WILLIAM K. DURR • JOHN PESCOSOLIDO • GORDON A. HAYWARD

CONSULTANTS • PAUL McKEE • MARCELLA T. JOHNSON

Diversity

HOUGHTON MIFFLIN COMPANY • BOSTON

ATLANTA • DALLAS • GENEVA, ILLINOIS • HOPEWELL, NEW JERSEY • PALO ALTO

ACKNOWLEDGMENTS

For each of the selections listed below, grateful acknowledgment is made for permission to adapt and/or reprint original or copyrighted material, as follows:

"Another Kind of Courage," from *Walk in the Sky* by Jack Ishmole. Copyright © 1972 by Jack Ishmole. All rights reserved. Reprinted by permission of Dodd, Mead & Company, Inc., the author, and the author's agent, Theron Raines Agency.

"Bats," reprinted with permission of The Macmillan Company from *The Bat-Poet* by Randall Jarrell. Copyright © The Macmillan Company 1963, 1964.

"Be Kind," from "Silent Mountains," in *Song of a Woods Colt* by Billy Edd Wheeler, Droke House Publishers, © 1969. Reprinted by permission.

"Billy Beans Lived Here," by Jean McCord. Copyright © 1968 by Jean McCord. From *Deep Where the Octopi Lie*. Used by permission of Atheneum Publishers.

"A Blessing," reprinted from *The Branch Will Not Break*, by James Wright, by permission of Wesleyan University Press. Copyright © 1961 by James Wright. This poem was first published in *Poetry*.

"The Boy Who Predicted Earthquakes," by Margaret St. Clair. Copyright © 1950 by Margaret St. Clair. Appeared originally in *Maclean's*. Reprinted by permission of McIntosh and Otis, Inc.

"Cat and the Weather" (copyright 1963 May Swenson) is reprinted by permission of Charles Scribner's Sons from *To Mix With Time* by May Swenson.

"Chinese: Synonym for *Superior*," from *Ancient China* by Edward H. Schafer and the Editors of TIME-LIFE BOOKS. Copyright © 1967 Time Inc. Used by permission.

"Colonizing the Moon," excerpt (slightly adapted) from *Tomorrow's Moon* by George E. Henry, pages 53–63. 21ST CENTURY MONOGRAFICS #6. © 1969 General Learning Corporation. Reprinted by permission.

"A Couple of Lost Squadrons," from *Lost Legends of the West* by Brad Williams and Choral Pepper. Copyright © 1970 by Brad Williams and Choral Pepper. Reprinted by permission of Holt, Rinehart and Winston, Inc.

"Creature of the Snows," by William Sambrot. This story originally appeared in the *Saturday Evening Post*. Reprinted by permission of Curtis Brown, Ltd. Copyright © 1960 by William Sambrot.

"A Cup of Tea," by Jill Paton Walsh. Reprinted with the permission of Farrar, Straus & Giroux, Inc., from *Fireweed* by Jill Paton Walsh, copyright © 1969 by Jill Paton Walsh, and with the permission of Macmillan Services Limited, London and Basingstoke.

"Dr. Dan," by Louis Haber. This is an abridgment of the chapter "Daniel Hale Williams," somewhat adapted, from *Black Pioneers of Science and Invention* by Louis Haber © 1970 by Harcourt Brace Jovanovich, Inc., and reprinted with their permission.

"The Eighth Wonder of the World," from *The Long Rampart: The Story of the Great Wall of China*, by Robert Silverberg. Copyright © 1966 by the author. Reprinted with the permission of the publisher, Chilton Book Company, Philadelphia.

"Fame," by Emily Dickinson. Reprinted by permission of the publishers and the Trustees of Amherst College from Thomas H. Johnson, Editor, *The Poems of Emily Dickinson*, Cambridge, Mass.: The Belknap Press of Harvard University Press, Copyright, 1951, 1955, by The President and Fellows of Harvard College.

"First U.S. Olympic Hero . . . ," adapted from "First U.S. Olympic hero unsung," by Barbara Craig. Reprinted by permission from *The Christian Science Monitor*. © 1972 The Christian Science Publishing Society. All rights reserved.

"Frozen Assets," adapted from *The Great American Ice Cream Book* by Paul Dickson. Copyright © 1972 by Paul Dickson. Reprinted by permission of Atheneum Publishers and The Sterling Lord Agency, Inc.

PRINTED IN THE U.S.A.   ISBN: 0-395-16272-6

CONTENTS

Cadences

Affinities

Prisms

Tapestry

Cadences

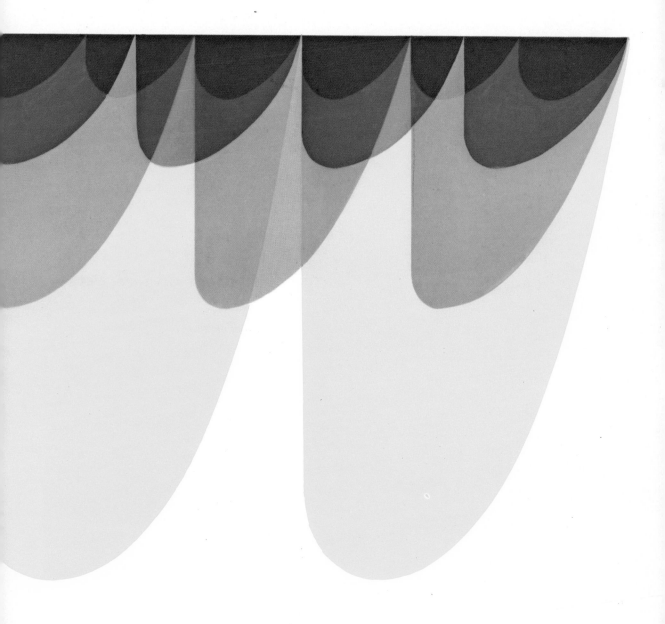

Contents

Cadences

A Cup of Tea

by Jill Paton Walsh

*Separated from their families, Bill and Julie had met by
chance in wartime London. The two homeless teen-agers
joined forces, determined to get along on their own and somehow survive the prolonged 1940 blitz. In the following story
Bill describes one of the harrowing experiences they shared.*

We wandered on. "Now that we've got a rucksack to put things
in," I said thoughtfully, "there are a lot of things from home I wish
I had."

"What sort of things?"

"My penknife, for a start. And my torch. And something to read
when I can't get to sleep in those shelters. And I'd very much like
a shave."

"*Shave?*" Julie said, incredulous. "You don't need to shave!"

"I jolly well do! About once a week or so."

"Well, I can't see any beard on you." She stared at my chin.

I raised my hand instinctively and stroked the soft, pale down that
grew there.

She laughed again. "Really, Bill, you don't need to shave *that* off!
That's not a beard!"

"It makes me feel a fool," I said sourly.

"Oh. Oh, I'm sorry. Well, let's go back to your house."

"I suppose I really ought to go and see if my aunt's there again now," I said. I hadn't really meant to go back right away. I felt very reluctant, as though something nasty would happen if I saw anyone I knew.

We went home on an Underground train. It was very smelly down there, because of all the night shelterers. A barricade was across the road. The doorstep was dirty, and all the windows looked dead. I don't know how it is that one can see from the glass, as one can in human eyes, when there's nobody at home, but it's true. We didn't walk straight up the street, to be caught and warned off by the warden, but slipped around the little lane that led between the small gardens at the back. There was a notice, UNEXPLODED BOMB, propped up against an old oil can, but we just walked past it.

I opened the gate at the end of our garden, and we went down the path. It looked different: the leaves were all golden yellow on the apple tree, and the grass had grown long and was jeweled with dew, even then, in the afternoon. At the end of the garden, next to the house, was a deep pit about six feet wide, into which the windows of the basement looked. It had stone steps into it, which led to the back door. And lying in this sunken place, lodged against the kitchen windowsill on one side and against my aunt's parsley and mint patch on the other, was the bomb. Its nose cone was on the windowsill, poking through a broken pane, and its finned tail was on the herb bed. We stared at it, fascinated. Looking up, I saw broken branches in the apple tree, and looking down, I saw a long, scuffed mark on the lawn.

"Look, Julie," I said, excited. "It fell into the tree; that must have broken its fall a bit and turned it sideways, so that it slithered along the lawn instead of falling on its nose, and that's why it didn't go off. It just slipped along there and stuck." Indeed, the scuff marks and scratches on its gray sides were already bright with new rust; and where the leaky gutter spilled over it, it had grown a streak of livid green algae, absurdly, as though it meant just to stay there and weather into the surroundings like a fallen tree.

"I don't like it," she said. "Let's go."

I think I would have said it if she hadn't, but now that she had, I felt different. "No," I said. "I want my things."

Her face whitened visibly as I watched. "But we'd have to go right under it!" she said.

"Cowardy, cowardy custard!" I said, to make myself feel brave.

"Are you really going to?" she asked.

"Yes," I said. "Really."

"Well, if you are, I'm coming too," she said firmly, taking a tight hold of my hand and marching me toward it.

So we went. We walked down the steps and across the narrow yard, stooping under the bomb, past it, and getting to the door. I slipped my hand around the doorpost and found the key, as always, wedged between the doorpost and the wall, where the fit was bad. I turned it in the lock and let us in.

It was dark; the bomb blocked out a lot of the light. Its nasty snout was nearly resting on the draining board beside the sink. Broken glass from the window lay across the floor, and dust lay thick on the table and the dresser. Julie was shivering; I heard her teeth. You know, people say teeth chatter, and that's just what hers were doing. I don't know what came over me, but I looked and looked, and saw how she was, shivering, hugging herself with her arms, her eyes looking huge and dark, and it made me feel cruel.

"I want a cup of tea," I said. "I'm going to shave. Make me a cup of tea."

We both looked around the place, seeing the horror of what I had just said. There were the cups and the teapot on the dresser, about five steps away. Then five steps back to get the kettle from the stove. Then the tap, about three inches from the surface of the bomb. Then the stove again.

"The gas!" she said breathlessly. "They'll have turned off the gas! They must have turned it off, must have! It might explode," she added in a more normal tone.

"It's an electric stove," I said brutally. "And the mains switch on just above it."

Full of manly strength, I went off up the stairs, three at a time, to the bathroom.

I was sorry by the time I had lathered my face. I hoped she would come up and join me, but she didn't. I hoped she wouldn't set it off; I supposed she would kill me too if she did, and that made it all right to be up there shaving. It wasn't as if I was safe. My razor blades had got rusty, and the water was cold, so it took some time. Then I went and fetched my torch and penknife from my room, and some clean socks while I was at it, and a shirt, and my copy of *Kidnapped*. Then I went downstairs to the kitchen.

She had the tea made, cups laid on the table. The table had been dusted too. She had even found a packet of biscuits in the larder and put them out. Her own tea was poured out, and she was sitting there reading one of my aunt's copies of *Picture Post*.

I stood in the doorway, looking at her. I expected her to be triumphant, gloating, or maybe to reproach me for my monstrous behavior. Instead, she looked up and grinned at me and said, "Come and have some tea! Look at this."

"This" was a picture of St. Paul's Cathedral. The heading was: UNEXPLODED BOMB THREATENS ST. PAUL'S. We could see a great yawning black hole in the pavement outside the south transept. Heads together while we drank tea, we read about the bomb-disposal squad that was trying to deal with the bomb. They had dug down thirty feet before reaching it and were still trying to defuse it when the paper went to press.

"You know," she said, "it's supposed to be good."

"What is?"

"St. Paul's."

"How do you mean, good?"

"It's supposed to be good architecture. People who know think so. And I've only seen it once, when I was quite young, and I didn't like it much then. I'd like to go and see it again, just once more, while it's still there."

"It will still be there," I said. "These bomb gangs are dealing with it."

"Bill," she said slowly, "do you know anything much about bombs?"

"Well, no, only what I've read in the papers."

"My father used to do them in the first war. Get the fuses out, you know. It's very dangerous."

"Well, as long as you don't give them a great knock on the nose cone. That's what makes them go off, isn't it?"

"You've got it a bit muddled, I think," she said, pouring out more tea. "Some of the ones that don't go off are duds or ordinary ones that, just by some chance, didn't fall on the trigger mechanism, but some of them are real time bombs, meant not to go off till someone touches them. They make a lot of trouble, you see, making people leave the area and all that. And those, Daddy said, are especially made to go off at the lightest touch, anywhere on them. Or even at a loud noise. Or even at a change in temperature. The people who deal with those bombs are just about the bravest people there are, Mummy says."

"Golly," I said. "I should think your mother's right. O.K., we'll take a bus back to town. There's one that goes right by St. Paul's, and you can take your last look."

It was a sort of delayed reaction, like the way a wave breaks, and then the backwash breaks again. I was still chatting about the bomb at St. Paul's when I remembered the one behind me.

"Julie," I said. My throat was quite dry. Very slowly I picked up my cup of tea and gulped some. "Julie, which sort do you think this is: the accident sort, or the time-bomb go-off-at-any-time sort?"

"I honestly don't know," she said, looking up at me calmly, with dark, limpid eyes. "I haven't a clue."

And I had made her make the tea. "Come on," I said. "Let's get out of here!"

"Let's!" she said, getting up at once. Then at the door she said, "Have you got your things?"

"Yes," I said. "I put them in the rucksack." I was whispering.

"Good," she said. "I wouldn't like you to make us come back for them!"

I have never closed a door so gently in my life as I closed that kitchen door behind me.

The bomb went up some time after we left. How long after, I'm not sure. It wrecked the houses on either side of my aunt's and two houses across the road, and it blew in the windows all the way down the street. Where our house had been, there was nothing left but a great hole. But the apple tree, split in two right to the root, sent up a shoot the following spring and survived.

DISCUSSION

1. What was the Underground, and in what two ways did it serve the people of London?
2. Why did Bill want to return to his house? When Julie and Bill reached his neighborhood, what did they find?
3. Why was Julie afraid to enter the house? How did Bill respond to her fear?
4. Why did Bill's fuzzy beard make him "feel a fool"? How do you think he wanted to feel about himself?
5. By insisting on going into the house, did Bill prove himself braver than Julie? Why or why not?
6. Reread the final paragraph of the story. Why do you think the apple tree made an impression on Bill?
7. Who do you think was stronger in character, Bill or Julie? Why do you think as you do?
8. Do you think Julie's actions were prompted primarily by bravery or by her friendship for Bill? Why do you think that?
9. Imagine yourself in Julie's place. What would your feelings have been as you made the tea and waited for Bill to finish shaving?

AUTHOR

Born in London, England, in 1937, Jill Paton Walsh specialized in English at Oxford University and graduated with honors. Before her marriage to Anthony Paton Walsh, who is also an Oxford graduate, she taught for several years at a girls' school. Writing is one of her favorite occupations, but now, as the mother of three children, she has difficulty finding as much time for it as she would like. Other occupations she enjoys are studying old churches and having friends to dinner at her London home. Mrs. Paton Walsh is an avid reader and is very much interested in history, especially the Anglo-Saxon period. Besides *Fireweed,* from which "A Cup of Tea" is taken, she has written three other books for young people, *Hengest's Tale, The Dolphin Crossing,* and *Goldengrove.* She is also co-author with Kevin Crossley-Holland of *Wordhoard,* a collection of short stories about Anglo-Saxon times.

COLONIZING THE MOON

by George E. Henry

Colonizing the moon will be like fighting a war. A thousand things will need doing, and they can't all be done first. No matter how the priorities are stacked, there is never an ideal sequence. One can only hope to come close to being right. Even this will take imagination, insight, and judgment.

Geologists would like the future moon base to be near the crater Aristarchus (ăr'ĭs-tär'kəs), a site of suspected recent volcanic activity. The astronomers want to be around on the far side. Various other groups will probably want to set up shop in one of the walled plains, where there may be meteoritic iron.

But unfortunately, all five of the ringed seas lie outside the 20°-wide equatorial zone that is favored by the space-flight operations officials. These men have to think about the cost, in extra spacecraft propulsion, of putting down in the higher latitudes. They would prefer a base in the Sea of Tranquillity, the Sea of Fecundity, or the Ocean of Storms, maybe somewhere near an Apollo touchdown point.

This tangle of conflicting interests is not easy to resolve. Possibly, in the end, crew safety will prove to be the deciding factor. Despite the extra cost, the prime base may well be placed close to the north pole or, equally well, close to the south pole. To understand the advantages of near-polar location, one has only to imagine what could happen to a moon colonist out on the surface somewhere when an emergency arises. Suppose the man finds himself at some distance from base with a serious malfunction in his spacesuit temperature control. At worst, the mechanism could fail completely. The man would then be at the mercy of his environment. He could roast, or freeze, in just a few minutes.

Early in the morning, or late in the afternoon, the boulders throw long shadows. The man has a chance to survive. He can face away from the sun and step into and out of the shade of the biggest piece of rock he can find. He can make the best of a most uncomfortable situation by alternating between extremes. In time, a search party will come to his rescue. The man will owe his life to the fact that the sun is low in the sky. And therein, very simply, lies one great advantage of the polar regions: The sun is never more than a few degrees above the horizon.

The idea of a polar base deserves close scrutiny. There, better than anywhere else on the moon, one could build a snug fortress against every threat of the hostile forces of nature. Significant benefits are conferred by an ever-present, circling, horizon-hugging sun.

A high peak would be selected, as close to the pole as possible. Tunnels would be bored all the way through the mountain, at several levels. At the very highest level, just below the summit, intersecting tunnels, their mouths close together all around, would form in effect a single, large, circular room. Walls would be left standing here and there to support the mass overhead. This room, then, would have windows facing out around 32 points of the compass. These windows, made of thick, heavy glass, would be permanently sealed shut. Special curtains would operate to soften the sun's glare, streaming horizontally inward. Almost half the windows, the ones directed away from the sun, could have their curtains drawn back. Throughout the course of the lunar month, automatic controls

would keep track of the sun's position. The curtains on the edge of the advancing sunlight would progressively be closed, while the curtains on the other side would be opened.

A polar roundhouse claims a long list of practical advantages. It is functional; it makes the most of the distinctive features of a very peculiar location. The heating and cooling cost is near zero. In this respect it is a lot like an unmanned spacecraft. The sunshine is almost always there, on one side or the other, and shadow is always there too, on the opposite side. By controlling the amount of light you allow to come in, and at the same time juggling the rate of heat radiating away on the cold side, you can have just about any temperature you want.

Meanwhile, the availability of sun and shadow provides a made-to-order condition for the efficient generation of electric power. There would be no need to worry about heavy-duty storage devices, to last through the long lunar night. Here there is no night, only an occasional eclipse of the sun. A few batteries would take care of emergencies and meet the power needs during the predictably frequent eclipses. Finally, there is a chance of finding water nearby, in the form of ice, possibly on the floor of some crater a thousand yards down the steep slope.

Convenience aside, there are good reasons for going to the lunar poles in quest of scientific data. This fact is recognized in the 1967 recommendations of the President's Scientific Advisory Committee. The possibility of finding ice there has been discussed by many reputable scientists. Granted, this possibility is not limited strictly to the polar regions. Ice can exist wherever a valley floor lies deep enough to rest in perpetual shadow. As a practical matter, however, the farther one goes away from the poles, the deeper the canyon has to be, and the steeper its walls, to meet the criterion of sunlessness. About half of 1 per cent of the moon's surface is permanently shielded from the sun's direct rays, with some 40 per cent of this amount being located quite close to the poles.

The whole question of finding ice is vitally important. There are other ways of getting water, to be sure, but only at considerable cost. Ready-made ice beds would be a treasure.

Let's take a look at the interior of the colony inside the mountain. The place is livable. It enjoys the safety features of an underground location without having to pay the penalty. There would be windows affording a view of the sky. The sight would be magnificent. Only the view on the nightside would be exposed. The twelve constellations of the zodiac would line the horizon, passing ever so slowly in review. Part of the time, the full earth could be seen, glowing white and sapphire-blue on the moon's rim.

Inside, the arrangement is complex. It will be easy to dig in the moon, so the tunnels go every which way, up and down as well as crosswise. There is no need to limit the number of levels; getting up and down is no problem. It is easier, indeed, to move vertically than to walk along on the level.

Naturally, there would be no stairways. The fireman's pole is a handy substitute, and not just for sliding down. Some people would be able to jump from one floor to the one above. It would be best to make the jump with one hand lightly touching the pole, for aiming and control. This would prevent bumping into the ceiling. At the crest of the jump, a slight extra tug on the pole would provide a lift for the remaining few inches up to the next floor.

New feelings about space, mass, direction, and distance will exert a

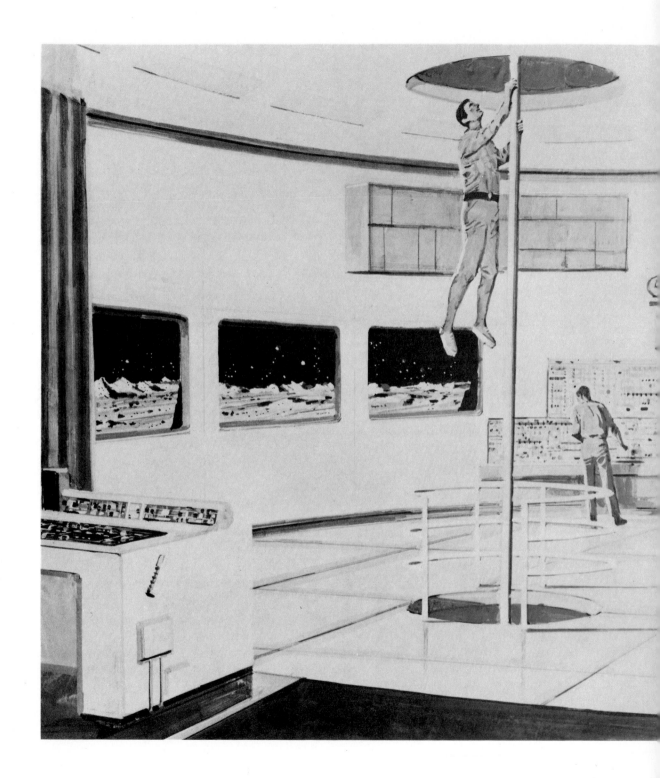

subtle but pervasive influence on everything people do. On Earth we tend to think of the size of a room or a building in terms of its floor space, our habits of motion being, by and large, two-dimensional. On the moon, we will become more nearly free to move in all three dimensions, and we will think of available space by its cubage.

More things will be hung from the ceiling, where they are out of the way, yet accessible. Bookshelves will go all the way up, with no need for ladders in front. There are handholds, perhaps, jutting out from the framework, and a few additional grips embedded in the ceiling.

There will be games available in the gymnasium, but not tennis. It is interesting to consider what would happen if we tried to play tennis on a court in the usual pattern, with familiar earthly equipment.

The balls can be driven almost as hard as ever, but not quite. The player's footing fails to provide the anchoring that allows a good solid stroke. A righthander's forehand swing twists his body clockwise, and his feet do some skidding.

The ball sails off just the same, and it appears to fly in a straight line. Either it hits the net or it goes out of bounds. But that is probably just as well, for the opposing player cannot reach the ball to strike back unless the first player completely ignores the game's strategy and aims the shot at his opponent's racket.

Quick starts and stops, and quick changes of direction, are almost impossible on the moon. Gravity is less there, but mass remains the same. It is this new relationship between mass and weight that is going to be hard to learn. But learn we will or else be as awkward as an impatient puppy on a slick new linoleum floor.

It might help to have suction cups on the shoes or a handy set of ski poles. Something of the sort will be required for general travel, but more than that will be needed to salvage the game of tennis.

Other sports will be invented. One writer, Robert Heinlein, has even suggested flying. Outsized artificial wings, fitted to the limbs of the body, would enable a person to fly by muscle power alone. This would be done in a pressurized cavity, deep within the moon.

Swimming should be fun, and this is the one sport that would be almost the same as on Earth. The swimmer's body would be lighter, but the surrounding buoyant medium would be lighter too. The most notable new sensation might come when the swimmer treads water. By working his hands and feet in an extra effort, he could thrust himself momentarily clear of the surface.

Doing the crawl stroke, a swimmer might ride a little higher in the water and go a little faster, but not much. The resistance to motion in

16

water comes not so much from the weight of the liquid as from its inertia and viscosity, both of which will still be the same on the moon.

Under water, a swimmer might have the illusion that he is right back on the home planet again. This is important! A regular workout in the pool could be the salvation of moon dwellers, for they must attempt to maintain muscle tone in order to return someday to Earth.

A strange new life is awaiting the moon pioneers. They will be pushing frontiers, not only with respect to territory but in human experience. The call to go out into space, and into the dark body of the moon, is full upon us. Let us not shrink back from this greatest of all adventures.

DISCUSSION

1. According to the author, what will be the most likely location for the first moon colony? What main advantage will this location have?
2. Describe a lunar roundhouse.
3. Why will various groups disagree on the most desirable location for the first moon colony?
4. Why is it easier to move vertically than horizontally on the moon?
5. Why will moon colonists be comfortable in rooms with less floor space than on Earth?
6. Why will flying be done only in a pressurized cavity rather than above the moon's surface?
7. What experience do you think you would enjoy most on the moon? What would be most unpleasant?
8. How likely do you think it is that the predictions of this article will become reality?
9. Do you think that there are good reasons for colonizing the moon? If so, what are those reasons?

To Kate,
Skating Better
Than Her Date

David Daiches

Wait, Kate! You skate at such a rate
You leave behind your skating mate.
Your splendid speed won't you abate?
He's lagging far behind you, Kate.
He brought you on this skating date
His shy affection thus to state,
But you on skating concentrate
And leave him with a woeful weight
Pressed on his heart. Oh, what a state
A man gets into, how irate
He's bound to be with life and fate
If, when he tries to promulgate
His love, the loved one turns to skate
Far, far ahead to demonstrate
Superior speed and skill. Oh, hate
Is sure to come of love, dear Kate,
If you so treat your skating mate.
Turn again, Kate, or simply wait
Until he comes, then him berate
(Coyly) for catching up so late.
For, Kate, he *knows* your skating's great,
He's *seen* your splendid figure eight,
He is not here to contemplate
Your supersonic skating rate —
That is not why he made the date.
He's anxious to expatiate
On how he wants you for his mate.
And don't you want to hear him, Kate?

Toni Cade Bambara

Raymond's RUN

I don't have much work to do around the house like some girls. My mother does that. And I don't have to earn my pocket money; George runs errands for the big boys and sells Christmas cards. And anything else that's got to get done, my father does. All I have to do in life is mind my brother Raymond, which is enough.

Sometimes I slip and say my little brother Raymond. But as any fool can see, he's much bigger and he's older too. But a lot of people call him my little brother 'cause he needs looking after 'cause he's not quite right. And a lot of smart mouths got lots to say about that too, especially when George was minding him. But now, if anybody has anything to say to Raymond, anything to say about his big head, they have to come by me. And I don't play the dozens[1] or believe in standing around with somebody in my face doing a lot of talking. I much

rather just knock you down and take my chances even if I am a little girl with skinny arms and a squeaky voice, which is how I got the name Squeaky. And if things get too rough, I run. And as anybody can tell you, I'm the fastest thing on two feet.

There is no track meet that I don't win the first-place medal. I use to win the twenty-yard dash when I was a little kid in kindergarten. Nowadays it's the fifty-yard dash. And tomorrow I am subject to run the quarter-mile relay all by myself and come in first, second, and third. The big kids call me Mercury 'cause I'm the swiftest thing in the neighborhood. Everybody knows that — except two people who know better, my father and me.

He can beat me to Amsterdam Avenue with me having a headstart of two fire hydrants and him running with his hands in his pockets, whistling. But that's private information. 'Cause can you imagine some thirty-five-year-old man stuffing himself into PAL shorts to race little kids? So as

---

[1] **play the dozens**, make rude remarks about the members of another person's family.

20

far as everyone's concerned, I'm the fastest; and that goes for Gretchen too, who has put out the tale that she is going to win the first-place medal this year. Ridiculous. In the second place, she's got short legs. In the third place, she's got freckles. And in the first place, no one can beat me, and that's all there is to it.

I'm standing on the corner admiring the weather and about to take a stroll down Broadway so I can practice my breathing exercises, and I've got Raymond walking on the inside close to the buildings 'cause he's subject to fits of fantasy and starts thinking he's a circus performer and that the curb is a tightrope strung high in the air. And sometimes after a rain he likes to step down off his tightrope right into the gutter and slosh around getting his shoes and cuffs wet. Then I get hit when I get home. Or sometimes if you don't watch him, he'll dash across traffic to the island in the middle of Broadway and give the pigeons a fit. Then I have to go behind him apologizing to all the old people sitting around trying to get some sun and getting all upset with the pigeons fluttering around them, scattering their newspapers and upsetting the wax-paper lunches in their laps. So I keep Raymond on the inside of me, and he plays like he's driving a stagecoach, which is O.K. by me so long as he doesn't run me over or interrupt my breathing exercises, which I have to do on account of I'm serious about my running and don't care who knows it.

Now, some people like to act like things come easy to them, won't let on that they practice. Not me. I'll high prance down 34th Street like a rodeo pony to keep my knees strong even if it does get my mother uptight, so that she walks ahead like she's not with me, don't know me, is all by herself on a shopping trip, and I am somebody else's crazy child.

Now, you take Cynthia Procter for instance. She's just the opposite. If there's a test tomorrow, she'll say something like, "Oh, I guess I'll play handball this afternoon and watch television tonight," just to let you know she ain't thinking about the test. Or like last week when she won the spelling bee for the millionth time, "A good thing you got *receive,* Squeaky, 'cause I would have got it wrong. I completely forgot about the spelling bee." And she'll clutch the lace on her blouse like it was a narrow escape. Oh, brother.

But of course when I pass her house on my early morning trots around the block, she is practicing the scales on the piano over and over and over and over. Then in music class, she always lets herself get bumped around so she falls accidentally on purpose onto the piano stool and is so surprised to find herself sitting there and so decides just for fun to try out the ole keys, and what do you know — Chopin's waltzes just spring out of her fingertips, and she's the most surprised thing in the world. A regular prodigy. I could kill people like that.

I stay up all night studying the words for the spelling bee. And you can see me any time of day practicing running. I never walk if I can trot, and shame on Raymond if he can't keep up. But of course he does, 'cause if he hangs back, someone's liable to walk up to him and get smart, or take his allowance from him, or ask him where he got that great big pumpkin head. People are so stupid sometimes.

So I'm strolling down Broadway, breathing out and breathing in on counts of seven, which is my lucky number, and here comes Gretchen and her sidekicks — Mary Louise, who used to be a friend of mine when she first moved to Harlem from Baltimore and got beat up by everybody till I took up for her on account of her mother and my mother used to sing in the same choir when they were young girls, but people ain't grateful, so now she hangs out with the new girl, Gretchen, and talks about me like a dog; and Rosie, who is as fat as I am skinny and has a big mouth where Raymond is concerned and is too stupid to know that there is not a big deal of difference between herself and Raymond and that she can't afford to throw stones. So they are steady coming up Broadway, and I see right away that it's going to be one of those Dodge City scenes 'cause the street ain't that big and they're close to the buildings just as we are. First I think I'll step into the candy store and look over the new comics and let them pass. But that's chicken, and I've got

a reputation to consider. So then I think I'll just walk straight on through them or over them if necessary. But as they get to me, they slow down. I'm ready to fight 'cause, like I said, I don't feature a whole lot of chitchat; I much prefer to just knock you down right from the jump and save everybody a lotta precious time.

"You signing up for the May Day races?" smiles Mary Louise, only it's not a smile at all.

A dumb question like that doesn't deserve an answer. Besides, there's just me and Gretchen standing there really, so no use wasting my breath talking to shadows.

"I don't think you're going to win this time," says Rosie, trying to signify with her hands on her hips, all salty, completely forgetting that I have whupped her many times for less salt than that.

"I always win 'cause I'm the best," I say straight at Gretchen, who is, as far as I'm concerned, the only one talking in this ventriloquist-dummy routine.

Gretchen smiles, but it's not a smile, and I'm thinking that girls never really smile at each other because they don't know how and don't want to know how, and there's probably no one to teach us how 'cause grown-up girls don't know either. Then they all look at Raymond, who has just brought his mule team to a standstill. And they're about to see what kind of trouble they can get into through him.

"What grade you in now, Raymond?" asks Mary Louise.

"You got anything to say to him, say it to me, Mary Louise Williams of Raggedy Town, Baltimore."

"What are you, his mother?" sasses Rosie.

"That's right, Fatso. And the next word out of anybody and I'll be their mother too." So they just stand there, and Gretchen puts her hands on her hips and is about to say something with her freckle-face self but doesn't. Then she walks around me, looking me up and down, but keeps walking up Broadway, and her sidekicks follow her. So me and Raymond smile at each other, and he says "Gidyap" to his team, and I continue with my breathing exercises, strolling down Broadway toward 145th with not a care in the world 'cause I am Miss Quicksilver herself.

I take my time getting to the park on May Day because the track meet is the last thing on the program. The biggest thing on the program is the Maypole dancing, which I can do without, thank you, even if my mother thinks it's a shame I don't take part and act like a girl for a change. You'd think my mother'd be grateful not to have to make me a white organdy dress with a big satin sash and buy me new white baby-doll shoes that can't be taken out of the box till the big day. You'd think she'd be glad her daughter ain't out there prancing around a Maypole, getting the new clothes all dirty and sweaty and trying

to act like a fairy or a flower or whatever you're supposed to be when you should be trying to be yourself, whatever that is, which is, as far as I am concerned, a poor black girl who really can't afford to buy shoes and a new dress you only wear once a lifetime 'cause it won't fit next year.

I was once a strawberry in a Hansel and Gretel pageant when I was in nursery school and didn't have no better sense than to dance on tiptoe with my arms in a circle over my head, doing umbrella steps and being a perfect fool just so my mother and father could come dressed up and clap. You'd think they'd know better than to encourage that kind of nonsense. I am not a strawberry. I do not dance on my toes. I run. That is what I am all about. So I always come late to the May Day program, just in time to get my number pinned on, and I lay in the grass till they announce the fifty-yard dash.

I put Raymond in the little swings, which is a tight squeeze this year and will be impossible next year. Then I look around for Mr. Pearson, who pins the numbers on. I'm really looking for Gretchen, if you want to know the truth, but she's not around. The park is jam-packed. Parents in hats and corsages and breast-pocket handkerchiefs peeking up. Kids in white dresses and light-blue suits. The park-ees unfolding chairs and chasing the rowdy kids from Lenox as if they had no right to be there. The big guys with their caps on backwards, leaning against the fence, swirling the basket-balls on the tips of their fingers, waiting for all these crazy people to clear out the park so they can play. Most of the kids in my class are carrying bass drums and glockenspiels and flutes. You'd think they'd put in a few bongos or something for real like that.

Then here comes Mr. Pearson with his clipboard and his cards and pencils and whistles and safety pins and fifty million other things he's always dropping all over the place with his clumsy self. He sticks out in a crowd 'cause he's on stilts. We used to call him Jack and the Beanstalk to get him mad. But I'm the only one that can outrun him and get away, and I'm too grown for that silliness now.

"Well, Squeaky," he says, checking my name off the list and handing me number seven and two pins. And I'm thinking he's got no right to call me Squeaky if I can't call him Beanstalk.

"Hazel Elizabeth Deborah Parker," I correct him and tell him to write it down on his board.

"Well, Hazel Elizabeth Deborah Parker, going to give someone else a break this year?" I squint at him real hard to see if he is seriously thinking I should lose the race on purpose just to give someone else a break.

"Only six girls running this time," he continues, shaking his head sadly like it's my fault all of New York didn't turn out in sneakers. "That new girl should give you a run for your money." He looks around the park for Gretchen like a periscope in

a submarine movie. Then he says, "Wouldn't it be a nice gesture if you were . . . to ahhh . . ."

I give him such a look he couldn't finish putting that idea into words. Grownups got a lot of nerve sometimes. I pin number seven to myself and stomp away — I'm so burnt. And I go straight for the track and stretch out on the grass while the band winds up with "Oh, the Monkey Wrapped His Tail Around the Flagpole," which my teacher calls by some other name. The man on the loudspeaker is calling everyone over to the track, and I'm on my back looking at the sky, trying to pretend I'm in the country, but I can't, because even grass in the city feels hard as sidewalk and there's just no pretending that you are anywhere but in a "concrete jungle," as my grandfather says.

The twenty-yard dash takes all of two minutes 'cause most of the little kids don't know no better than to run off the track or run the wrong way or run smack into the fence and fall down and cry. One little kid, though, has got the good sense to run straight for the white ribbon up ahead, so he wins. Then the second graders line up for the thirty-yard dash, and I don't even bother to turn my head to watch 'cause Raphael Perez always wins. He wins before he even begins by psyching the runners, telling them they're going to trip on their shoelaces and fall on their faces or lose their shorts or something, which he doesn't really have to do since he is very fast, almost as fast as I am. After that is the forty-yard dash, which I use to run when I was in first grade. Raymond is hollering from the swings 'cause he knows I'm about to do my thing 'cause the man on the loudspeaker has just announced the fifty-yard dash, although he might just as well be giving a recipe for angel food cake 'cause you can hardly make out what he's saying for the static. I get up and slip off my sweat pants, and then I see Gretchen standing at the starting line, kicking her legs out like a pro. Then as I get into place, I see that ole Raymond is in line on the other side of the fence, bending down, with his fingers on the ground just like he knew what he was doing. I was going to yell at him, but then I didn't. It burns up your energy to holler.

Every time, just before I take off in a race, I always feel like I'm in a dream, the kind of dream you have when you're sick with fever and feel all hot and weightless. I dream I'm flying over a sandy beach in the early morning sun, kissing the leaves of the trees as I fly by. And there's always the smell of apples, just like in the country when I was little and use to think I was a choochoo train, running through the fields of corn and chugging up the hill to the orchard. And all the time I'm dreaming this, I get lighter and lighter until I'm flying over the beach again, getting blown through the sky like a feather that weighs nothing at all. But once I spread my fingers in the dirt and

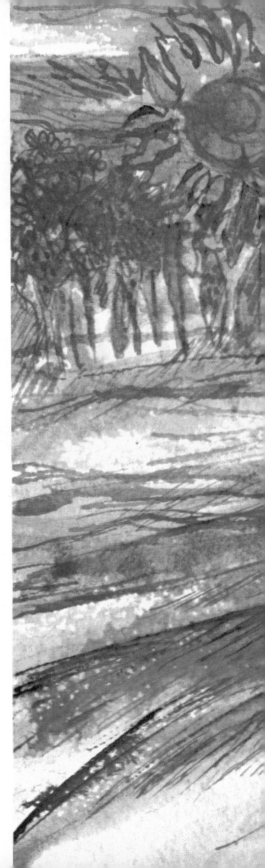

crouch over for the Get on Your Mark, the dream is gone, and I am solid again and am telling myself, "Squeaky, you must win, you must win; you are the fastest thing in the world; you can even beat your father up Amsterdam if you really try." And then I feel my weight coming back just behind my knees, then down to my feet, then into the earth, and the pistol shot explodes in my blood, and I am off and weightless again, flying past the other runners, my arms pumping up and down, and the whole world is quiet except for the crunch as I zoom over the gravel in the track. I glance to my left, and there is no one. To the right a blurred Gretchen, who's got her chin jutting out as if it would win the race all by itself. And on the other side of the fence is Raymond with his arms down to his side and the palms tucked up behind him, running in his very own style, and the first time I ever saw that, and I almost stop to watch my brother Raymond on his first run. But the white ribbon is bouncing toward me, and I tear past it, racing into the distance till my feet with a mind of their own start digging up footfuls of dirt and brake me short. Then all the kids standing on the side pile on me, banging me on the back and slapping my head with their May Day programs, for I have won again, and everybody on 151st Street can walk tall for another year.

"In first place . . ." The man on the loudspeaker is just as clear as a bell now. But then he pauses, and the loudspeaker starts to whine. Then static. And I lean down to catch my breath, and here comes Gretchen, walking back, for she's overshot the finish line too, huffing and puffing with her hands on her hips, taking it slow, breathing in steady time like a real pro, and I sort of like her a little for the first time. "In first place . . ." and then three or four voices get all mixed up on the loudspeaker, and I dig my sneaker into the grass and stare at Gretchen, who's staring back, we both wondering just who did win. I can hear old Beanstalk arguing with the man on the loudspeaker and then a few others running their mouths about what the stopwatches say.

Then I hear Raymond yanking at the fence to call me, and I wave to shush him, but he keeps rattling the fence like a gorilla in a cage like in them gorilla movies; but then like a dancer or something he starts climbing up nice and easy but very fast. And it occurs to me, watching how smoothly he climbs hand over hand and remembering how he looked running with his arms down to his side and with the wind pulling his mouth back and his teeth showing and all, it occurred to me that Raymond would make a very fine runner. Doesn't he always keep up with me on my trots? And he surely knows how to breathe in counts of seven 'cause he's always doing it at the dinner table, which drives my brother George up the wall. And I'm smiling to beat the band 'cause if I've lost this race, or if me and Gretchen tied, or even if I've won, I can always retire as a runner and begin a whole new career as a coach with Raymond as my champion. After all, with a little more study I can beat Cynthia and her phony self at the spelling bee. And if I bugged my mother, I could get piano lessons and become a star. And I have a big rep as the baddest thing around. And I've got a roomful of ribbons and medals and awards. But what has Raymond got to call his own?

So I stand there with my new plan, laughing out loud by this time, as Raymond jumps down from the fence and runs over with his teeth showing and his arms down to the side, which no one before him has quite mastered as a running style. And by the time he comes over, I'm jumping up and down, so glad to see him — my brother Raymond, a great runner in the family tradition. But of course everyone thinks I'm jumping up and down because the men on the loudspeaker have finally gotten themselves together and compared notes and are announcing, "In first place — Miss Hazel Elizabeth Deborah Parker." (Dig that.) "In second place — Miss Gretchen P. Lewis." And I look over at Gretchen, wondering what the P stands for. And I smile. 'Cause she's good, no doubt about it. Maybe she'd like to help me coach Raymond; she obviously is serious about running, as any fool can see. And she nods to congratulate me, and then she smiles. And I smile. We stand there with this big smile of respect between us. It's about as real a smile as girls' can do for each other, considering we don't practice real smiling every day, you know, 'cause maybe we are much too busy being flowers or fairies or strawberries instead of something honest and worthy of respect . . . you know . . . like being people.

DISCUSSION

1. What responsibility did Squeaky's family assign to her? What made Squeaky's assignment difficult?
2. What annual event was of great importance to Squeaky? Why? How did Squeaky get ready for it?
3. What surprising discovery did Squeaky make about Raymond?
4. How do you think Squeaky felt about herself? About Raymond?
5. Squeaky referred to Rosie as standing "with her hands on her hips, all salty." What do you think she meant by *salty?*

6. What suggestion do you think Mr. Pearson would have made if Squeaky's look had not stopped him? Why would such a suggestion have been unacceptable to Squeaky?
7. Would you say that Squeaky had too high an opinion of herself? Why do you think as you do?
8. How did Squeaky think girls usually treat each other? Do you agree with her? Why or why not?
9. How did Raymond's run change Squeaky's attitude toward him? Toward herself? Toward others?
10. How did Squeaky get her nickname? How appropriate do you think the nickname was for her? What other nicknames can you suggest for her?

AUTHOR

Toni Cade Bambara has had an interesting and varied career since graduating from Queens College in 1959. Positions she has held include investigator for the New York State Department of Welfare, free-lance writer at the Ministry of Museums in Venice, Italy, and director of recreation in the psychiatry department of Metropolitan Hospital in New York City. At present she is an associate professor of English at Rutgers. Her educational background, too, is varied and interesting, for the places at which she studied after graduation from college include Katherine Dunham Dance Studio, Clark Center of Performing Arts, and Studio Museum of Harlem Film Institute as well as a school of mime in Paris and the University of Florence in Italy.

"Raymond's Run" is from a collection entitled *Tales and Stories for Black Folks,* which Toni Cade Bambara edited, and other stories she has written have appeared in anthologies and in magazines. She has also contributed articles and book and film reviews to such periodicals as *Negro Digest, Redbook, Prairie Schooner, New York Times Book Review,* and *Massachusetts Review.*

SKILL LESSON 1

GETTING MEANING FROM CONTEXT

Every year you add hundreds of new words to your vocabulary. You learn their meanings, and you learn to use those words with correct meaning in speaking and in writing.

When you meet a word in your reading that you don't know the meaning of, how can you find out by yourself what the meaning is? One thing you can do is to try to figure out the meaning from what is said by the rest of the sentence in which you see the word. This technique is called GETTING MEANING FROM CONTEXT or USING CONTEXT CLUES. When you use context clues, you are using the sense of the sentence to help you determine the meaning of a word whose meaning you don't yet know.

Do you know the meaning of the word *cerulean?* If not, use the context in the following sentence to try to figure out the meaning.

At noontime the cerulean sky provided a colorful background for the few white clouds that floated high above the earth on this perfect summer's day.

Did you conclude that *cerulean* means *blue,* in particular, *sky blue?* In determining that meaning for the word, you used the meanings of words you know well in the sentence and your understanding of the sense of the sentence.

Sometimes an author uses a word for which you already know one or more meanings, but you may discover that no one of those meanings fits the context of the sentence you are reading. By using the meanings of other words you know in the sentence, you may be able to determine the proper meaning. For example, you probably know one or more meanings for the word *range*. Do any of the meanings you know make sense in this sentence?

The ponies range over the prairies in search of food and shelter from winter storms.

If none of the meanings you know fit into the context of the sentence, you still may be able to determine the meaning by using the context clues. You are aware that the ponies are moving about and looking for food and shelter, so the meaning of *range* in the sentence will suggest *move about* or *roam*. Now read the sentence again using one of those meanings. Does the sentence make sense now?

Try using context clues to determine the meaning of the italicized word in each of these paragraphs:

Scientists have had difficulty in curing certain rare diseases because there is no information as to causes and treatment. This *dearth* of information makes a solution to problems difficult and time consuming.

His quick and very bold actions marked him as an *impetuous* man. He often did things without thinking beforehand whether his actions would be wise.

You can use several types of context clues to help you figure out the meanings of strange words. Among those types are DEFINITION CLUES, COMPARISON CLUES, CONTRAST CLUES, and SENSE OF PASSAGE CLUES.

A. DEFINITION CLUES

The type of context clue easiest to use is the definition clue. The sentence itself defines an unknown word. What is the meaning of the italicized word in each sentence at the top of page 33?

1. *A tyrant* is a ruler who uses power cruelly.
2. *Rapacious* means greedy.
3. An *ophthalmologist,* an eye doctor, should be consulted for eye problems.

Did you notice the words *is* and *means?* Those words are often used in the definition type of context clue. In the third sentence the definition is given by setting it off with commas rather than by using *is* or *means.*

Decide what the meaning of the italicized word is in each of the following sentences.

1. *Durum* is a kind of wheat used to make spaghetti.
2. The *poniard,* or sharp dagger, gleamed in the light.

B. COMPARISON CLUES

Sometimes the meaning of an unknown word is made clear by a direct comparison with a known word. In the following sentence, notice how the known word *relies* could help you with the meaning of the word *competent* if it were unknown: *Mr. Jones is a competent worker, so his foreman relies on him often.* One would rely on a *qualified* or *capable* individual; therefore, the meaning of *competent* could be either *qualified* or *capable.*

Can you decide what the meaning of the italicized word is in each of the following sentences?

1. A souvenir of miniature palm trees would serve as a *memento* of their trip to the islands.
2. The fog completely covered the area and *enveloped* the cars and people.

In the first sentence the words *souvenir* and *memento* are synonyms, words that mean about the same thing. In the second sentence *completely covered* and *enveloped* mean about the same thing. By comparing the meaning of an unknown word in a sentence with a known word or group of words, you can quite often get the meaning of the unknown word. The known word may often be a synonym of the unknown word.

What does the italicized word mean in each sentence below?

1. The team members were *despondent* when the score became 13–0, and their being so depressed made the situation hopeless.
2. The *minuscule* figures in the photograph could not be recognized for the very reason that they were so tiny.

C. CONTRAST CLUES

The contrast type of context clue is similar to the comparison clue except that the meaning of the known word is the opposite of the meaning of the unknown word. In the following sentence, how could the meaning of the known word *late* help you with the meaning of the word *punctual* if it were unknown?

John is usually late, but Larry is usually punctual.

The word *but* is a negative word which sometimes indicates that what follows is going to be in some way the opposite of the first part. In the case of the words that follow *John is usually late,* a contrast is made between Larry and John. If John is usually *late* and Larry is usually *punctual,* then *punctual* must mean the opposite of *late. Punctual,* therefore, must mean *prompt* or *on time.*

You will often find such words and terms as *but, however, not, on the other hand* used in sentences to indicate a contrast.

In each of the following sentences use the contrast clue to determine the meaning of the italicized word.

1. Mr. Smith is usually very clear in giving directions; however, the message I received from him was quite *vague.*
2. You would expect the manager to show mature behavior, but his *puerile* conduct during the incident was most surprising.
3. His *fallacious* arguments were, however, easily disproved by the logical answers of the speaker.

D. SENSE OF PASSAGE CLUES

Sometimes you can determine the meaning of an unknown word in a paragraph by thinking about the meaning of other parts of the paragraph. This type of context clue is called *sense of passage,* and the helpful parts in the context may come before, after, or both before and after the unknown word.

The unknown word in the following passage is *bovine.* Decide on its meaning by thinking about the meaning of the sentences that precede and follow the sentence that contains the word *bovine.*

Have you ever stopped to thank a cow? Without the gifts of this animal, your day would be a lot duller. This morning you probably poured milk on your favorite cereal. Your lunchtime meal owes much to the cow also. Rolls and bread depend on milk for their delicious flavor. You wouldn't be enjoying life quite so much if it weren't for our bovine friend. Even your favorite desserts — ice cream, cake, milkshakes — all make use of the products of the cow.

The entire passage is about the contributions of the cow. So you can conclude that *bovine* is a word that refers to *cow.*

What is the meaning of *pilfer* in the following passage?

Pack rats have been known to pilfer all kinds of items. Usually, they have no real use for what they take, but they have a curious nature that compels them to carry home small objects.

A special kind of meaning problem is that of getting the meaning of an idiom from context clues. An idiom is a group of words whose meaning is quite different from the meaning the words usually have. To determine the meaning of an idiom, you must look at the words in the context of the whole sentence. Suppose your principal had put this notice on the bulletin board: "There will be no exceptions made to the hard and fast rule about the length of the lunch period." You may know what the words *hard* and *fast* usually mean, but the words are used in a different way in the context of that sentence. From the remainder of the sentence the phrase *hard and fast* suggests a rule that is rigid and allows no exceptions.

In each of the following sentences determine the meaning of the italicized idiom from its context in the sentence:

1. With all the students arguing among themselves, the meeting was completely *out of hand.*
2. Sally was *walking on air* after Joe asked her to go to the prom.

Discussion

Help your class answer these questions:
1. What is meant by *getting meaning from context?*
2. What is the easiest type of context clue to use?
3. What punctuation marks are sometimes used with a definition clue?
4. What clue words are often used with the contrast type of context clue?
5. What is an idiom?
6. What meaning do the words *durum* and *poniard* have on page 33?
7. What are the meanings of *out of hand* and *walking on air* in the sentences at the top of this page?
8. What are synonyms for the words *despondent* and *minuscule* on page 34?
9. What meaning does *pilfer* have in the paragraph on page 35?

On your own

Number on a sheet of paper 1 to 7 to stand for the seven sentences that follow. After each numeral, write the letter before the word that explains what the italicized word means in the sentence that has the same numeral.

1. The driver entered the highway at a speed of twenty miles per hour. Soon he *accelerated* to sixty miles an hour.
   a. reduced   b. increased   c. reversed   d. corrected

2. When you pull an elastic, it will expand. Upon release, it will *contract.*

    a. stretch   b. become smaller   c. agree   d. dissolve

3. Immanuel Kant is a most difficult philosopher to read because his ideas are very *abstruse.*

    a. clear   b. foreign   c. obscure   d. important

4. Bill is very confident, not *timorous,* when he gives a speech.

    a. slow   b. loud   c. positive   d. timid

5. The Supreme Court decision *annulled* a state law that was found to be unconstitutional.

    a. repealed   b. added   c. signified   d. approved

6. As a land developer, Mr. Jones has had great success; however, his most recent project was a *fiasco.*

    a. success   b. failure   c. building   d. victory

7. A *vagrant* is one who moves from place to place.

    a. holder   b. speeder   c. wanderer   d. loser

Checking your work

If you are asked to do so, read aloud the answers you wrote to one or more questions. Can you tell what kind of clue you used? If you made a mistake in any answer, find out why it is a mistake.

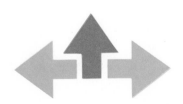

Question

Why isn't there
A light bulb
On the top of
Your head
That lights up
Each time
I strike you
With a
Brilliant thought?

Like a
Tree that,
Crashing from
A stroke of
Lightning,
Lets you
Know it's
Been hit.

Or a
Buzzer
On a
Washing machine
That tells
You,
"It's time to
take the
clothes out."

Instead
You sit there
With your
Mouth closed
and
Sometimes
Your
Eyes
And perhaps
Your mind?

BARBARA RITCHEY

Two-Wheeled Sport

by Charles Coombs

Sooner or later, nearly every motorcyclist yearns to pit his riding skills against those of others. Although there are a few professional motorcycle racers, just as there are professional racing-car drivers, the overwhelming majority of cycle riders retain their amateur standing. They race around dirt ovals, climb precarious hillsides, slog through swamps or woodlands, and battle the clock for the sheer joy and excitement of competition.

Two or more people on motorcycles can measure their riding skills against each other in many informal ways. The contest can be anything from a simple treasure hunt to a soccer game on lightweight machines or an impromptu race along a vacant stretch of beach that ends up as a free-for-all struggle to reach the top of a distant hill.

As in any type of motorcycle riding, the prime considerations in competition are riding experience and attention to safety factors.

Much of this competition is spontaneous and unorganized. However, cyclists who have tasted the heady delights of neighborhood victories and wish to take part in more highly organized contests can consider joining the American Motorcycle Association (AMA) or other organizations for cycles.

The AMA encourages formation of motorcycling clubs and sanctions some four thousand different competitive amateur and professional meets a year. Only members of the AMA are allowed to enter these contests so that sponsors and contestants can be reasonably sure that each rider has experience, practices proper safety, and will not become a hazard in competition. The AMA has headquarters in Worthington, Ohio, and local district representatives govern activities within their own areas. All groups adhere to basic AMA rules and bylaws.

A motorcyclist who competes in AMA-sanctioned events in which prize money is paid loses his amateur standing, and he must carry a competition license indicating his professional status. Most cycling competition, however, is composed of amateur events in which, at most, a trophy may be offered.

As in almost any other sport, there is a small group of trained professional motorcycle riders who manage to make a living by barnstorming around the country, entering different motorcycling events. Many of them operate dealerships or motorcycle shops during the off-season, and a few lucky ones are sponsored by cycle manufacturers.

As important as the prize money these professionals collect is the pursuit of the national championship of motorcycling. National championships are based on an accumulation of points earned in a variety of nationwide events. The current national champion has the privilege of sporting a number 1 on his cycle.

A wide assortment of competitive motorcycling events takes place in this country. Each requires varying degrees of skill and stamina. Only by scouting around and trying a few of them out can the eager new rider determine which best suits his abilities and interests. Plenty of riders have a great deal of fun, while at the same time improving their cycling skills, by entering informally organized field meets. These competitions may take place on vacant lots,

in parks, or on some field on the outskirts of town. Success depends largely upon the enthusiasm of the cyclists and on there being enough spirited members of the group with a knack for thinking up a series of events that are challenging to perform on a motorcycle.

A field meet is a funfest, a collection of games on two wheels, with hazards kept at a minimum. One common event is a Slow Race. Here contestants race the clock backwards, taking as much time as possible to ride between two points without losing balance and having to dab a foot (touch the ground), leave the course path, or kill the engine. There's a Boot Race in which all contestants' boots are tossed in a pile. En route to victory, the riders must find and don their own boots. Naturally, in the search, loose boots get thrown wildly in all directions.

Then there are contests in which riders try to build a hot dog, mustard and all, without stopping their machines, a difficult feat, since one hand is always needed on the throttle. There are barrel-rolling contests and any number of other stunts to perform while chugging along on a cycle. Such field meets are like picnics or Sunday outings. They really need no sanction or sponsorship other than a bunch of cheerful cyclists out for a good time and off-road fun. As a by-product of the horseplay, however, beginning cyclists gain valuable experience. Of

course, such cycling games are illegal on public thoroughfares.

As a rider becomes more proficient on his machine, he may enter more-advanced events. The popular English trials provide a danger-free race in which riders traverse rough terrain on a course that has been marked out in tape. Similar to a miniature golf course, a trials course may cover very little ground but have obstacles such as sand traps, water hazards, steep slopes, gullies, sharp curves, and so forth. Speed is no great factor, but control of the machine is. The rider loses points for dabbing a foot to the ground, crossing taped course lines, stopping, stalling the engine, or showing any other indications of poor control over his vehicle.

Having acquired full confidence and mastered his motorcycle, the amateur rider may progress to the road run, an event like a sports-car rally, except it is for two-wheeled vehicles instead of four-wheeled ones. A road run is both a race and an exercise in navigation. Routes are established, checkpoints are set up, and each contestant must follow clues in order to be first to reach his destination and the winner's circle.

While the race is going on, the cyclist also may find himself cruising through some scenic country. The road run, like straight touring for pleasure, is on prepared surfaces, including both paved highways and gravel or graded back roads. It is easy on machines and riders and is much preferred by many cyclists who don't relish such tire-pounding events as scrambles or enduros.

A scramble is a race conducted over a closed-circuit, dirt-track obstacle course. Here the rider must contend with sand, jumps, twists, turns, and assorted other riding hazards. There is no standard course for scrambles. As long as the route is difficult to maneuver around, it will suffice.

Actually, Grand Prix motorcycle racing — which requires a high degree of skill — is a form of scrambling but over longer and more rugged courses.

An endurance race, called an enduro, is a clocked event over an unfamiliar course having a full share of woods, desert, or other rough terrain. Contests usually run for two days or so, cover upwards of three hundred rugged miles, and really test the staying power of both man and machine. The rider tries, not to beat the clock, but to ride on a fixed schedule and hit each checkpoint on the split second if possible. Being too fast costs points as well as being too slow.

One of the favorite endurance races is the hare-and-hounds. Dozens of cycles usually participate in this grueling event. Any cross-country course that includes little-used roads, dirt trails, hilly and difficult terrain, can become the scene of a hare-and-hounds event.

Prior to the race, the long course is established by the hare, who marks the route with sporadic splashes of lime. The riders — the hounds — must hit assorted checkpoints during the pursuit. Other than that requirement, the race is to the swift. Some hare-and-hound races include a class for motorcycles with sidecars. That is a rough way to travel!

A racing event of great magnitude is the hare-and-hounds race which takes place periodically on California's Mojave Desert. As the sun rises, casting long shadows from gnarled Joshua trees, spiny cactus, and scrub brush of all kinds, hundreds of contestants kick their two-wheelers to life and roar off across the sandy, rock-strewn desert.

Before the day is over, many contestants have dropped by the wayside from sheer fatigue, or their cycles have been put out of working order by fouled spark plugs, flat tires, broken chains, or any of numerous other mischances that may befall a cyclist along the scorching (up to 130 degrees) course. Fortunately, due to frequent checkpoints and constant patrolling, by the end of the day all riders are accounted for. The broken-down machines are wrestled out of prickly barricades of underbrush or wallows of deep sand. A tired, grimy, but happy winner is declared.

Days later, riders are still nursing bruises, scratches, and sore muscles while busily repairing abused machines. The Mojave Desert hare-and-hounds is a race that no one in his right mind would try a second time; yet most riders who have done it once can't wait to tackle it again.

Many variations exist in scrambles, enduros, cross-country, hare-and-hounds, and Grand Prix motorcycle racing. All the races, however, call upon a full measure of endurance from both men and machines.

Other riders prefer motorcycle hill climbing. In this timed event the cyclists begin at a starting line at the bottom and ride to the top of a steep dirt hill. Although the event produces a fair share of spills, few serious accidents occur because the cycle's motor is rigged to cut off automatically when there's an upset. For the occasional cyclist who uses his vehicle mostly for transportation to school or for simple everyday riding, hill climbing is a better sport to watch than to enter. Hill-climbing cycles usually are stripped-down models that will not be damaged easily. Still, moderate hills attract all riders, and rare is the two-wheeler who has not tried his hand at the slopes.

Drag racing on motorcycles is almost as popular as the four-wheeled drags. The cycles use the same quarter-mile strip, burn lots of rubber leaving the starting gate, and can hit fantastic speeds of around 150 miles per hour in the ten seconds sometimes necessary to cover the distance. The drag-racing cycles are invariably custom-built. They are fueled with special exotic mixes and use oversize rear tires which furnish the essential traction for the blast-off and sprint. Drag races may be either time trials or races between individual contestants, and the various divisions are organized by type of cycle and size of engine.

Some communities conduct open competition for standard cycles ridden by sufficiently qualified and experienced cyclists. In any case, drag racing has its full share of dangers. It should never be attempted on neighborhood streets or, for that matter, anywhere except on an approved strip, and it should always be under proper supervision.

For the ultimate in two-wheeled speed, each August motorcyclists in specially built machines head for the vast, smooth salt flats of Bonneville, Utah, where all world speed records on land have been set. There, huddled inside streamlined, cigar-shaped wind fairings, the drivers of two-wheelers that hardly resemble motorcycles at all have exceeded speeds of 255 miles per hour. At this time, speed cyclists are striving for 300 miles per hour. That, indeed, is an event in which few participate.

Also limited to a special group of cyclists is the track racing on dirt or boards that one sees on television or at country fairs. This racing is strictly a spectator sport, except for the small handful of professional cyclists who broadside around the curves with an iron-shod left shoe scraping the dirt for balance and stability. The cycles used in such races are without brakes, and the contestants usually wear long-sleeved leather clothing, called simply leathers, to offer them some protection in the event of a high-speed spill. Although this type of racing is perhaps not strictly for professionals, it definitely does require professional skills.

All in all, whether the competition is organized or merely confined to a few eager enthusiasts anxious to pit their riding skills against each other, cycling for sport accounts for a large percentage of all motorcycling.

But no matter for what type of work, sport, or simple pleasure the cyclist uses his machine, his success and enjoyment will depend on the practiced skill and concern for safety with which he rides. Motorcycling is a two-wheeled world that is opening ever wider to exploration by the adventurous young.

DISCUSSION

1. What is the AMA? Why are AMA contests for members only? What special privilege is granted to the national AMA champion?
2. What are some contests suitable for beginning cyclists? For more advanced? For highly skilled?
3. Choose one of the contests or events mentioned in the article and describe it.
4. Would you say that professional motorcyclists make a lot of money? What makes you think that?
5. How do you think the author feels about motorcycling? Point out passages that suggest how he feels.
6. Judging from the article, what may be some of the attractions of motorcycling for those who ride for pleasure rather than as competitors?
7. What limits does the author feel that cyclists should place on their enthusiasm for the sport? Do you think that his cautions are generally followed? Why do you think that?

8. What motorcycling activities described in the article would you enjoy most? Why? Which ones would you leave for someone else? Why?

9. Have you heard people comment negatively about motorcycling and motorcyclists? What are some possible reasons for their feelings? After reading this article, do you think you could persuade them to change their feelings? If so, how would you do that?

AUTHOR

After working for many years at farming, carpentry, and merchandising, Charles Coombs decided in 1946 to become a full-time writer. His decision was unquestionably a wise one, for the great number and popularity of the books he has written testify to his unusual gifts as an author.

Many of his earliest publications were collections of adventure, sports, or detective stories, but currently he is best known for his writings about aerospace and other technical subjects. To obtain accurate background material, he travels extensively, usually by air — which is no hardship for Mr. Coombs, who at one time hoped to become a pilot. The research he does for many of his projects is carried on with the help and cooperation of the National Aeronautics and Space Administration and other governmental agencies.

In addition to writing more than five hundred short stories, most of which appeared originally in magazines for young people, Mr. Coombs is the author of over two hundred articles on a wide range of topics. He has a special ability to explain even the most complicated subjects in a way that makes them easily understood and exciting. His skill as a technical writer is evident in such recent books as *Motorcycling,* of which "Two-Wheeled Sport" is a chapter, *Aerospace Pilot, Cleared for Takeoff: Behind the Scenes at an Airport,* and *Deep-Sea World: The Story of Oceanography.*

The Boy Who Predicted Earthquakes

by Margaret St. Clair

"Naturally, you're skeptical," Wellman said. He poured water from a carafe, put a pill on his tongue, washed the pill down. "Naturally, understandably. I don't blame you, wouldn't dream of blaming you. A good many of us here at the studio had your attitude, I'm afraid, when we started programming this boy Herbert. I don't mind telling you, just between ourselves, that I myself was pretty doubtful that a show of that sort would be good television."

Wellman scratched behind an ear while Read looked on with scientific interest. "Well, I was wrong," Wellman said, putting the hand down again. "I'm pleased to say that I was 1,000 per cent wrong. The kid's first, unannounced, unadvertised show brought nearly fourteen hundred pieces of mail. And his rating nowadays . . ." He leaned toward Read and whispered a figure.

"Oh," Read said.

"We haven't given it out yet, because those buzzards at Purple simply wouldn't believe us. But it's the plain simple truth. There isn't another TV personality today who has the following the kid has. He's on short wave, too, and people tune him in all over the globe. Every time he has a show, the post office has to send two special trucks with his mail. I can't tell you how happy I am, Read, that you scientists are thinking about making a study of him at last. I'm terrifically sincere about this."

"What's he like personally?" Read asked.

"The kid? Oh, very simple, very quiet, very, very sincere. I like him tremendously. His father — well, he's a real character."

"How does the program work?"

"You mean how does Herbert do it? Frankly, Read, that's something for you researchers to find out. We haven't the faintest idea what happens, really.

"I can tell you the program details, of course. The kid has a show twice a week, Mondays and Fridays. He won't use a script" — Wellman grimaced — "which is pretty much a headache for us. He says a script dries him up. He's on the air for twelve minutes. Most of that time he just talks, telling the viewers about what he's been doing in school, the books he's been reading, and so on. The kind of stuff you'd hear from any nice, quiet boy. But he always makes one or two predictions, always at least one, and never more than three. They are always things that will happen within forty-eight hours. Herbert says he can't see any farther ahead than that."

"And they do happen?" Read said. It was less a question than statement.

"They do," Wellman replied, somewhat heavily. He puffed out his lips. "Herbert predicted the stratosphere-liner wreck off Guam last April, the Gulf States hurricane, the election results. He predicted the submarine disaster in the Tortugas. Do you realize that the FBI has an agent sitting in the studio with him during every show out of range of the scanners? That's so he can be taken off the air immediately if he says anything that might be contrary to public policy. They take him that seriously.

"I went over the kid's record yesterday when I heard the university was thinking of studying him. His show has been going out now for a year and a half, twice a week. He's made 206 predictions during that time. And every one of them, every single one of them, has come true. By now the general public has such confidence in him that" — Wellman licked his lips and hunted for a comparison — "that they'd believe him if he predicted the end of the world or the winner of the Irish Sweepstakes.

"I'm sincere about this, Read, terrifically sincere. Herbert is the biggest thing in TV since the invention of the selenium cell. You can't overestimate him or his importance. And now, shall we go take in his show? It's just about time for him to go on."

Wellman got up from his desk chair, smoothing into place the design of pink and purple penguins on his necktie. He led Read through

the corridors of the station to the observation room of studio 8G, where Herbert Pinner was.

Herbert looked, Read thought, like a nice, quiet boy. He was about fifteen, tall for his age, with a pleasant, intelligent, somewhat careworn face. He went about the preparation for his show with perfect composure, which might hide a touch of distaste.

"... I have been reading a very interesting book," Herbert said to the TV audience. "Its name is *The Count of Monte Cristo.* I think almost anybody might enjoy it." He held up the book for the viewers to see. "I have also begun a book on astronomy by a man named Duncan. Reading that book has made me want a telescope. My father says that if I work hard and get good grades in school, I can have a small telescope at the end of the term. I will tell you what I can see with the telescope after we buy it.

"There will be an earthquake, not a bad one, in the North Atlantic States tonight. There will be considerable property damage, but no one will be killed. Tomorrow morning about ten o'clock they will find Gwendolyn Box, who has been lost in the Sierras since Thursday. Her leg is broken, but she will still be alive.

"After I get the telescope, I hope to become a member of the Society of Variable Star Observers. Variable stars are stars whose brightness varies because of internal changes or because of external causes . . ."

At the end of the program Read was introduced to young Pinner. He found the boy polite and cooperative but a little remote.

"I don't know just how I do do it, Mr. Read," Herbert said when a number of preliminary questions had been put. "It isn't pictures, the way you suggested, and it isn't words. It's just — it just comes into my mind.

"One thing I've noticed is that I can't predict anything unless I more or less know what it is. I could predict about the earthquake because everybody knows what a quake is, pretty much. But I couldn't have predicted about Gwendolyn Box if I hadn't known she was missing. I'd just have had a feeling that somebody or something was going to be found."

"You mean you can't make predictions about anything unless it's in your consciousness previously?" Read asked intently.

Herbert hesitated. "I guess so," he said. "It makes a . . . a spot in my mind, but I can't identify it. It's like looking at a light with your eyes shut. You know a light is there, but that's all you know about it. That's the reason why I read so many books. The more things I know about, the more things I can predict.

"Sometimes I miss important things too. I don't know why that is. There was the time the atomic pile exploded and so many people were killed. All I had for that day was an increase in employment.

"I don't know how it works, really, Mr. Read. I just know it does."

Herbert's father came up. He was a small, bouncing man with the extrovert's persuasive personality. "So you're going to investigate Herbie, hum?" he said when the introductions had been performed. "Well, that's fine. It's time he was investigated."

"I believe we are," Read answered with a touch of caution. "I'll have to have the appropriation for the project approved first."

Mr. Pinner looked at him shrewdly. "You want to see whether there's an earthquake first, isn't that it? It's different when you hear him saying it himself. Well, there will be. It's a terrible thing, an earthquake." He clicked his tongue deprecatingly. "But nobody will be killed, that's one good thing. And they'll find that Miss Box the way Herbie says they will."

The earthquake arrived about nine fifteen, when Read was sitting under the bridge lamp reading a report from the Society for Psychical Research. There was an ominous muttering rumble and then a long, swaying, seasick roll.

Next morning Read had his secretary put through a call to Haffner, a seismologist with whom he had a casual acquaintanceship. Haffner, over the phone, was definite and brusque.

"Certainly there's no way of foretelling a quake," he snapped. "Not even an hour in advance. If there were, we'd issue warnings and get people out in time. There'd never be any loss of life. We can tell in a general way where a quake is likely, yes. We've known for years that this area was in for one. But as for setting the exact time — you might as well ask an astronomer to predict a nova for you. He doesn't know, and neither do we. What brought this up, anyway? The prediction made by that Pinner kid?"

"Yes. We're thinking of observing him."

"Thinking of it? You mean you're only just now getting around to him? Lord, what ivory towers you research psychologists must live in!"

"You think he's genuine?"

"The answer is an unqualified yes."

Read hung up. When he went out to lunch, he saw by the headlines that Gwendolyn Box had been found just as Herbert had predicted on his television program.

Still he hesitated. It was not until Thursday that he realized that he was hesitating, not because he was afraid of wasting the university's money on a fake, but because he was all too sure that Herbert Pinner was genuine. He didn't at bottom want to start this study. He was afraid.

The realization shocked him. He got the dean on the phone at once, asked for his appropriation, and was told there would be no difficulty about it. Friday morning he selected his two assistants for the project, and by the time Herbert's program was nearly due to go out, they were at the station.

They found Herbert sitting tensely on a chair in studio 8G with Wellman and five or six other station executives clustered around him. His father was dancing about excitedly, wringing his hands. Even the FBI man had abandoned his usual detachment and was joining warmly in the argument. And Herbert, in the middle, was shaking his head and saying, "No, no, I can't," over and over again doggedly.

"But why not, Herbie?" his father wailed. "Please tell me why not. Why won't you give your show?"

"I can't," Herbert said. "Please don't ask me. I just can't." Read noticed how white the boy was around the mouth.

"But, Herbie, you can have anything you want, anything, if you only will! That telescope — I'll buy it for you tomorrow. I'll buy it tonight!"

"I don't want a telescope," young Pinner said wanly. "I don't want to look through it."

"I'll get you a pony, a motorboat, a swimming pool! Herbie, I'll get you anything!"

"No," Herbert said.

Mr. Pinner looked around him desperately. His eyes fell on Read, standing in the corner, and he hurried over to him. "See what you can do with him, Mr. Read," he panted.

Read chewed his lower lip. In a sense it was his business. He pushed his way through the crowd to Herbert and put his hand on his shoulder. "What's this I hear about you not wanting to give your show today, Herbert?" he asked.

Herbert looked up at him. The harassed expression in his eyes made Read feel guilty and contrite. "I just can't," he said. "Don't you start asking me too, Mr. Read."

Once more Read chewed his lip. Part of the technique of parapsychology lies in getting subjects to cooperate. "If you don't go on the air, Herbert," he said, "a lot of people are going to be disappointed."

Herbert's face took on a tinge of sullenness. "I can't help it," he said.

"More than that, a lot of people are going to be frightened. They won't know why you aren't going on the air, and they'll imagine things. All sorts of things. If they don't view you, an awful lot of people are going to be scared."

"I —" Herbert said. He rubbed his cheek. "Maybe that's right," he answered slowly. "Only . . ."

"You've got to go on with your show."

Herbert capitulated suddenly. "All right," he said, "I'll try."

Everyone in the studio sighed deeply. There was a general motion toward the door of the observation room. Voices were raised in high-pitched, rather nervous chatter. The crisis was over; the worst would not occur.

The first part of Herbert's show was much like the others had been. The boy's voice was a trifle unsteady, and his hands had a tendency to shake, but these abnormalities would have passed the average viewer unnoticed. When perhaps five minutes of the show had gone, Herbert put aside the books and drawings he had been showing his audience (he had been discussing mechanical drawing) and began to speak with great seriousness.

"I want to tell you about tomorrow," he said. "Tomorrow" — he stopped and swallowed — "tomorrow is going to be different from what anything in the past has been. Tomorrow is going to be the start of a new and better world for all of us."

Read, listening in the glass-enclosed room, felt an incredulous thrill race over him at the words. He glanced around at the faces of the others and saw that they were listening intently, their faces strained and rapt. Wellman's lower jaw dropped a little, and he absently fingered the unicorns on his tie.

"In the past," young Pinner said, "we've had a pretty bad time. We've had wars — so many wars — and famines and pestilences. We've had depressions and haven't known what caused them; we've had people starving when there was food and dying of diseases for which we knew the cure. We've seen the wealth of the world wasted shamelessly, the rivers running black with the washed-off soil, while hunger for all of us got surer and nearer every day. We've suffered; we've had a hard time.

"Beginning tomorrow" — his voice grew louder and more deep — "all that is going to be changed. There won't be any more wars. We're going to live side by side like brothers. We're going to forget about killing and breaking and bombs. From pole to pole the world will be one great garden, full of richness and fruit, and it will be for all of us to have and use and enjoy. People will live a long time and live happily, and when they die, it will be from old age. Nobody will be afraid anymore. For the first time since human beings lived on earth, we're going to live the way human beings should.

"The cities will be full of the richness of culture, full of art and music and books. And every race on earth will contribute to that culture, each in its degree. We're going to be wiser and happier and richer than any people have ever been. And pretty soon" — he hesitated for a moment, as if his thought had stumbled — "pretty soon we're going to send out rocket ships to Mars and Venus and Jupiter. We'll go to the limits of our solar system to see what Uranus and Pluto are like. And maybe from there — it's possible — we'll go on and visit the stars.

"Tomorrow is going to be the beginning of all that. That's all for now. Good-by. Good night."

For a moment after he had ceased, no one moved or spoke. Then voices began to babble deliriously. Read, glancing at the people around him, noticed how white their faces were and how dilated their eyes.

"Wonder what effect the new setup will have on TV?" Wellman said, as if to himself. His tie was flopping wildly about. "There'll be TV, that's certain — it's part of the good life." And then, to Pinner, who was blowing his nose and wiping his eyes, "Get him out of here, Pinner, right away. He'll be mobbed if he stays here."

Herbert's father nodded. He dashed into the studio after Herbert, who was already surrounded, and came back with him. With Read running interference, they fought their way through the corridor and down to the street level at the back of the station.

Read got into the car uninvited and sat down opposite Herbert on one of the folding seats. The boy looked quite exhausted, but his lips wore a faint smile. "You'd better have the chauffeur take you to some quiet hotel," Read said to the senior Pinner. "You'd be besieged if you went to your usual place."

Pinner nodded. "Hotel Triller," he said to the driver of the car. "Go slow, cabby. We want to think."

He slipped his arm around his son and hugged him. His eyes were shining. "I'm proud of you, Herbie," he declared solemnly, "as proud as can be. What you said — those were wonderful, wonderful things."

The driver had made no move to start the car. Now he turned round and spoke. "It's young Mr. Pinner, isn't it? I was watching you just now. Could I shake your hand?"

After a moment Herbert leaned forward and extended it. The chauffeur accepted it almost reverently. "I just want to thank you — just want to thank you — excuse me, Mr. Herbert. But what you said meant a lot to me. I was in the last war."

The car slid away from the curb. As it moved downtown, Read saw that Pinner's injunction to the driver to go slow had been unnecessary. People were thronging the streets already. The sidewalks were choked. People began to spill over onto the pavements. The car slowed to a walk, to a crawl, and still they poured out. Read snapped the blinds down for fear Herbert would be recognized.

Newsboys were screaming on the corners in raucous hysteria. As the car came to a halt, Pinner opened the door and slipped out. He came scrambling back with an armload of papers he had bought.

"NEW WORLD COMING!" one read, another "MILLENNIUM TO-MORROW!" and another quite simply, "JOY TO THE WORLD!" Read spread the papers out and began to read the story in one of them.

"A 15-year-old boy told the world that its troubles were over beginning tomorrow, and the world went wild with joy. The boy, Herbert Pinner, whose uncannily accurate predictions have won him a worldwide following, predicted an era of peace, abundance, and prosperity such as the world has never known before . . ."

"Isn't it wonderful, Herbert?" Pinner panted. His eyes were blazing. He shook Herbert's arm. "Isn't it wonderful? Aren't you glad?"

"Yes," Herbert said.

They got to the hotel at last and registered. They were given a suite on the sixteenth floor. Even at this height they could faintly hear the excitement of the crowd below.

"Lie down and rest, Herbert," Mr. Pinner said. "You look worn out. Telling all that — it was hard on you." He bounced around the room for a moment and then turned to Herbert apologetically. "You'll excuse me if I go out, son, won't you? I'm too excited to be quiet. I want to see what's going on outside." His hand was on the knob of the door.

"Yes, go ahead," Herbert answered. He had sunk down in a chair.

Read and Herbert were alone in the room. There was silence for a moment. Herbert laced his fingers over his forehead and sighed.

"Herbert," Read said softly, "I thought you couldn't see into the future for more than forty-eight hours ahead."

"That's right," Herbert replied without looking up.

"Then how could you foresee all the things you predicted tonight?"

The question seemed to sink into the silence of the room like a stone dropped into a pond. Ripples spread out from it. Herbert said, "Do you really want to know?"

For a moment Read had to hunt for the name of the emotion he felt. It was fear. He answered, "Yes."

Herbert got up and went over to the window. He stood looking out, not at the crowded streets, but at the sky — where, thanks to daylight-saving time, a faint sunset glow yet lingered.

"I wouldn't have known if I hadn't read the book," he said, turning around, the words coming out in a rush. "I'd just have known something big — big — was going to happen. But now I know. I read about it in my astronomy book.

"Look over here." He pointed to the west, where the sun had been. "Tomorrow it won't be like this."

"What do you mean?" Read cried. His voice was sharp with anxiety. "What are you trying to say?"

"That . . . tomorrow the sun will be different. Maybe it's better this way. I wanted them to be happy. You mustn't hold it against me, Mr. Read, that I lied to them."

Read turned on him fiercely. "What is it? What's going to happen tomorrow? You've got to say!"

"Why, tomorrow the sun — I've forgotten the word. What is it they call it when a star flares up suddenly, when it becomes a billion times hotter than it was before?"

"A nova?" Read cried.

"That's it. Tomorrow . . . the sun is going to explode."

DISCUSSION

1. Why did the public have such tremendous confidence in Herbert's predictions?
2. What limitations were there on Herbert's power to predict? What had Herbert been reading that made it possible for him to know what was going to happen to the sun?
3. On Read's second visit to the TV studio, what had Herbert done to upset everyone?
4. What prediction did Herbert make on TV after agreeing to do the show? How did he change his prediction when he talked with Read?
5. When Herbert's father was trying to get him to do the TV show and offered to buy him a telescope immediately, why did Herbert no longer want it?
6. After he had refused to do the show, why do you think Herbert changed his mind and agreed to do it?
7. Why do you think Herbert told the truth to Read rather than to his father?
8. Why do you think Herbert's TV show was such a success?
9. In your opinion, what sort of person was Read?
10. Do you think that Read should keep the secret that Herbert shared with him? Why do you think as you do?
11. Would you like to have the power to foretell the future? Why or why not?

Owl Quartet

by Arline Thomas

She had no special training or equipment, but she did have a way with the injured or abandoned birds she rescued in the shoe box she called her ambulance. Here Arline Thomas tells about three baby owls that had been toppled from their nest by jays and about what happened when she added a fourth member to her trio.

As they crouched in their shoe-box ambulance, they were three shapeless lumps of feathers, punctuated by round, yellow eyes. As if their outsized beaks were too heavy for them, they hung their heads. Their feathered ear tufts, as well as their size, identified them as screech owls, a bird that has the distinction of coming in either of two colors: red-brown or gray. This color difference is found in both male and female screech owls regardless of age or season of the year. Of my three, one was reddish, the other two gray.

Deciding to put the little owls in a larger carton, I reached for the reddish one, which was also the smallest. He backed away and snapped his beak. Just guessing at his sex, I named him Snapper.

After consulting the zoo, I offered them all some raw hamburger. Snapper and the middle-sized one looked bewildered at this substitute for their mouse-grasshopper diet, but the largest one scrambled over to me and began eating out of my hand. Known from then on as Wimpy, he turned out to be a lovable extrovert and the leader of the gang. Though normally nocturnal, the youngsters quickly got used to a daytime schedule, thriving on three meals of raw beef. At night they slept quietly in their carton.

Mornings, after spreading newspapers, I let them loose in the kitchen. Like three little gnomes, they toured the room. Exploring the furniture, Wimpy blinked in wide-eyed surprise when the garbage-can lid snapped. After a while they grew bold enough to run and skip, waving their stumpy wings in flight practice. Snapper often slipped and fell on his face — then, gravely righting himself, slowed down to a toddle. Soon they could flutter to the chair backs and later to the windowsill. From there their keen eyes watched the affairs of the neighborhood. Contrary to widespread belief, owls are certainly not blind in daylight. In fact, they see very well, but most see better at dusk because their eyes, adapted for night hunting, are so sensitive that the iris almost closes in strong light.

Watching an airplane overhead or an animal in the street, my owls would crane their necks and swivel their heads until they looked straight back over their shoulders. Then — a trick that often alarmed me — they would snap their heads frontward so fast that it seemed as though they had turned them in a complete circle. This was only an illusion, but the movement, made easy by their fourteen neck bones against our seven, is responsible for the old folktale that the sure way to kill an owl is to walk around and around it — as it keeps twisting its head to follow you, it will soon wring its own neck.

While I was getting some firsthand knowledge about owls, Simone, a friend from Paris, visited me. Fascinated by the birds, she offered to help me care for them. As a reward, she was allowed to name the middle-sized one. Touching his head lightly with a drop of perfume, she translated his family name (owl) into French, calling him Hibou (ē′bōo).

And such is the magic of words — and owls — that Hibou really seemed French. Like all of his kin, he had a nearly human face. Rings of short flattened feathers formed a "face" for his round eyes. His beak, bordered by a silky mustache, was very like a nose. But his flexible ear tufts, which he often held at a rakish angle, gave him his personality. Simone assured me he needed only a white boutonniere on his gray shoulder to complete the illusion of a jaunty boulevardier.

"Look at him, my gallant Hibou," she called to me once. "See how he takes care to sheathe his talons when I hold him on my finger." Tickled silly by all the attention, the rascal flattened his ear tufts, a picture of demure sweetness as he coyly bent his head sideways.

Simone spoiled him terribly, often taking him out of the cage and whispering endearments in French to him. She also fed him bits of feathered skin, which she scissored from the chicken heads that were part of his diet. Like all birds of prey, he had to have either fur or feathers in his diet to stimulate his digestion and clean out his stomach. Some hours after his meal, he spat up an oval pellet consisting of feathers with indigestible matter neatly wrapped inside.

For days after Simone left, Hibou seemed to listen for her footsteps, turning expectantly toward the doorway through which she no longer appeared. He moped, too, and even neglected his fastidious preening.

Although Hibou was never as friendly with me as he was with Simone, all the birds became quite tame. Even Snapper flew readily to me. Wimpy, the gregarious showoff, often rode around the house perched on my shoulder. He was just as amiable with the neighborhood children who loved to drop in and see the owls. Looking like a character from a Disney film, Wimpy fluffed his feathers and perched on their fingers, waiting expectantly to be petted.

While the owls were very young, they needed no water to drink. But later, one hot day, I put some in a shallow pan on the floor. As curious as monkeys, they glided down from the sill and peered over the rim. Steeling himself to get up his courage, Wimpy took a long drink, letting the water slowly trickle down his throat like rare wine. Reassured, Hibou and Snapper did the same. Then eventually Wimpy stepped into the pan. Astounded at his daring, he stood gazing at his submerged feet until, getting braver, he sat down on the water and dunked his tail. Ruffling his feathers, he began to bathe, flailing his wings and dipping his face until his fluffy plumage was sodden, thereby revealing an unbelievably skinny neck and legs.

Hibou tried it out next, repeating Wimpy's vigorous actions and scattering still more water on the floor, which left an almost empty pan for Snapper.

Recklessly he threw himself on his face and slid his breast along the bottom, trying to scoop up as much moisture as he could. Then keeling over sideways, he attempted to wet first one wing and then the other, until he lost his balance and rolled out onto the floor.

As frolicsome as kittens, the owls loved to play. One of the games was pounce, a preparation for their role as hunters. By now they had lost their baby fluffiness; their wing feathers were firm and strong except at the edges, which would remain soft and downy all their lives. This is a characteristic of all owls that lets them fly in ghostlike silence and drop quietly down on their prey. Understandably, the Indian name for owl means "hush-wing." The game went something like this. While the owls sat on a perch, I held out a feather. They waited until I let it fall, meanwhile swaying their heads like pendulums to focus their eyes. Gliding like shad-

ows, they swooped, trying to clutch it with their flexible claws. When it drifted away, they chased it across the room, bumping their heads together and tumbling over one another, all the while whinnying with excitement. Even when they were older, they did not screech unpleasantly but gave a warbling *whoo-whoo* call.

When the three owls were about half-grown, an acquaintance who was a naturalist asked me to take on another one. Rescued during a cloudburst in New Jersey, it had been leading a pampered but lonely life in his city apartment, living on white mice that cost fifty cents apiece. The newcomer, named Jersey, was about the size of Snapper, the small red owl, but his feathers were gray like those of the other two.

A meek little bird, Jersey never adjusted to the rowdy ways of my lively trio, yet he followed them around, hoping to make friends. He often edged up to them and timidly flut-

tered his wings, but they either
jumped on his head or stepped on his
face. At feeding time, too, they gave
him no peace. A slow eater, Jersey
liked to pause and look around between bites. Hurriedly bolting their
own food, the others took turns
snatching his away. Always treating
him like a rank outsider, they never
let him join in any owl games, except
one in which he was "it."

I saw them start this one warm
morning when they were all sitting on
the windowsill and staring outdoors,
Wimpy at one end, Jersey the other.
Turning his head, Wimpy nudged
Hibou, who in turn pushed Snapper.
Closing ranks, the three sidled along
the sill. They pressed their bodies together at a crazy angle, leaning their
combined weight against Jersey to
squeeze him against the window
frame until he began to pant. Finally,
almost suffocated, he dropped to the
floor and gazed up at his tormentors
in puzzled innocence. Then, fairly

chuckling with glee, they spread out again with plenty of room to spare.

Although more or less resigned to being pushed around, once when the going got too tough, Jersey tried to escape. Making a wild dive to the floor, he jumped headlong into the black border of the linoleum, mistaking it for a hole. Backing away, he tried again, this time banging his head against the wall. Baffled by his failure to find a hiding place, he walked slowly away, shaking his tail. That afternoon he disappeared, and though I looked everywhere in the house, I couldn't find him. I even searched the garden in the belief that, rejected by his peers, he had slipped out the door and run away. It was almost evening when I reached into a cabinet drawer and felt something soft. Pulling out the drawer, I found Jersey huddled in a corner behind my knife box. I stroked his head, gave him an extra large piece of meat to comfort him, and put him back on the window with the rest. A few minutes later, he was crouching abjectly while the others, walking back and forth along the sill, planted their feet squarely on his neck and clobbered him with their beaks.

After that, he rarely sat with them; instead, he perched on the towel rack, where he watched me do my chores or stared at the wall. At night, too, he kept apart from the rest, sitting on the lower perch in their carton, while the others perched above him.

By midsummer the nearly grown birds were ten inches tall and flying well. However, as often happens with birds that people raise, they were too tame to release in a residential neighborhood. The problem was solved when the Audubon Society proposed keeping them for the rest of the summer at their Greenwich, Connecticut, camp, where conservation courses are given to teachers, scout leaders, and bird lovers.

After the owls were settled in their new home, I went to visit them. Kept in a picturesque red barn that had been converted into a nature museum, they were the only live exhibits there at the time. Groups of students gathered around their cage as the camp biologist discussed owls, food chains, and the primeval accident that some four hundred million years ago resulted in the creation of green plants. My four owls turned unusually solemn when the lecturer described their background, mentioning that in prehistoric times the cavemen believed owls to be the playmates of devils. As I approached their cage later, they recognized me and whimpered to be let out. When I opened the door, they swarmed over me, while the campers ran for their cameras.

While I was at camp, the biologist who had charge of the owls came over and talked to me about them. He had been teaching them to forage by letting them out every once in a while in a nearby field so they could learn to catch grasshoppers before their final release. Screech owls eat grasshoppers and moths all during their lifetime, and this hunting practice was to insure their survival in the wild.

"For an amateur, you did a good job raising them," he complimented. "They're healthy little birds and must have gotten a proper diet."

Although flattered by his praise, I was still concerned about my low bird on the totem pole, meek little Jersey.

Almost afraid of his answer, I asked, "The smallest gray one, how's he getting along?"

"A whiz at hunting grasshoppers," he astounded me by saying, "and the only one so far to catch a mouse."

Like the parent of an underachiever who has suddenly made good, I glowed with pride.

DISCUSSION

1. What kind of owls did the author rescue? How was she able to identify them?
2. What two common beliefs about owls does the author dispute? What are the facts?
3. What special food did Simone feed to Hibou? Why?
4. How was Jersey treated by the other owls? Why do you think they behaved toward him as they did?
5. Do most owls hunt grasshoppers? Why did these owls need special training in this activity?
6. Why was the author particularly pleased by Jersey's success in hunting?
7. Do you think that the owls' treatment of Jersey was typical of all living creatures? Would you expect the same behavior from human beings? Why or why not?
8. Was the author a trained naturalist? Why do you think she was successful in caring for the owls?
9. How does the author's description of the owls and their behavior differ from a scientist's description such as you would find in an encyclopedia article? Point out specific passages in "Owl Quartet" to support your answer.

The Good-Luck Frog
by Hal Higdon

It is the age of the electronic Olympics, and in Olympic Village in the small country of Scandia, engineers have installed all kinds of scientific marvels. The most impressive is a giant computer known as PED-72, which is the pride of its builder, Peter Powell. It is the official and sole judge of each Olympic event and instantly announces the winner. Connected to sensors, cameras, and other devices, and programmed to know what would be a perfect performance, the computer can judge even events like gymnastics and diving where athletes are scored on form and style rather than speed or distance.

Stacy Randolph, a member of the American team, has made it to the finals of the women's platform diving. But she has lost her good-luck charm and is facing the last day of competition without it. When a young photographer named Dave Henderson finds Stacy's metal frog, he tries to get it to her at the swim palace before she has to make her final three dives.

When Dave reached the bus depot, none of the buses were moving. He suddenly recalled that buses to the other side of town were being halted for three hours today. Traffic was being blocked because of the marathon, a long-distance running race that wound through the city streets. At the Mexico City Olympics, a swimmer missed his event because he got stuck in traffic on the day of the marathon.

Dave ran quickly back to his room and rummaged through the closet. He found what he wanted in a bag — a pair of roller shoes. They looked like regular track shoes but had roller bearings instead of spikes. "The bus traffic may be stopped," he thought, "but I can get through wearing these." He hurriedly laced the shoes onto his feet and grabbed Stacy's frog.

He moved quickly to the elevator. Soon Dave was skating swiftly along the streets. He reached the boulevard, where soldiers serving as traffic guards had traffic blocked for the marathoners, and darted quickly across.

"Hey, where are you going?" shouted one of the guards.

"Swim palace," said Dave, but he did not stop.

"Come back here!" shouted another guard.

At that moment a captain of the guards arrived in a jeep and wanted to know the cause of the commotion. The two guards explained about the jaywalking roller skater.

"He can't get away with that," snorted the captain. "Which way was he going?"

"To the swim palace," answered the two guards.

The captain motioned for his two men to climb into the jeep. Then he turned to his driver and said, "Follow that roller skater!" With a clashing of gears, the jeep full of guards roared off in Dave's wake.

Dave skated rapidly into the swim palace in time to see Stacy poised on top of the diving platform. "My gosh, I'm too late," he thought.

"Let's see your ticket," asked one of the guards.

Dave flashed him his press pass. He wondered for a minute how he could get Stacy's attention. He wanted her to know that he had her frog in hand.

He began to move toward the diving area. *Scrape, scrape* went his roller skates against the tile of the pool. A number of Olympic officials sitting in the grandstand turned around and glared at him. "Shhhhh," they said.

At that moment Stacy hurled herself off the platform, turning and twisting and knifing smoothly into the water. Immediately the scoreboard lit up: 83.04 POINTS. A cheer rose from the crowd.

"Holy cow," thought Dave. "That's her best dive so far. And she did it without her good-luck frog."

Stacy was climbing out of the water to the applause of the crowd. She toweled herself dry, then turned and watched another diver go off the board.

Dave wondered if he should call to her and tell her he was here. But she had gotten her best score believing that the frog was lost. He decided to keep quiet.

"Dave, you brought my frog." It was too late; Stacy had spotted him.

"Good dive, Stacy," he said. She reached toward the stainless-steel frog in his hand. He held it away from her. "You don't need the frog, Stacy. See how well you dove without it."

"Don't be silly," Stacy said, taking the frog from his hand. "If I dove that well without the frog, think how well I can dive with it." She turned back toward the diving platform.

Dave shouted, "Stacy, you've got to break this frog habit."

One of the Olympic officials turned and glared at him again. "Young man, if you don't keep quiet, you're going out of here."

"Yes, sir," said Dave.

He watched as another diver cut into the water. Her dive hadn't been as good as Stacy's last one. Stacy had moved up from fourth to second place. Maybe there was a chance of her winning a gold medal.

It was Stacy's turn again. She set her frog near the side of the pool, then ascended to the top of the platform. The crowd hushed. Stacy launched herself into space. She twisted and turned, slicing into the water — an even more perfect dive than the last one.

But the computer didn't seem to think so. It scored her dive 77.39 points. The crowd groaned. That would cost Stacy dearly.

"She was robbed!" Dave shouted. "Kill the computer!"

Peter Powell, sitting in the group of Olympic officials, looked around and glared, trying to spot the person insulting his computer. Dave decided he'd better keep quiet.

The next dive was by an East German girl. It dropped Stacy to fourth, and another diver pushed her back to fifth. She had only one more dive left to try to make her gold medal.

Once more Stacy moved toward the diving platform. She placed her frog by the water's edge and started up the ladder.

Dave sat watching. Why should she dive so well without the frog and so badly with it? As Stacy reached the top of the platform, he stared at the steel frog sitting right above one of the sensor lenses.

Suddenly Dave stood up. "That's it," he realized. The frog was interfering with the sensor lens at that point. The steel would affect the magnetic circuits leading to the computer. Stacy could not get full credit for her dives.

"Wait!" he shouted and lunged forward.

But Dave had lunged forgetting he had roller skates on his feet. Suddenly he slid out of balance toward the diving platform.

Peter Powell stood up in the official's box. "You!" he shouted.

Dave skidded on his skates toward the side of the pool and over its side. *Splash!* In the last second before he tumbled into the water, he grabbed Stacy's metal frog.

"Seize that man!" shouted Powell to several guards near the grandstand.

Dave's head bobbed up in the water. He looked up at the top of the platform toward the diver. "Stacy," he shouted. "It's the frog. It's been shorting the computer."

Powell was red with rage. He pointed at Dave Henderson treading water in the diving area. "Stop him."

Three ushers stood by the side of the pool. They looked at one another, shrugged, then dove in.

"Oh, my gosh," said Dave. Still holding the frog, he began to paddle toward the other end of the pool.

Two of the ushers began paddling after him. But the third usher was thrashing and struggling. "Help," he shouted. "I forgot I can't swim." One of the ushers turned back to save him.

As Dave swam the length of the pool, Powell stood on the edge. "I'll have you arrested," he raged. "I'll have you hung! I'll revoke your Olympic pass!"

Dave found himself at the shallow end of the pool. He started to climb out. At that moment the captain of the traffic guards burst into the pool, followed by his two men.

"There he is!" shouted the captain. "The jaywalker!"

"I surrender," said Dave, standing in water up to his neck.

"Get that man out of the pool!" shouted Powell.

The two guards reached down and grabbed Dave. They hauled him out of the pool by his armpits and pushed him away from the water's edge. The three ushers also climbed out of the pool. They all now stood next to the PED-72 computer, which scored all the swimming and diving events.

The captain of the guards snatched the frog from Dave's hands. "What's this?" he asked.

"A frog," Dave replied.

The captain grabbed Dave by the throat. "Confess," he said. "What is the meaning of this frog?"

"Quiet!" Peter Powell silenced everybody. He pointed toward the other end of the arena where Stacy stood on top of the diving platform. "The Olympics must go on. We'll deal with this fool later."

Powell began to walk back to his seat. The captain relaxed his grip on Dave's neck. While awaiting the dive, he placed the steel frog on top of the computer.

"No, wait —" Dave began. A glare from the captain silenced him. The two guards tightened their hold on his arms.

Stacy stood at the edge of the platform. The crowd quieted and turned its attention toward her. But the commotion had been too much for her. She started to dive, stopped, then suddenly lost her balance. She fell through the air feet first, thrashing with her arms. She landed in the water with a big *Buh-loomp.*

"Poor Stacy," Dave groaned.

Stacy surfaced. At that instant the computer scoreboard began flashing: 473,928.07 POINTS.

Powell was standing again. "What?"

The computer scoreboard continued its flashing: STACY RANDOLPH'S TOTAL: 89,354,625,911.72 POINTS.

"That dive wasn't worth half a point," raged Powell. "Somebody's been tampering with my computer."

STACY RANDOLPH IS THE NEW OLYMPIC CHAMPION, announced the computer scoreboard.

"It's the frog," Dave tried to explain. "This time it shorted the entire computer."

Powell stood before Dave, his face a mask of hate. "This time you're really in trouble." The captain grabbed Dave again by the neck.

"Ggllmpghh," said Dave.

At that moment the scoreboard lit up in red, white, and blue — the American flag. "The Star-Spangled Banner" began to play through the electronic sound system.

Automatically the captain and his two guards relaxed their hold on Dave, turned, and snapped to attention. They saluted smartly, as PED-72 began to spell out: OH, SAY CAN YOU SEE . . .

Dave suddenly found himself free. He began to skate as fast as he could toward the nearest exit.

"Come back here!" Powell screamed after him. "Don't you know it's unpatriotic to escape during the playing of the national anthem!"

DISCUSSION

1. What problem did Dave have in trying to take the frog to Stacy? How did he solve it?
2. Why was the frog so important to Stacy? What did Dave say that showed how important he thought it was?
3. What unexpected effects did the frog have on Stacy's score?
4. A character in a baseball story might say, "Kill the umpire!" What did Dave say that could be compared with this?
5. In spite of his opinion of the frog, why do you think Dave went to so much trouble to take it to Stacy?
6. Compare Dave's and Powell's reactions to the computer's rating of Stacy's last two dives. Why did their reactions change?
7. In what ways did Powell probably expect the computer to be superior to human judges?
8. Do you think Stacy changed her ideas about good-luck charms? Why do you think that?
9. What do you think is the author's opinion of computers as substitutes for humans?
10. If you were the Olympic official in charge of this diving event, what would you do in order to determine the winner?

AUTHOR

Hal Higdon's special interests — humor and sports — go back many years and are reflected in his writings. As a youngster, he was an enthusiastic collector of comic books and also enjoyed creating and drawing his own cartoons. One sport he is serious about is running. He is a champion amateur distance runner and has won several titles. In the 1964 Boston Marathon, he was the first American to cross the finish line, and only a knee injury kept him from attaining a place on the United States Olympic team. He feels that he actually has two careers, one as a writer and the other as a long-distance runner.

Mr. Higdon was born in Chicago in 1931 and graduated from Carleton College in Northfield, Minnesota. After working briefly as a magazine editor, he became a free-lance writer in 1959. His articles have appeared in numerous popular magazines, and he has published many books — some humorous, some serious — about sports. One of his books is the delightful *Electronic Olympics* from which "The Good-Luck Frog" was taken. Others include *Heroes of the Olympics; The Horse That Played Center Field; Pro Football, USA; Champions of the Tennis Court;* and *Thirty Days in May: The "Indy" 500.*

Mr. Higdon lives with his wife and three children in Michigan City, Indiana, and now does much of his running for pleasure along the shores of Lake Michigan.

First U.S. Olympic Hero...

by Barbara Craig

The United States' first Olympic winner was James B. Connolly, who, in his later years, became a well-known writer of sea stories. He won the hop, hop, and a jump competition in the first modern Olympics held in Athens in 1896.

But no cheering throngs or big brass bands greeted the athlete when he returned home in triumph to Boston. He was practically ignored. In those days, Olympic gold-medal winners were not the celebrities they are now.

In fact, Mr. Connolly, a sophomore at Harvard University, almost didn't make it to the Olympics. His dean refused him permission to leave classes so he could compete in Athens. Young Connolly finally had to quit school.

In addition, he had to pay his own way to Greece. He represented "the little Suffolk Athletic Club" in his hometown of South Boston, and the organization didn't have a penny in its treasury. .

Mr. Connolly later wrote: "Only one American college [Princeton] and one athletic club besides my own, the Boston Athletic Association, were represented on that first Olympic team. . . ." The small squad left New York on March 20 aboard a German steamer and reached Athens seventeen days later.

Wrote Mr. Connolly: "It was nine o'clock at night when we reached our hotel in Athens. Tom Burke [of the Boston club] and I roomed together. About four o'clock we came wide awake together. There were soldiers parading and a powerful band *whaling* away.

"It was too late to bother with any more sleep, so we had breakfast, remarking what a lucky thing it was we had twelve days to get in shape after that long seventeen-day trip. Then two members of some committee came in and handed us the programs for the games. Right then and there we discovered we were supposed to compete in the Olympics that very day.

"We soon discovered that the athletic officials back home who had given out the data for the opening of the games had made a mistake of twelve days, the difference between the Greek calendar and ours."

When Mr. Connolly arrived at the stadium a few hours later, he discovered one more problem. He learned his competitors were all doing a hop, hop, and a jump, and not the hop, step, and jump he expected to use. The hop, hop, and jump, it should be noted, is ancient Olympic form.

Mr. Connolly recalled:

"Some said 100,000 people filled the stadium. The hills above and just outside the walls were packed with men, women, and children. It was the day of days, the first day of the first Olympiad after fifteen hundred years. . . .

"I was the last to jump. I gripped my hands for the last time — I had the right feeling now — and started for the takeoff. And a curious thing happened to me. I had intended to do a hop, step, and a jump, but what I said to myself as I waited there was: 'Me, too, for the two hops and a jump.'

"As I landed in the pit, a tremendous cheer went up. There had been no great cheering before that from the seats.

"By and by, I took my second try. Another roar went up. An Englishman named Perry was leveling off the pit after each jump. After my second try, I said to him: 'They ought to tell how far each man jumps. Then a fellow won't be breaking his back when there's no need to it.'

"To that he said: 'As far as the measurements go, there's nobody within a yard of you.' "

Mr. Connolly won the double hop and a jump with an effort of forty-five feet, which was three feet three inches ahead of his closest rival.

"A band of two hundred pieces was grouped at the foot of a lofty flagstaff in the center of the arena," he went on. "Before I woke up to what the band was playing, I saw a group of San Francisco bluejackets from the good ship *Liberty,* which was in Greece at the time. They were standing at attention and saluting.

"I came wide awake then. That big band was booming out the opening notes of 'The Star-Spangled Banner,' and two Greek sailors were slowly hoisting an American flag to the top of that high staff. The thousands and thousands of spectators sat or stood in hushed attention.

"It was a moment in a young fellow's life. I had won an Olympic victory for my country, and atop of that I was the first Olympic victor in fifteen hundred years, since my competition was the first event scheduled. South Boston, I thought happily, would be pleased to get word of that."

·   ·   ·

En route home, Mr. Connolly stopped off in Paris for a visit.

He wrote: "I left Paris with my ticket home and three dollars in change. I arrived at Park Square station, but there was no mob busting down the station gates. Nobody but myself knew I was there.

"I had two nickels and two coppers left, one of the coppers being a white one. It was a hot day in May. I bought a soda with one nickel and boarded a trolley with the other. With the coppers I bought a paper, which made a cleanup of the pile.

"I got off the car in South Boston, the conductor helping me off with my bundles. I had two suitcases; a light spring coat and a heavy winter one; an Olympic diploma in a three-foot cylindrical cardboard box; a silver and gold cup given me by Prince George of Greece; a bust of some celebrated Greek done by another celebrated Greek, in a paper package; a wreath of wild olives from the groves of the old Olympia; three souvenir canes tied together with a string; and twenty yards of silk, the makings of a dress for my mother."

Last, but not least, he added: "My Olympic medal I had tucked away in my hip pocket."

DISCUSSION

1. When and where were the first modern Olympic games held?
2. How was Connolly's experience as an Olympic gold-medal winner different from that of present-day winners?
3. Who paid for Connolly's trip to the Olympics?
4. How many American organizations sponsored athletes in the 1896 games?
5. How would you contrast Connolly's reception in Greece with that in Boston?
6. Why do you think Connolly received so little recognition at home?
7. Do you think Connolly's victory resulted from his training or from natural ability? Why?
8. What do you think is the purpose of the Olympic games? Do the facts in this article about the 1896 games suggest that the purpose was achieved in any way? Why do you think that?
9. If you had been Connolly, which would have impressed you more — winning the medal or being the first winner in fifteen hundred years? Why?
10. Do you think that Connolly's returning to Boston an unsung hero should have mattered much to him? Why do you think that?

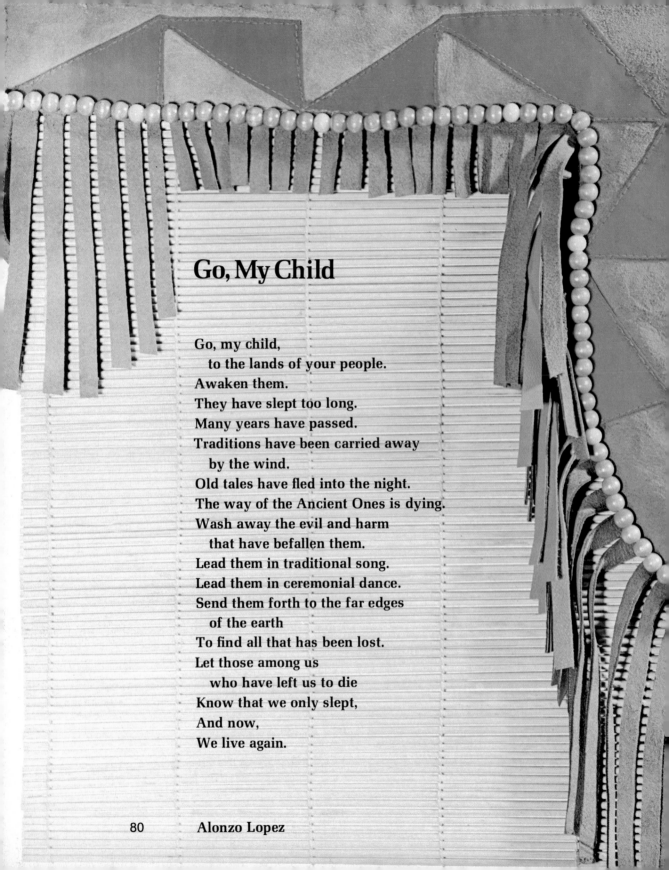

Go, My Child

Go, my child,
    to the lands of your people.
Awaken them.
They have slept too long.
Many years have passed.
Traditions have been carried away
    by the wind.
Old tales have fled into the night.
The way of the Ancient Ones is dying.
Wash away the evil and harm
    that have befallen them.
Lead them in traditional song.
Lead them in ceremonial dance.
Send them forth to the far edges
    of the earth
To find all that has been lost.
Let those among us
    who have left us to die
Know that we only slept,
And now,
We live again.

Alonzo Lopez

The *Green River* Skinner

by Annabel and Edgar Johnson

A good blade — the kind the mountain men carried away from the Green River Rendezvous each year. Right above the hilt, the letters G. R. made it official. Worth a couple of prime beaver pelts — even here at the post it cost three dollars in silver, which had taken months to earn. But there was no time to enjoy it — somebody upstairs was calling, "Boy! Where's that boy?" A certain way people said it, Rue always knew they meant him.

"I'm coming!" He stuck the skinner in his belt and pulled the shirt-tail down over it. As he ran up the stairs, old Palmer loomed at the top. Fancy ruffled front and monstrous gold watch chain — he'd found the crack in the crystal bowl, holding it delicately in his white Englishman hands.

"R-r-r-rudolph, what were you doing in the storeroom?"

"Just picked out something I bought with my own money I earned. If you don't believe me, ask the clerk."

"I'm sure you wouldn't lie — about that or about this." The major-domo held up the cracked bowl in his fingertips. "Mr. McKenzie's favorite piece; it came in a ship all the way from Italy, half around the world, across this continent and up the entire length of the Missouri River a thousand miles, to provide a little beauty in this wretched wilderness. Now destroyed — thanks to your carelessness."

"Yes, sir. I'm sorry." And he was — Rue knew he was all thumbs when it came to handling glass and fine china. Growing up in an Indian village you don't worry about such foolishness. All his life, the best plates in his mother's lodge had been made of buffalo shoulder blade, which doesn't break if you slightly drop it. In his own defense he dared say a further word. "My father sent me here to the fort to learn to read and write. I don't reckon he knew I'd wash dishes."

Palmer's face, soft as bear fat, puckered in a frown. "Mr. Beckwourth was well aware that you'd be earning your keep, my lad. To serve your superiors is to learn a whole lesson in itself — the problems of responsibility. Now, take the loss of this bowl; obviously it must rest heavy on your shoulders. And since you can't pay for it in gold, I suggest you work it out — two hours each evening you may scrub the chamber pots, which don't break so easily."

"Each evening until when?" Rue asked reluctantly.

"Until I decide you have settled your debt. Until you prove nimble enough to wait on us at table properly. Mr. McKenzie wants you eventually to take over the entire serving duties — a fine step up the ladder for a young man of your color. Now go to the scullery; you're tardy."

Down a long carpeted hallway — *young man of my color?* — through the pantry and across the kitchen, steaming with good odors — *serve my superiors?* Rue kicked the swinging door to the scullery with such a bang, the old man in the corner leaped up with his knife, ready to do battle. A trapper, he was wild as some animal in that floppy cap of beaver fur, greasy hair down over the shoulders of his long, fringed buckskins. Crusted, rusted, warped, and hawk-nosed as only the deep country can make a man.

"Wagh!" he hooted. "I thought ye was a whole tribe of Blackfoot."

Sinking down again at the chopping block where a platter of hot meat was set, he picked up the chunk in his hand and sank his teeth into it, slicing off the bite close to his lips. When he'd chewed a while, he shook his head. "Pure foolishment, servin' up old bull on a piece of chiney."

Rue put on his apron, aware that the mountain man was watching him narrowly. A curious breed they were, sour and lonely and tough on man or animal. They'd as soon eat the mule they rode, if game failed. And forever dirty — this one was a shade worse than most.

"So 'the King' got hisself a slave boy to trot the stew out." The old man was scheming something. "Listen, then, could ye search up some light bread? Or pancakes better — this hoss is plumb froze for a bit of flap-doodle and molasses."

"I'm no slave," Rue told him curtly. "My father's Beckwourth, the trader. He sent me here to get schooling — I only work because I want to earn my own way."

"Not a slave, eh? Me, I been slavin' for McKenzie nigh onto three years — they don't call him 'King of the Missouri' fer nothing. Got me a bellyful, I do. I'm gone beaver, soon's I've et. Sure now, you can make some pancakes come, bright young feller like you?"

"What'll you give me?" The natural law of the mountains, to drive a bargain.

The old man appreciated it too. "Trouble is, old Jeremy's cleaned. Got into a game throwin' the bones last night and lost the whole cache." He broke off, cocking his head; then with a fast wink went back to eating as Palmer strutted in.

"Lingering, Rudolph?" He looked coldly at both of them. "Jeremy, you well know that Mr. McKenzie feeds only those in his employ."

"Which includes this hoss. Yes sirree" — he hacked off another chaw — "for 'bout five more minutes, I'm still one of the help."

Palmer turned to Rue. "Boy, get to your duties at once. And as for you, sir, we'll expect to see your dust within the hour unless you care to change your mind and sign articles again with the Company."

When he'd stalked out again, Jeremy chuckled and sniffed behind his grubby beard. "The King must be some worried if he's got to be so all-fired unfriendly. He knows it's us free-trappers that'll fix his flint one of these times."

It had a ring to it that Rue liked. "Sir" — the idea took shape even as he spoke — "could you use a partner? I was born in the woods, I can read sign, I've got good eyes. From five miles off I can tell you elk's elk."

"Pardner?" The seamy face contorted and twitched at the joke.

Rue shrugged and turned away, musing to himself. "Pancakes . . .

drippy with syrup and raisins on top, with sugar . . . real cow's butter all melting down . . ."

Behind him Jeremy said grudgingly, "You're singin' the right song, black boy."

"Don't call me 'boy,'" Rue warned. "I can't ride with anybody talks down on me."

"You do sound some like Beckwourth at that." Jeremy eyed him thoughtfully. "How'd you cut a haunch of meat?"

"Down-grain."

"Who made my mocs?"

"They're Sioux pattern, but a Crow squaw made them."

"How'd you get the graybacks out of a old shirt?"

"Lay it on an anthill."

The old man chewed silently a while. Then he said, "Don't suppose ye got your own hossflesh?"

"My father took my horse back with him. He knew if he left me a pony I'd cut out of here. He was bound I should get an education, but he didn't know what kind it would be. He'd never want me to be taken for a slave."

"Wagh!" Jeremy shook his head. "Well, I got a extry mule along to pack supplies, and now there's none to load on her. She's mean as a kinkajou, but when it comes to smellin' trouble, she'll shine. If that's good enough for your swamper-ship, ye can tag along. Now go fetch them pancakes."

From scullery work to swamper overnight — now there was truly a fine "step up the ladder." Rue gave a last unkindly thought to Palmer that next morning as they rode away from the fort. Gray against gray, the log stockade stood small behind them in the midst of the wintry plains. And yet a mist was rising off the river where the channel flowed between its ice packs — some drift of warmer air, a hint of spring on the way.

Rue was glad to be shut of that crude castle and its king. McKenzie was too white, too cold, too full of foreign fancies such as painted china and crystal. And tight clothes — it was good to be in buckskins again.

So what was making him feel some tinge of regret? In the first sunlight a scrap of color was inching up the pole — the flag of a country somewhere far to the east, called the United States. It had a proud look, but when Rue had mentioned that once to his father, Beckwourth had laughed oddly.

"A place where men can be stood on a block and auctioned off like so many trading trinkets," he said.

Rue couldn't quite picture that — what it would feel like to be sold, body, brain, and heart. He couldn't connect it with the fluttering pennant and its bright, extravagant colors. Instead, the flag only stood for the life he'd known till now; for in spite of Beckwourth's bitterness, he still flew the Stars and Stripes above his lodge.

So I'm homesick. The idea nearly made Rue laugh. All the same, he wished he could tell his family why he was doing this. *You'll see, I will learn,* he promised them silently. *I'll learn every lesson I can from this trapper. Things more useful than they could ever teach at the fort — I was getting soft, living indoors for so long. You wouldn't want me to grow weak?*

He was so sure he could make his people understand this escape, on impulse he rode to catch up with Jeremy. "Sir, if you have time to swing down through Absaroka, my father would give us meat. I could get my horse — "

"Not likely." The old man went on riding, keeping a bleak eye out this way and that.

"But you don't know him."

"Don't, huh? Beckwourth's been tradin' with the Crow ever since they first let traders shine. He takes their beaver to McKenzie, don't he? Means he's beholden to the Company, eh? And the word is, Company *nor* Crow don't keer very sweetly about free-trappers. Start pokin' around Absarokee and we're 'the opposition.' Which is more'n a man oughter have t'explain to a campkicker." He nudged his horse ahead, and where the trail forked, he took the way westward.

Rue let the mule mosey, a little disconcerted at the idea of being on the other side. He'd hardly given much thought to the competition between fur companies. But it was true, no free-trappers ever stuck their noses into McKenzie's Crow country. And now — that meant him. For the first time, it came over him that he couldn't turn back.

In the deep snowy creases of the mountain, the ponds lay like patches of black glass fringed with naked willows. Staying well up the slope, the old man studied them as he rode, and when they stopped about sundown, he shouldered his traps. "Picket where the critters can dig for grass," he told Rue, "and set your fire keerful. You can get the pot a-boilin'."

Though for what? They had no jerky, much less pemmican or tallow or cornmeal. Neither beans nor bacon, and scant powder to get meat. But a little fire would feel good. Rue dug a hole the size of the stewpot and filled it with dry pine needles. When a few small sticks were burning quietly, he set the pan on top and filled it with snow.

Then he went about peeling bark from a small cottonwood tree near the stream. The mule was having a time finding enough dry grass to get a mouthful, pawing the snow, snuffling in disgust. When Rue piled the bark in front of her, she laid her long ears back, but she wasn't too haughty to accept the favor. Crunching and chomping — the

sound almost lulled Rue into a doze until abruptly it ceased and he started awake.

Coming back through the dark, Jeremy said, "Had a time findin' you." He sounded almost satisfied. "Build 'er up some more. There ain't a Injun this side the mountains or I'll eat old bull."

"Wouldn't mind some myself," Rue joshed carelessly, as he added kindling.

"Hungry?" The old man pretended to be surprised. "Wagh! If I knowed ye was that sort, I wouldn't of brung ye. Half-starved, ye say? Then y'won't be fussy." He took from his sack a porcupine, skinned and cleaned. "Cook her up. We'll sleep with full bellies tonight, come Blackfoot, come McKenzie, come Jim Bridger."

And that was a name to turn Rue's thoughts. One that was heard around the fort often enough — muttered, cursed. McKenzie's ruddy face would turn morbid at the mere mention of it. In the early morning hours, as Rue drifted half-awake, he pictured a towering giant of a trapper who had dared to set his own fur brigades against the might of "the King."

"Will you deal with Bridger at the Rendezvous?" he asked Jeremy in the gray dawn as they boiled a thin ration of tea.

"When we git there, it'll be trade with the first hoss that's got the most brass bells." The old man was gulping the hot drink noisily. "Which means we got to have somethin' to trade with." He slung his sack across his shoulder. "You can be cuttin' alders — so thick" — he held up a thumb — "and 'bout as long as your arm. Peel 'em and bend 'em; two tied together'll make a circle. Then sharp your skinner. Watch for smoke and listen ten miles all around."

So it went those days, Jeremy always on the move, setting his traps by late afternoon and slipping out again at daybreak to collect them. When he came back, his buckskins would be wet to the waist, crusted with ice some of these cold days. He limped as if his joints ached, yet he'd covered miles of stream, bringing a half-dozen pelts over his shoulder. To Rue went the work of graining — stretching them on the willow hoops, cleaning them of all meat so they could be turned to the sun to dry.

A moody partnership, with sometimes scarcely a word spoken between them in a day. Wary, suspicious of every twig floating downstream, every bird that flew up from the brush, the old man kept them on the move, searching out new ponds each day. Rue, so used to the easy-come ways of the Indian, sometimes wondered what made the trapper drive himself like that, to where he was a weary, dripping ruination. Only once did Jeremy give some clue — the one time Rue had asked to learn something about trapping.

"Learn, eh?" Jeremy let out a whinny of laughter. "In a hundred years, maybe. Think y'can just stroll out and set traps? Ain't nothin' on earth leery as a beaver. Smart critters, any little thing'll put 'em off — man scent, man noise, even a floatpole that weren't thrown by another beaver. Makes 'em worry. They'll circle your bait, spring your trap with a stick, pull it up, and carry it to deep water. Seen 'em bury a trap two foot in mud." He spoke now with open admiration. "Them's the keenest animiles ever lived. Ye don't treat 'em careless. That's why ye walk the middle of the creek and never mind the ice chunkin' your shins. Climb their dam quiet, don't touch the traps with your own skin — you seen me rub the smell off with wood ash? Float your stick gentle and don't even shiver, just ease on upstream, nobody been along here but us wolves." A pride, a look of contest, lit his fierce old eyes as if he spoke of a noble kind of game. "It ain't a job for no chee-ild."

Rue sat silent and bristling under the word.

Jeremy enjoyed it a while. "Tell ye what, though. Tomorrow ye can learn to cache."

Which meant to dig a pit. A huge joke — Rue up to his neck in a five-foot-deep hole while the old man lolled and smoked his pipe. "Go down 'nother foot or two." When it finally suited him, they gathered dead branches to cut in lengths and lay crisscross on the bottom; then the beaver plews, folded fur-side-in and tied in tight packets, finally covered with the blanket that had been Rue's saddle. "Tough young black Injun like you" — the old man had a wicked gleam — "shouldn't mind ridin' bare."

When they'd filled in the hole, stamped it hard and solid, and scattered rocks and pine needles over the ground, Jeremy took a willow branch and brushed the whole place clean of tracks. "There's the treasure vault" — he broke into a sudden jig — "there's our cash box, safe as a banker's pokey! That's our ticket, case of fire and earthquakes and acts o' God — there's security, wagh!"

It was good to travel light again. Rue quieted the hungry stirring of his innards with the thought that the furs were safe. And by now his eye was educated enough to size up the new territory as they crossed onto another range. The best trapping grounds yet.

A long, high, swampy valley laced with ponds and beaver runs — land so untouched it seemed no man had ever ridden here. Even Jeremy lost his moroseness and scanned each spring and freshet eagerly, like a general bracing for battle. *Go on* — he waved impatiently to Rue — *on farther.* All day they kept at a steady pace down to the most distant end of the meadows, starting to lose their fields of snow now. Wet spring-smell all around and the restless crunch and crack of winter breaking up.

"There's a thaw comin', got to make tracks," the old man said that night. Camped close under a shelf of rock, they ate the last of a chance feast — deer meat. Another sign of spring, the animals were moving up out of the valleys. Sniffing the air, Jeremy laid his plans. "Tomorrow mornin' we'll risk it — no sign of competition — we'll move out by daylight. Backtrack upstream to the first fork and start settin' traps over that way —"

"Oh, now, ye wouldn't!" The new voice broke in on them, husky and cool as the shadows. A mud-spattered figure stepped forward into the firelight — a short, scarred scarecrow of a man in flapping, greasy old buckskins. Rue could hardly believe it, that he hadn't heard a sound, and even more incredible — Jeremy hadn't.

The old man's face was blank as a rainy sky while he watched the newcomer make himself at home, squatting comfortably on the far side of the fire.

"Been a long time, old hoss."

Jeremy went on chawing the meat, finally shoved some toward the visitor. "Might as well feed, Jim." Then glancing at Rue, he shrugged. "This here's just my campkicker. Boy, say howdy to Bridger."

In the last of the firelight, the two shaggy figures stood jaw to jaw like stubborn bull buffalo.

"Better think on it some more." Bridger said a last word. "Whiles you and me been palaverin' here, my first brigade's moved up the south side of the ponds and second's fannin' out north. Oh, come on along, old hoss, I could use another good hand."

Jeremy shook his head. "No more articles; I swore I ain't gonna sign with nobody."

Hunching his shoulders, Bridger flapped a hand at them. "Wouldn't want to see a friend come onto bad luck. But then, 'tis a free country." And he was gone, off into the night again.

After the old man came back to the fire, Rue asked in a low tone, "Will this finish the place for us?"

A mighty twitch went through Jeremy's bent frame. "Oh, he'll take the cream off th' top, never doubt. But this critter knows a few tricks maybe he don't. We'll dig in here a spell; he's got some rough coots in his brigades. They travel by twos and threes — don't share traps with nobody. When he pulls out, we'll see."

But next day he kept a worried eye upon the sky, where the clouds gathered thicker; a wet, warm wind

stirred the trees, and when a drizzle set in, he swore. "Here's damp powder for sure!"

Itching with restlessness, Rue said, "I think I'll scout around, see if they've moved on."

"Well, mebbe. Mebbe you won't get noticed," Jeremy allowed. "Ye got the dangedest way of slippin' along — a body could mistake ye for a dark painter-cat."

It surprised Rue a little; the old man wasn't one to pass out compliments. Keeping to the rocky ridges, he skirted the valley, but it seemed deserted clear to the upper end. As he roamed, watching for the ripple across the face of the ponds, it came to him that something was different. Where were the beaver houses? Suddenly he realized there were no round huts of brush and sapling out in the midst of those waters. All that was left, here and there, was a jumble of sticks — and current rushing through a gap in a broken dam. Rue turned back on a fast trot.

"Wrecked the trappin' grounds?" Old Jeremy stood blinking. "Why'd he do that? Account of us — but we ain't so big a competition. Mebbe he thinks we're still workin' for Mc-Kenzie."

"Beavers build back." Rue couldn't believe they were finished so easily. "A few weeks and the dams will be repaired."

"Not with thaw comin' down. It'll sweep out every pond along the line, kittens be scattered up the small creeks — they won't build again till they mate. Summer fur's puny. Nope, there's going to be no beaver took here till next fall. And then reckon I can guess who will be the first in. Ol' Bridger. Ol' Jim. Wagh!" Jeremy almost laughed. "Funny — the King used to say same thing, 'It's a free country.' Free fer sneakin' and grabbin' and stranglin' out the opposition. Free to ruin the land. Free to gut and hamstring and bust the feller that don't knuckle down easy."

The words kept rankling in Rue as they rode back to their cache — twice as cautious as ever now. Traveling the open stretches by night, they took their bearings from a cleft in the rimrock. Back across a stream that had been only knee-deep two weeks ago, now roiling fast, racing away southeast. Jeremy pulled up on the bank as if another trail tempted him.

"Fer a nickel I'd take my fur to Bent's," he muttered. "I hear tell they deal honest. Where-at is that, you say? A big fort down on the Arkansas River — long ways from here, near to Mexico. And Mexico's full of wild furriners. Nope, I reckon I'll stick in these parts."

"Doesn't Bridger run things at Rendezvous?" Rue asked.

"Not quite, he don't. McKenzie'll have traders on the scene. Mebbe two — three gents from back east'll send out agents to get a piece of the business." And when they reached the cache, his spirits seemed to rise. Counting off twenty-six steps north from a rocky outcropping, then due east nineteen paces, he grabbed the short spade off his pack and began to dig feverishly. "We ain't rubbed out yet, no sirree. We ain't so bad off — get these plews to Rendezvous, it'll shine."

And shine was the word for it, that early summer morning as they rode across grassy meadows with the sun blazing on the big tents of the traders, circled around by the white cones of tipis. Nez Percé, Shoshoni, Arapahoe, Cheyenne — all had set aside their war paint and come in to barter their furs.

The thunder of drums shook the air, dogs barking everywhere, men whooping as the young braves raced their horses along the bank of the stream — this river that the Indians called Siskadee but white men had named the Green. Straight into those milling throngs Jeremy rode, hailing the trappers who loafed about — swampers, Frenchmen in stocking caps, and traders who looked as British as old Palmer, astraddle finicky eastern horses. Everywhere the smell of beaver.

"What're they bringin'?" Jeremy called to one or another man, and when he turned to Rue his old eyes were glittery with new hope. "D'ye hear? Nine dollars the pound! They're in a sweat, must need a million tall hats for all them princes and gents across th' ocean."

Rue was doing some figuring, the kind his own father had taught him better than any school. With each pelt weighing over a pound — and they must have sixty or more — it added up to wealth. Enough to buy himself a wool blanket, maybe a rifle and powder, some bacon — his mouth began to water at the thought. And yet there were chores to be done first.

While the old man went to barter his packs, Rue made camp and looked for a place to stake the mule. But with hundreds of pack trains trampling and grubbing for grass, fodder was skimpy already. And she was so gaunt, Rue thought he'd better make sure she fed well. Leading her upriver, he found a secluded meadow where she could graze while he climbed a low bluff to keep watch.

From that vantage point he could enjoy the whole clutter and color of the "fair," as they called it. Though he'd never seen one before, the word seemed to fit. Over the biggest tent, lifting and fluttering, was the flag — it pricked a sudden sharp twinge of welcome in him, the sight of those familiar stars. They brought a swarm of memories of home, of his father. And of the last time he'd seen them, far away to the north on a cold winter's day. That recollection brought him a certain

slight worry, which became much stronger when he got back to camp and there was still no sign of Jeremy. Starting off on the prowl through the late dusk, he saw that high spirits were turning rowdy all over the encampment.

The loudest clamor came from behind the big trading tent — some premonition made Rue hurry that way. And there he found his partner. In a circle of men, Jeremy was on hands and knees, throwing a set of Indian bones, blowing on them and rolling them, while sweat trickled down his hollow cheeks. In a voice hoarse with desperation he pleaded, "Come, dang ye, come!"

Sick as if a mule had kicked him in the belly, Rue saw that everything was lost. Only a few coins remained in front of the old man. In a fury he rushed forward to grip Jeremy's arm. "Didn't you save us even a little?"

The trapper shoved him off hotly. "Git away! You been bad luck to this hoss — git, black boy!"

"Not too far, though." An eastern trader, leaning against his packs, gave Rue a slit of a smile. "I just bought me a nigger."

That strange, filthy word held Rue frozen. He'd never heard it before, but he knew what it meant. Stunned speechless, he turned on Jeremy.

The old man wouldn't meet his look. "I don't need ye no more, I signed on with Bridger," he mumbled. "What difference anyways? What's so good about free? Half-starvin', wore down t' the bone — ye could get plumb skunked by all this-here liberty."

"Go on over to my tent," the trader told his property in that cold drawl. "I'll give orders later."

Rue couldn't even pretend to obey. With a terrible surge of hatred he turned and ran — some strange instinct came afire in him as he dashed between the tents, across the open field. Frenchmen over there were dancing the farandole — Rue plunged through the circle, scattering them aside. The Indian villages were just ahead. Darting around tipis, he dodged racks of drying meat, Indian curs yapping at his heels all the way. And still, behind him, came the yelling, cursing sound of the chase. Others had joined in now; he could hear the trader's voice urging them on. Gaining on him . . .

Go for the river! Rue burst onto its bank and plunged down into dark water, bubbling cold about his ears. He swam until he touched gravel and pulled himself into the willows on the far side. Holding his breath, he watched the lanterns dance across the night. A temptation as they got closer — he wanted to climb out and run again, but his newfound sixth sense told him to keep dead still. Words whispered in his mind from long ago, his father's voice . . . "Black on black,

that's the secret of the jungle." And he'd wondered what a jungle was. Now he knew.

On the slope of the foothills, lying flat in the sagebrush, Rue watched the sun come up with a shiver of relief. It had been a chilly night, spent without blanket or fire — even summertime, here in the high country, it could get cold. The valley would have been warmer, but pure fear had driven him on a good ten miles through the dark last night, until grass gave way to high brush and he felt the ground steepen.

Hidden now, he scanned the meadows below, but there was no sign of pursuit. Only the trader's last furious words following him, ringing in his ears: "You'll crawl back when you get hungry. And when you do, get ready for the strap!"

Hungry — no. But his belly was caving in with emptiness. So nervous yesterday, he hadn't eaten a scrap. Now as the sun rose higher, he searched his pockets — flint and whetstone, that was all. No wire for snares, no string to catch fish, no traps nor gun. Only the Green River knife. I can go stab a buffalo for dinner, he told himself sarcastically, wondering how many blows it would take with that puny blade to make an old bull even notice him. Or maybe run down a goose on the wing?

Stiffly he got to his feet and headed for higher land where the heavy stands of timber began. Maybe a porcupine up there — though how many of those would you find in a thousand miles, and how long would it take you to wander the forest, looking? All he knew was that he'd better get moving before fear seized him any tighter.

He kept trying to summon that sense of quickness he'd felt last night when the chase was on — a rushing of the blood, a keen, aware feeling. With that hidden strength, for a little while he could have outrun an antelope. Something his father had told him once — he searched a moment for the recollection — some wild tale of a far-away place where all people were black. Where the antelopes were as big as horses, and other creatures had noses six feet long or necks ten feet high or stripes all over them. Beckwourth was a good man with a tall story.

In the jungle, as he called it, the young boys had to prove their manhood by hunting lions twice as big as the biggest painter-cat in these hills. They must kill the cat, armed only with a spear. It had all sounded like a fable, and yet now, as he considered it, a spear could be a handy thing to have, especially when it comes to sticking a porcupine without getting a dose of quills.

So search for a good shaft. All around, the young saplings grew slender as lodgepoles, reaching straight up for a few inches of sunlight, in the dense woods. Rue cut one and peeled it, split the end; with a whang of leather off his buckskins, he tied the knife into the cleft. It looked right enough, and when it flew, the weight of steel gave it good distance. As it stuck, quivering, in the ground, his spirits vibrated with new determination. He'd once been pretty good at pitching arrows with the young Crow.

But a miss is a miss, and first a rabbit plunged into the brush untouched, then a fat rock chuck escaped down its hole. Rue crouched nearby for a half-hour till it stuck its head out — threw and missed again. As darkness closed down, he had to curl up and try to get to sleep on a bellyful of spring water.

Next morning, a little light-headed, he leaned back against a crumbling boulder and watched more dust rising from the Rendez-vous, as the Indians began to move out too. Grinding inside with hunger now, Rue stripped off his buckskins to let the crisp air stream along his naked flanks, slipped out of his moccasins too. His only pair, he'd need them for rocky stretches. Carrying the little bundle of clothes, he moved out at a trot across the slopes, through a vast quiet.

Only once he looked back a minute to where a whole haze of dust lay over the valley. Rendezvous breaking up, everyone scattering — soon he'd not be able to find a master if he wanted one. A strange feeling; his heart rocked unevenly, but he ran on until it steadied. He saw a covey of grouse ahead. *And this time I've got to hit one.*

Down on all fours he stalked until he was close enough to hear their clucking. Cautiously he rose and studied his shot. As they squawked and flew, the spear whistled on the air, and Rue had himself a chicken dinner.

Never so good a meal! Hardly able to wait while it cooked, he tore at the hot meat, sizzling juice down his chin, great, great! Worth the whole risk, this pure taste of independence. And loneliness — even that brought a certain joy. Nobody to talk to? Nobody talking down at him either. Time to think — what next?

Those days, as summer mounted, the sun toughened his skin, and his muscles strengthened. He could keep going over the bad stretches with only a mouthful of water from the pouch he'd made out of a badger's pelt. When game turned scarce, he learned to roast rattlesnake and, in the firelight, wrapped the diamond skin around the grip of his spear. Handsome it was, and it gave him a secret sense of pride. Of

rightness. He didn't have to show it to anyone to know that it was good. He didn't have to ask anybody what to do — it came to him naturally. As if he owned this whole silent land.

The wretched wilderness, old Palmer had called it. But then, most white men seemed to feel it was some old adversary, as if the animals were there to be plundered — the great, terrible game of life that Jeremy had waged. Rue wondered about it as he lay stretched out on the warm granite (dark on dark, the words kept coming back to him), blending into the earth as if he'd sprung from it full-grown.

A time of perfect balance ... it was bound to end. The golden sky was taking on a tinge of bronze as the days grew shorter. And Rue hadn't found a way south yet. Roaming eastward along a new river for weeks, he had skirted a high mountain range, following a broad, hard-beaten mule trail, which meant people ahead somewhere.

Then one night the wind swung around, coming down out of the north, bringing a scud of clouds and dousing summer at a single blow. With his skin prickling under the cold rain, Rue put on his buckskins and, with them, some mood out of the past. A gray uncertainty settled like the sparse, wet snow.

For of course he knew he couldn't go on into cold weather without a blanket or a buffalo-skin robe. He'd need powder and shot, a gun to hunt with. And that meant he'd have to earn some money from the men with power and cash and white skins. The thought filled him with a sort of despair that quickened, late one day, as he came over a rise and sighted the fort ahead.

Almost like the one he'd left far up on the Missouri — a log stockade with Indians camped around the big gates and the flag hanging idle in the thin sundown light. Rue hunkered in the tall grass, staring across at it in sudden sorrow — it came over him how much white there was in that beautiful banner.

He looked down at his own long dark hands, strong and able now, the wrists hanging out of his shirt sleeves. Going to carry platters of food to other men? Learn to wash the carved glass bowls? "Come here, boy!" And a terrible rebellion rose in his throat like a yell of defiance. *Boy, no more!*

In fierce anger, he took to the woods again, moving in a long circle away from the place. With darkness coming on, he held the spear ready — to tackle a bear or buffalo. What if the odds weren't good? They never had been very great. *All I need is one hide to make a robe,* he told himself. *If I can stay alive long enough to get south —*

As the last daylight closed down, he stumbled across a trail leading off that way — a track around the mountains? At least other men were on it. In the dusk ahead he saw the flicker of a campfire. A party of traders were pulling the heavy saddles from their horses — delicate, beautiful animals with small feet and long necks. The men were different too — good dark skin, a warmer brown than his own, more golden than an Indian's. He was reminded of Jeremy's words — "wild furriners" from Mexico — and for a minute he hesitated.

Then taking a chance, he stepped forward into their firelight. They started up, curious, and one came to confront him, eyeing the spear, looking at Rue, puzzled. "¿*Cómo, señor?*"[1] Strange words, but the tone was right.

"You go south — I would like to travel with you. I'll work." Rue could see they hardly understood him. And yet they did.

With a wave of the hand, the trader motioned him to join them at the fire. They watched curiously, but Rue could stand their stares — no contempt in them at all. Why should there be? It takes a good man to walk in out of the wilderness alone.

From a big pot one of the Mexicans dipped a steaming bowl of beans, speaking again in that foreign tongue. "¿*Frijoles?*"[2]

---

[1] ¿**Cómo, señor?** (kō′mō sän-yôr′): What is it, sir?

[2] ¿**Frijoles?** (frē-hō′läs): Beans?

Rue caught the first part of the word — it sounded as though the man said something about "free." Which brought back one lingering memory of Jeremy. With the hot food spreading warmth through his belly, Rue couldn't really hate the old man.

The main thing was how to keep clear of such a fate? Because anyone must work sometime for others. But to do it with dignity — there was the trick, he thought. And never to forget how it felt, once, to run naked down the trail alone in the summer sun.

DISCUSSION

1. Why had Rue's father sent him to the fort? How did Rue feel about his life there? What means did Rue find to leave the fort?
2. How did Jeremy and Rue divide their work?
3. What treacherous thing did Jeremy do to Rue?
4. How did Rue survive after his escape?
5. Whom did Rue meet on the trail leading south? How did they treat him?
6. What two classes of trappers did Jeremy mention as he and Rue left the fort? Which kind was Jeremy? Why was Rue upset when he realized that, having joined Jeremy, he could not turn back?
7. How did Jeremy appear to react when Jim Bridger arrived? How do you think he really felt? Why?
8. Why do you think Jeremy spoke of liberty and freedom as unimportant when he tried to excuse his treachery to Rue? Was Rue the only one he was trying to convince? Why do you think as you do?
9. Do you think Jeremy had reason to be proud of his skill as a trapper? Why do you think that? Was Jeremy's bitterness toward McKenzie and Bridger justified? Why or why not?
10. Both Jeremy and Rue had to choose between working for themselves or working for others. At the end of the story, which choice did each of them make? Which of them do you think was more likely to be content with his choice? Why?

11. Why do you think Rue could not really hate Jeremy? Have you ever been badly let down by someone? If so, how did you feel toward that person? How did the circumstances in which the person acted affect your feeling?

AUTHORS

Annabel and Edgar Johnson are a husband-and-wife writing team whose life together reads like an adventure story. After their marriage, they spent more than twelve years touring the country in a small trailer, spending as much time as possible out-of-doors. In winter they would camp in the warm desert; in summer, in the mountains. When they ran short of money, they would get temporary or part-time jobs to tide them over. Both of them have had a lifelong interest in the West and its history, and the research they did in museums and libraries provided them with a wealth of fascinating information and story ideas. Sometimes, if they were lucky, they would run across old-timers who could give them firsthand accounts of long-ago days in the West. When they had gathered background material for a book, the Johnsons would hide themselves away in the solitude of one of the national forests and write their story.

The Johnsons' early writing was prompted by the desire to share the exciting stories they had discovered with young people of today, especially those living in cities far removed from any wilderness area. Some of their more recent books, however, are stories that deal with the present and the problems confronting youth in the complex modern world. They have written over a dozen books for young readers, many of which have been awarded honors and prizes. Among their titles are *The Grizzly, Torrie, Wilderness Bride, The Bearcat, Pickpocket Run, Count Me Gone,* and *The Last Knife,* from which "The Green River Skinner" was taken.

The Johnsons maintain a home in Denver, Colorado, but continue to travel widely. When they are not busy with their writing and research, they take pleasure in their many hobbies. Trained as an artist, Mr. Johnson is well known for his work in ceramics and is a craftsman in silver and wood. He is also an ardent fisherman and is interested in seventeenth-century music and ancient musical instruments. Mrs. Johnson's leisure enjoyment comes mainly from hand weaving and tying flies for trout fishing.

Insect
Mail

by M. W. Martin

The world of animals is the most common theme found on post-age stamps, and the ubiquitous insects have not been neglected. Though the United States has never issued a stamp showing an in-sect, other countries have issued hundreds of them. In 1971 alone, twenty countries issued a hundred and fifteen stamps with insects in their designs.

Though the colorful moth, the graceful butterfly, and the photo-genic beetle are the insects shown most often, the whole class is well represented. A recent count indicated that more than eighty countries have issued insect stamps showing as many as four hun-dred different species belonging to fifty-seven families grouped in seven orders.

The insect most often pictured on a postage stamp is no pretty butterfly but the deadly malaria-bearing mosquito. Various species of this mosquito have been shown on the stamps of some thirty na-tions, as well as the United Nations, as part of different anti-malarial campaigns. Another killer is the little-known tsetse fly, a carrier of sleeping sickness. It is shown on stamps from Cameroon, where the dreaded disease is still prevalent.

Another insect has recently become the object of a widespread campaign of extermination. It is the locust, once considered a tasty dish but known as a plague since the beginning of recorded history. Several species of short-horned grasshoppers may be regarded as lo-custs, and they occur in many parts of the world. A dozen countries have issued stamps commemorating the "war on locusts."

Insects beneficial to mankind have been displayed on stamps of many nations. The honeybee holds first place, with ten countries issuing stamps in its honor. The silkworm moth has been shown on stamps of several countries, but curiously enough, neither China (where silk originated) nor Japan (which produces the finest silks) has issued stamps commemorating the spinner.

Perhaps the most famous of all insects is the scarab, a large, black beetle worshiped by ancient Egyptians as a symbol of resurrection and immortality. Modern-day Egypt no longer pays homage to this beetle, but it does appear on a French stamp.

Of the better-known insects, the ant appears on stamps of both East Germany and Poland. Termites have not yet been the subject of stamps, but their nests have been pictured on stamps issued by several African nations. Various species of the bumblebee are shown on Finnish, Polish, and Swiss stamps. The beneficial, seven-spotted ladybird beetle appears on stamps of several countries, and so does the praying mantis.

Moths and butterflies appear on stamps of almost all countries that have issued insect stamps; some countries have issued stamps showing only these beautiful insects and no others. The swallowtails are probably the butterflies most often pictured, and dozens of species of this butterfly appear on stamps of many countries.

The family of the giant silkworm moth is also well represented and includes the Atlas moth, which is shown on stamps of several Asian countries. The Atlas moth is sometimes called the biggest moth in the world, but in New Guinea and Australia lives the Hercules moth. Its wings are less than ten inches across, but they are so broad and ample that they reach a total surface area of nearly a hundred square inches, which probably makes the Hercules the largest of all moths.

Because of their abundance, a collection of insect stamps can be put together without spending a great deal of money. Such a collection lends itself to many interesting presentations, and it can easily be kept up-to-date by selections from the many new stamps that appear each year. Language is no problem here because insect stamps are almost always issued with labels showing Latin designations in addition to the common names in the language of the issuing country.

SKILL LESSON 2

READING FOR DIFFERENT PURPOSES

In or out of school, you usually read a piece of informative material for a specific purpose. You may read a sports account to find out who scored the most goals in a game, or you may read a set of directions to find out how to make something. In reading a paragraph, your purpose may be to get information on a question you want answered or to decide what the topic of that paragraph is. Your purpose in reading a longer selection may be to decide what its main idea is or to understand well and remember all the information it gives on a certain point. Whenever you read a piece of informative material for a specific purpose, you can read more efficiently if you keep that purpose in mind as you read. The purpose you have can help you select an appropriate rate of reading. It can also direct your attention to the kinds of information which will be most helpful.

For example, if your purpose is to determine the general information in a selection, you know that you can read it at a fairly rapid rate. If you keep that purpose in mind as you read, you can also mentally select out those points that seem to contribute to the general ideas instead of concentrating on minute details that do not fit in with your purpose of getting general information.

Read the following newspaper account for general information. Keep that purpose in mind as you read.

The Miss Hilldale Beauty Pageant produced a surprised winner last night on the stage of the Elm Theater. Donna Lee, a freshman at Hilldale College, was named winner over five other contestants. Because she had fallen twice while dancing in the talent contest, the general feeling was that these mishaps would keep her from winning the title. Donna Lee will compete next month in Lennox for the state title. A victory in the state contest would help Donna in her ambition to become a professional model.

The important general information in the newspaper account you just read is that Donna Lee won the Miss Hilldale Beauty Pageant in spite of falling in the talent contest and will go on to compete for the state title. Other information in the account consists of details that you would not remember unless, of course, you were reading it for the purpose of remembering details.

What is the important general information in the following news story?

A large bull moose wandered into the downtown area of Dixville early Saturday morning. It was first sighted by Harry Wilcox, who was just opening up his hardware store. The animal remained in the area of Main and Water Streets for about fifteen minutes before it ambled off toward the wooded area beyond the fire station. Not many people caught a glimpse of the moose on Saturday, but those who did claim it is the same moose spotted near the Back Road in the last two weeks. Animal conservation officials were notified, and they plan to make a wide search for the animal to determine if it is in poor health or in danger from roving dogs. All future sightings should be reported to the Animal Conservation Commission in Belleville.

Sometimes you will read a passage to get information that will be appropriate for you to include in a brief talk that you plan to give to your class. You must consider (1) the things you think will be most interesting to the audience and (2) the things you believe will give new and important information to the audience. To read a passage for the purpose of getting information to use in a talk, you should first read the whole passage carefully. Then decide which ideas you want to include on the basis of the two points suggested. Finally, read those parts again carefully enough to be sure you understand the ideas they present. You may decide to make notes about the ideas you plan to include in your talk.

Write on a separate sheet of paper brief notes on ideas that the following paragraph tells and that you would include if you were preparing a talk for your class:

Cartoons have been read by men and women for many years. Readers have enjoyed them for their humor but have also found that they can deliver important messages. Cartoons have at times been used for very serious purposes. They have brought social and political evils to the attention of the public and have led to reforms. Cartoons have also had international impact. During World War I the Raemacker cartoons were so effective in directing public sentiment against the German cause that the German government offered a large reward for the capture of the artist. In the 1920's and 30's, cartoons depicting extremely poor working conditions aided in the creation of work laws because they increased public awareness. Even in politics cartoons have played an important role. The Nast cartoons led to the over-throw of powerful political bosses in New York early in this century. The cartoonist's pen has been a strong weapon in its role as public informant.

Your purpose for reading the selection was to get information to use in preparing a brief talk for your class. Does your audience realize the broad uses of cartoons? If not, then you would have noted their international use during World War I in directing public sentiment against the Germans. The social importance of cartoons should be noted in the example depicting poor working conditions. The political

events as shown by political bosses should also be included. All other details in the article add to or support the general idea of the many uses of cartoons.

Another purpose you may have for reading an informative passage is to answer a general question. Although the passage itself does not state an answer to that question, you may, by noting important information that relates to it, draw a conclusion and formulate an answer for yourself.

What conclusion would you draw if you were reading the following passage to answer this question: *How have the purposes of the American school system changed?*

1. The American educational system is one of the great achievements of our society. 2. It is a system open to all people, without regard to race, color, creed, economic or social circumstance. 3. Motivation for the first schools in America was essentially religious. 4. Pioneers in New England and in the Virginia colonies formulated their code of behavior from the church. 5. Reading was an important and essential skill because it was the key to unlocking God's truth in Scripture. 6. The purpose then of the early schools was mainly religious. 7. Immediately following the American Revolution various proposals were made regarding education. 8. It was in this period that Jefferson proposed the establishment of a complete system of public education. 9. There was a need at the time to increase the knowledge of people in all fields, and this became the purpose of the schools in this era.

10. The year 1872 saw the establishment of the first public high school. 11. To finance the extension of grammar schools, additional taxes were levied on local property. 12. The early high schools usually reproduced the curricular offerings of the private academies with emphasis upon college-entrance subjects.

13. Toward the end of the 1800's and into the present century the demands of industry grew so that more and more skilled personnel were needed. 14. There was a similar increase in the

need for people qualified to serve in government agencies. 15. Business and law became increasingly complex and required persons with special training. 16. Most recently, medicine and the environment are calling upon the educational system for qualified personnel to resolve problems. 17. The curriculum of the modern school encompasses numerous areas of study and provides a wide variety of courses.

Perhaps you noticed that the paragraphs spoke about the different purposes of schools at different times in our country's history. That could lead you to the plausible conclusion that the purposes of schools have changed over the years to meet the ever changing needs of our society.

Sentences 3 and 4 established the type of society in the Colonial Period. Sentence 6 pointed out the role and the purpose of the schools for that period.

Sentence 9 indicated the need in the Revolutionary Period for increased knowledge, and this became the purpose of the schools.

Sentences 13, 14, 15, and 16 depicted the increased needs of society in industry, government, business, law, medicine, and environment. Sentence 17 pointed out that modern schools offer a wide variety of courses to meet these needs.

The article seemed to show how the needs of society changed and how, with each change, the schools tried to meet the needs of the time. It should be noted that not all the information in the article was used to form the conclusion. Sentences 7 and 8, for example, although related to the general subject, did not tie in directly with the "purpose of the schools."

Perhaps you were aware that you read the article on cartoons in a different manner from the way you read the one on schools. The reason is that you had a different purpose for reading each one. Having the purpose for reading clearly in mind helps you read more efficiently because it directs your attention to the information that will be most helpful to you and helps you avoid details that do not relate to your purpose.

Discussion

Help your class answer these questions:

1. For what kinds of purposes might you read a piece of informative material?
2. When you read to get information for a talk, what things should you keep in mind?
3. When you read to formulate a conclusion, what do you look for in an article?
4. What general information did you consider to be important in the second news story on page 106?
5. Are all sentences in an article likely to be used when you read to formulate a conclusion? Why or why not?

On your own

Read the following paragraph for the purpose of getting the most important general information that is in it. On a separate sheet of paper write the information that you consider to be important in the paragraph.

The lengths of days and nights vary from season to season. On or about March 21 and September 23, the length of day and night are practically equal everywhere because the sun is exactly over the earth's equator. At the time of the summer solstice, about June 21, the sun is farthest north and the day is longest in the Northern Hemisphere and shortest in the Southern Hemisphere. At the time of the winter solstice, about December 22, the reverse is true: the sun is farthest south and the day is longest in the Southern Hemisphere and shortest in the Northern Hemisphere. If you live in the Northern Hemisphere, days grow longer from December 22 to June 21. From June 22, they grow shorter to December 21.

What information in the following paragraph would you use in preparing a brief talk for your class? On a separate sheet of paper write notes on the information you choose. Remember to keep in mind the suggestions made on pages 106–108 for choosing information to include in a brief talk.

Many persons feel that price supports for food growers should continue. They argue that farming is different from industry. An adequate food supply is necessary for national well-being. Farming success depends on much besides planning and hard work. Too great a rainfall or too long a dry period may ruin a crop. The hours of labor on farms are long, and there is a growing movement of workers away from the farm to the city. Such persons hope to have an easier life and more income. Price supports seek to encourage people to stay on the farm.

What conclusion would you draw from information given in the following paragraph to answer the question *Is there a high mortality rate among migrating birds?*

Snows, lighthouses, hunters, sudden freezes, gales, droughts, floods, and grass and forest fires all take their toll of migrating birds, sometimes in terms so appalling that for years afterward woodcock, bluebirds, and swallows have been unable to restore their numbers over areas the size of New England. Death on a large scale is the price birds pay for the benefits of migration. A late blizzard in Minnesota killed more than a million small migrating birds; thousands of migrating ducks on the St. Lawrence River died from oil that soaked their feathers when a tanker went aground. The dangers of migration make the life expectancy only three to five years for most small species.

Checking your work

If you are asked to do so, read the general information you considered to be important in the article about the length of days and nights. You may also be asked to deliver a brief talk to your class about price supports. Listen to suggestions others make concerning your notes or your talk. If you are asked to do so, tell what conclusion you drew from the article about birds.

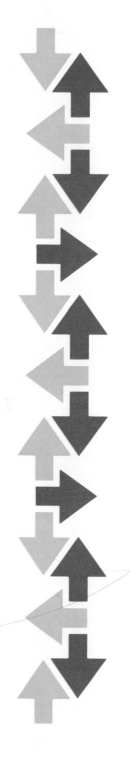

A Couple of Lost Squadrons

Brad Williams and Choral Pepper

The United States Navy has always prided itself on the caliber of its officers, with particular reference to their ability to follow orders. A good example of this discipline can be found to this day upon a rocky section of the Pacific Coast some twenty-five miles north of Santa Barbara. On the evening of September 9, 1923, a squadron of seven destroyers was heading south a few miles off the shore. The weather was a little foggy, but the flotilla was proceeding in close formation and at full speed. The captain of the lead destroyer absent-mindedly made a left-hand turn, and the whole flotilla sailed at full speed into the rocky shore. The destroyers were upended like plastic boats in a bathtub, but miraculously, although the injured list was long, only twenty-two sailors were drowned.

The committees investigating the disaster could understand how one commanding officer, a skipper, could inadvertently run his ship at full steam into the shore. But they found it odd that the six other skippers would blindly follow him to destruction, until someone explained that,

in the Navy, officers were taught to follow orders and that this was a prime example of disciplinary responsibility.

In view of this prime example of the Navy's sense of duty and discipline, it is rather difficult to explain how the Navy ever came to commission one Thomas Ap Catesby Jones as a commodore some three quarters of a century earlier. Possibly it was because of Jones that the Navy no longer boasts the rank of commodore. In the historical annals of the United States Navy, the adventures of Commodore Jones are conveniently overlooked, and one can easily understand why if he understands the Navy's sensitivity toward discipline.

Jones came from a proper New England family and was appointed to the Naval Academy, where he was graduated without an indication that he might be inclined to erratic behavior. It took him fifteen years to rise in rank from ensign to commodore, which was about average, and he had to wait an additional two years before he was finally given a command of his own.

On December 4, 1841, the Secretary of the Navy, Abel Upshur, announced that because of the unsettled conditions in the Northern Hemisphere, he was increasing the size of the United States naval force in the Pacific Ocean by one squadron. The squadron consisted of six ships and was placed under the command of Commodore Thomas Ap Catesby Jones. The commodore took his fleet on a leisurely voyage around the Horn and eventually reached the California coast. California at this time was owned by Mexico.

For several weeks, the fleet tarried in San Diego as guests of the Mexican government, then slowly proceeded up the coast, eventually reaching the Mexican capital of California at Monterey. At this time, the United States was at peace with Mexico, but as Jones said several years later, he had no way of knowing this because communications were extraordinarily poor between the fleet in the Pacific and the Navy headquarters in Washington. As a result, on a warm spring day in 1842, Commodore Jones sailed his fleet into the harbor of Monterey and proceeded to capture it. The capture was not a difficult feat. His warships lobbed a few cännonballs into the hills in back of the town. He sent a landing party ashore to arrest Governor Micheltorena (mē-chĕl-tō-rä′nä) and a few other assorted government officials. He then granted liberty to most of his men to celebrate the occasion.

The citizens of the community did not seem particularly upset over this turn of events, but the capture of a state capital of a friendly nation was not received in good favor by either the United States or Mexico when the news eventually reached their heads of government. The United States Secretary of State, Daniel Webster, personally apologized to the ambassador from Mexico in Washington. The American ambassador was ordered to convey his regrets to the government of Mexico in Mexico City. It took several days to get word to Commodore Jones that he was to turn Governor Micheltorena loose along with his assistants and to get his sailors out of Monterey and back on the ships.

Reluctantly, Commodore Jones complied, but he kept his squadron in Monterey Harbor "in case hostilities did break out" and because there had been no orders issued for him to resume cruising. Once again the Mexican government protested, and once again the heads of state apologized to each other. Commodore Jones was to get out of Monterey Harbor and, additionally, he was to be relieved of his command as soon as Commodore Dallas could arrive to take over. Jones was ordered to return to Washington "in such mode as be most convenient and agreeable" to himself. With typical military efficiency, the Navy also forgot to mention a spot where Jones could meet Dallas.

The phraseology of the orders apparently was the custom of the time in correspondence between officers and gentlemen, but it is unlikely that anyone in Washington had any idea as to how Commodore Jones would interpret his instructions. He found it most convenient and agreeable to set sail with his fleet from Monterey to Hawaii, an area with which Washington found it even more difficult to maintain communications than Monterey.

Several months later, word was received in the nation's capital that its missing squadron was anchored off the shores of Honolulu. A few weeks after this, word was passed to Commodore Dallas as to where he could make his rendezvous. Dallas was sent across the Pacific in the frigate *Erie* to take over his command and to explain to Commodore Jones that a detour via Hawaii was not what the Navy had in mind when it told him to return in the "mode most convenient and agreeable" to himself.

When Dallas arrived in Honolulu, however, he found no squadron, and he learned from some other sailors and natives that the squadron had sailed a few weeks earlier for an unknown destination in the South Pacific. How long Dallas waited in Hawaii before he learned that the missing squadron of Commodore Jones was anchored in Tahiti is not on record.

Once again Dallas took off in pursuit, only to discover, when he arrived in Papeete (pə-pē′tē), that Commodore Jones again had set sail, with his next stop scheduled at Valparaiso (văl′pə-rī′zō) in Chile. Weeks later, Dallas arrived in Valparaiso, where he learned that Commodore Jones had sailed north the day after the first cold snap of winter had struck the city. Well aware of Commodore Jones's preference for a balmy tropical climate, Dallas immediately sailed north, but still he could find no

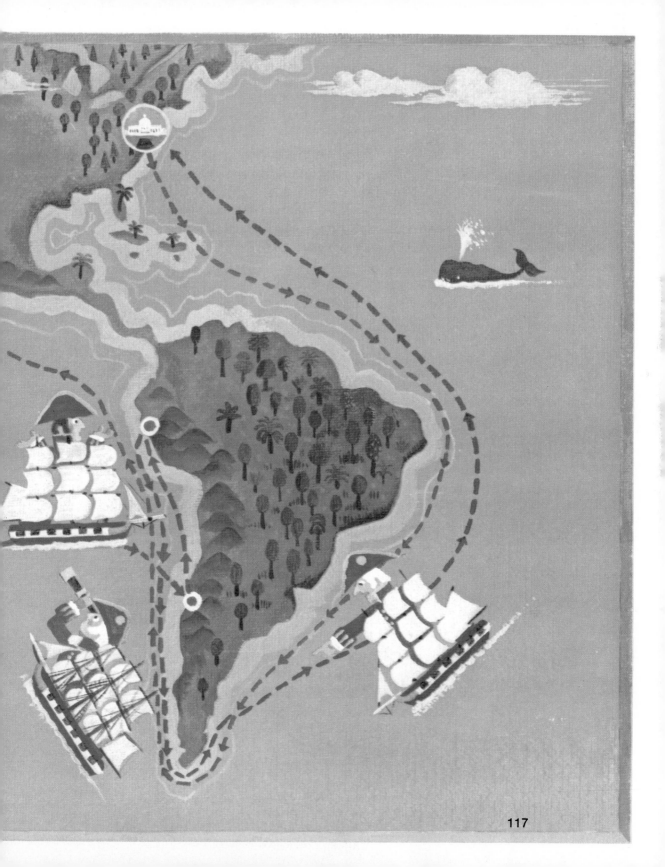

trace of the missing fleet. Dallas never did. Ironically, he died in Callao (kä-yä′ō), Peru, some three weeks before Commodore Jones sailed into the same port for refueling and reprovisioning.

It was here that the cruise of Commodore Jones took a more definite turn. Daniel Webster had secured orders from the Navy which were more explicit in ordering the wandering commodore to return to his base, and copies had been given to every consul general or his representative at every port where Jones might put in for reprovisioning. In Callao, the consul general boarded Jones's flagship almost before it dropped anchor and personally ordered Jones to go home immediately and in the most direct manner possible.

A good Navy man, Commodore Jones did not disobey his new orders. Once again he sailed south for the trip around the Horn. He paused at Valparaiso for supplies, and while his ships were being provisioned, another U.S. Navy ship sailed into the bay. On board this ship was Commodore John Drake Sloat. He had been sent out to pick up the chase from the late Commodore Dallas and was overjoyed at running into the elusive Catesby Jones so early in the game.

Jones welcomed Sloat aboard and studied Sloat's orders carefully. He noted that although they had come from the Navy Department, they bore an earlier date than the instructions he had received in Callao, and he presumed, therefore, they must be void. He refused to give up his command, and with the new commodore along as his guest, he sailed the squadron back to Washington, arriving there shortly after the inauguration of President James Knox Polk in 1845, more than three years after his departure.

The Navy Department apparently was most understanding. It agreed that there was some confusion over the orders that Sloat carried, but this was straightened out with a minimum of difficulty. Commodore Sloat was put in command of the squadron after Jones was relieved of command, and once again the flotilla was sent around the Horn to patrol the California coast.

No action ever was taken against Catesby Jones. Relations with Mexico at this time no longer were friendly, and Commodore Jones was lauded by President Polk for his "elevated principles of duty." Neither Polk nor anyone else ever asked how the Navy could lose an entire squadron of ships for three years.

Catesby Jones was given a new assignment, but it was on shore. Never again was he given the opportunity to command a ship.

A few months after Commodore Sloat arrived in California, he sailed his squadron into Monterey Bay, lobbed a few cannonballs over the town into the hills, then sent a landing party ashore to take possession of the town. This time there was no problem. The United States was at war with Mexico.

A statue still stands in Monterey commemorating Commodore Sloat's capture of the city. There's not even a plaque to Catesby Jones.

DISCUSSION

1. What ordinarily good quality, developed in its men by the Navy, was responsible for the wreck of all seven destroyers?
2. How did Commodore Jones first displease the United States government?
3. What places did Commodore Jones visit on his way from Monterey to Washington?
4. What possible reasons do you think Commodore Jones could have had for his actions in Monterey?
5. How was Commodore Jones ordered to return to Washington? Do you think the authors were serious in saying that those orders were issued with "typical military efficiency"? Why do you think that?
6. In your opinion, why did the Navy fail to take action against Commodore Jones for delaying so long in returning to Washington?
7. Do you think Commodore Jones should have been punished for any of his actions? Why do you think as you do?

Bats

A bat is born
Naked and blind and pale.
His mother makes a pocket of her tail
And catches him. He clings to her long fur
By his thumbs and toes and teeth.
And then the mother dances through the night
Doubling and looping, soaring, somersaulting —
Her baby hangs on underneath.
All night, in happiness, she hunts and flies.
Her high sharp cries
Like shining needlepoints of sound
Go out into the night and, echoing back,
Tell her what they have touched.
She hears how far it is, how big it is,
Which way it's going:
She lives by hearing.
The mother eats the moths and gnats she catches
In full flight; in full flight
The mother drinks the water of the pond
She skims across. Her baby hangs on tight.
Her baby drinks the milk she makes him
In moonlight or starlight, in mid-air.
Their single shadow, printed on the moon
Or fluttering across the stars,
Whirls on all night; at daybreak
The tired mother flaps home to her rafter.
The others all are there.
They hang themselves up by their toes,
They wrap themselves in their brown wings.
Bunched upside-down, they sleep in air.
Their sharp ears, their sharp teeth, their quick sharp faces
Are dull and slow and mild.
All the bright day, as the mother sleeps,
She folds her wings about her sleeping child.

Randall Jarrell

The Three GARRIDEBS

by Sir Arthur Conan Doyle

It may have been a comedy, or it may have been a tragedy. It cost one man his reason, it cost me a blood-letting, and it cost yet another man the penalties of the law. Yet there was certainly an element of comedy. Well, you shall judge for yourselves.

I remember the date very well, for it was in the same month that Sherlock Holmes refused a knighthood for services which may perhaps some day be described. I only refer to the matter in passing, for in my position of partner and confidant I am obliged to be particularly careful to avoid any indiscretion. I repeat, however, that this enables me to fix the date, which was the latter end of June, 1902, shortly after the conclusion of the South African War. Holmes had spent several days in bed, as was his habit from time to time, but he emerged that morning with a long foolscap document in his hand and a twinkle of amusement in his austere gray eyes.

"There is a chance for you to make some money, friend Watson," said he. "Have you ever heard the name of Garrideb?"

I admitted that I had not.

"Well, if you can lay your hand upon a Garrideb, there's money in it."

"Why?"

"Ah, that's a long story — rather a whimsical one, too. I don't think in all our explorations of human complexities we have ever come upon anything more singular. The fellow will be here presently for cross-examination, so I won't open the matter up till he comes. But, meanwhile, that's the name we want."

The telephone directory lay on the table beside me, and I turned over the pages in a rather hopeless quest. But to my amazement there was this strange name in its due place. I gave a cry of triumph.

"Here you are, Holmes! Here it is!"

Holmes took the book from my hand.

" 'Garrideb, N.,' " he read, " '136 Little Ryder Street, W.' Sorry to disappoint you, my dear Watson, but this is the man himself. That is the address upon his letter. We want another to match him."

Mrs. Hudson had come in with a card upon a tray. I took it up and glanced at it.

"Why, here it is!" I cried in amazement. "This is a different initial. John Garrideb, Counsellor at Law, Moorville, Kansas, U.S.A."

Holmes smiled as he looked at the card. "I am afraid you must make yet another effort, Watson," said he. "This gentleman is also in the plot already, though I certainly did not expect to see him this morning. However, he is in a position to tell us a good deal which I want to know."

A moment later he was in the room. Mr. John Garrideb, Counsellor at Law, was a short, powerful man with the round, fresh, clean-shaven face characteristic of so many American men of affairs. The general effect was chubby and rather childlike, so that one received the impression of quite a young man with a broad set smile upon his face. His eyes, however,

were arresting. Seldom in any human head have I seen a pair which bespoke a more intense inward life, so bright were they, so alert, so responsive to every change of thought. His accent was American but was not accompanied by any eccentricity of speech.

"Mr. Holmes?" he asked, glancing from one to the other. "Ah, yes! Your pictures are not unlike you, sir, if I may say so. I believe you have had a letter from my namesake, Mr. Nathan Garrideb, have you not?"

"Pray sit down," said Sherlock Holmes. "We shall, I fancy, have a good deal to discuss." He took up his sheets of foolscap. "You are, of course, the Mr. John Garrideb mentioned in this document. But surely you have been in England some time?"

"Why do you say that, Mr. Holmes?" I seemed to read sudden suspicion in those expressive eyes.

"Your whole outfit is English."

Mr. Garrideb forced a laugh. "I've read of your tricks, Mr. Holmes, but I never thought I would be the subject of them. Where do you read that?"

"The shoulder cut of your coat, the toes of your boots — could anyone doubt it?"

"Well, well, I had no idea I was so obvious a Britisher. But business brought me over here some time ago, and so, as you say, my outfit is nearly all London. However, I guess your time is of value, and we did not meet to talk about the cut of my socks. What about getting down to that paper you hold in your hand?"

Holmes had in some way ruffled our visitor, whose chubby face had assumed a far less amiable expression.

"Patience! Patience, Mr. Garrideb!" said my friend in a soothing voice. "Dr. Watson would tell you that these little digressions of mine sometimes prove in the end to have some bearing on the matter. But why did Mr. Nathan Garrideb not come with you?"

"Why did he ever drag you into it at all?" asked our visitor with a sudden outflame of anger. "What in thunder had you to do with it? Here was a bit of professional business between two gentlemen, and one of them must needs call in a detective! I saw him this morning, and he told me this fool-trick he had played me, and that's why I am here. But I feel bad about it, all the same."

"There was no reflection upon you, Mr. Garrideb. It was simply zeal upon his part to gain your end — an end which is, I understand, equally vital for both of you. He knew that I had means of getting information, and, therefore, it was very natural that he should apply to me."

Our visitor's angry face gradually cleared.

"Well, that puts it different," said he. "When I went to see him this morning and he told me he had sent to a detective, I just asked for your address and came right away. I don't want police butting into a private matter. But if you are content just to help us find the man, there can be no harm in that."

"Well, that is just how it stands," said Holmes. "And now, sir, since you are here, we had best have a clear account from your own lips. My friend here knows nothing of the details."

Mr. Garrideb surveyed me with not too friendly a gaze.

"Need he know?" he asked.

"We usually work together."

"Well, there's no reason it should be kept a secret. I'll give you the facts as short as I can make them. If you came from Kansas, I would not need to explain to you who Alexander Hamilton Garrideb was. He made his money in real estate, and afterwards in the wheat pit at Chicago, but he spent it in buying up as much land as would easily make one of your counties, lying along the Arkansas River, west of Fort Dodge. It's grazing-land and lumber-land and arable-land and mineralized-land and just every sort of land that brings dollars to the man that owns it.

"He had no kith nor kin — or, if he had, I never heard of it. But he did take a kind of pride in the queerness of his name. That was

what brought us together. I was in the law at Topeka, and one day I had a visit from the old man, and he was tickled to death to meet another man with his own name. It was his pet fad, and he was dead set to find out if there were any more Garridebs in the world. 'Find me another!' said he. I told him I was a busy man and could not spend my life hiking round the world in search of Garridebs. 'None the less,' said he, 'that is just what you will do if things pan out as I planned them.' I thought he was joking, but there was a powerful lot of meaning in the words, as I was soon to discover.

"For he died within a year of saying them, and he left a will behind him. It was the queerest will that has ever been filed in the state of Kansas. His property was divided into three parts, and I was to have one on condition that I found two Garridebs who would share the remainder. It's five million dollars for each if it is a cent, but we can't lay a finger on it until we all three stand in a row.

"It was so big a chance that I just let my legal practice slide and I set forth looking for Garridebs. There is not one in the United States. I went through it, sir, with a fine-toothed comb, and never a Garrideb could I catch. Then I tried the old country. Sure enough, there was the name in the London telephone directory. I went after him two days ago and explained the whole matter to him. But he is a lone man, like myself, with some women relations, but no men. It says three adult men in the will. So you see we still have a vacancy, and if you can help to fill it, we will be very ready to pay your charges."

"Well, Watson," said Holmes with a smile, "I said it was rather whimsical, did I not? I should have thought, sir, that your obvious way was to advertise in the agony columns of the papers."

"I have done that, Mr. Holmes. No replies."

"Dear me! Well, it is certainly a most curious little problem. I may take a glance at it in my leisure. By the way, it is curious that you should have come from Topeka. I used to have a correspondent — he is dead now — old Dr. Lysander Starr, who was mayor in 1890."

"Good old Dr. Starr!" said our visitor. "His name is still honoured. Well, Mr. Holmes, I suppose all we can do is to report to you and let you know how we progress. I reckon you will hear within a day or two." With this assurance our American bowed and departed.

Holmes had lit his pipe, and he sat for some time with a curious smile upon his face.

"Well?" I asked at last.

"I am wondering, Watson — just wondering!"

"At what?"

Holmes took his pipe from his lips.

"I was wondering, Watson, what on earth could be the object of this man in telling us such a rigmarole of lies. I nearly asked him so — for there are times when a brutal frontal attack is the best policy — but I judged it better to let him think he had fooled us. Here is a man with an English coat frayed at the elbow and trousers bagged at the knee with a year's wear, and yet by this document and by his own account he is a provincial American lately landed in London. There have been no advertisements in the agony columns. You know that I miss nothing there. They are my favourite covert for putting up a bird, and I would never have overlooked such a cock pheasant as that. I never knew a Dr. Lysander Starr, of Topeka. Touch him where you would, he was false. I think the fellow is really an American, but he has worn his accent smooth with years of London. What is his game, then, and what motive lies behind this preposterous search for Garridebs? It's worth our attention, for, granting that the man is a rascal, he is certainly a complex and ingenious one. We must now find out if our other correspondent is a fraud also. Just ring him up, Watson."

I did so and heard a thin, quavering voice at the other end of the line.

"Yes, yes, I am Mr. Nathan Garrideb. Is Mr. Holmes there? I should very much like to have a word with Mr. Holmes."

My friend took the instrument, and I heard the usual syncopated dialogue.

"Yes, he has been here. I understand that you don't know him.... How long?... Only two days!... Yes, yes, of course, it is a most captivating prospect. Will you be at home this evening? I suppose your namesake will not be there?... Very good, we will come then, for I would rather have a chat without him.... Dr. Watson will come with me.... I understood from your note that you did not go out often.... Well, we shall be round about six. You need not mention it to the American lawyer.... Very good. Good-bye!"

It was twilight of a lovely spring evening, and even Little Ryder Street, one of the smaller offshoots from the Edgware Road, looked golden and wonderful in the slanting rays of the setting sun. The particular house to which we were directed was a large, old-fashioned, Early Georgian edifice, with a flat brick face broken only by two deep bay windows on the ground floor. It was on this ground floor that our client lived, and, indeed, the low windows proved to be the front of the huge room in which he spent his waking hours. Holmes pointed, as

we passed, to the small brass plate which bore the curious name.

"Up some years obviously, Watson," he remarked, indicating its discoloured surface. "It's *his* real name, anyhow, and that is something to note."

The house had a common stair, and there were a number of names painted in the hall, some indicating offices and some private chambers. It was not a collection of residential flats but, rather, the abode of Bohemian bachelors. Our client opened the door for us himself and apologized by saying that the woman in charge left at four o'clock. Mr. Nathan Garrideb proved to be a very tall, loose-jointed, round-backed person, gaunt and bald, some sixty-odd years of age. He had a cadaverous face, with the dull dead skin of a man to whom exercise was unknown. Large round spectacles and a small projecting goat's beard combined with his stooping attitude to give him an expression of peering curiosity. The general effect, however, was quite amiable, though eccentric.

The room was as curious as its occupant. It looked like a small museum. It was both broad and deep, with cupboards and cabinets all round, crowded with specimens, geological and anatomical. Cases of butterflies and moths flanked each side of the entrance. A large table in the centre was littered with all sorts of débris, while the tall brass tube of a powerful microscope bristled up among them. As I glanced round, I was surprised at the universality of the man's interests. Here was a case of ancient coins. There was a cabinet of flint instruments. Behind his central table was a large cupboard of fossil bones. Above was a line of plaster skulls with such names as "Neanderthal," "Heidelberg," "Cro-Magnon" printed beneath them. It was clear that he was a student of many subjects. As he stood in front of us now, he held a piece of chamois leather in his right hand with which he was polishing a coin.

"Syracusan — of the best period," he explained, holding it up. "They degenerated greatly towards the end. At their best I hold them supreme, though some prefer the Alexandrian school. You will find a chair here, Mr. Holmes. Pray allow me to clear these bones. And you, sir — ah, yes, Dr. Watson — if you would have the goodness to put the Japanese vase to one side. You see round me my little interests in life. My doctor lectures me about never going out, but why should I go out when I have so much to hold me here? I can assure you that the adequate cataloguing of one of those cabinets would take me three good months."

Holmes looked round him with curiosity.

"But do you tell me that you *never* go out?" he said.

"Now and again I drive down to Sotheby's or Christie's.[1] Otherwise I very seldom leave my room. I am not too strong, and my researches are very absorbing. But you can imagine, Mr. Holmes, what a terrific shock — pleasant but terrific — it was for me when I heard of this unparalleled good fortune. It only needs one more Garrideb to complete the matter, and surely we can find one. I had a brother, but he is dead, and female relatives are disqualified. But there must surely be others in the world. I had heard that you handled strange cases, and that was why I sent to you. Of course, this American gentleman is right. I should have taken his advice first, but I acted for the best."

"I think you acted very wisely indeed," said Holmes. "But are you really anxious to acquire an estate in America?"

"Certainly not, sir. Nothing would induce me to leave my collection. But this gentleman has assured me that he will buy me out as soon as we have established our claim. Five million dollars was the sum named. There are a dozen specimens in the market at the present moment which fill gaps in my collection and which I am unable to purchase for want of a few hundred pounds. Just think what I could do with five million dollars.

---

[1] **Sotheby's** and **Christie's**, London auction galleries dealing in ancient relics.

Why, I have the nucleus of a national collection. I shall be the Hans Sloane[2] of my age."

His eyes gleamed behind his great spectacles. It was very clear that no pains would be spared by Mr. Nathan Garrideb in attempting to find a namesake.

"I merely called to make your acquaintance, and there is no reason why I should interrupt your studies," said Holmes. "I prefer to establish personal touch with those with whom I do business. There are few questions I need ask, for I have your very clear narrative in my pocket, and I filled up the blanks when this American gentleman called. I understand that up to this week you were unaware of his existence."

"That is so. He called Tuesday."

"Did he tell you of our interview to-day?"

"Yes, he came straight back to me. He had been very angry."

"Why should he be angry?"

"He seemed to think it was some reflection on his honour. But he was quite cheerful again when he returned."

"Did he suggest any course of action?"

"No, sir, he did not."

"Has he had, or asked for, any money from you?"

"No, sir, never!"

"You see no possible object he has in view?"

"None, except what he states."

"Did you tell him of our telephone appointment?"

"Yes, sir, I did."

Holmes was lost in thought. I could see that he was puzzled.

"Have you any articles of great value in your collection?"

"No, sir. I am not a rich man. It is a good collection but not a very valuable one."

"You have no fear of burglars?"

"Not the least."

"How long have you been in these rooms?"

"Nearly five years."

Holmes's cross-examination was interrupted by an imperative knocking at the door. No sooner had our client unlatched it than the American lawyer burst excitedly into the room.

"Here you are!" he cried, waving a paper over his head. "I thought I should be in time to get you. Mr. Nathan Garrideb, my congratulations! You are a rich man, sir. Our business is happily finished and all is well. As to you, Mr. Holmes, we can only say we are sorry if we have given you any useless trouble."

He handed over the paper to our client, who stood staring at a marked advertisement. Holmes and I leaned forward and read it over his shoulder. This is how it ran:

---

[2] **Hans Sloane,** English physician whose collections of books and curiosities formed the nucleus of the British Museum.

HOWARD GARRIDEB

Constructor of Agricultural Machinery

Binders, reapers, steam and hand plows, drills, harrows, farmers' carts, buckboards, and all other appliances.

Estimates for Artesian Wells.

Apply Grosvenor Buildings, Aston.

Our host gasped. "Glorious! That makes our third man."

"I had opened up inquiries in Birmingham," said the American, "and my agent there has sent me this advertisement from a local paper. We must hustle and put the thing through. I have written to this man and told him that you will see him in his office to-morrow afternoon at four o'clock."

"You want *me* to see him?"

"What do you say, Mr. Holmes? Don't you think it would be wiser? Here am I, a wandering American with a wonderful tale. Why should he believe what I tell him? But you are a Britisher with solid references, and he is bound to take notice of what you say. I would go with you if you wished, but I have a very

busy day to-morrow, and I could always follow you if you are in any trouble."

"Well, I have not made such a journey for years."

"It is nothing, Mr. Garrideb. I have figured out your connections. You leave at twelve and should be there soon after two. Then you can be back the same night. All you have to do is to see this man, explain the matter, and get an affidavit of his existence. By the Lord!" he added hotly, "considering I've come all the way from the centre of America, it is surely little enough if you go a hundred miles in order to put this matter through."

"Quite so," said Holmes. "I think what this gentleman says is very true."

Mr. Nathan Garrideb shrugged his shoulders with a disconsolate air. "Well, if you insist, I shall go," said he. "It is certainly hard for me to refuse you anything, considering the glory of hope that you have brought into my life."

"Then that is agreed," said Holmes, "and no doubt you will let me have a report as soon as you can."

"I'll see to that," said the American. "Well," he added, looking at his watch, "I'll have to get on. I'll call to-morrow, Mr. Nathan, and see you off to Birmingham. Coming my way, Mr. Holmes? Well, then, good-bye, and we may have good news for you to-morrow night."

I noticed that my friend's face cleared when the American left the room, and the look of thoughtful perplexity had vanished.

"I wish I could look over your collection, Mr. Garrideb," Holmes said. "In my profession all sorts of odd knowledge comes useful, and this room is a storehouse of it."

Our client shone with pleasure, and his eyes gleamed from behind his big glasses.

"I had always heard, sir, that you were a very intelligent man," said he. "I could take you round now if you have the time."

"Unfortunately, I have not. But these specimens are so well labelled and classified that they hardly need your personal explanation. If to-morrow I should be able to look in, I presume that there would be no objection to my glancing over them?"

"None at all. You are most welcome. The place will, of course, be shut up, but Mrs. Saunders is in the basement up to four o'clock and would let you in with her key."

"Well, I happen to be clear to-morrow afternoon. If you would say a word to Mrs. Saunders, it would be quite in order. By the way, who is your house-agent?"

Our client was amazed at this sudden question.

"Holloway and Steele, in the Edgware Road. But why?"

"I am a bit of an archaeologist myself when it comes to houses," said Holmes, laughing. "I was wondering if this was Queen Anne or Georgian."

"Georgian, beyond doubt."

"Really. I should have thought a little earlier. However, it is easily ascertained. Well, good-bye, Mr. Garrideb, and may you have every success in your journey to Birmingham."

The house-agent's was close by, but we found that it was closed for the day, so we made our way back to Baker Street. It was not till after dinner that Holmes reverted to the subject.

"Our little problem draws to a close," said he. "No doubt you have outlined the solution in your own mind."

"I can make neither head nor tail of it."

"The head is surely clear enough, and to-morrow we should see the tail. Did you notice nothing curious about that advertisement?"

"I saw that the word 'plough' was misspelt."

"Oh, you did notice that, did you? Come, Watson, you improve all the time. Yes, it was bad English but good American. The printer had set it up as received. Then the buckboards. That is American also. And artesian wells are commoner with them than with us. It was a typical American advertisement, but purporting to be from an English firm. What do you make of that?"

"I can only suppose that this American lawyer put it in himself. What his object was I fail to understand."

"Well, there are alternative explanations. Anyhow, he wanted to get this good old fossil up to Birmingham. That is very clear. I might have told him that he was clearly going on a wild-goose chase, but, on second thoughts, it seemed better to clear the stage by letting him go. To-morrow, Watson — well, to-morrow will speak for itself."

Holmes was up and out early. When he returned at lunchtime, I noticed his face was very grave.

"This is a more serious matter than I had expected, Watson," said he. "It is fair to tell you so, though I know it will only be an additional reason to you for running your head into danger. I should know my Watson by now. But there *is* danger, and you should know it."

"Well, it is not the first we have shared, Holmes. I hope it may not be the last. What is the particular danger this time?"

"We are up against a very hard case. I have identified Mr. John Garrideb, Counsellor at Law. He is none other than 'Killer' Evans, of sinister and murderous reputation."

"I fear I am none the wiser."

"Ah, it is not part of your profession to carry about a portable Newgate[3] Calendar in your memory. I

---

[3] **Newgate**, a famous London prison.

have been down to see friend Lestrade at the Yard. There may be an occasional want of imaginative intuition down there, but they lead the world for thoroughness and method. I had an idea that we might get on the track of our American friend in their records. Sure enough, I found his chubby face smiling up at me from the rogues' portrait gallery. 'James Winter, alias Morecroft, alias Killer Evans' was the inscription below." Holmes drew an envelope from his pocket. "I scribbled down a few points from his dossier: Aged forty-four. Native of Chicago. Known to have shot three men in the States. Escaped from penitentiary through political influence. Came to London in 1893. Shot a man over cards in a night-club in the Waterloo Road in January, 1895. Man died, but he was shown to have been the aggressor in the row. Dead man was identified as Rodger Prescott, famous as forger and coiner in Chicago. Killer Evans released in 1901. Has been under police supervision since, but so far as known has led an honest life. Very dangerous man, usually carries arms and is prepared to use them. That is our bird, Watson — a sporting bird, as you must admit."

"But what is his game?"

"Well, it begins to define itself. I have been to the house-agent's. Our client, as he told us, has been there five years. It was unlet for a year before then. The previous tenant was a gentleman at large named Waldron. Waldron's appearance was well remembered at the office. He had suddenly vanished and nothing more been heard of him. He was a tall, bearded man with very dark features. Now, Prescott, the man whom Killer Evans had shot, was, according to Scotland Yard, a tall, dark man with a beard. As a working hypothesis, I think we may take it that Prescott, the American criminal, used to live in the very room which our innocent friend now devotes to his museum. So at last we get a link, you see."

"And the next link?"

"We must now look for that."

He took a revolver from the drawer and handed it to me.

"I have my old favourite with me. If our Wild West friend tries to live up to his nickname, we must be ready for him. I'll give you an hour for a siesta, Watson, and then I think it will be time for our Ryder Street adventure."

It was just four o'clock when we reached the curious apartment of Nathan Garrideb. Mrs. Saunders, the caretaker, was about to leave, but she had no hesitation in admitting us, for the door shut with a spring lock, and Holmes promised to see that all was safe before we left. Shortly afterwards the outer door closed, her bonnet passed the bow window, and we knew that we were alone in the lower floor of the house. Holmes made a rapid examination of the premises. There was one cupboard in a dark corner which stood out a little from the wall. It was behind this that we eventually crouched while Holmes in a whisper outlined his intentions.

"He wanted to get our amiable friend out of his room — that is very clear, and, as the collector never went out, it took some planning to do it. The whole of this Garrideb invention was apparently for no other end. I must say, Watson, that there is a certain devilish ingenuity about it, even if the queer name of the tenant did give him an opening which he could hardly have expected. He wove his plot with remarkable cunning."

"But what did he want?"

"Well, that is what we are here to find out. It has nothing whatever to do with our client, so far as I can read the situation. It is something connected with the man he murdered — the man who may have been his confederate in crime. There is some guilty secret in the room. That is how I read it. At first I thought our friend might have something in his collection more valuable than he knew — something worth the attention of a big criminal. But the fact that Rodger Prescott of evil memory inhabited these rooms points to some deeper reason. Well, Watson, we can but possess our souls in patience and see what the hour may bring."

That hour was not long in striking. We crouched closer in the shadow as we heard the outer door open and shut. Then came the sharp, metallic snap of a key, and the American was in the room. He closed the door softly behind him, took a sharp glance around him to see that all was safe, threw off his overcoat, and walked up to the central table with the brisk manner of one who knows exactly what he has to do and how to do it. He pushed the table to one side, tore up the square of carpet on which it rested, rolled it completely back, and then, drawing a jemmy from his inside pocket, he knelt down and worked vigorously upon the floor. Presently we heard the sound of sliding boards, and an instant later a square had opened in the planks. Killer Evans struck a match, lit a stump of candle, and vanished from our view.

Clearly our moment had come. Holmes touched my wrist as a signal, and together we stole across to the open trap-door. Gently as we moved, however, the old floor must have creaked under our feet, for the head of our American, peering anxiously round, emerged suddenly from the open space. His face turned upon us with a glare of baffled rage, which gradually softened into a rather shamefaced grin as he realized that two pistols were pointed at his head.

"Well, well!" said he coolly as he scrambled to the surface. "I guess you have been one too many for me, Mr. Holmes. Saw through my game, I suppose, and played me for a sucker from the first. I hand it to you; you have me beat and —"

In an instant he had whisked out a revolver from his breast and had fired two shots. I felt a sudden hot sear as if a red-hot iron had been

pressed to my thigh. There was a crash as Holmes's pistol came down on the man's head. I had a vision of him sprawling upon the floor with blood running down his face while Holmes rummaged him for weapons. Then my friend's wiry arms were round me, and he was leading me to a chair.

"You're not hurt, Watson? For God's sake, say you are not hurt!"

It was worth a wound — it was worth many wounds — to know the depth of loyalty and love which lay behind that cold mask. The clear, hard eyes were dimmed for a moment, and the firm lips were shaking. For the one and only time, I caught a glimpse of a great heart as well as of a great brain. All my years of humble but single-minded service culminated in that moment of revelation.

"It's nothing, Holmes. It's a mere scratch."

He had ripped up my trousers with his pocket-knife.

"You are right," he cried with an immense sigh of relief. "It is quite superficial." His face set like flint as he glared at our prisoner, who was sitting up with a dazed face. "By the Lord, it is as well for you. If you had killed Watson, you would not have got out of this room alive. Now, sir, what have you to say for yourself?"

He had nothing to say for himself. He only sat and scowled. I leaned on Holmes's arm, and together we looked down into the small cellar which had been disclosed by the secret flap. It was still illuminated by the candle which Evans had taken down with him. Our eyes fell upon a mass of rusted machinery, great rolls of paper, a litter of bottles, and, neatly arranged upon a small table, a number of neat little bundles.

"A printing press — a counterfeiter's outfit," said Holmes.

"Yes, sir," said our prisoner, staggering slowly to his feet and then sinking into the chair. "The greatest counterfeiter London ever saw. That's Prescott's machine, and the bundles are two thousand of Prescott's notes, worth a hundred each and fit to pass anywhere. Help yourselves, gentlemen. Call it a deal and let me beat it."

Holmes laughed.

"We don't do things like that, Mr. Evans. There is no bolt-hole for you in this country. You shot this man Prescott, did you not?"

"Yes, sir, and got five years for it, though it was he who pulled on me. Five years — when I should have had a medal the size of a soup plate. No living man could tell a Prescott from a Bank of England, and if I hadn't put him out, he would have flooded London with them. I was the only one in the world who knew where he made them. Can you wonder that I wanted to get to the place? And can you wonder that when I found this crazy boob of a bug-hunter with the queer name squatting right on the top of it, and never quitting his room, I had to do the best I could to shift him? Maybe I would have been wiser if I had put him away. It would have been easy enough, but I'm a soft-hearted guy that can't begin shooting unless the other man has a gun also. But say, Mr. Holmes, what have I done wrong anyhow? I've not used this plant. I've not hurt this old stiff. Where do you get me?''

"Only attempted murder, so far as I can see," said Holmes. "But that's not our job. They take that at the next stage. What we wanted at present was just your sweet self, Mr. Evans. Please give the Yard a call now, Watson. It won't be entirely unexpected."

So those were the facts about Killer Evans and his remarkable invention of the three Garridebs. We heard later that our poor old friend never got over the shock of his dissipated dreams. When his castle in the air fell down, it buried him beneath the ruins. He was last heard of at a nursing-home in Brixton. It was a glad day at the Yard when the Prescott outfit was discovered, for, though they knew that it existed, they had never been able, after the death of the man, to find out where it was. Evans had indeed done great service and caused several worthy C.I.D.[4] men to sleep the sounder, for the counterfeiter stands in a class by himself as a public danger. They would willingly have subscribed to that soup-plate medal of which the criminal had spoken, but the bench took a less favourable view, and the Killer returned to those shades from which he had just emerged.

---

[4] C.I.D., Criminal Investigation Department.

DISCUSSION

1. Holmes knew that in their first discussion John Garrideb had lied to him on three counts. What were they, and how did Holmes know that each was a lie?
2. According to John Garrideb, how was Alexander Hamilton Garrideb's fortune to be distributed after his death? Why had he supposedly made such an unusual will?

3. How did Nathan Garrideb spend his time? Why was he interested in finding a third Garrideb?
4. How and where was the third Garrideb supposedly located? What made Holmes suspicious about him?
5. Why had John Garrideb devised his scheme? What was John Garrideb's real identity, and how did Holmes uncover it?
6. Why was Watson so moved by Holmes's reaction to his gunshot wound? How do you think Watson felt about Holmes?
7. Why was John Garrideb so disturbed during his first visit to Holmes?
8. What did Killer Evans mean when he said that no one "could tell a Prescott from a Bank of England"?
9. What is Scotland Yard? What was Holmes's opinion of it? How did Holmes's attitude compare with that of modern movie and television "private eyes" toward the police?
10. Watson felt that the counterfeiter was "in a class by himself as a public danger." Is counterfeiting a major public danger in the United States today? Why do you think that? In your opinion, what are our greatest public dangers? Why?
11. Since Sherlock Holmes was obviously capable of carrying on his investigations by himself, why do you think the author included the character of Dr. Watson?

AUTHOR

Although he was a doctor, historian, novelist, war correspondent, and dramatist and was knighted for his services during the Boer War, it is as the creator of Sherlock Holmes that Sir Arthur Conan Doyle is best remembered. His famous detective appeared in fifty-six short stories and four novels, and as the writer Christopher Morley commented, "Perhaps no fiction character ever created has become so charmingly real to his readers."

Yet the master detective might never have come into existence if Sir Arthur Conan Doyle had been more successful with his early medical practice. Born in 1859 in Edinburgh, Scotland, he received his medical degree from Edinburgh University and later studied in Vienna to become an eye specialist. After two voyages as a ship's doctor, he set up his practice in a suburb of Portsmouth, England, in 1882. But very few patients came to his office, and to pass the time, he started to write. For his character of Sherlock Holmes, he drew on his recollections of a Scottish surgeon who had been his instructor, Dr. Joseph Bell. Dr. Bell constantly urged his students to develop their powers of deduction and observation to help them diagnose patients' ailments, and when he demonstrated his own highly developed powers in the classroom, the results were astonishing. So it was that Sherlock Holmes emerged as a detective with an amazing ability to solve crimes through the use of reason and observation.

The first Sherlock Holmes novel, *A Study in Scarlet,* was published in 1887. Within a few years, his stories brought him such success that Sir Arthur Conan Doyle gave up his medical practice in order to devote more time to his writing. Eventually he tired of the character he had created and wrote a story in which Sherlock Holmes was killed, but the public protested so vehemently that he was persuaded to bring Holmes back to life for further adventures. Sir Arthur Conan Doyle died in 1930.

FROM THE BOOKSHELF

THIS IS A RECORDING, *by Barbara Corcoran*
Marianne resents being sent to Montana to visit an actress-grandmother she cannot remember. Her amusing tape-recorded diary shows how the people she met helped her discover new ways of looking at things.

THE ANGRY PLANET, *by John Keir Cross*
Two boys and a girl stow away on a rocket ship that a Scottish scientist and an English novelist are flying to Mars.

WHOSE TOWN? *by Lorenz Graham*
A black family's hopes of finding a peaceful existence in a new town are shattered when their teen-age son is attacked by a gang.

THE UNTOLD TALE, *by Erik C. Haugaard*
This seventeenth-century adventure story describes the experiences of an orphan boy during the time Denmark was at war with Sweden.

MIGRANT GIRL, *by Carli Laklan*
The plight of Dacey Cotter and her family is a story of the hardships endured by all migrant workers.

THE YOUNG UNICORNS, *by Madeleine L'Engle*
The invention of Dr. Austin's micro-laser enmeshes his family in a bizarre plot to use it to control men's minds.

BRUMBIE DUST, *by Reginald Ottley*
Wild horses and the tough and lonely men who hunt them are the central figures in these stories of the Australian outback.

PEOPLE IN TWILIGHT: VANISHING AND CHANGING CULTURES,
by Adrien Stoutenburg
This is a fascinating account of what happens when primitive peoples are confronted by modern civilization.

140

Affinities

Contents

Affinities

Another Kind of Courage

by Jack Ishmole

Joey Montagne is a young Mohawk born in the North Gowanus section of Brooklyn where his family settled two generations ago after
leaving the Indian reservation in Canada. Following Mohawk tradition,
his grandfather (Papa), his father (Big Joe), and his uncle (Mike) have
all been ironworkers who have braved the dangers of construction work
atop skyscrapers and bridges. After Joey's father was killed in a fall from
a high beam, Mike became head of the household and leader of the
ironworkers, and he expects Joey to keep the Montagne chain unbroken
by joining his crew after finishing high school. But Joey has decided
that high steel is not for him and that he must stand up to Mike and
be what he wants to be — a musical performer. Mike looks on the boy
as a coward and a deserter, but Joey's mother (Lily) and his girl friend
(Birdie Le Brun) approve his choice of a career and encourage him to
apply for the Ironworkers' Union Scholarship that will enable him to
further his musical education.

Joey's performance in a school musical leads to an audition for Hal
Golding, the proprietor of a Greenwich Village coffee house called The
Living End. When Golding suddenly has to find a substitute for a rock
group whose appearance is canceled, he calls on Joey to fill in for two
weeks. Now Joey faces his first real chance to prove his talents in the
highly competitive field he has chosen.

Golding's phone call had brought confusion along with excitement. Did Joey have a glossy photo they could blow up for out front at The Living End? And for publicity? No. Well, it wasn't important. They would do a quick hand-painted poster, and releases would be sent to the city newspapers announcing the substitution. Did Joey have a special costume he would wear? No. How about one of those white ruffled-front shirts with ruffled sleeves, and a tight-fitting pair of black trousers? No shirt like that? Pick up one at one of the mod boutiques in the Village on the way over. Black boots? Yes, Joey had those. Could you tie some red streamers onto the guitar? Why? Just a bit of color to add to the stark quality of only black and white. Birdie could do that. What time for showing up at The Living End? Three hours before show time, for a run-through, at five o'clock. Bring your family along as our guests. Got it all straight, Joey? See you soon. Click.

The hours passed heavily until Saturday afternoon, and after the initial excitement had worn off, Lily and Papa tried not to talk about it with Joey. If he had a need to talk with them, he would. At school he had had to talk about half his classmates out of showing up at The Living End on Saturday night. He was pleased and flattered by the response of his friends, and the kids in his classes, and many of the teachers, and the basketball team wanting to show en masse.[1] It was too much, and he didn't want to risk being more nervous than he should be. An audience of friends and neighbors and classmates and relatives would never allow him to measure his performance objectively. It would not be fair to him, nor to Golding, to have his first audiences neatly wrapped, tied with a bow, and delivered like the canned laughter he hated on television.

Saturday afternoon. Only three o'clock. Joey sat on the edge of his bed, rehearsing his songs. He was pleased with the way his voice sounded and with the sureness with which his fingers moved across the guitar strings. Birdie had bought some red ribbon at the five-and-ten, cut it into short and long streamers which hung gracefully from the guitar. They did add something — Golding knew his business — but Joey wanted to get used to them, to see that they did not distract him. He stood and tried a song from that position. He had not thought too much about stage movement before this. Would he stand through all of the songs? Would he sit? Would he move around? Golding would help him, he was sure. He wished he could

_____

[1] **en masse** (ĕn măs'), in a group.

145

plan his moves himself, but that would have to wait until he got to The Living End.

On the table near his bed lay a sandwich and glass of milk Lily had brought to his room. He found the food sticking in his throat, so he abandoned the sandwich after a few bites. The milk he gulped down in great swallows.

He packed his guitar carefully in its case, folding the ribbons over gently so they would not be creased.

Three thirty. He washed his face with cool water, patted it dry, and contemplated himself in the bathroom mirror. He hoped he would not need to wear make-up. That would depend on the lighting, and Golding's advice. He walked to the closet and took out his black trousers, leaving them on the hanger, wrapped in plastic.

As he opened his bedroom door, he heard Birdie's voice at the bottom of the stairs, talking with Lily and Papa, going over the directions on how to get to The Living End.

Birdie was not sure whether Lily and Papa would be coming by subway until Papa told her Mike was driving them in. So Mike would be coming too. It was better to have him there, even grudgingly, than absent, with all the tension that would follow his not being there.

Joey and Birdie said good-by and walked toward the subway. He carried his guitar case; she, the trousers. On Eighth Street, they saw the shirt Golding had described in the window of the Village Esquire. Joey tried it on, and it looked fine, so he bought it, asking them not to wrap it up but to put it on the trouser hanger instead. Twelve dollars, which Golding had told Joey he would be glad to reimburse. On the way to Bleecker Street, they paused to look at a record-shop window. Cascading from left to right were all the latest hit albums . . . the Beatles, Sonny and Cher, Harry Belafonte, faces or weird artistic designs to attract and please the millions of young people all over the world who were their fans. Joey and Birdie looked at each other and smiled, silently sharing the same thought, the same hope. Those names had started somewhere, facing their first audiences in Liverpool, or California, or Trinidad. They had made their mark, with hard work, and patience, and luck, and the loyalty of their fans, and the special talent that made each one of them unique and memorable.

Maybe . . . maybe.

A few minutes later, Joey and Birdie were standing outside The Living End. Large black letters on a poster announced the name: Lonny Arlen. In smaller letters, below, were printed the words:

EXTRA ATTRACTION

Joey Montagne

The Singing Mohawk

Joey was furious. Golding had said something about a poster. But not "The Singing Mohawk." Not that!

Birdie could see his angry look. "What's wrong, Joey?"

"Look at that, will you?"

"I still don't see what's wrong."

"Birdie Le Brun, don't you go getting me angry too!"

He went toward the poster, and Birdie thought he was about to rip it from the frame.

"I don't want to be known as a 'Singing Mohawk'! I just want to be a good entertainer. Do they bill Tony Bennett as the Singing Italian, or Sidney Poitier as the Acting Negro? Don't you see, Birdie, this makes me some kind of freak! They'll expect me to come out in moccasins, carrying a tom-tom, and then go into my rain dance! Or maybe they expect me to wear a feather headdress down to my knees. That's not what I want!"

"Gee, Joey, I never thought about it that way. We're proud of being Mohawk. I can't see any harm in letting anyone know about it."

"Not this way, Birdie. It's cheap. It's like a side-show act in a carnival. I don't mind anyone knowing about my Indian blood, but first I'd like to show them I can sing, that I have myself to offer — not some novelty, some gimmick."

"Joey, don't say anything until after tonight. I don't think it's a good idea. Besides, I'm sure Gold-

ing didn't mean any harm. Wait — you can tell him about it later."

"Maybe you're right, Birdie. But just wait till after I'm finished. I'll give him a piece of my Indian mind!"

They entered the coffee house, empty now except for two waitresses who were busy behind the counter, getting huge urns of coffee ready. A large espresso machine gleamed in the dim light, and under a canopy of Plexiglas on the counter top and in display cases were a varied assortment of pastries and cakes, looking like a patchwork quilt.

Joey asked for Hal Golding and was directed to the dressing rooms in the rear, behind a huge screen covered with old theater posters.

Joey knocked at the door, and Golding's voice invited them to enter.

"Hello, Mr. Golding, I'd like you to meet my friend, Birdie Le Brun."

"Hello, Birdie. Joey, baby, am I ever so glad to see you! I just got here not five minutes ago myself."

Joey wondered if he should say anything about the poster. Birdie's look scared him away. Instead he asked, "Can we try a run-through, Mr. Golding?"

"Sure, Joey. Champing at the bit, are you? Well, I don't blame you for wanting to get going. You'll like working with Lonny Arlen." His confidence reached across to Joey and put him at ease.

"Ready, kids? Follow me."

He guided them into the large room. Birdie asked Golding if she would be intruding if she watched Joey rehearse.

"You can sit with me, if you'd like to, Birdie. I can yell lighting cues from back there. Why don't you go change, Joey, and make it out here as fast as you can. I'd like you to meet Lonny Arlen. He'll be here in a few minutes."

As Birdie sat with Golding, her eyes growing accustomed to the dim lighting, she realized how really attractive Golding had made his little club.

One wall, opposite the long counter, was canopied in bright red-and-white striped canvas, making that side of the room look like a large, raised porch, with its small tables and chairs.

From the ceiling, Tiffany lamps hung every few feet, a forest of them, glowing softly beneath their stained-glass kaleidoscopes. The tables were covered with red-checked cloths, and each table was crowned with a small potted fern plant.

The performing area was the most unusual, she observed. There was a simple, red-bricked wall on which hung literally dozens of antique mirrors, all sizes, all colors — gold, black, and some in silver frames. Anyone standing before the wall during a performance would cast dozens of fragmented reflections at those sitting in the audience. It was breathtaking. In the center of the floor, the focal point of the entire room, was a large old-fashioned potbellied stove painted stark white. Overhead, a long rack of pin-spots in amber, blue, and pink bathed the area around the stove.

Golding turned to Birdie. "About an hour from now, they'll be swinging from the rafters."

"It's a very good-looking room, Mr. Golding."

"Well, thanks, I think so too. And you know, young lady, I keep getting new kids in here all the time. I can't begin to tell you how great it makes me feel to be giving them their first break. Some of them have gone on to better things. Ever seen Lonny Arlen?"

"No, but I've heard about him and read about him."

"Nice talent, good soft comedy. It's not that rat-tat-tat old-fashioned kind. He pokes fun at serious things and gets people to laugh at 'em. There he is now. Hey, Lonny! Come here a minute."

Golding introduced Birdie and said to Lonny, "Sit down. Joey Montagne'll be out in a minute. I'd like you to let me know what you think."

"Sure thing," said Arlen.

Almost on cue, Joey emerged from behind the curtain screen. Birdie had no idea what the others thought. She only knew that he looked very handsome, almost like a

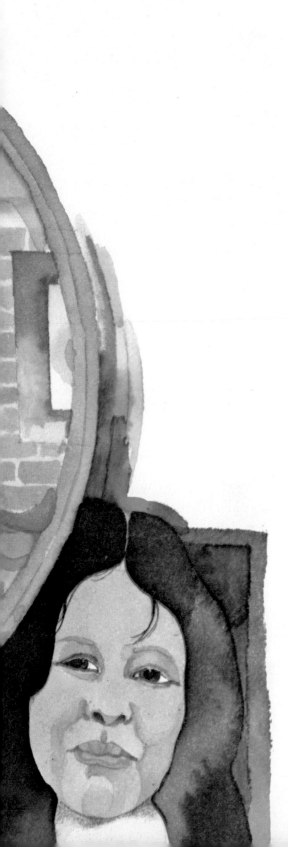

portrait she'd once seen at the Metropolitan Museum of Art. The simplicity of the white shirt and the coal-black trousers was given added elegance by the brilliant red silk streamers she had tied to the guitar.

Golding beckoned. "Over there, Joey — right alongside the stove."

Joey walked to the place indicated by the voice.

"Okay." Golding yelled over his shoulder, "Johnny, let's have the white spot!"

A sharp beam of light haloed Joey from hair to toes.

"Okay." Then Golding instructed, "Bring it down to a pin — just on the face."

Joey's body disappeared in the diminished light. Only the face stood out. Light spilled over onto the surface of the guitar. It was stark, impressive, clean.

"Goya! A painting by Goya, that's who you are, Joey, baby," Golding shouted.

"Rita," he called to one of the waitresses, "get a chair and put it out there, on his right!"

A quick scurrying sound, and a chair was in its place.

"All right, Joey, let's see how it looks when you sit, and you, Johnny, give me a circle of blue on that floor — around the chair!"

"Great," said Arlen, "the kid looks great!"

"You betcha life, Lonny. It's the Golding touch." He was kidding, but his pride was evident.

"I'd say his parents had something to do with it," joked Arlen.

While the others were arranging some further changes in Joey's setup, Birdie wondered about Golding's use of the words "The Singing Mohawk" and whether or not she should try to dissuade Joey from complaining about it until he had thought about it for a few days. Anyone could see that Golding wasn't trying to present Joey to the public as his token Indian. He seemed to want to present him as a talented performer, showing him off to the best advantage.

Everything was ready.

"Okay, Joey, how about a number now? Let's have a standard; then you can switch from standing to sitting, or whatever you like, and then you can do one of your own."

Golding sat down. The waitresses stopped their preparations behind the counter; three bus boys came from the kitchen; even the cashier stood quietly in front of the screen leading to the dressing rooms. Complete silence. Then the soft, sweet sound of Joey's voice floated into the far corners of the room, radiating outward from the central point. The harmony of voice and guitar was perfection; his voice had the freshness of youth which Golding had found in the first audition. He finished the number. The onlookers applauded.

"Cut that!" shouted Golding. "The kid's tryin' to build a mood.

You ought to know better than that."

The room quieted. Embarrassed silence.

Slowly Joey stood, gracefully placing one leg so that his foot rested on the seat of the chair. The stance seemed almost flamenco — classic, elegant.

He looked directly at Golding, as he had done during his audition. His voice was confident and clear.

"Ladies and gentlemen. Some of you have forgotten what it's like to be puzzled by your youth and by your innocence. We forget about the ways in which the world separates one generation from another. I'd like to sing a song called 'Fathers and Sons' which speaks for itself."

And across the darkened room, with only the stark image of his strong face bathed in a sea of blue light, came the words and music of his song.

As his voice disappeared in the whispered tones of the last few words, Golding's advice was forgotten, even by Golding himself. Everyone was applauding. Birdie was on her feet. Her excitement at the triumph of voice and music, of lighting and atmosphere, could not be expressed sitting down. Golding and Arlen were also on their feet; the applause seemed to last for a minute, sounding louder than the sounds made by a dozen frenzied clapping hands. It was overwhelming!

Joey looked jubilant, in the knowledge that everything seemed to be working out well.

"Okay, Joey, take ten!" Golding shouted.

The magical moment finally vanished as the regular lights blinked on around the room. Joey had gone back into the dressing room.

Birdie could overhear Golding and Arlen discussing Joey's performance.

"Well, what do you think of him, Lonny?"

"You sure know how to pick 'em, Hal. The kid's going to be a knockout. Are any of the papers coming?"

"I told *Show Business* and *Backstage* to catch the act early next week. Maybe *Variety*'ll send down their New Acts reporter."

Birdie excused herself and rushed backstage to be with Joey.

It was nine o'clock. Joey stood behind the screen, listening to the uncontrolled laughter of the audience reacting to Arlen's routine. Birdie had kept everyone from visiting him until after his first performance. Now she was sitting out there with Papa and Lily. Many of the other small tables were filled with their friends and neighbors from Gowanus who had heard about Joey and had come to lend support. Many of the ironworkers were sitting stiffly in their seats, looking uncomfortably formal in their shirts and ties, hair combed back and shiny looking. This was their own Joey, Big Joe's boy, and they were here to give him a big hand.

Joey was standing near the stove, the center of all eyes — then he sat through two numbers, as he sang. He moved naturally and gracefully, the songs pouring out without a trace of the nervousness that usually comes with a first professional performance. Through the smoky haze and dim light, he could see his family and the Le Bruns, and he sang as if they were the only audience. At one point, he caught Birdie's face, aglow with pride and excitement, and he winked slightly, making her grin from ear to ear.

Back in Golding's office, after the first performance, Joey sat on the couch, feeling both tired and triumphant. He had been applauded and cheered and whistled at and, at the end, had been given a standing ovation. But those were people he knew, people who had watched him grow up, people woven into his life like the sacred shells in a wampum belt. What did Golding think?

Golding paced back and forth, came out from behind his desk.

"You've got something, Joey. I knew it when we first met. Now, I'm going to level with you. If I praise you to the skies, I'd be phony. If I tell you that you can be much better, that's closer to the truth, but it sounds depressing. So I'm going to give it to you Golding's way . . . straight from the shoulder.

Right now, you're like a hundred other kids I've seen the past year. Green, eager to please, with talent in every finger. When I signed you, I signed you not for what you are now but for what I know you can be, in a few years. If you work at what you've got — and I mean really work hard — I think it'll happen. You were okay tonight . . . fresh, somebody new, and they were rooting for you, even those strangers out there who never saw you before. You'll get better as the nights pass. And then the two weeks are up. You're going to need to study, Joey. To train, to vocalize, to build your voice.

"Your music is something else. Keep it going. Your ideas are good, and your lyrics know where they're going, right along with your music.

"Just one more thing. If you have no plans for your summer, I'd like to get you to try summer stock, doing chorus work, or even some juvenile parts. It's a different kind of exposure, and it will do you good. And then, think about school, like the Berghof outfit, right here in the Village, or the American Academy uptown. If you're serious about a show-biz career, you're not too young to get started."

It came at Joey like a barrage — words, ideas, the honesty, the sincerity, the whole final judgment of Hal Golding.

"Wow," he sighed.

"*Wow* is right. I like you, Joey, and I'd like to get my kicks watching you come along, like I've watched a few others. Their names aren't important . . . and I don't want to scare you or impress you. It's all a matter of luck . . . and persistence. I better let you go. You ought to rest before the eleven o'clock show. There's a comfortable sofa in your dressing room. Try it out for size. And I want you to know that I listened very carefully to you tonight, kid. Every single note and chord. I hope you've listened to me."

"I have, Mr. Golding."

"By the way, Joey. I almost fainted when I saw that poster outside. It's not there anymore. My secretary got frantic, and I've been so busy I didn't get a chance to talk to Tony Parrilla, who handles my publicity. She told him you were young, good-looking, and an Indian. So the jerk goes ahead and stupidly does what you saw out there. I apologize — for Tony, for my secretary, and for The Living End. We'll do you justice tomorrow. A photographer will be here at about seven. We'll get something up there, something good."

Joey was relieved to hear the explanation.

"Thanks, Mr. Golding. Thanks very much."

"Well now, scoot. Beat it."

Joey walked back to the dressing room to face the people who were eager to share his first hours as a professional performer.

Each night, during Joey's engagement, Birdie showed up at The Living End about half an hour before he was through with his performance. She waited for the applause to rise, signaling his closing number.

They would leave The Living End, making their way through the streets to the subway. The Village was always lively, especially late at night. They couldn't resist stopping here and there to window-shop. Jewelry shops, displaying unique rings and bracelets; clothing shops with the latest mod fashions from London strewn casually over racks and counters; antique stores hoarding strange combinations of junk and fine, attractive Victorian pieces. Sometimes they would stop for a hamburger and coke and then remind themselves that both families were still up, waiting for them.

School was another matter. Joey was tired. He knew he needed more sleep, but it was a strange, almost good, sense of fatigue. His teachers seemed to conspire to make no demands on him, as though they knew that perhaps his future lay elsewhere, far away from textbooks and assignments. He was sure to make up any of the work he would postpone for two weeks. And in his classes, and in the cafeteria and the halls, the backslapping, handshaking, and fingers pointing showed that the school had a new celebrity.

One night, after taking Birdie home, Joey found Lily waiting for him, flushed and excited.

"Joey, this letter came today. It's addressed to you. When I saw it was from the union, I knew it must be about the scholarship. I couldn't help myself. I hope you don't mind that I opened it. I was worried."

"Of course not, Mom. Let's see if I can guess what it says. No, don't come closer — I want to read it in your face."

Lily was smiling as she ran to her son and embraced him.

"Joey, I'm so proud of you. I —" She began to cry. "If only your dad were here to share it with us."

"Yes, I wish he were, Mom. Does Mike know about it?"

"I told him, Joey. I wondered if I ought to wait until you came home, but Papa told me not to wait. It seemed to mean something special to him, to tell Mike right away."

"What did he say?" Joey asked.

"I'm not sure. He mumbled something — sounded like 'Well, if that's what he wants.' I told him it *was* what you wanted. And then I broke down and told him it was what I wanted too. All these years he's been hoping to have you up there with him as part of his crew. But I knew I couldn't go through that whole thing all over again. Me, waiting at home for you to come

down each day, wondering if it'll happen again — to you — like it happened to Big Joe. Mike's inside watching the 'Late Show.' Speak with him. Please."

"In a minute, Mom."

Joey opened the envelope and slowly drew out the letter.

Dear Joey:

It is with great pride and pleasure that I am privileged to announce the Board's choice of Joseph Montagne, Jr., as winner of this year's John Harper Scholarship Award.

As you know, the prize pays $4,000 toward tuition for a four-year period of higher education at an institution of the winner's choice.

A committee of eminent educators chose you from a field of eleven applicants. Your outstanding scholastic record and your leadership in community youth activities have won for you the unanimous decision of the judges.

We are proud of you as a young man with a fine potential, and we are doubly proud that you are the son of one of our most highly revered friends and workers, the late Joseph Montagne.

Good luck, Joey, and the best from all of us here at the Ironworkers' Local.

Affectionately,

Sam Simpson

DISCUSSION

1. Why had Joey discouraged many friends and classmates from attending his first performance?
2. Why was Joey angry about the poster outside The Living End? What did Birdie advise him to do about it? What happened after the first performance that proved Birdie's advice was good?
3. Who observed Joey's rehearsal? How was it received?
4. What advice did Golding give Joey about his career?
5. What hopes did Mike have about a career for Joey?
6. Why do you think this story was given the title "Another Kind of Courage"?
7. Why did Lily want Joey to speak to Mike right away about the letter from the union?

8. What did Birdie mean by the phrase "token Indian"?
9. Do you think Mike was selfish in his attitude toward Joey's ambitions? Why do you think that?
10. Which do you think had more influence on Mike — Joey's success as an entertainer or the letter from the union? Why?
11. Would you advise Joey to go to a college where he could study other things besides acting and music or would you advise him to go to a school where he would receive training exclusively in the performing arts? Why?
12. Have you ever given someone a piece of your mind, as Joey was tempted to do, and later been sorry? Why is it often best to wait until you have cooled down before saying anything?

AUTHOR

Jack Ishmole is a native of New York City and teaches film producing, radio broadcasting, and English at a Long Island junior high school. His great interest in the Mohawk Indians led him to investigate their feats as ironworkers, or boomers, in the construction of the skyscrapers and bridges which he saw all around him. His research gave him the idea for his book *Walk in the Sky,* of which "Another Kind of Courage" is a chapter. He has also edited an anthology for young readers entitled *New York Portrait: A Literary Look at the Empire State.* Mr. Ishmole's hobbies include directing productions of community theaters, art collecting, and traveling to the sites of ancient civilizations.

THE PROPHET

by Nancy Wilson Ross

Abigail Scott's home in Illinois stood within a few hundred feet of a main highway, then little more than a rough dirt road, that passed between the towns of Pekin and Peoria. Along this road there had begun to pass during every spring and summer of the late 1840's long lines of covered wagons moving westward.

Abigail could remember all her life the children of these emigrants, barefooted and often dirty, who would come at sundown to the Scott house, bringing sticks of hickory or walnut in order to carry off to their own campfires some of the live coals that her mother kept covered with ashes on the hearth all day long to make her own cooking easier. Mrs. Scott always gave generously of her fire for the sake of the poor homeless women — whom she very much pitied — camping out down the road, with a brood of children and a restless husband.

Not all the people who passed the Scott property were bound for the Pacific Ocean. Many, coming out of Kentucky, Indiana, Ohio, and other parts of Illinois, planned to go no farther than Missouri, then considered part of the Far West. But Abigail's father's imagination was fired, like that of many other men of the time, by the thought of the distant land of the Pacific Northwest. He caught "Oregon fever" in a bad way.

Abigail's mother did not wish to leave her home in Illinois. Physically frail, worn out with the bearing of a large family of children and too much heavy work, she both dreaded and feared the long, uncertain journey. Her protests were, however, in vain. It was Mr. Scott who made the decisions for the family, and his mind was made up. In 1852, over the mother's desperate pleas to remain where they were, the family packed everything they were able to carry and set off. . . .

Her mother's unwillingness to go west, and the seemingly little influence this had on her father, deeply affected the young girl of seventeen. It may even be fair to surmise that they were partly responsible for the fact that some years later Abigail became a suffragette and went forth to preach the doctrine of equal rights for women.

All Mrs. Scott's fears and apprehensions were realized on the exhausting and difficult westward trek. Tired and frail, she succumbed easily to the cholera epidemic that was raging then along the trail of the emigrants. Her untimely death was a blow from which none of her children ever quite recovered. . . .

Why was a woman's lot so hard? Abigail was to ask herself this question many times in the years to come, and when she finally had the answer, she made up her mind to do something about it. . . .

After the Scotts reached Oregon, Abigail was able to get a job teaching school. But very soon she was married to a neighboring farmer named Ben Duniway. On her marriage, she had to give up teaching to become, as she bitterly said, "a servant without wages."

Abigail, though not frail in mind, spirit, or will power, was — like her mother — frail in body. And, like her mother, she found herself caught in an endless round of work that was too heavy for her: scrubbing, milking, churning, sewing, canning — not only for her children, her husband, and the hired men but also for assorted bachelor friends of Ben's who liked to drop in at mealtimes at what Abigail sometimes in despair referred to as "the Duniway Hotel."

By a curious turn of fate, Abigail's opportunity to show what she really had in her came as a result of seeming ill fortune.

One day while she was plucking a goose for feathers for pillows and beds (for there was no ready-made bedding in those days), a man came to call on her husband. Abigail overheard their conversation. The man was asking Ben to sign his name to a note which would allow the man to borrow a large sum of money.

When she heard her husband agreeing to this proposal, Abigail went into the room to protest. She knew that if the man was not able to pay up when the note fell due, Ben would lose his farm, which he was putting up as security. But her husband would not listen to her. Women were not supposed to understand business details. This was a man's world. Ben went right ahead and signed the note.

In time, Abigail's worst fears came to pass. The note fell due. The man could not pay. Ben Duniway had to put up the money, and in order to raise it, he had to sell the farm and everything they owned.

When the sheriff came to serve the papers that let the Duniways know they were to be sued if they didn't pay the man's note, Ben was not at home. Abigail, who had had no legal right to prevent the signing of the note (since a woman at that time had no legal position of any kind), found, however, that the sheriff, in her husband's absence, could make her accept and sign

PROCLAMATION

outrageous in the

Women of

D STEEL WALKING PLOW
Made in STUBBLE and TURF AND

YOU CANNOT
NO MATT

ABIGAIL

MARRIAGE

BEN DUNIWAY

1862

the United States, she

liable to be treated as a woman of the

her

INDIAN ROOT
PILLS

OMSTOCK'S

the papers he had come to serve. This seemed to her the highest form of injustice. It was all a part of a process, however, that she referred to later as "opening her eyes."

When Ben sold the farm, the Duniway family, now penniless, moved to the little town of Lafayette. And here the second serious blow struck them. Ben was injured in an accident with a runaway horse. He could never do farm work again, and farming was all he knew. It now fell to Abigail's lot to earn the income for the family.

She returned, not without a certain joy, to teaching school. Although she had to rise at three in summer and four in winter to clean house and prepare breakfast for her six children, her husband, and the boarders she had taken in to help make ends meet, she did not complain. She was interested in her work. . . .

But Abigail was a hard-headed realist. Although education was more important to her than anything else in the world, she soon found she could not make a living at it. She saw that if she was to continue as the family's main support, she must somehow get into business.

She decided to move her family to the nearby larger town of Albany. Here she turned her schoolhouse into a store with counters, shelves, and showcases. She had managed to save thirty dollars, and with this sum to spend on goods, she journeyed to Portland to interview the town's richest merchant, Jacob Meier.

Mr. Meier, a man both kind and astute, insisted that she take twelve hundred dollars' worth of goods on credit. Abigail's head whirled. She had come to Portland with thirty dollars and was being offered more than a thousand! Should she plunge? Did she dare to? She decided to plunge.

In just three weeks she was back, her entire debt paid. This time she asked for three thousand dollars' worth of goods and got it without a question.

It was millinery, oddly enough, that led Abigail out farther and farther into life. In her prosperous shop, to which women began to come from all the neighboring villages and farms of the countryside, she had a chance to meet and talk to women from every kind of life and many different backgrounds. What she saw of the women around her led Abigail to remark with wry humor, "Half of us are dolls, half of us are drudges, and all of us are fools."

The thing that upset her the most was the part she was asked to play in little games of deceit by which women — who had in those days no allowance of any kind and no financial independence — deceived their husbands about money. A woman would, for instance, pretend to her husband that she was buying cheap straw hats for her children at Abigail's shop and, when his back was turned, persuade Abigail to exchange the hats for more practical and also more expensive ones. The woman would go into debt for her children's hats and then pay off the debt bit by bit by pilfering small change from her husband's pockets when he was asleep.

When Abigail, horrified and troubled by this kind of experience, went to another merchant of the town to talk to him about such a shocking state of affairs, he only laughed at her and said, "We merchants couldn't make any profit on fancy goods at all if it wasn't for what the women steal from their husbands."

This did not seem a very satisfactory answer to Abigail. She went on thinking her troubled thoughts about the wrongness of the whole situation. It was true that women stole from their husbands, but the men stole from their wives too. Only in the case of the men there was a difference. When, for instance, a man helped himself to his wife's precious "butter money" or "egg money" — the one kind of small savings that country women had a right to in those days by a sort of unspoken law, since it was the women who did the churning and raised the hens — *he* did not need to do it in the dark of the night. He just helped himself, and he had a legal right to do so, for everything his wife owned legally belonged to him. . . .

Plainly something was terribly wrong! But what to do about it — that was the question. . . .

Abigail did a lot of thinking and talking, and even a good deal of fuming, over things of this kind and the general lot of women. She was thirty-six years old when, as she said, finally "the light broke" on her. She always gave her husband, Ben, the full credit for pointing out the truth to her. One day as she was protesting some injustice, he put his hand fondly on the top of her head and told her she could go on fuming all she pleased about the "slavery of women" but nothing could change until all women had "the right to vote and equal rights with men before the law."

It is not easy today — when people like Abigail Duniway have made it possible for all women to vote, to have an education, to earn money in jobs and professions, to have a right to their own money and to their own property and all the rest of the things now taken for granted — to realize just what it meant in Abigail's day to declare oneself in favor of equal rights, to become that dreaded kind of female, a suffragette.

Suffragettes were already making a stir in the eastern part of the United States. They were considered by most people to be freaks or fiends, and all, without exception, were said to be manhaters. The truth is that most of them came from fine backgrounds, were handsome, gentle-voiced, educated, and dedicated. . . .

When Abigail had committed herself to becoming a fighter in the cause of equal rights, she gave up her Albany store and moved with her family to Portland, the largest town in the state. She had a new plan. She was going to found a newspaper. Her brother, Harvey Scott, had become the editor of the *Oregonian,* the leading newspaper of that part of the country. But she did not turn to him for any help or advice. She simply rented two bedrooms in a plain frame house, hired a foreman at twenty-five dollars a week, set her sons to learning printing, and was soon embarked on the next stage of her career. Only when the paper was well launched did she invite Harvey in to have a look. His sincere praise and great surprise warmed her heart.

She called her newspaper *The New Northwest.* In the same year that she founded it, the great feminist, Susan B. Anthony, came to the Pacific Coast from New York State to talk on women's rights.

Since the end of the Civil War, Susan B. Anthony had been talking to women everywhere — and men too — about the fact that Abraham Lincoln had himself said, when he freed the slaves and gave them the right to vote, that equality belonged to all Americans "and by no means excluding women." But even these words of a great President had not yet given women equality nor kept those who preached the new doctrine from being badly treated. Once when Miss Anthony had dared — back in New York State where she lived — to go to the polls and try to vote, she had been fined a hundred dollars for her crime!

So when the famous (some said "infamous") Miss Anthony came to the Far West and Abigail Duniway became her manager during her visit, curious people began to buy *The New Northwest,* hoping to read about the dangerous doings of these two frightening "manhaters." The circulation of Abigail's paper boomed.

But Abigail was much too astute to fill her newspaper simply with propaganda. She always said that her life as a milliner had taught her a lot about the psychology of the average woman. She believed that she could best interest women in the problem of their legal rights by dealing also with such everyday matters as how long skirts were going to be that year, how you could cut over an out-of-date dress, how you could make mutton stew more appetizing. So she began a Free Advice to Readers column. . . . Subtly, Abigail kept hammering away on the theme of equality and on the theme of women growing up to their full stature. . . .

It was inevitable that Abigail, with her gift of words and her fiery interest in the subject of women's rights, should soon take to the public platform. To do such a thing was the most shocking step so far. Not many years before she herself became a public speaker, Abigail had been hissed for daring to enter a hall on her husband's arm just to listen to a male lecturer!

Abigail of course realized that as a woman speaker, traveling alone, talking in public, she would be considered a greater freak than ever. But she was willing to face this new ridicule if by so doing she could plant the seeds of rebellion in other feminine hearts or make men, too, see the light. For Abigail, always a realist, knew very well that it was men who would finally decide the question of votes for women. Men alone had the right to vote, and they alone could grant this privilege to their wives, sisters, daughters, and mothers — or forever keep it from them. She also always felt that the women of the Far West would be the first to win the vote because they had so clearly shown — in the days of the great emigrations — just what stuff they were made of and how they could equal men in enduring danger and hardships.

Before long, Abigail had become a familiar figure on riverboats and stagecoaches of the pioneer period. With her strong, handsome face under its conservative but always smart and expensive hat (Abigail was aware of the importance of such details!), with her sensible shoes to make walking easier, her neat gloves, her inevitable umbrella (sometimes useful as a weapon of defense), she would buy a ticket on one of the comfortable boats that made their slow way up the Columbia River from the green seacoast to the dry inland country. When the steamer reached the sluggish parts of the river where there were no rapids to excite the passengers and where the scenery had become monotonous, Abigail would ask the captain's permission to make a speech. She had found that passengers would listen to anyone when they were bored — and besides, equal rights was hardly a boring subject! People felt strongly on it one way or another! When she had finished her little talk, she would, with quiet dignity, take up a collection for the cause. When the steamer tied up for the night at some riverside village, Abigail would bravely go ashore, alone, a stranger in a strange town, and try to find a room large enough in which to hold another meeting, make another speech.

She had great courage and a sense of humor. Without these traits of her character she could never have survived. She was able even to see the irony in the fact that the Pixley Sisters — with a daring, even shocking, song-and-dance act — could get a hall in any town sooner than she with her dignified talks on suffrage for women. . . .

She spoke in stores, in schools, in hotel lobbies, in private houses, in blacksmiths' shops, in stables, once even in the back room of a saloon. (That was on a night when the key of the hall she had engaged had mysteriously disappeared.) By the yellow light of kerosene lamps she would stand in quiet dignity making her vivid pictures — and Abigail, the word-user, knew how to describe injustice in the lives of women. Over

"The debt that each generation owes to the past it must pay to the future."

Abigail Scott Duniway

, May 15, 18

o. 28.

United States
from the wo-
ew Orleans, in
rference
here-

T

JULY 22. 18

VICTORY

'95

20 21 2
27 28 29

and over she would stress the unfairness of the fact that the women who bore the country's children still had no legal right to decide the laws of the land to which these children belonged.

One of the favorite questions often put to timid women who had begun to think they really did have a right to the vote and might like to exercise that right was the silly question, "But how would you like to serve on a jury and be locked in a room with eleven men?" The very idea was called indecent. "Indecent!" Abigail would cry. "Is it more indecent than the fact that though women may not sit on juries, juries can try them for their very lives?"

. . . Once when she was riding on a stagecoach through eastern Washington — the only woman among men, as she so often had to be — a fellow traveler . . . decided to make Abigail the butt of some sarcastic remarks for the benefit of the other travelers. "Madam," he said, in ending these remarks, "you ought to be at home enjoying yourself, as my wife is doing. I want to bear all the hardships of life myself and let her sit by the fire, toasting her footsies." Abigail . . . later enjoyed an unexpected revenge when the man was dropped before his house beside the road. There in the thickly falling snow stood his poor wife, chopping away at the woodpile. Abigail couldn't resist this opportunity to make a point. She leaned out of the coach and called cheerfully to her tormentor, "Good-by. I see that your wife is toasting her footsies." She could still laugh at that one when she was in her seventies. . . .

After her fame had spread across America, she made a number of trips east. On one of these trips to attend a suffrage convention, she met the great Horace Greeley, the editor of the *New York Tribune.* Greeley was running for the Presidency of the United States. He received Abigail warmly because he had been told that she had made a speech in his favor. But when Abigail spoke of her mission — which was to ask him to endorse the suffrage movement in his political platform — Greeley at once grew extremely irritable. Stroking his much-caricatured white chin whiskers, he said in a voice suddenly "as hard as hailstones": "I don't want women to be men."

"Neither do I," replied Abigail, getting at once to her feet, preparing to leave with no more talk. "I wouldn't be a man if I could! And now, Mr. Greeley, mark my words: You'll never be President! You will find that women can tear down if they are not permitted to build up."

Her prophecy came true. Greeley never became President.

It was 1912 when Abigail Scott Duniway, by now an old woman in a lace cap, was at last able to sign the Equal Suffrage Proclamation for her state of Oregon. She had written the proclamation herself — an event said to be as significant in the long unrecorded history of women as the writing of the Constitution of the United States was to humanity in general. No woman had ever before been entrusted with the framing of so important a paper.

Abigail Scott Duniway died three years later, in 1915. . . . Right up to the day of her death, she was reminding American women and girls of the gratitude they should feel for the hard fight that certain indomitable females had made in their behalf.

"The young women of today," she once said, "free to study, to speak, to write, to choose their occupations, should remember that every inch of this freedom was bought for them at a great price. It is for them to show their gratitude by helping onward the reforms of their own times, by spreading the light of freedom and truth still wider."

And, finally, she voiced one great and simple challenge: "The debt that each generation owes to the past it must pay to the future."

Thus Abigail, the pioneer pathbreaker and prophet, pointed all American women on their way to an ever-widening world!

DISCUSSION

1. In what way was Abigail's mother a victim of "Oregon fever"? What was there about the relationship between Abigail's mother and father that later influenced Abigail to become a suffragette?

2. What two misfortunes radically changed Abigail's married life? What did Abigail feel was especially unjust about the first of those misfortunes? By what three means did she manage to support the family after those misfortunes?

3. What did Abigail's husband say to her that finally convinced her she should become a suffragette?

4. Why did it take unusual courage for Abigail to become a public speaker?

5. What do you think Abigail meant when she said, "Half of us are dolls, half of us are drudges, and all of us are fools"?

6. Why do you think riverboat captains were willing to let Abigail give talks on women's rights to their passengers?

7. Women were not allowed to vote, but how might Abigail have helped make her prophecy about Horace Greeley come true?

8. What did Abigail mean by saying, "The debt that each generation owes to the past it must pay to the future"?

9. Which do you think was more difficult — to convince women that they should demand equal rights or to convince men that these rights should be granted? Which was more important? Why?

10. Why do you think many men in Abigail's day were opposed to letting women vote? Do you know of any similar injustices in present-day America? If so, what are they and how might they be eliminated?

11. If Abigail were alive today, do you think she would be fighting for some other cause? Why do you think as you do?

AUTHOR

Nancy Wilson Ross was born in Olympia, Washington, in 1907. After graduating from the University of Oregon, she studied at an art school in Germany, and art and writing have always been her two major interests. She has from childhood been a constant reader, and she is also enthusiastic about travel. During World War II she served as a war correspondent in North Africa and Europe.

Her Pacific Northwest background is reflected in several of her books, including *Heroines of the Early West,* from which "The Prophet" is taken, and *Farthest Reach: The Story of Oregon and Washington.* When some of her writing resulted in accusations almost thirty years ago that she was a feminist, she countered by voicing her opinion that American women were in general "our greatest unused national resource."

She and her husband, publisher and playwright Stanley Young, now live in Old Westbury, Long Island.

A Blessing

Just off the highway to Rochester, Minnesota,
Twilight bounds softly forth on the grass.
And the eyes of those two Indian ponies
Darken with kindness.
They have come gladly out of the willows
To welcome my friend and me.
We step over the barbed wire into the pasture
Where they have been grazing all day, alone.
They ripple tensely, they can hardly contain their happiness
That we have come.
They bow shyly as wet swans. They love each other.
There is no loneliness like theirs.
At home once more,
They begin munching the young tufts of spring in the darkness.
I would like to hold the slenderer one in my arms,
For she has walked over to me
And nuzzled my left hand.
She is black and white,
Her mane falls wild on her forehead,
And the light breeze moves me to caress her long ear
That is delicate as the skin over a girl's wrist.
Suddenly I realize
That if I stepped out of my body I would break
Into blossom.

James Wright

171

FROZEN ASSETS

by Paul Dickson

Ice cream cannot be fully appreciated in a vacuum; it must be seen in light of the many glorious forms in which it is presented to us. Scant attention has been paid to these edible institutions in the past — unfair, since many of us grew up knowing more than we wanted to know about Eli Whitney and his cotton gin (1793, right?) and nothing about the more relevant Eskimo Pie or sundae. To rectify this educational injustice, the stories behind some of these lip-smacking institutions have been assembled. Sadly, several defy historical sleuthing and seem just to have appeared around the turn of the century. Such is the case with the ice-cream sandwich, the banana split, and also the float — and for lack of data the songs of their hero-inventors must go unsung. Fortunately this is not the case with the ice-cream soda, the sundae, and the cone.

As is true with almost every worthy ice-cream discovery, there is more than one claim to the construction of the first ice-cream soda. Unlike other cases, however, the evidence in this one clearly leads us away from a host of pretenders to a Philadelphian who dealt in dispensers of carbonated water. This generally acknowledged creator of the ice-cream soda is Robert M. Green, who fathered it in October, 1874, at the semicentennial celebration of the Franklin Institute in Philadelphia, where he was a concessionaire selling soda-fountain drinks from a three-foot-square dispenser. At the beginning of the exhibition he was serving a popular drink of the time which was a mixture of sweet cream, syrup, and carbonated water. During one of the early days of the celebration, however, he ran out of cream and began substituting vanilla ice cream. The customers gave their hearty approval to the new drink as evidenced by the fact that Green, who had been averaging $6 a day with the first drink, was taking in over $600 a day for ice-cream sodas by the end of the exhibition. Green went on to make a fortune as a soda manufacturer, and when he died in 1920, his will called for a large monument to be erected over his grave with the inscription: ORIGINATOR OF THE ICE-CREAM SODA. His firm, Robt. M. Green and Sons, continued to flourish until after World War II, when national priorities turned against the amenity of the soda fountain.

Two years after Green's soda first appeared, it had become such a sensation that James W. Tufts, another pioneer soda-fountain manufacturer, paid $50,000 for the sole right to dispense ice-cream sodas at the Philadelphia Centennial, which was held to commemorate the hundredth anniversary of the Declaration of Independence. By 1893 an American magazine had heralded the ice-cream soda as "the national beverage," and it was being served in every corner of the land.

In no time at all the ice-cream soda became a fresh new menace for the more excitable members of the American clergy. As Stewart H. Holbrook observes in his *Lost Men of American History:* "In the author's native town of Newport, Vermont, as late as 1890, a powerful sermon was preached against 'sucking soda' and eating ice cream in drugstores on the Sabbath; and in certain Midwest towns laws were passed against the abomination, and the selling of soda water on Sunday was prohibited." Such actions begged for another fountain concoction — one that would be so constructed as to skirt the intolerant Sunday blue laws legally.

Just as there are scads of local claims on the ice-cream soda, so there are scads more on the sundae — and it would be futile to try to list all the communities insisting that they be honored as the birthplace of the sundae. Sifting out the chaff, these facts remain. The ice-cream sundae emerged in the late 1890's and became extremely popular around the turn of the century. This popularity was substantially aided by laws prohibiting the sale of sodas on Sunday, and for this reason the concoction was first known as the "Sunday" or the "Soda-less Soda." The more elegant -ae ending probably came about when those who orated from the pulpit on the sinful soda went to work on the sacrilegious use of the name of the Sabbath for its stand-in.

As for the specific birthplace of the dish, two possibilities emerge as the most likely among many contenders. Neither place can offer conclusive dates, so one can pick between "Heavenston" (favored by the National Dairy Council, among others) and Two Rivers (championed by such diverse sources as the old *Ice Cream Review* and H. L. Mencken in his *American Language*).

The first claim goes back to the 1890's in Evanston, Illinois (then widely known as "Chicago's Heaven" or "Heavenston"), where civic piety had reached such a state that it became the first American community to recognize and legislate against the "Sunday Soda Menace." This prompted confectioners to create Sundays so that they could do business on the Sabbath.

The Two Rivers, Wisconsin, claim goes back to the same era and, so the story goes, was created when a youth named George Hallauer went into Ed Berner's soda fountain for a dish of ice cream. As the ice cream was being scooped, the daring Hallauer spied a bottle of chocolate syrup, normally used in sodas, and asked Berner to pour some of it over his ice cream. Berner sampled the concoction and liked it enough to begin featuring "ice cream with syrup" in his shop for the same price as a dish of ice cream. The name *sundae* was given to the dish when George Giffy, an ice-cream parlor proprietor in nearby Manitowoc, was forced by customer demand to serve the popular Berner concoction. Giffy was convinced that the nickel dish would put him out of business and at first served it only as a Sunday loss leader. In Manitowoc it soon became known as "the Sunday." Giffy then found that he was making money on the dish and began advertising his "Ice Cream Sundaes," with the spelling changed so that it would lose its Sunday-only association.

Regardless of the origin, by 1900 midwestern soda-fountain supply salesmen were carrying samples of tulip-shaped "Sundae Specials." Within a few more years they would be carrying an even hotter new item: the World's Fair Cornucopia, later known as the ice-cream cone.

On April 28, 1954, the pooh-bahs of the cone and ice-cream industries assembled in St. Louis to celebrate the golden anniversary of the ice-cream cone. Under the sponsorship of the International Association of Ice Cream Manufacturers (IAICM), a two-day celebration and convention was held at the Chase Hotel, built atop the very spot where the Association had determined that the first ice-cream cone had been made.

It was a festive affair honoring the late Ernest A. Hamwi, a Syrian who had come to St. Louis from Damascus in 1903. Based on the IAICM's investigations, the birth of the cone goes like this. In 1904 the St. Louis Exposition — also known as the St. Louis World's Fair and the Louisiana Purchase Exposition — opened, and Hamwi obtained a concession there to sell zalabia, a crisp waferlike Persian pastry baked on a flat waffle iron and served with sugar and other sweets. Close to Hamwi's stand was an ice-cream concessionaire who was selling his product in ten-cent-store dishes. One extremely busy day, the ice-cream stand ran out of dishes, and the alert Hamwi rolled one of his wafers into a cornucopia, let it cool, and put a scoop of ice cream in its mouth. The ice-cream vendor was intrigued with the idea, and the "World's Fair Cornucopia" was born. It was an immediate hit.

The cone gained popularity quickly. Before the Fair was over, St. Louis foundries were banging out baking molds for making the World's Fair Cornucopia, and those who played a part in its introduction fanned out to popularize and profit from the novelty. Hamwi went on to run the Cornucopia Waffle Company and later founded the Missouri Cone Company. At the time of the cone semicentennial in 1954, his nephew was still in the cone business in St. Louis.

The ice-cream cone industry developed rapidly, and in 1924 an estimated 245 million cones were produced. The competition to create best-seller cone designs became fierce.

Such was competition in the cone business by the 1930's that companies would bring out a new line each year. The Turnbull Cone Company, for example, ran ads reading "Turnbull's Cones for 1935" which featured pictures of such ornate new models as "Royalty," "Big Head," "Baby Grand," and "Gold Leaf." The burden of this intense activity fell on the U.S. Patent Office, which had to pass on the hundreds of applications for variations on the basic theme. Each issue of *The Ice Cream Review* carried a section on new cones along with little sketches. Many of these were only flamboyant embellishments on the basic design, but others were ingenious examples of micro-engineering. There were cones with a side pouch for an extra scoop, spiral cones, cones that stood on the table, those that looked like rocket ships (or Gothic spires), those that borrowed from turn-of-the-century bathtub designs, and "dripless" models of every description.

This decade-long flurry of intense creative activity, when inventors throughout the land dreamed of originating *the* great American cone, is half-forgotten history today. Several major cone companies emerged to dominate, and today all we are offered from them is a basic cake-and-sugar cone, with a few minor variations from firm to firm. Form now follows function to the letter, and there are no longer new-model years and creative touches. The cone has become the Volkswagen of the ice-cream world. But do not let this trend to simplicity obscure a great virtue of the cone. As an environmentally concerned Department of Health, Education, and Welfare official said on television recently: "The ice-cream cone is the only ecologically sound package known. It is the perfect package."

DISCUSSION

1. Under what circumstances was the ice-cream soda invented?
2. What difficulties did the ice-cream-soda business encounter, and how did they lead to the development of the sundae?
3. How did the ice-cream cone originate?
4. What does the author mean by his statement that "The cone has become the Volkswagen of the ice-cream world"?
5. Why was the ice-cream cone called "the only ecologically sound package known"?
6. What unfairness does the author point out in the first two sentences of his article? Does he appear to be completely serious in his complaint? Why do you think that?
7. To what extent were luck and accident important in bringing about the invention of the ice-cream cone and soda? What traits did the inventors possess that enabled them to take advantage of their situation?

Robert Arthur

Larceny
and
Old Lace

Florence Usher prides herself on her youthfulness — she is only seventy, two years younger than her sister Grace. Both are retired schoolteachers who have long been avid readers of mystery stories, and at last they have unexpectedly come upon an adventure of their own. A nephew they haven't seen for many years has suddenly died and left them his big old house in Milwaukee. Thrilled at the happy prospect of living in the city, they have cut their lifelong ties in the little town of Kiskishaw and have come to the nephew's lawyer, Mr. Bingham, to get the keys to the Milwaukee house.

Mr. Bingham set down his teacup with a clatter.

"Really," he said, his tone hollow, "I advise you to sell. The house is run down, taxes are high, the neighborhood unsavory —"

But Grace merely shook her head.

"We will cope," she said. "Now please tell us something about poor Walter. After all, we haven't seen him in the last twenty-five years."

"How did he die?" Florence asked, pressing her gloved hands together in eager interest.

"Well" — Mr. Bingham rubbed his high forehead distractedly — "he died of a form of heart failure —"

"I suppose," Grace agreed, "that you could call three bullets in the heart a form of heart failure. However —"

"*Two* bullets in the heart," Florence corrected. "The coroner's report said the other missed by several inches. You see, Mr. Bingham, we read all about it in the paper before your letter arrived. We follow all the crime news. Of course, we didn't know then it was our nephew who had been killed. We weren't very much surprised to find out, though. We always felt Walter would come to a bad end."

"As a boy, he used to torment puppies," Grace added. "I'm sure whoever did it had a very good reason." She patted her lips fastidiously. "When Walter was young, we often wanted to kill him ourselves."

Mr. Bingham mopped his brow.

"Eh, yes, of course," he said. He looked unhappily at the two little old ladies, bright as crickets for all their sober, small-town dresses, their old-fashioned bonnets, and gray hair.

"But again, dear ladies, let me urge you to sell your nephew's house. It is really in a shady neighborhood, tainted by a murder, and I have a purchaser who wants to tear it down and build a —"

"No. We intend to live there and run a boarding house for writers and artists," Grace told him firmly. "Now, Mr. Bingham, please let us have the key and the address, and a taxi will take us there."

Mr. Bingham, who had once had an iron-willed aunt, produced the key and wrote down an address.

"There," he croaked unhappily, "I do hope you have a — ah — a peaceful night. I do hope so."

"Why shouldn't we?" Grace asked. "Come, Florence, I'm all eagerness to see our inheritance."

They rustled out. From the window Mr. Bingham saw them lift their umbrellas and hail a taxi. He groaned, hesitated, then went down the gloomy hall to another door on which he knocked timidly before entering. The door bore the legend *Gordon Enterprises, Inc.* Inside, a large man in a discreetly tailored suit lounged in a leather chair, smoking a cigar.

Harry Gordon blew a smoke ring as Bingham entered.

"Well, Ed, how much did the house cost me?"

Bingham mopped his brow again. "They won't sell, Harry."

"Won't sell?" The big man brought his feet down solidly on the floor. "Maybe you didn't persuade them right."

"They're going to open a boarding house."

Bingham lowered himself into a chair.

"They're tired of hick towns." He sighed dismally. "They want to reside in a metropolis like Milwaukee and live the life artistic. They're two little old ladies, and they have wills of steel."

"You told them about their nephew being bumped off?"

"Yes. I told them the place had a sinister reputation, their nephew was a man of mystery — all that stuff."

"You didn't tell them he was the smartest blackmailer who ever put the bite on Harry Gordon?"

"Of course not."

Harry Gordon scowled. "I wished I knew where the devil he hid those ledger sheets he lifted," he said. "They've got to be in that house someplace —"

"If we couldn't find the papers, they'll stay hid," Bingham said. "Those two old dames will get tired of that gloomy morgue soon. Then we'll be able to buy it cheap and tear it down. There's nothing to worry about."

"Anyway, they'll get a scare that may send them running," the big man grunted. "I sent Tiny Tinker to the house tonight for another look around. If they bump into him, they may decide to sell, and sell fast. Tiny isn't the kind of guy two little old ladies would care to meet in a dark old house late at night!"

"Well," Florence Usher said doubtfully, "it *is* a big house, isn't it? And awfully dark."

"All houses are dark until the lights are lit," Grace informed her. "Let's go inside and put on some lights."

They picked up their suitcases and went up the flagstoned walk that led from a dimly lit street to the old, brown, somehow sinister house that sat back amid scraggly trees. A shutter creaked, and Florence gave a little gasp.

"Please, Florence," Grace said, "control yourself. Every mystery story is full of sound effects like creaking shutters. They mean nothing except that some hinge needs a little oil. Give me the key and we'll go in."

Florence handed her the key. Grace inserted it into a very modern lock in a very heavy front door, and the door opened. This time there were no creaks. They stepped into a hall and fumbled until Florence found a light switch. The overhead light snapped on.

"Well!" Grace said approvingly. "Very nice furnishings. Walter was certainly getting money from some source, though I doubt if he was earning it . . . Florence, what *is* it?"

"I heard a noise," Florence said in a strained whisper. "There's someone upstairs."

"You must not let your imagination . . . there *is* someone upstairs." Grace lowered her voice. "It must be a burglar — someone who knew the house was empty and took the opportunity to search it."

"Let's leave at once," Florence whispered between trembling lips. "Let's send for the police and — and spend the night at a hotel."

"Don't be a chicken, Florence! After all, we both know all about the best technique for trapping burglars — it's thoroughly explained in many mystery novels. Remember your Arsène Lupin and Raffles.[1]

---

[1] **Arsène Lupin,** hero of detective novels by a French writer, Maurice Leblanc. **Raffles,** a gentleman crook created by English novelist E. W. Hornung.

Besides, it is well known that burglars dislike violence. A criminal sticks to his trade, and burglars burgle. Follow my orders and we will teach Mr. Burglar a thing or two!"

"I — I'd rather not," Florence objected, but Grace was tiptoeing already toward the stairs. She removed her shoes, motioned to her sister to do the same, and in stocking feet, only their skirts whispering, the two slowly climbed the stairs.

As they reached the second floor, the sound of someone moving about became louder. The sound came from behind a closed door near the head of the stairs. Grace and Florence tiptoed toward the door. Grace looked quite confident, and Florence looked unhappy.

"No noise. Let me peek through the keyhole." Grace bent and put her eye to the old-fashioned keyhole. Inside, a light was on. A short, heavyset man with a face like a dish of scrambled eggs was tapping the walls with his knuckles. Tiny Tinker had once been a heavyweight prizefighter, but he was not a very good one.

"There's a man in there looking for something," Grace reported. "We must get him to come out."

"I don't *want* him to come out!" Florence wailed. "Please, let's *go*."

Grace ignored the plea.

"After reading all those mysteries, we certainly know how to handle this," she retorted. "Practically all of them agree that the heel of a woman's shoe is splendid as a weapon. As we wear Dr. Borden's Sensible Shoes, with extra-heavy heels, I'm sure we're well equipped. Now, I'll stand on one side of the door, you stand on the other. We'll each hold a shoe in our right hand. Then I'll toss my other shoe down the stairs —"

A moment later Tiny Tinker, inside the room, heard a clattering noise. "Rats," he muttered to himself and went on rapping the walls. But the noise was repeated a few moments later (when Florence, after some urging, threw her left shoe down the stairs). Tiny, never a great brain, decided the time had come to investigate. He opened the door and stuck his head out, blinking into the darkness.

"Whazzat?" he asked. Then all the knockouts he had ever suffered came back to haunt him. Even a skull like his was not made to withstand the impact of two heels on Dr. Borden's Sensible Shoes.

Tiny went down for the long count.

"Well, we're making progress," Grace Usher said determinedly.

She looked down at Tiny Tinker, who lay on the floor of the room. They had been able to drag him in but not to lift him onto the couch. So they had stretched him out, and with a lot of brightly colored neckties from a rack beside the door they had lashed his legs to the couch and his hands, stretched up over his head, to a lovely cherry-wood desk.

"*Now* can we call the police?" Florence asked.

"Certainly not. Take a look at this burglar. See how well dressed he is. He's no ordinary burglar." (He wasn't. Tiny was Harry Gordon's bodyguard.)

"What of it? He's so ugly it makes me nervous to look at him."

"Florence, I am very much disappointed in you." Grace surveyed her sister disapprovingly. "After all these years we've talked about living life and having adventures, and now that we're really doing it, you keep wanting to call the police. We have to question this man first."

"Question him about what?"

"About Walter's death and about what he is looking for — something Walter must have hidden. My goodness, don't you see? This is a real mystery! We're plunged right into the middle of it. It's a chance we never dreamed we'd have."

"Well, all right," Florence agreed. "But first we must scan the room for possible places of hiding."

Together they scanned the room. It was a sort of library-den.

"Look," Florence said. "The picture of you and me with Walter when he finally managed to graduate from high school twenty-five years ago. I confess I've always felt a little guilty about giving him a passing grade in civics."

"As things turned out, he certainly didn't deserve it," Grace agreed, studying the faded photo of themselves, with Walter, a head taller, standing between them.

"Anyway," said Florence, "it proves there was some good in Walter. He did remember us even after all these years. And he thought enough of us to leave us his house. Perhaps we always thought too harshly of him."

Together they looked down at Tiny Tinker. His face twitched with the pain of approaching consciousness.

"Florence," Grace soon remarked thoughtfully, "I wonder if this man killed Walter and now has come back to the scene of the crime to look for something he couldn't find at the time?"

"Killed Walter? Oh —" Florence jumped a little. "Then he's not just a burglar — he's a murderer. Grace, we *must* call the police!"

"Did you ever read a detective story where the police solved the case?"

"Well —"

"Of course not. Therefore it's up to us. We must see justice done for dear Walter, even if he was a crook of some kind. This creature is regaining consciousness. We'll question him."

Tiny Tinker opened one eye and looked up at them blearily.

Florence shuddered. "And what makes you think he'll answer our questions?" she asked.

"Surely one thousand mystery novels have taught us the correct procedure as to how to question a gangster! We can't be polite about it. If brutality is called for, we'll have to be brutal."

"You've never hurt a fly in your life," Florence retorted. "How can you start being cruel now?"

Grace ignored the question. "Sssh! He's opening his other eye."

Tiny Tinker blinked painfully up at them.

"What hit me?" he asked.

"We hit you, young man," Grace told him. "Now we have your hands and feet tied securely so you cannot take it on the lam or make a getaway."

Tiny Tinker yanked his arms and legs, found the facts as stated, and looked up with a tinge of awe on his scrambled features.

"The Usher sisters," he announced. "That's who you dames must be!"

"We find your knowledge of our identity very suspicious," Florence told him, bolder now that she saw the neckties were going to hold.

"Say, you two better untie me," Tiny Tinker said menacingly, "if you know what's good for you. Harry will be looking for me."

"Florence," Grace instructed, "make a note that this person is employed by someone named Harry."

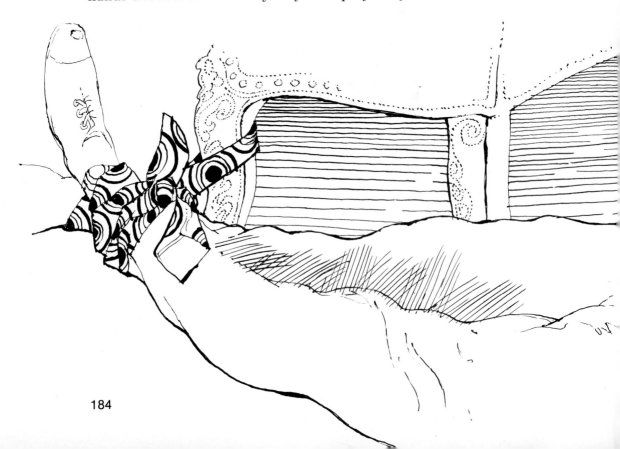

"Yes, certainly." Florence found paper and pencil in the desk and jotted down *Emply by smne nmd Harry.* A trace of alarm appeared on the captive's face.

"I didn't say nothing!" he protested. "What're you two up to, anyway?"

"It's quite simple," Grace said. "You killed our nephew Walter —"

The alarm on Tiny Tinker's face grew astoundingly. "How'd you know that? I mean, I didn't neither. You're crazy."

"Aha!" Grace turned a look of triumph on her sister. "We *are* making progress. This man admits he killed poor Walter."

"I don't!" Tiny shouted. "Nothing of the kind. I didn't kill him, and I didn't admit nothing. If you know what's good for you, you'll untie me double-quick. You're messing in something that's a lot too big for you."

"Aha!" Grace gave a chortle. "Florence, make a note. The prisoner admits he is part of a large criminal conspiracy."

"Yes, Grace." Florence made a note.

Tiny writhed harder. "I didn't! I didn't admit no such thing! What're you two trying to pin on me?"

"We are simply solving a crime in the accepted manner — just as we have learned it from more than one thousand mystery novels," Grace told him. "Now, young man, who's the Big Brain?"

"Who's the what?"

"The Big Brain. Mr. Big . . . oh, whom do you work for, stupid?"

"I work for Harry Gordon, and don't call me stupid. Who can tell what you two dames are talking about?"

"Florence, make a note. Prisoner identifies the mastermind of the criminal conspiracy as one Harry Gordon."

"Wait a minute, wait a minute!" Tiny almost wept from sheer frustration. "I didn't never say no such thing."

"*Two* double negatives in one sentence!" Florence exclaimed. "Where did you go to school?"

"Where did I go to school?" Tiny blinked. "What's that got to do with it?" Tiny could hold out against a team of expert detectives for forty-eight hours, but the methods of the Usher sisters confused him.

"Never mind," Grace said loftily. "Now let us sum up. You have admitted that you killed our nephew Walter, that you work for one Harry Gordon, that he is head of a vast criminal enterprise, and presumably you were searching this house for something of Walter's which Harry Gordon wants. Now what is it? Dope? Hot ice? Stolen bonds? Plates for counterfeit money? You might as well tell us, for we'll get it out of you anyway."

Tiny stared up at two pairs of steel-gray eyes giving him the same looks that had made generations of schoolboys quail. He shuddered.

"Yeah," he gulped, "I guess you will."

Tiny Tinker started talking, and Florence started making notes. Tiny had his eye on the clock. If he could talk long enough, eventually Harry would get there, and Harry would know how to take care of two sharp old witches like these.

"So there we have the picture!" Grace said when at last Tiny had finished talking. "Walter was a bookkeeper for this Harry Gordon. Walter stole some records of Gordon's criminal activity. But instead of turning them over to the police, Walter hid them and blackmailed Gordon, who got tired of paying and sent this — what is your name?"

"Just call me Tiny." Tiny sighed.

"Sent this Mr. Tiny to search the house. Walter came home too soon, and Mr. Tiny shot him. Since then, no one has been able to find the incriminating documents. They're still somewhere in the house."

"Which must be why Mr. Bingham tried to discourage us from coming here!" Florence exclaimed. "He's in it too!"

"And now we are on the point of smashing this criminal ring!" Grace breathed, her eyes shining.

"I think —" Florence began, but a voice from the door interrupted her and made both sisters whirl around with little eeeking sounds.

"Please go right ahead, ladies. But you don't mind if I come in?"

Harry Gordon advanced into the room, puffing on his cigar. Mr. Bingham danced nervously behind him. Harry Gordon came toward Grace and Florence like a truck about to crush two small gray kittens. He stopped and fixed them with a sardonic glance.

"Well, ladies, you've had a ball with my boy Tiny, haven't you? But the party's over now. This is the end of the line. Sit down in those two chairs until Ed and I get Tiny untied. Then we'll decide what to do with you!"

Tiny Tinker, released from the neckties, sat gratefully in a corner. Harry Gordon sat back in one of the easy chairs and pointed his cigar at Grace and Florence, who were huddled on the sofa beyond the desk, subdued but still defiant.

"They made Tiny talk," Gordon rumbled. "I say we ought to put them in cold storage."

"No, no, Harry," Mr. Bingham urged, nervously rubbing his forehead. "Get them out of town and make sure they never come back."

"My way, they'd be sure never to come back."

"If you think you can intimidate us, you're very much mistaken!" Grace bristled. Florence turned on her furiously.

"He is not mistaken. He *has* intimidated us. He's intimidated *me*, anyway, and I'm willing to make a bargain with him."

A flicker of interest showed in Harry Gordon's black eyes.

"What kind of a bargain, sister?"

"You want this house because it has certain papers hidden in it. All right, we'll sell you the house, just as it is, and you can find the papers for yourself."

"Go on."

"We'll take a trip around the world, leaving as soon as we have the money."

"Florence, I will not bargain with criminals!" Grace cried.

"Be quiet, Grace. You've been the boss up until now. Well, now I'm in charge. Mr. Gordon, how about it?"

"Pay 'em off and get rid of 'em," Bingham pleaded. "We'll find the papers if we have to tear the house down."

"I dunno." Harry Gordon puffed a cloud of smoke. "It'd be cheaper just to bury them."

"We wouldn't stay buried, do you hear?" Florence told him. "We'd — we'd rise up and haunt you."

"I wouldn't be surprised if you did at that," Harry Gordon said. "All right, I'll give you ten thousand in cash for the house, and you leave town tonight."

"Fifteen!" Florence retorted.

"Why, this house is worth at least twenty thousand dollars!" Grace said in great indignation.

"You're in no position to bargain, lady," Harry Gordon said. "All right, fifteen thousand."

"In cash. And you drive us directly to the station," Florence stipulated.

"A deal. We'll pick up the cash at my office. Come on, let's get going," Gordon growled.

"Just midnight," Grace said in their Pullman compartment, her tone discontented. "Florence, do you realize we were in Milwaukee only three hours?"

"But my, they were exciting hours." Florence yawned. "Really, we must go to bed. We need our sleep."

"How can you expect to sleep after having sold out to a gang of thugs and cutthroats? I certainly won't. Why, we've let Walter's murderers go free, and for just a few thousand dollars!"

"Walter was always a rapscallion," Florence answered. "I certainly did not intend to lose my life over him."

"Just the same, nothing like this ever happened in *any* of the books we have read. I feel mortified."

"I don't think you should, Grace." Florence reached into her enormous purse and pulled out of it a framed photograph — the one which showed herself, Grace, and Walter. Less than an hour before, it had stood on Walter's desk.

"Walter had as much sentiment as a rattlesnake," she said. "Why should he keep a picture of himself with us? Only because a picture of yourself and two maiden aunts is about as unsuspicious as anything can be. Nobody gave it a second thought."

"But how did you get it?" Grace asked. "I didn't see you take it."

"In the confusion when Mr. Gordon and Mr. Bingham were bending over to untie Mr. Tiny, I just slipped it into my purse. Now, if my analysis is correct, all we have to do is open it up and inside, in back of our picture, we shall find microfilms of the documents which will send Mr. Harry Gordon and all the others to the state penitentiary. Now, Grace, let us look."

The microfilms were there.

"Ellery Queen[2] would be proud of you," Grace said, for she was never one to deny credit where credit was due.

---

[2] **Ellery Queen**, pen name and also main character of detective stories written by Frederic Dannay and Manfred B. Lee.

DISCUSSION

1. How had the Usher sisters come to own the house in the story? What were they planning to do with it? Who else wanted the house? Why?

2. What danger did the sisters first encounter? How did they deal with it?

3. How had the sisters gotten their know-how as crime fighters? What else in their background helped them get the truth out of Tiny?

4. Why was Florence sure she had the microfilms of the stolen records?

5. What deal did the sisters make with Gordon, and who suggested it? What had happened earlier that would lead you to think Florence was a person who was easily intimidated? Was she really intimidated by Gordon? Why do you think that?

6. Why do you think Bingham opposed Gordon's idea of putting the sisters "in cold storage"?

7. What clues did the author use very early to indicate that the lawyer was involved in something shady? What early clues let you know that the nephew, too, had probably been doing something unlawful?

8. Do you think the sisters succeeded because of brilliant detective work, because of fantastic luck, or because of just plain stupidity on the part of the criminals? Why do you think that?

9. Did the sisters take detective stories seriously? Do you think the author wishes you to take them seriously? Why do you think as you do?

10. In the title of the story, to what characters does the word *Larceny* refer? To whom do the words *Old Lace* refer? Is the title a good one for this story? Give reasons for your answer.

11. If you had been involved in this episode, at what point would you have called the police? Do you think the police would have been able to solve the mystery as well as the sisters did? What makes you think that?

AUTHOR

Born on the island of Corregidor in the Philippines, where his father was stationed with the United States Army, Robert Arthur studied at William and Mary College and the University of Michigan. After working for several years as a magazine editor, he became a free-lance writer and the author of short stories and books as well as radio and television scripts. He also was a story consultant for motion-picture and television producer Alfred Hitchcock. Among the books Mr. Arthur wrote or edited are *Mystery and More Mystery,* from which "Larceny and Old Lace" is taken, *Spies and More Spies, Thrillers and More Thrillers, Davy Jones' Haunted Locker,* and *Monster Mix: Thirteen Chilling Tales.*

Duke Kahanamoku (kä-hä-nä-mō'kōo) *was a famous Hawaiian surfer and an Olympic swimming champion. Here he describes an unforgettable surfing experience off Waikiki Beach, Honolulu.*

That Legendary Ride

by Duke Kahanamoku

Much seems to have been made of that once-in-a-lifetime ride of mine from the outer steamer lane off Waikiki, and now is as good a time as any to put the record straight. The incident has been written up before but might bear repeating. I can remember the details as though it all happened yesterday, for, in retrospect, I have relived the ride many a time. I think my memory plays me no tricks on this one.

Pride was in it with me those days, and I was still striving to build bigger and better boards, ride taller and faster waves, and develop more dexterity from day to day. Also, vanity probably had much to do with my trying to delight the crowds at Waikiki with spectacular rides on the long, glassy, sloping waves.

But the day I caught the Big One was a day when I was not thinking in terms of awing any tourists or *kamaainas*[1] on Waikiki Beach. It was simply an early morning when mammoth ground swells were rolling in sporadically from the horizon, and I saw that no one was paddling out to try them. Frankly, they were the largest I'd ever seen. The yell of ''The surf is up!'' was the understatement of the century.

In fact, it was that rare morning when the word was out that the big ''bluebirds'' were rolling in; this is the name for gigantic waves that sweep in from the horizon on extraordinary occasions. Sometimes years elapse with no evidence of them. They are spawned far out at sea and are the result of certain cataclysms of nature — either great

---

[1] **kamaainas** (kä'mä-ī'näs), old-timers.

atmospheric disturbances or subterranean agitation like underwater earthquakes and volcanic eruptions.

True, as waves go, the experts will agree that bigness alone is not what supplies outstandingly good surfing. Sometimes giant waves make for bad surfing in spite of their size, and the reason often is that there is an onshore wind that pushes the top of the waves down and makes them break too fast with lots of white water. It takes an off-shore wind to make the waves stand up to their full height. This day we had stiff trade winds blowing from the high Koolau (kō′ō-lä′ōo) Range, and they were making those bluebirds tower up like the Himalayas. Man, I was pulling my breath from way down at sight of them.

It put me in mind of the winter storm waves that roar in at Kaena (kä-ä′nä) Point on the North Shore. Big-wave surfers, even then, were doing much speculating on whether those Kaena waves could be ridden with any degree of safety. The bluebirds facing me were easily thirty-plus waves, and they looked as though, with the right equipment — plus a lot of luck — they just might be makable.

The danger lay in the prone-out or wipe-out. Studying the waves made me wonder if any man's body could withstand the unbelievable force of a thirty- to fifty-foot wall of water when it crashes. And, too, could even a top swimmer like myself manage to battle the currents and explosive water that would necessarily accompany the aftermath of such a wave?

Well, the answer seemed to be simply — *don't get wiped out!*

From the shore you could see those high glassy ridges building up in the outer Diamond Head region. The bluebirds were swarming across the bay in a solid line as far northwest as Honolulu Harbor. They were tall, steep, and fast. The closer-in ones crumbled and showed their teeth with a fury that I had never seen before. I wondered if I could even push through the acres of white water to get to the outer area where the build-ups were taking place.

But, like the mountain climbers with Mount Everest, you try it "just because it's there." Some days a man does not take time to analyze what motivates him. All I knew was that I was suddenly trying to shove through that incoming sea — and having the fight of my life. I was using my *Papa-nui* (pä′pä-nōo′ē), the sixteen-foot, 114-pound semihollow board, and it was like trying to jam a log through the flood of a dam break.

Again and again it was necessary to turn turtle with the big board and hang on tightly underneath — arms and legs wrapped around a thing that bucked like a bronco gone berserk. The shoreward-bound torrents of water ground overhead, making all the racket of a string of freight cars roaring over a trestle. The prone paddling between combers was a demanding thing because the water was wild. It was a case of wrestling the board through block-busting breakers, and it was a miracle that I ever gained the outlying waters.

Bushed from the long fight to get seaward, I sat my board and watched the long humps of water peaking into ridges that marched like animated foothills. I let a slew of them lift and drop me with their silent, threatening glide. I could hardly believe that such perpendicular walls of water could be built up like that. The troughs between the swells had the depth of elevator shafts, and I wondered again what it would be like to be buried under tons of water when it curled and detonated. There was something eerie about watching the shimmering backs of the ridges as they passed me and rolled on toward Waikiki.

I let a lot of them career by, wondering in my own heart whether I was passing them up because of their unholy height or whether I was really waiting for the big right one. A man begins to doubt himself at a time like that. Then I was suddenly wheeling and turning to catch the towering blue ridge bearing toward me. I was prone and stroking hard at the water with my hands.

Strangely, it was more as though the wave had selected me, rather than I had chosen it. It seemed like a very personal and special wave — the kind I had seen in my mind's eye during a night of tangled dreaming. There was no backing out on this one; the two of us had something to settle between us. The rioting breakers between me and shore no longer bugged me. There was just this one ridge and myself — no more. Could I master it? I doubted it, but I was willing to die in the attempt to harness it.

Instinctively I got to my feet when the pitch, slant, and speed seemed right. Left foot forward, knees slightly bent, I rode the board down that precipitous slope like a man tobogganing down a glacier.

Sliding left along the watery monster's face, I didn't know I was at
the beginning of a ride that would become a celebrated and mem-
oried thing. All I knew was that I had come to grips with the tallest,
bulkiest, fastest wave I had ever seen. I realized, too, more than ever,
that to be trapped under its curling bulk would be the same as letting
a factory cave in upon you.

This lethal avalanche of water swept shoreward swiftly and spook-
ily. The board began hissing from the traction as the wave leaned
forward with greater and more incredible speed and power. I shifted
my weight, cut left at more of an angle, and shot into the big Castle
Surf which was building and adding to the wave I was on. Spray was
spuming up wildly from my rails, and I had never before seen it
spout up like that. I rode it for city-long blocks, the wind almost
sucking the breath out of me. Diamond Head itself seemed to have
come alive and was leaping in at me from the right.

Then I was slamming into Elk's Club Surf, still sliding left and still fighting for balance, for position, for everything and anything that would keep me upright. The drumming of the water under the board had become a madman's tattoo. Elk's Surf rioted me along, high and steep, until I skidded and slanted through into Public Baths Surf. By then it amounted to three surfs combined into one; big, rumbling, and exploding. I was not sure I could make it on this ever-steepening ridge. A curl broke to my right and almost engulfed me, so I swung even farther left, shuffled back a little on the board to keep from purling.

Left it was; left and more left, with the board veeing a jet of water on both sides and making a snarl that told of speed and stress and thrust. The wind was tugging my hair with frantic hands. Then suddenly it looked as if I might, with more luck, make it into the back of Queen's Surf! The build-up had developed into something approximating what I had heard of tidal waves, and I wondered if it would ever flatten out at all. White water was pounding to my right, so I angled farther from it to avoid its wiping me out and burying me in the sudsy depths.

Borrowing on the Cunha Surf for all it was worth — and it was worth several hundred yards — I managed to manipulate the board into the now towering Queen's Surf. One mistake — just one small one — could well spill me into the maelstrom to my right. I teetered for some panic-ridden seconds, caught control again, and made it down on that last forward rush, sliding and bouncing through lunatic water. The breaker gave me all the tossing of a bucking bronco. Still luckily erect, I could see the people standing there on the beach, their hands shading their eyes against the sun, and watching me complete this crazy, unbelievable one-and-three-quarter-mile ride.

I made it into the shallows in one last surging flood. A little dazedly I wound up in hip-deep water, where I stepped off and pushed my board shoreward through the bubbly surf. That improbable ride gave me the sense of being an unlickable guy for the moment. I heisted my board to my hip, locked both arms around it, and lugged it up the beach.

Without looking at the people clustered around, I walked on, hearing them murmur fine, exciting things which I wanted to remember in days to come. I told myself this was the ride to end all rides. I grinned my thanks to those who stepped close and slapped me on the shoulders, and I smiled to those who told me this was the greatest. I trudged on and on, knowing this would be a shining memory for me that I could take out in years to come and relive in all its full glory. This had been *it*.

I never caught another wave anything like that one. And now with the birthdays piled up on my back, I know I never shall. But they cannot take that memory away from me. It is a golden one that I treasure, and I'm grateful that God gave it to me.

DISCUSSION

1. What were the "bluebirds" referred to by Duke? How often do they occur? What causes them? Why does an offshore wind make for the best surfing?
2. About how big and heavy was Duke's surfboard? Was it harder or easier to handle in the surf than on land? Why?
3. What two things did Duke have to do over and over again in alternation to get his surfboard out beyond the breakers? What did he then have to do to start riding the wave he chose?
4. In what ways would Duke's life have been endangered by the water if he had not succeeded in riding the wave all the way in?
5. What were some of the different emotions that Duke probably felt as he rode toward the shore?
6. Do you think the people watching Duke knew much about surfing? What makes you think that? How did Duke react to their praise? Do you think his reaction showed that he was conceited? Why do you think that?
7. Suppose no one had been watching. Do you think Duke would have treasured the memory of his feat as much as he did? Why do you think as you do?

8. Do you think Duke's achievement was worth the risk he took? What makes you think that?

9. Have you ever tried, like Duke, to do something dangerous just to prove to yourself that you could? What was it? Did you have enough knowledge and skill to give you a reasonable chance of success? If asked to do so, tell about your experience.

10. What other sports do you know of that are tests of an individual's skill and courage in doing something by himself? Which of them would interest you most? Why?

AUTHOR

A pure-blooded Hawaiian, Duke Paoa (pä-ō'ä) Kahanamoku was born in Honolulu in 1890. Duke was his given name, not a title or nickname. His medal-winning swimming performance at the Stockholm Olympics brought him his first acclaim in 1912 and focused the attention of the aquatic world on his Hawaiian homeland. He was a member of three subsequent United States Olympic teams and at one time or another held almost every swimming record there is. But surfing was his real love, and many experts consider him the master surfer, the greatest of all time. This ancient Polynesian sport had fallen into decline by the turn of the century, and Duke Kahanamoku was primarily responsible for reviving it and bringing it to its present popularity. Generations of youngsters learned to surf with him as their teacher, and he constantly worked to improve surfing equipment and standards. He introduced the sport to the United States mainland, Australia, and New Zealand, and wherever he gave demonstrations, people caught and shared his enthusiasm.

In spite of his fame, Duke Kahanamoku remained a modest and friendly man, greatly loved and respected by the people of Hawaii. He was elected to thirteen consecutive terms as Sheriff of Honolulu, and for over half a century he was probably Hawaii's best-known citizen. Until his death in 1968, he was Ambassador-at-large for the state of Hawaii and also Official Greeter of the City and County of Honolulu.

"That Legendary Ride" is an excerpt from *Duke Kahanamoku's World of Surfing,* a book he finished shortly before his death in collaboration with sports writer Joe Brennan.

LOCATING INFORMATION QUICKLY

The first step in quickly locating information that you need on a question is to use the most helpful reference material. In much of your work you will generally use one or more reference aids, such as an almanac, an atlas, a dictionary, an encyclopedia, and a textbook. Here are brief descriptions of these aids:

ALMANAC: A yearly publication of facts, often in the form of tables, lists, and charts.

ATLAS: A bound collection of maps.

DICTIONARY: A book containing an alphabetical list of words with information on each word. Such information will show for a word its separation into syllables if it has more than one syllable, its pronunciation, its meanings, and sometimes its etymology, its usage, and its synonyms.

ENCYCLOPEDIA: A book or set of books containing articles that are arranged in alphabetical order and that cover a wide variety of subjects.

TEXTBOOK: A book used for the study of a particular subject.

According to the definitions you just read and your own experience, which of the reference aids would you most likely use to find the answer to each of the following questions?

1. *How did the art of stonecutting originate?*
2. *What is the meaning of* pangolin?
3. *What are the basic techniques of addition and subtraction?*
4. *How far is it from Salt Lake City, Utah, to Miami, Florida?*
5. *What was the production of wheat in the United States in 1973?*

The answer to the first question could certainly be found in an encyclopedia; the answer to the second, in a dictionary. A mathematics textbook could provide a thorough answer to the third question, although an encyclopedia might give some answers. The answer to the fourth question could be found in an atlas; the answer to the fifth, in an almanac.

Except for a dictionary, each of the five reference aids has an index that helps you find the information you are looking for. An atlas has a special kind of index, one that helps you locate countries, states, cities, and towns on the maps. Almanacs, encyclopedias, and textbooks have indexes that list in alphabetical order all the important topics that are presented in the books. The entries in an index are called MAIN TOPICS, and they are arranged in alphabetical order. Some main topics have SUBTOPICS, also arranged in alphabetical order.

A portion of an index from a book of science facts is shown on page 203. Notice that the main topics appear in heavy black type. Notice also that some of the main topics have subtopics, which are run in under their main topics. To see how a main topic with subtopics appears in an index, look at the entry *Storms*. After each subtopic are numerals that tell you on which pages information about that subtopic may be found. A dash between two numerals, such as 51–53, indicates that the discussion starts somewhere on page 51 and ends somewhere on page 53. Commas between numerals indicate that information is on only the pages for which numerals are given. On how many pages is there information about *White rats?* On how many pages is there information about *X-rays?*

In using an index, you must first decide on the word you will look for among the main topics. Such a word is called a KEY WORD.

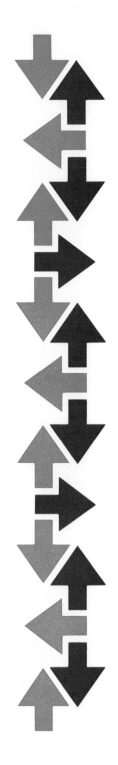

Frequently, a key word is one of the words in a question for which you are trying to find an answer. What word would you use as a key word for each of the following questions?

1. *Why are differences in soil important for growing things?*
2. *How does walking help keep you fit?*

In the first question you are searching for an answer to a question about *differences in soil.* Essentially the question has to do with *soil,* and that would be the key word. Does the part of an index on page 203 contain the main topic *Soil?* Indented under that main topic are a number of subtopics. You are looking for differences in soil. Is that listed among the subtopics? If so, on what pages would you look to find your information?

What would you use as the key word for the second question? Is it listed as a main topic in the part of an index? Since page 239 contains information about *walking as an exercise,* you would probably find an answer to your question on that page.

What would you use as a key word in looking for answers to each of these questions?

1. *In what ways are rats harmful to man?*
2. *What makes sugar sweet?*

Sometimes it is necessary to use more than one key word in a question to find all the information that you need. Look at the following questions and determine what you would use as key words in each one.

1. *What effect do volcanoes have on the formation of rocks?*
2. *How does the life cycle of snakes compare with that of other reptiles?*

In the first question the information under *Volcanoes* may give you only part of the answer. You may also need to use the main topic *Rocks* in order to obtain all the information you need. The key words in the question are *volcanoes* and *rocks.* What key words would you use to answer the second question? One key word would be *snakes* and further information may be obtained by referring to *reptiles.* Find each main topic in the part of an index. Notice the words "*See also* Lizards; Snakes; Turtles" that come after the subtopics listed

for *Reptiles.* This is a cross-reference, which means that more information concerning *Reptiles* may be found under the main topics *Lizards, Snakes,* and *Turtles.*

In each of the following questions what two words might be used as key words?

1. *What vitamins do you find in most vegetables?*
2. *What happens when a high wind blows over sand?*

In searching for the answer to a question, you may sometimes need to use a key word that is not in the question. Suppose you were seeking an answer to the question: *What is the growing season of cabbages, potatoes, and spinach?* If the index you are using does not list *cabbages, potatoes,* and *spinach* as main topics, does it mean you could not find the answer to the question in the book? You might look for another main topic before deciding no information is available. Since cabbages, potatoes, and spinach are *vegetables,* that would be a logical key word. If you look at the portion of an index on page 203, you will find that information about your question could be found by using *vegetables* as a key word.

The key word you need is not included in each of the following questions. What word would you try to use as a key word to answer each question?

1. *In what months are Venus and Mars closest to the earth?*
2. *Which of the following is the largest in size: New York, Chicago, or Los Angeles?*

An index tells you on which page or pages to look for information. It does not tell you just where the specific information you are seeking is on the page or pages given in the index. Frequently you can spend more time reading line after line of print to locate an answer than it took you to find the appropriate page. After you have turned to the page indicated by the index, read the first two or three sentences of the first paragraph and decide whether they give you information in answer to your questions. If they do, then read the whole paragraph as carefully as you need to in order to understand and remember the information. If the first three or four sentences do not give you the information you need, go on to succeeding paragraphs.

The paragraphs below are about hailstorms and hailstones. Use the way of locating information just described in finding an answer to the question *How are hailstones formed?*

A hailstorm is a storm in which balls or irregular lumps of ice fall from the clouds. Hailstones are closely associated with thunderstorms. The hailstones are formed when snow and ice crystals meet with water droplets in cold areas of clouds. When the hailstones become heavy enough, they fall from the clouds to the ground.

The hailstones that fall during a hailstorm sometimes cause great damage. Most hailstones are about the size of peas, but some may be as big as oranges. Hailstones of that size do tremendous damage to crops and to livestock. Even automobiles and airplanes can suffer extensive damage during a severe hailstorm.

Find as quickly as you can the paragraph in the following article that gives information that will answer the question *How many meteors can be seen in a meteor shower?*

1. A meteor is a small stony or metallic particle traveling around the sun. The earth collides with many millions of these particles every day. Most of them are the size of very fine grains of dust, although some range up to one or two pounds. A meteor that reaches earth before burning up is called a meteorite.

2. Meteors plunge into our atmosphere at speeds from 8 to 42 miles per second. The smallest meteors are slowed down by the atmosphere and float to earth unseen and unnoticed. Larger meteors are quickly heated to incandescence through collisions with air molecules and produce the brief streak across the sky known as a meteor trail. These trails are popularly called shooting stars.

3. The earth occasionally collides with a swarm of meteors traveling relatively close together. The result of this collision is

called a meteor shower. During a meteor shower as many as 100 meteors per minute can be seen. Even in the densest swarm, however, each meteor is separated by many miles from the other meteors of the swarm.

If you quickly moved through paragraphs 1 and 2, you followed the correct procedure and then came upon the answer in paragraph 3. Practice this technique each time you are trying to locate a specific piece of information quickly.

Discussion

Help your class answer these questions:
1. What kind of information does an almanac provide? An atlas?
2. How does a textbook differ from a volume of an encyclopedia?
3. What is an index?
4. What is a main topic in an index?
5. How are a key word and a main topic related?
6. What are the words or groups of words listed after a main topic called? What is their function in an index?
7. What is a cross-reference? Why would you use a cross-reference?
8. After locating the page that is likely to contain an answer to your question, how should you proceed?

On your own

On a piece of paper, copy the numeral and letter for each question and write your answer.
1. Which reference aid or aids would you use to find an answer to each of these questions?
   a. *In what year did Lindbergh make his most famous solo flight?*
   b. *What states border Tennessee?*
   c. *What is the pronunciation of* gratis?
   d. *Who won the major auto-racing event in 1973?*

2. On which page or pages listed in the part of an index on page 203 would you look for an answer to each of these questions?

  a. *In which direction does the wind generally blow in the Northern Hemisphere?*

  b. *What is a major cause of river pollution?*

  c. *What is the difference between a stalactite and a stalagmite?*

  d. *For what purpose are crops rotated?*

  e. *Should a person be exposed to more than four x-rays a year?*

  f. *What should the size of fir and spruce trees be before they can be successfully transplanted?*

Checking your work

If you are asked to do so, read aloud the answers you wrote to one or more questions. If you made a mistake in any answer, find out why it is a mistake.

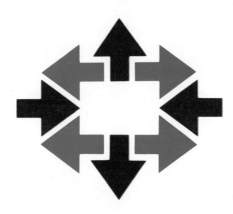

CREATURE OF THE SNOWS

by William Sambrot

Ed McKale straightened up under his load of cameras and equipment, squinting against the blasting wind, peering, staring, sweeping the jagged, unending expanse of snow and wind-scoured rock. Looking, searching, as he'd been doing now for two months, cameras at the ready.

Nothing. Nothing but the towering Himalayas, thrusting miles high on all sides, stretching in awesome grandeur from horizon to horizon, each pinnacle tipped with immense banners of snow plumes, streaming out in the wind, vivid against the darkly blue sky. The vista was one of surpassing beauty. Viewing it, Ed automatically thought of light settings, focal length, color filters — but just as automatically rejected the thought. He was here on top of the world to photograph something infinitely more newsworthy, if only he could find it.

The expedition paused, strung out along a ridge of blue snow, with shadows falling away to the right and left into terrifying abysses, and Ed sucked for air. Twenty thousand feet is really quite high, although many of the peaks beyond rose nearly ten thousand feet above him.

Up ahead, the Sherpa porters (each one a marvelous shot: gap-toothed, ebullient grins, seamed faces, leathery brown) bowed under stupendous loads for this altitude, leaning on their coolie crutches, waiting for Dr. Schenk to make up his mind. Schenk, the expedition leader, was arguing with the guides again, his breath spurting little puffs of vapor, waving his arms, pointing down.

Obviously Schenk was calling it quits. He was within his rights, Ed knew; two months was all Schenk had contracted for. Two months of probing snow and ice; scrambling over crevasses, up rotten rock cliffs, wind-ravaged and bleak, stretching endlessly toward Tibet and the

209

never-never lands beyond. Two months of searching for footprints where none should be. Searching for odors, for droppings, anything to disclose the presence of creatures other than themselves. Without success.

Two months of nothing. Big, fat nothing.

The expedition was a bust. The goofiest assignment of this or any other century, as Ed felt it would be from the moment he'd sat across the desk from the big boss in the picture magazine's New York office two months ago, looking at a blurred photograph while the boss filled him in on the weird details.

The photograph, his boss had told Ed gravely, had been taken in the Himalayan mountains, at an altitude of twenty-one thousand feet, by a man who had been soaring overhead in a motorless glider.

"A glider," Ed had said noncommittally, staring at the fuzzy, enlarged snapshot of a great expanse of snow and rocky ledges, full of harsh light and shadows, a sort of roughly bowl-shaped plateau apparently, and in the middle of it, a group of indistinct figures, tiny, lost against the immensity of great ice pinnacles. Ed looked closer. Were the figures people? If so, what had happened to their clothes?

"A glider," his boss reiterated firmly. The pilot, the boss said, was maneuvering in an updraft, attempting to do the incredible — soar over Mount Everest in a homemade glider. The wide-winged glider had been unable to achieve the flight over Everest, but flitting silently about seeking updrafts, it cleared a jagged pinnacle, and there, less than a thousand feet below, the pilot saw movement where none should have been. And dropping lower, startled, he'd seen, the boss said dryly, "Creatures — creatures that looked exactly like a group of naked men and women and kids playing in the snow — at an altitude of twenty thousand five hundred feet." He'd had the presence of mind to take a few hasty snapshots before the group disappeared. Only one of the pictures had developed.

Looking at the snapshot with professional scorn, Ed had said, "These things are indistinct. I think he's selling you a bill of goods."

"No," the boss said, "we checked on the guy. He really did make the glider flight. We've had experts go over that blowup. The picture's genuine. Those are naked, biped, erect-walking creatures." Then he flipped the picture irritably. "I can't publish this thing. I want close-ups, action shots, the sort of thing that our subscribers have come to expect of us."

He'd lighted a cigar slowly. "Bring me back some pictures I can publish, Ed, and you can write your own ticket."

"You're asking me to climb Mount Everest," Ed said carefully, keeping the sarcasm out of his voice, "to search for this plateau here" — he tapped the shoddy photograph — "and take pix of — what are they — biped, erect-walking creatures, you say?"

The boss cleared his throat. "Not Mount Everest, Ed. It's Gauri Sankar (gou′rĭ sŭng′kər), one of the peaks not far from Mount Everest. Roughly, it's only about twenty-three thousand feet or so high."

"That's pretty rough," Ed said.

The boss looked pained. "Actually it's not Gauri Sankar either. Just one of the lesser peaks of the Gauri Sankar massif. Well under twenty-three thousand. Certainly nothing to bother a hotshot exparatrooper like you, Ed."

Ed winced, and the boss continued: "This guy — this glider pilot — wasn't able to pinpoint the spot, but he did come up with a pretty fair map of the terrain, for a pretty fair price. We've checked it out with the American Alpine Club; it conforms well with their own charts of the general area. Several expeditions have been in the vicinity but not at this exact spot, they tell me. It's not a piece of cake by any means; however, it's far from being another Annapurna or K2 for accessibility."

He sucked at his cigar thoughtfully. "The Alpine Club says we've got only about two months of good weather before the inevitable monsoons hit that area, so time, as they say, is of the essence, Ed. But two months for this kind of thing ought to be plenty. Everything will be first class — we're even including these new gas guns that shoot hypodermic needles or something similar. We'll fly the essentials in to Katmandu and airdrop everything possible along the route up to your base" — he squinted at the map — "Namche Bazar (näm′chē bä′zär), a Sherpa village which is twelve thousand feet high."

He smiled amiably at Ed. "That's a couple of weeks' march up from the nearest railhead and ought to get you acclimatized nicely. Plenty of experienced porters at Namche, all Sherpas. We've lined up a couple of expert mountain climbers with Himalayan backgrounds. And the expedition leader will be Dr. Schenk. He's the top man in his field."

"What is his field?" Ed asked gloomily.

"Zoology. Whatever these things are in this picture, they're animal, which is his field. Everyone will be sworn to secrecy. You'll be the only one permitted to use a camera, Ed. This could be the biggest thing you'll ever cover, if these things are what I think they are."

"What do you think they are?"

"An unknown species of man — or subman," his boss said, and prudently Ed remained silent. Two months would tell the tale.

But two months didn't tell.

Oh, there were plenty of wild rumors by the Nepalese all along the upper route. Hushed stories of the two-legged creature that walked like a man. A monster the Sherpas spoke of as Yeti (yĕ'tē). Legends. Strange encounters; drums sounding from snow-swept heights; wild snatches of song drifting down from peaks that were inaccessible to ordinary men. And one concrete fact: a ban, laid on by the Buddhist monks, against the taking of any life in the high Himalayas. What life? Ed wondered.

Stories, legends — but nothing else.

Two months of it. Starting from the tropical flatlands, up through a lush, exotic rain forest, where the sun struggled through immense trees festooned with orchids. Two months, moving up into the arid foothills, where foliage abruptly ceased and the rocks and wind took over. Up and ever up to where the first heavy snowpack lay. And higher still, following the trail laid out by the glider pilot. (And what impelled a man, Ed wondered, to soar over Mount Everest in a home-made glider?)

Two months during which Ed had come to dislike Dr. Schenk intensely. Tall, saturnine, smelling strongly of formaldehyde, Schenk classified everything into terms of vertebrate, invertebrate.

So now, standing on this wind-scoured ridge with the shadows falling into the abysses on either side, Ed peered through his ice-encrusted goggles, watching Schenk arguing with the guides. He motioned to the ledge above, and obediently the Sherpas moved toward it. Obviously that would be the final camping spot. The two months were over by several days; Schenk was within his rights to call it quits. It was only Ed's assurances that the plateau they were seeking lay just ahead that had kept Schenk from bowing out exactly on the appointed time — that and the burning desire to secure his niche in zoology forever with a new specimen: biped, erect-walking — what?

But the plateau just ahead and the one after that and all the rest beyond had proved just as empty as those behind.

A bust. Whatever the unknown creatures were that the glider pilot had photographed, they would remain just that — unknown.

And yet as Ed slogged slowly up toward where the porters were setting up the bright blue and yellow nylon tents, he was nagged by a feeling that the odd-shaped pinnacle ahead looked awfully much like the one in the blurred photograph. With his unfailing memory for pictures, Ed remembered the tall, jagged cone that had cast a black shadow across a snowy plateau, pointing directly toward the little group that was in the center of the picture.

But Schenk wasn't having any more plateaus. He shook his head vehemently, white-daubed lips a grim line on his sun-blistered face. "Last camp, Ed," he said firmly. "We agreed this would be the final plateau. I'm already a week behind schedule. If the monsoons hit us, we could be in serious trouble below. We have to get started back. I know exactly how you feel, but I'm afraid this is it."

Later that night, while the wind moved ceaselessly, sucking at the tent, they burrowed in sleeping bags, talking.

"There must be some basis of fact in those stories," Ed said to Dr. Schenk. "I've given them a lot of thought. Has it occurred to you that every one of the sightings, the few face-to-face meetings of the natives and these — these unknowns, has generally been just around dawn and usually when the native was alone?"

Schenk smiled rather dubiously. "Whatever this creature may be — and I am convinced that it's either a species of large bear or one of the great anthropoids — it certainly must keep off the well-traveled routes. There are very few passes through these peaks, of course, and it would be quite simple for them to avoid these locales."

"But we're not on any known trail," Ed said thoughtfully. "I believe our methods have been all wrong, stringing out a bunch of men, looking for trails in the snow. All we've done is announce our presence to anything with ears for miles around. That glider pilot made no sound; he came on them without warning."

Ed looked intently at Schenk. "I'd like to try that peak up ahead and the plateau beyond." When Schenk uttered a protesting cry, Ed said, "Wait — this time I'll go alone with just one Sherpa guide. We could leave several hours before daybreak. No equipment, other than oxygen, food for one meal — and my cameras, of course. Maintain a strict silence. We could be back before noon. Will you wait long enough for this one last try?" Schenk hesitated. "Only a few hours more," Ed urged.

Schenk stared at him; then he nodded slowly. "Agreed. But aren't you forgetting the most important item of all?" When Ed looked blank, Schenk smiled. "The gas gun. If you should run across one, we'll need more proof than just your word for it."

There was very little wind, no moon, but cold, the cold approaching that of outer space, as Ed and one Sherpa porter started away from the sleeping camp, up the shattered floor of an ice river that swept down from the jagged peak ahead.

They moved up, hearing only the squeak of equipment, the peculiar gritty sound of crampons biting into packed snow, an occasional hollow crash of falling ice blocks. To the east a faint line of gray was already visible; daylight was hours away, but at this tremendous height sunrise came early. They moved slowly, breathing through woolen masks, the thin air cutting cruelly into their lungs, moving up, up.

They stopped once for hot chocolate from a thermos, and Ed slapped the Sherpa's shoulder, grinning, pointing ahead to where the jagged peak glowed pink and gold in the first slanting rays of the sun. The Sherpa looked at the peak and quickly shifted his glance to the sky. He gave a long, careful look at the gathering clouds in the east, then muttered something, shaking his head, pointing back, back down to where the camp was hidden in the inky shadows of enormous boulders.

When Ed resumed the climb, the Sherpa removed the long nylon line which had joined them. The route was comparatively level, on a huge sweeping expanse of snow-covered glacier that flowed about at the base of the peak. The Sherpa, no longer in the lead, began dropping behind as Ed pressed eagerly forward.

The sun was up, and with it the wind began keening again, bitterly sharp, bringing with it a scent of coming snow. In the east, beyond the jagged peak just ahead, the immense escarpment of the Himalayas was lost in approaching cloud. Ed hurried as best he could; it would snow, and soon. He'd have to make better time.

But above, the sky was blue, infinitely blue; and behind, the sun was well up, although the camp was still lost in night below. The peak thrust up ahead, near, with what appeared to be a natural pass skirting its flank. Ed made for it. As he circled an upthrust ridge of reddish rotten rock, he glanced ahead. The plateau spread out before him, gently sloping, a natural amphitheater full of deep, smooth snow, with peaks surrounding it and the central peak thrusting a long, black shadow directly across the center. He paused, glancing back. The Sherpa had stopped well below him, his face a dark blur, looking up, gesticulating frantically, pointing to the clouds. Ed motioned, then moved around, leaning against the rock, peering ahead.

That great shadow against the snow was certainly similar to the one in the photo, only, of course, the shadow pointed west now, when later it would point northwest as the sun swung to the south. And when it did, most certainly it was the precise — Ed sucked in a sharp, lung-piercing breath.

He stared, squinting against the rising wind that seemed to blow from the earth's outermost reaches. Three figures stirred slightly and suddenly leaped into focus, almost perfectly camouflaged against the snow and wind-blasted rock. Three figures not more than a hundred feet below him. Two small, one larger.

He leaned forward, his heart thudding terribly at this twenty-thousand-foot height. A tremor of excitement shook him. It was true. They existed. He was looking at what was undeniably a female and two smaller — what? Apes?

They were covered with downy hair, nearly white, resembling nothing so much as tight-fitting leotards. The female was exactly like any woman on earth except for the hair. No larger than most women, with arms slightly longer, more muscular. Thighs heavier, legs out of proportion to the trunk, shorter.

Not apes.

Hardly breathing, Ed squinted, staring, motionless. Not apes. Not standing so erectly. Not with those broad, high brows. Not with the undeniable intelligence of the two young, now capering about their mother. Not — and on seeing this, Ed trembled against the rock — not with the sudden affectionate sweep of the female as she lifted the smaller and pressed it to her breast, smoothing back hair from its face with a motion common to every human mother on earth. A wonderfully tender gesture.

What were they? Less than human? Perhaps. He couldn't be certain, but he thought he heard a faint gurgle of laughter from the female, fondling the small one, and the sound stirred him strangely. Dr. Schenk had assured him that no animal was capable of genuine laughter; only man.

But they laughed, those three, and hearing it, watching the mother tickling the youngest one, watching its delighted squirming, Ed knew that in that marvelous little grouping below, perfectly lighted, perfectly staged, he was privileged to observe one of the earth's most-guarded secrets.

He should get started shooting his pictures; afterward, he should stun the group into unconsciousness with the gas gun and then send the Sherpa back down for Dr. Schenk and the others. Clouds were massing, immensities of blue-black. Already the first few flakes of snow, huge, wet, drifted against his face.

But for a long moment more he remained motionless, oddly unwilling to do anything to destroy the harmony, the aching purity of the scene below, so vividly etched in brilliant light and shadow. The female, child slung casually on one hip, stood erect, hand shading her eyes, and Ed grinned. Artless, but perfectly posed. She was looking carefully about and above, scanning the great outcroppings of rock, obviously searching for something. Then she paused.

She was staring directly at him.

Ed froze, even though he knew he was perfectly concealed by the deep shadows of the high cliff behind him. She was still looking directly at him, and then, slowly, her hand came up.

She waved.

He shivered uncontrollably in the biting wind, trying hard to remain motionless.

Then the two young ones suddenly began to jump up and down and show every evidence of joy. And suddenly Ed knew.

He turned slowly, very slowly, and with the sensation of a freezing knife plunging deeply into his chest, he saw the male less than five yards away.

It was huge, by far twice the size of the female below. (And crazily Ed thought of Schenk's little lecture, given what seemed like eons ago, six weeks before, in the incredible tropical grove far below, where rhododendrons grew in wild profusion and enormous butterflies flitted above: "In primitive man," Schenk had said, "as in the great apes today, the male was far larger than the female.")

The gas gun was hopelessly out of reach, securely strapped to his shoulder pack. Ed stared, knowing there was absolutely nothing he could do to protect himself before this creature, fully eight feet tall, with arms as big as Ed's own thighs and eyes (*blue* eyes!) that were boring into his. There was a light of savage intelligence there — and something else.

The creature (man?) made no move against him, and Ed stared at it, breathing rapidly, shallowly, and with difficulty, noting with his photographer's eyes the immense chest span, the easy rise and fall of his breathing, the large, square, white teeth, the somber cast of his face. There was long sandy fur on the shoulders, chest, and back, shortening to off-white over the rest of the magnificent torso. Ears rather small and close to the head. Short, thick neck, rising up from the broad shoulders to the back of the head in a straight line. Toes long and definitely prehensile.

They looked silently at one another across the abyss of time and mystery. Man and — what? How long, Ed wondered, had it stood there observing him? Why hadn't it attacked? Had it been waiting for Ed to make a single threatening gesture such as pointing a gun or camera? Seeing the calm awareness in those long, slanting blue eyes, Ed sped a silent prayer of thanks upward; most certainly if he had made a move for camera or gun, that move would have been his last.

They looked at one another through a curtain of falling snow, and suddenly there was a perfect, instantaneous understanding between them. Ed made an awkward, half-frozen little bow, moving backward. The great creature stood motionless, merely watching, and then Ed did a strange thing. He held out his hands, palms out, gave a wry grin, and ducked quickly around the outcropping of rock and began a plunging, sliding return, down the way he'd come. In spite of the harsh, snow-laden wind, bitterly cold, he was perspiring.

Ed glanced back once. Nothing. Only the thickening veil of swift, glowing snow blanking out the pinnacle, erasing every trace, every proof that anyone, anything, had stood there moments before. Only the snow, only the rocks, only the unending, wind-filled silence of the top of the world. Nothing else.

The Sherpa was struggling up to him from below, terribly anxious to get started back; the storm was rising. Without a word they hooked up and began the groping, stumbling descent back to the last camp. They found the camp already broken, Sherpas already moving out. Schenk paused only long enough to give Ed a questioning look.

What could Ed say? Schenk was a scientist, demanding material proof. If not a corpse, at the very least a photograph. The only photographs Ed had were etched in his mind, not on film. And even if he could persuade Schenk to wait, when the storm cleared, the giant, forewarned, would be gone. Some farther peak, some remoter plateau, would echo to his young ones' laughter.

Feeling not a bit bad about it, Ed gave Schenk a barely perceptible

negative nod. Instantly Schenk shrugged, turned, and went plunging down into the thickening snow, back into the world of littler men. Ed trailed behind.

On the arduous trek back through that first great storm, through the snow line, through the rain forest, hot and humid, Ed thought of the giant back up there where the air was thin and pure.

Who, what, were he and his race? Castaways on this planet, forever marooned, yearning for a distant, never-to-be-reached home?

Or did they date in unbroken descent from the Pleistocene (plī'stə-sēn'), man's first beginning, when all the races of not-quite-man were giants, unable or unwilling to take the fork in the road that led to smaller, cleverer man; forced to retreat higher and higher, to more and more remote areas, until finally there was only one corner in all the earth left to them — the high Himalayas?

Or were he and his kind the earth's last reserves; not-yet-men, waiting for the opening of still another chapter in the earth's unending mystery story?

Whatever the giant was, his secret was safe with him, Ed thought. For who would believe it even if he chose to tell?

DISCUSSION

1. Who was sponsoring Ed's expedition? What was its purpose?
2. What two things did Ed's boss give him in New York to help Ed in his search? Which was more helpful to him?
3. What final attempt did Ed get Dr. Schenk to agree to? What were Ed's arguments in favor of his plan? Why did this have to be the last attempt?
4. How did Ed come to realize that one of the creatures must be very close to him? Why do you think the male did not attack him?
5. Do you think Ed was sorry he had not been able to take pictures? Why do you think that? Suppose he had brought back the desired pictures. What might have happened then?
6. What item of equipment did Dr. Schenk remind Ed to take with him? What did Dr. Schenk want Ed to do if he found what

he was looking for? Do you think this may have been one reason Ed did not like Dr. Schenk? What makes you think that?

7. Ed wondered repeatedly whether or not the creatures were human. Do you think he ever answered that question in his own mind? If so, how? What evidence from the story would support your answer?

8. Why do you think Ed lied to Dr. Schenk by signaling "No" with his head? Why do you think Ed decided not to tell anyone what he had seen? Would you have made the same decision? Why or why not?

9. Do you think Ed would ever support another expedition of this kind? Why do you think that? Do you think he should? What makes you think as you do?

AUTHOR

Born in 1920 in Pittsburgh, Pennsylvania, William Sambrot was educated at the University in Biarritz, France, and at the University of California. During World War II he served with the Medical Corps of the United States Army. After working for several years in advertising and other fields, he decided in 1954 to devote his time exclusively to writing. He is the author of nearly 150 short stories and has also written television scripts, including adaptations of some of his own work. Mr. Sambrot is particularly interested in science fiction and feels that it deserves greater respect from critics and reviewers. As one of his lifetime goals, he hopes through his writing to help elevate science fiction so that it will come to be esteemed as literature.

HOCKEY

The ice is smooth, smooth, smooth.
The air bites to the center
Of warmth and flesh, and I whirl.
It begins in a game . . .
The puck swims, skims, veers,
Goes leading my vision
Beyond the chasing reach of my stick.

The air is sharp, steel-sharp.
I suck needles of breathing,
And feel the players converge.
It grows to a science . . .
We clot, break, drive,
Electrons in motion
In the magnetic pull of the puck.

The play is fast, fierce, tense.
Sticks click and snap like teeth
Of wolves on the scent of a prey.
It ends in the kill . . .
I am one of the pack in a mad,
Taut leap of desperation
In the wild, slashing drive for the goal.

SCOTT BLAINE

THE WONDROUS WOODLANDS

When early European voyagers approached the land that is now the United States, they were enchanted by the land smell that told them they were nearing shore. This was actually the perfume of a dense, unbroken wilderness that extended from the seacoast to the Mississippi River, and to a man like Arthur Barlowe, who coasted along North Carolina in 1584 and reported his findings to Sir Walter Raleigh, it was a wondrous thing indeed. "The second of July," he wrote, "we found shole water, wher we smelt so sweet, and so strong a smel, as if we had bene in the midst of some delicate garden abounding with all kinde of odoriferous flowers, by which we were assured, that the land could not be farre distant. . . ." After going ashore and surveying the rich vegetation, Barlowe concluded that "in all the world the like abundance is not to be found: and my selfe having seene those parts of Europe that most abound, find such difference as were incredible to be written. . . ."

by Richard M. Ketchum

It had been hundreds of years since any other European had seen anything even remotely resembling what Barlowe witnessed. There are numerous references to forests in classical writings: Homer[1] speaks frequently of "wooded Samothrace"[2] or the "tall pines and oaks of Sicily," but these woodlands had largely disappeared from the ancient world. The forests had been cleared by man, and his sheep and goats and cattle had altered forever the nature of the landscape bordering parts of the Mediterranean and Aegean. Even at the time of Greece's glory, Plato[3] wrote, "What now remains compared with what then existed is like the skeleton of a sick man, all the fat and soft earth having been wasted away, and only the bare framework of the land being left."

---

[1] **Homer** (hō′mər), a Greek poet of the eighth century B.C.

[2] **Samothrace** (săm′ō-thrās), a Greek island in the Aegean Sea.

[3] **Plato** (plā′tō), a Greek philosopher living 427–347 B.C.

To the colonists settling America in the seventeenth and eighteenth centuries, the apparently endless woods, unbroken except by rivers and mountain crags, were a wonder that made an enduring impression. It was said that a squirrel could make its way from the eastern end of Pennsylvania to the western boundary without ever leaving the trees, so thick was the cover, and certainly only a bird flying over the ancient forest could take in its immensity. Parts of that area were called the "black forest" by pioneers because the vegetation shut out the sun so completely, and General Edward Braddock's route to destiny in 1755 took his army through an almost impenetrable gloom known locally as the "shades of death."

Evidently this rank deciduous and white-pine forest was a world of silence by day, for most of the songbirds that populate more-open woods today lived on the perimeters of the dense growth, along the Atlantic coastline and the river valleys and in the few openings that existed in the woodland.

Of an estimated four hundred thousand square miles of virgin forest that once covered the eastern half of the United States, less than two thousand square miles might be said to remain in anything like their primeval state. Only the more inaccessible reaches of the Appalachians and a few small scattered areas elsewhere are left to suggest what the whole region was like. For almost the first two hundred years of American settlement, pioneers claimed a farmstead by hacking one out of the forest, cutting down trees so large a man might chop for several days before he could fell one. At best, the pioneer farmer could clear a few acres each year, and one reason so many of the huge trees were girdled was to save a man the backbreaking toil of swinging an axe day after day.

By the beginning of the nineteenth century, frontier farmers reached the western edge of the great eastern forest, coming out into the pocket of the prairie that lies in what is now Illinois. There are records of the joy they felt upon emerging from the gloom and dark of the woods into sunny, open grasslands where they could see the full sweep of sky. The prairie soil was far richer for farming than the land they had left behind, but curiously enough, few of the first settlers knew this. In their experience, and that of earlier generations, something must be wrong with soil in which trees did not grow. And so they settled, at first, in the forest at the edge of the grass. Beyond the Mississippi, in colonial times as now, the woods ended almost completely, and the tall grass of the prairies began — for what reason, no one is entirely certain. Some believe that the Indians burned off the forest there to drive out the game and to improve the vegetation that supported it. Others think that the last glacier to slide down over America from the north may have retarded the forest. What is perhaps more likely is that a combination of soil and rainfall conditions was responsible, but no one knows for certain. The early settlers found the prairie grass unusually beautiful, especially when it was interlaced with flowers in the spring, and they wrote that it was so tall a man on foot could not see over it.

For years the New England states were filled with abandoned farms — lands that had been cleared of trees by generations of pioneers determined to scratch out a living from the stony soil. Farmers who were discouraged by increasingly poor yields, or lured by the promise of fertile western lands or the hope of finding gold or silver, packed up their families and belongings, took a last look at the old homestead, shut the door, and departed, leaving behind a few ruinous buildings and fields that had until recently been meadowland and pasture. In the 1870's and well into the 1890's farms were being abandoned wholesale, and one can read between the lines of statistics the profound changes that resulted from this population movement. By 1820 all but 27 per cent of the entire area of Connecticut had been cleared of woods. By 1910 the trees had come back, reclaiming 45 per cent of the land, and by 1955 forests occupied 63 per cent of the state. What happened in the years after New England's farms were abandoned reveals a great deal about the process that is called natural succession. Within a few months of a farmer's departure, a long trail of change began to take place — a change that eventually produced a forest to supersede the one cleared long ago at the cost of such hardship and pain.

Let us imagine that the time is spring, in the year the farm family departed: sunlight falls directly on the soil between the sparse growth in the fields, and by midsummer a collection of new plants has already invaded the territory. Most are weeds — annuals such as ragweed, dandelions, and chickweed — whose seeds blow into the fields by the millions or are dropped and spread by the birds. As time passes, other

226

plants seed themselves and begin to grow: goldenrod and Queen Anne's lace, joe-pye weed, black-eyed Susans, milkweed, and mullein. Woody plants like the burdock and blackberry take root; gradually, patches of soil are shaded from the sun, and more water is held in the earth by the growing number of plants. New animals and insects move into the fields, and an increasing variety of birds populate the area in search of food. Mice, rabbits, moles, and shrews come into the old fields, followed by the predators that feed on them — hawks of all kinds, owls, and snakes. Woodchucks dig their holes and multiple tunnels beneath the soil, and at every level — above and below ground — life proliferates.

Here and there a tree seed has germinated, and a scattering of them — a pine or red cedar, a few white birch and poplar, perhaps a wild cherry — begin to be prominent in the fields. Only those species whose seedlings tolerate direct sunlight move into the open land. In many areas of New England the white pine soon becomes predominant, elsewhere the birch and poplar fill the fields, but none of these species is destined to last permanently. By the time the pines are about fifteen or twenty years old, their branches may form a canopy that darkens the ground, smothering the old pasture grass and weeds, and may begin to form such a complete cover that their own seedlings have insufficient light for germination. And the birches and poplars, which tend to be relatively short-lived, begin to die when they have reached maturity. But these pioneer trees provide shade for still other species that are far more tolerant of it — trees that actually require a certain amount of protection from direct sunlight. Red oaks and maples, tulip poplars and ash, achieve a foothold under the pines or birches, infiltrating the woodland slowly but persistently. In the pinewoods the weeds disappear as they are deprived of sunlight, and with their departure the character of animal life alters too. Little animals that made nests of grass in the fields move out, deer move in, and the field birds are supplanted by those that live in or on the edges of forests. Chipmunks and squirrels are busy carrying acorns, butternuts, or hickory nuts into the woods, and some of these take root with the passing of time.

Inevitably, the pines begin to disappear one by one — some of them blown over by windstorms, some destroyed by fire or lightning, still others damaged by insects or disease — and as they topple over, their places are taken by trees that have been growing patiently on the forest floor — usually red maples, red oaks, or tulip trees. Similarly, the white birch is replaced by other types of trees: the line of succession is from the sun-loving pioneer trees to those that can grow in partial shade, and these latter form a forest that is still only in the intermediate stage. Like the pines, these trees eventually bring about their own destruction by growing so large that their own seedlings are incapable of surviving in their shade. During the passing decades the species that thrive in deep shade — sugar maples, hemlocks, beeches, white oaks, and hickories — have been taking over the forest floor from the other plants, forming a dense understory, and each time one of the red oaks or red maples succumbs to old age or some catastrophe, they are released and grow more quickly, filling in the space until the forest finally achieves what is called its climax stage. From this time on, unless a major calamity befalls the forest, only those seedlings that can grow in dense shade will survive. And below the understory the cycle of growth and decay, the building of humus and topsoil, is going on steadily, adding riches to the earth and creating the conditions of moisture and food that nurture the big climax trees.

From studies made of true wilderness tracts, it is estimated that a climax forest of this type — a balanced community of plant and animal life — takes between two and three hundred years to replicate. When woodland such as this is destroyed by man or by natural catastrophe, the entire cycle of succession must begin again, and it is a matter of centuries — not years — before the climax forest can re-create itself.

DISCUSSION

1. What made the eastern part of North America different from the lands from which the early settlers came? When had the European countryside been much more like what the settlers found in America? What had caused the change?

2. Approximately where were the east-west boundaries of the great eastern forest? The area of the primeval forest that still remains is only a half of 1 per cent of the original. What happened to the rest of it?

3. What kind of area lay just west of the eastern forest? What three possible reasons are given for the absence of forest in that area?

4. Why do you think songbirds did not inhabit the deep forest?

5. What is a climax forest? Was the primeval eastern forest a climax forest? Why do you think that?

6. Why was the establishing of farms in the East especially difficult? What do you think settlers did when they "girdled" trees? Why would they do that?

7. The author says that a climax forest is a balanced community of plant and animal life. Are prairies and deserts also balanced communities of plant and animal life? Why or why not? How can the balance in such a community be disturbed or changed?

8. Should the colonists have tried to conserve the original forest? Why or why not? Should much more land in the eastern states be allowed to become climax forest again? Why or why not? What are the advantages to man of such wilderness areas?

9. Have you seen evidence of the kind of forest regrowth described in this article? If so, tell about it.

I MEET MONEY

Prince Modupe

The author of the following selection was born in the early 1900's in a village of mud huts in what was French Guinea (gĭn'ē), West Africa. His grandfather was chief of the So-So tribe, and Prince Modupe (mō-dōo'pā) was in line to succeed him on the chief-stool, or throne. Like every So-So youth, the prince in his mid-teens had undergone the rituals of the Bondo Bush, which established him as a man of the tribe, and had proven his manhood by venturing alone into the jungle and killing a leopard.

The world of the So-So was limited to their tribal boundaries, and Prince Modupe's life would have been much like the lives of generations of So-So had a stranger not appeared in the village one day. His name was Paul Boolama. He was a member of a neighboring tribe, and he told the So-So that he had gone to school in a faraway place called Sierra Leone (sē-ĕr'ə lē-ōn') and had become what was known as a Christian. The purpose of his visit was to prepare the way for a white missionary who would soon come to the village to explain the wonders of white learning. When the missionary arrived, he made a tremendous impression on the chief and other tribesmen. He seemed to possess a new kind of power, different from that of the So-So medicine men. For the benefit of the tribe, it was decided that Prince Modupe should journey to the coast to study Christian ways.

The villagers stood on the bank of the Scarcis[1] to see me off to the world outside. Kende stood beside my mother in the front ranks. The pain of parting, especially from those two, almost unmanned me. Would they ever see me again? They feared not. In one way, they were right. When I returned several years later, I was not the same person who had left.

Muddy-tan water lapped at the sides of the dugout. Mapam, an older warrior, sat in front; I at the stern. A few strokes and we were in midstream. Although I was busy with my *batai* (bä-tī′), the paddle, I saw through tear-blur their gallant efforts to wave. The dugout swept easily around a bend, and we were out of sight.

A trip down the Scarcis is not easy. There are mud flats studded with crocodiles, there is quicksand, and in my day it was the vast playground of the huge river horses, the hippopotamuses. They are not man-eaters, but they love to frolic, and when any creature of almost elephant size gets playful with a human, it is dangerous. They love to submerge and surface, cavorting with the zest of a small-boy child. If one comes up under a canoe or even brushes the side of the shell-frail craft, over it goes. The crocodiles seem to grin as they wait and watch with small evil eyes.

---

[1] Scarcis, now spelled **Scarcies** (skär′sēz).

The first hippo we saw crossed directly in front of us. Others followed into the water, diving and breaking surface. There were too many of them to be traceable. All we could do was to alert ourselves and hope. One of them came up so close to us that my *batai* struck him at the finish of the stroke. Mapam and I ceased paddling; our full concern was to balance the craft by throwing our weights to one side. It steadied, settled. We bent again to our paddles. It was important to go as far as possible by daylight. There were few places on the bank where it seemed safe to stop. Reeds grew in the shallow water near shore. The banks were lined with huge trees, thick and twisted with lianas, making a screen and a mystery of what lay behind. Brilliant birds perched on overhanging limbs like noisy flowers. Monkeys played on the lianas, chattering defiance at our dugout. Toward evening we spied game at land's edge, antelope, chevrotain. We heard an elephant trumpet in the distance. For the most part, the day slipped away as quietly as the dugout glided. Yet it seemed more adventurous to me than anything which had happened previously because of the unknown quality of life ahead. Those things which had gone into making me a "complete savage" — the Bondo training, the test of manhood, the judgment poisonings, and the sacrificial executions I had witnessed —

were the expected shapes and colors of tribal life in the bush. I had been prepared for them since birth. For the unknown ahead, I had no qualification except a burning desire to know.

When night fell, we lit a palm-oil lamp in the dugout and continued to paddle in the moonless darkness. Crocodiles lie up on mud banks and sand flats at night. If we were lucky enough to avoid going aground on one of those, we would be all right. The hazard of the river was less than the dangers of the unknown, jungle-choked shore. We ate some food we had brought with us and continued downstream.

The morning of the next day we reached the village where it had been arranged on the drums that Paul Boolama was to wait for me. As I stepped from the dugout, he grasped my hand and wrung it, laughing at the startled expression on my face. Shaking hands was, he explained, the Christian mode of greeting a friend. I tucked this bit of information away for future use. I believe it would be safe to say that during my early years as a Christian, I was one of the most persistent of all handshakers. I shook the hand of everyone I met, man, woman, or child, often to the surprise or annoyance of the shakee. To thrust forward the hand was my first lesson in the rituals of civilization, learned on the bank of the muddy Scarcis.

After we had rested, Mapam started back toward Dubricka[2] alone, paddling against the current. A great pang clutched my heart as I watched him slowly disappear from view. Paul Boolama and I prepared to go in the other direction. The other direction! The river flows to the sea. Tides push it back upon itself for a space, then the tide reverses, is with the current, and all is swept before it. The waters of rivers merge with the sea.

A warrior sat in the front, another in the back of the new dugout. Paul Boolama and I sat between them. This was a larger boat. I asked for a *batai*. Paul explained that we would talk and the others would row. This seemed strange to me because I seemed to be the youngest member of the party, but then I supposed I would have to get used to all sorts of reversals of custom. Boolama was highly pleased that he was able to bring a protégé to his big-father, the missionary with whom he lived. He explained that after we reached Konakry,[3] he would send word to Freetown and arrange for my passage in a huge boat. The big-father in Sierra Leone would meet my boat in Freetown. He tried to make me understand that the message would be sent by something called a telegram rather than by talking drums, but I could make nothing of that. For one thing, I was too appalled at the news that Boolama was not going the entire journey with me. He had to visit more tribes in Guinea and give instruction in places he would revisit before he came back to Freetown. He was a Bambara and so the logical one to attend to the work in Guinea. I would be perfectly safe on the big coastal boat, he explained.

It was the beginning of a clear night when we approached Konakry. The water was choppy with tide wash and breeze. We swung around a bend. There before my eyes was the dazzling sight of the lights of the coastal city. The grandeur of those lights to my eyes, accustomed to palm-oil lamps, balks any effort of description. Thrill and disbelief quivered through me. The lights were shut off for a moment by a bend in the river. I thought they had been an illusion. They reappeared and were constantly visible like a skyful of stars snared in a net and brought to earth. Nothing in the missionary's kit of pictures conveyed the lovely sublimity of heaven as did those twinkling lights in front of me.

We passed the blurred outlines of huts of such size as I had never dreamed possible. In the wide span of water before us, huge canoes, with smoke coming out of their

---

[2] **Dubricka**, now spelled **Dubréka** (dōō-brā′kə).

[3] **Konakry**, now spelled **Conakry** (kän′ə-krē). It is the capital of the Republic of Guinea, which was formed in 1958.

round tops, lay offshore. The dug-out was turned toward the docks. These high piles of wooden structure frightened me as did all else. Only Paul Boolama's presence at my side gave me courage to keep my eyes open.

I was wearing my jungle attire. I was nude to the waist and had my spear and knives and bow and arrows. These were sufficient equipment to meet any unknown or known danger in the bush. I clutched them tighter, wondering whether they would be adequate to the dangers of the world. The dug-out was steadied for us. Boolama climbed out, and I followed. People on the dock stared at me and pointed. I had my full growth and was well muscled from an active life. I must have looked the savage that I was. The dock loungers could not have known that my heart pommeled my ribs with hard-knocking fear.

Boolama left me for a moment to find a conveyance, telling me to stay where I was and wait for him. Nearby I saw an African woman seated on the ground. Beside her was a calabash filled with *akara* (ä-kä'rä), fried bean bread. I was hungry, and it was good to see a familiar kind of food. She held some up to me, speaking in a language I did not understand. I accepted it and began eating. She spoke out sharply and held up her empty hand with the palm raised.

I did not understand. This must be some other ritual of the hands in the outer world. A small crowd gathered quickly as she shrilled at me. I would have run except that Boolama had told me with emphasis to stay where he left me.

A white-uniformed man came over and spoke sharply to me. I could not understand him either. He gestured for my weapons. I was not about to give those up without a struggle. I kept on eating because I was hungry and because I reasoned that if something terrible was about to happen to me, it would only be worse on an empty stomach. The uniformed man put a whistle to his lips and blew on it. The sound was penetrating. . . . Two more men came riding up on shiny-wheeled affairs. The crowd thinned at the sweep of their hands.

Paul Boolama came running to me just in time. He said something to the policemen which satisfied them, and he drew something shiny out of his pocket which satisfied the African woman.

We went to Boolama's friends in an affair which seemed like a small hut on wheels. On our way he tried to make me understand what money was and its uses. Food was not given for nothing in the civilized world. In fact, almost nothing one wanted could be had without money. It was the most important single thing to have and to know about. I was baffled. In our village everything we needed for food, clothing, shelter, entertainment, weapons, religion, was furnished by the Great Mother, Earth. If there was some small thing we lacked, such as a Foulah pot, we traded something we had to obtain it. I had met money, but I did not understand it. All I understood was an implication of the terrors of needing it and not having it.

Paul Boolama showed me a coin and explained how much rice it would purchase. My father had brought home similar coins from his trips to the coast. They were viewed by the women in our household as suitable source material for bangles to wear at the neck. Our village had no other use for silver. How was one ever to learn the relative value of these shiny little disks! The only thing we had which was in any way comparable was the cowrie shell, and a big one was not worth more than a slightly smaller one. From this to-do about money, I began to suspect that civilization was complicated. I was shaken by a great fear that I would never be able to master the complications.

At the home of Boolama's friends, clothes were brought for me. He helped me bathe and dress. The thing in which I bathed repulsed me because the used water stayed right there until one had finished, instead of sliding away like the stream water at home. The clothes seemed too many, too heavy, too tight. And the shoes! It took years for me to get accustomed to shoes. What torture! I knew I would have to get used to strange customs, but I did not expect any punishment as harsh as having to encase my feet in pinching leather.

Dinner was a nightmare. Was this food, this stuff laid out on a flat dish, a little green here, a little dab of red there, something yellow in one corner? At home everything was cooked together and cooked thoroughly. The meat at this meal was rare. Did Christians eat raw meat like forest beasts? Most frightening of all was the sharp, shiny pronged thing they called a fork. Were these people not at one with each other that they did not eat with their hands from a common bowl? I tried to do what Boolama did. I stuck my tongue with the fork. The food tasted awful. It needed seasoning, much hot pepper. In the bush it is indication of enmity not to eat proffered food, so I forced it all down, hating every bite, relieved that the portions were what would have seemed meager at home. Perhaps these people ate sparsely because the food was so unpalatable.

Shortly after we arose from the table, I had to go into the little room where I had bathed.... My stomach would not agree to keep the food I had made it accept.

I took off the leather which was torturing my feet and the socks which made them so hot. I sat ... thinking about the hardships which seemed to go with being a Christian. Being a savage was certainly more comfortable!

Boolama came looking for me, calling my name. I stood up dizzily and replied.... He took one look at me and led me to a cot in the next room. Just as I was ... I fell asleep. I dreamed of converging policemen blowing whistles and swinging clubs because I lacked something called money. Thus passed my first twenty-four hours in civilization.

DISCUSSION

1. How did Prince Modupe travel from his village to the outside world? What were the dangers of the trip?
2. Describe the prince's first experience with money. What did Paul Boolama tell the prince about money? What was the prince's reaction to what Boolama told him?

3. Although the prince did not explain why he was leaving his village, what details did he mention that indicated who had arranged his trip and why he was going?
4. What weapons did the prince take with him? What does the way he had armed himself tell you about his understanding of life outside his own village?
5. After his first day in civilization, do you think the prince may have felt he should never have left his village? Why do you think as you do?
6. Do you think the prince was surprised to find that many of the ways of civilization seemed inferior to his tribal ways? Why do you think that?
7. What unpleasant experiences did the prince have during his first evening at the missionary's home? Why were they unpleasant for him? Would they have been unpleasant for you? Why or why not?
8. Suppose you had been Prince Modupe. Do you think you would have felt any differently about money after living in civilization for a while than you did when you first learned about it? Why do you think that?
9. Have you ever had to learn new ways of doing things or new customs in a very short period of time? If so, describe your experience.

AUTHOR

In Freetown Prince Modupe lived at the home of the missionary, Father Perry, who paid for the boy's schooling. Father Perry was a kind and sympathetic man whom the prince recognized immediately as a friend. When the teen-age So-So warrior started his studies, he was humiliated to find himself in a class of first graders. But Prince Modupe had a fine, quick mind, and he also was driven by a desire to learn and to catch up with pupils of his own age, so his progress in school was remarkable. As soon as he had mastered his primers, he began to read directly from the Bible. When he finally reached high school, one of his teachers was a young African who had graduated from Oxford University and who urged the prince to continue his education there. The idea appealed to Prince Modupe, for he had come to realize that what he had learned was only a beginning and that there was much more he wanted to know. But how could he pay for further studies and a trip to England?

Prince Modupe returned to his village, where he was embarrassed by the deference shown him by the chief and elders. He could think of no way to explain to his family that in order to be eventually of greater help to the tribe, he must leave again and go on with his education. To add to his distress, he found that the world had discovered Dubricka and that many of the good things in the So-So culture were being lost. In the years he had been away, three new religious denominations had sent representatives to the village and were competing for the tribesmen's souls. The deceit and hatred these groups showed one another made a mockery of their words, and the prince became hopelessly disillusioned with all three.

As his family wished, he married Kende, whom he had loved since childhood. Soon after their marriage, they set off in a dugout to attempt to locate an elephant graveyard that was thought to be a few days' journey upriver. If they could find it, they could sell the ivory tusks to pay for Prince Modupe's studies and, now, for Kende to go to school too. They never did locate the graveyard, but they did obtain one pair of immense tusks from a dying elephant they trailed. On their return downstream, however, the dugout capsized, and Kende was drowned and swept away by the rapids. The prince was able to recover the tusks and sadly made his way eventually to Freetown. With the money they brought him, he was prepared to buy passage to England until by chance he met an American churchman who convinced him that he should go to the United States instead and study at Hampton Institute in Virginia. When word suddenly reached Freetown that the So-Sos were trying by every means possible to keep the twenty-year-old heir to the throne from leaving Africa, the prince felt fortunate to secure passage on a ship sailing almost immediately for America, and on May 22, 1922, he reached New York.

Prince Modupe's story of his early life is told in his book *A Royal African*, from which "I Meet Money" is taken. In the years he has been in the United States, he has earned his living in the motion-picture industry as an actor, director, and producer, and he has also been a professor of anthropology. The prince married again and has American-born children who, as youngsters, never tired of hearing him tell about his boyhood experiences. He now lives in Los Angeles and is at present trying to raise funds in this country with which he can found a school in Nigeria.

Perfect Number

Isaac Asimov

The ancient Greeks enjoyed playing games with numbers, and one of them was to add up the factors of particular integers. For instance, the factors of 12 (not counting the number itself) are 1, 2, 3, 4, and 6. Each of these numbers, but no others, will go evenly into 12. The sum of these factors is 16, which is greater than the number 12 itself, so that 12 was called an *abundant number*. The factors of 10, on the other hand, are 1, 2, and 5, which add up to 8. This is less than the number itself, so 10 is a *deficient number*.

But consider 6. Its factors are 1, 2, and 3, which add up to the number itself. The Greeks considered 6, therefore, a *perfect number*. Throughout ancient and medieval times, only four different perfect numbers were known. The second was 28, the factors of which are 1, 2, 4, 7, and 14. The third and fourth perfect numbers are 496 and 8,128. The fifth perfect number was not discovered till 1460, and the name of the discoverer is not known. It is 33,550,336.

There are no practical uses for the perfect numbers; they are merely a mathematical curiosity. Mathematicians, however, are curious and have worked out formulas that will yield perfect numbers if certain conditions are met. If even the fifth perfect number is over thirty million, those still higher are, you can well imagine, terribly tedious to work out.

The break came with the development of computers during and after World War II. To demonstrate what computers could do, one could set them to work solving formulas for perfect numbers. By now, twenty-one perfect numbers are known. The twenty-first perfect number, worked out in 1971, is a number with twelve thousand and three digits.

Such a number has no more practical use than any smaller perfect number, but wouldn't the Greeks have been astonished if they could have seen it!

POST EARLY FOR SPACE

Once we were wayfarers, then seafarers, then airfarers;
We shall be spacefarers soon,
Not voyaging from city to city or from coast to coast,
But from planet to planet and from moon to moon.

This is no fanciful flight of imagination,
No strange, incredible, utterly different thing;
It will come by obstinate thought and calculation
And the old resolve to spread an expanding wing.

We shall see homes established on distant planets,
Friends departing to take up a post on Mars;
They will have perils to meet, but they will meet them,
As the early settlers did on American shores.

We shall buy tickets later, as now we buy them
For a foreign vacation, reserve our seat or berth,
Then spending a holiday month on a moon of Saturn,
Look tenderly back to our little shining Earth.

And those who decide they will not make the journey
Will remember a son up there or a favorite niece,
Eagerly awaiting news from the old home-planet,
And will scribble a line to catch the post for space.

PETER J. HENNIKER-HEATON

SKILL LESSON 4

EFFECTIVE STUDY HABITS

Just what do you do in order to study for a school assignment? Do you read the material only once, perhaps somewhat as you would read a short story? Do you read the material a second time? If all you do is either or both of these things, you won't remember many of the ideas or details that the material contains.

A good step to take first in studying is to get quickly an overview of the information that the material supplies. You can do this either by referring to the table of contents at the front of the book or by turning the pages of the material rapidly to find the main headings. Suppose, for example, that in starting to study a chapter on plants, you find these main headings:

1. PARTS OF PLANTS
2. CELLS AND TISSUES
3. PHYSIOLOGICAL ACTIVITIES
4. REPRODUCTION
5. IMPORTANCE OF PLANTS

Immediately you know that the chapter discusses 1) the parts of plants, 2) cells and tissues that are part of a plant's structure, 3) the physiological activities that would probably tell how plants maintain life and grow, 4) the reproductive processes of plants, and 5) why plants are important. Thus, within just a few moments, you have clearly in mind the kinds of information you would expect to find in the five major parts of the chapter.

Assume that you are going to study material about Brazil. What would you learn by finding these main headings:

1. LOCATION IN SOUTH AMERICA
2. HISTORICAL PERSPECTIVES
3. CLIMATE AND RESOURCES
4. IMPORTS-EXPORTS
5. IMPORTANCE IN THE TWENTIETH CENTURY

Often the information that a chapter in a text or a long article in a reference book gives about a main heading is divided into sections. Each section is labeled with a word or group of words that is called a subheading. For example, in the discussion that a chapter on plants gives about the main heading PARTS OF PLANTS, you might find these subheadings: *Roots, Stems, Leaves, Flowers.* Now you have more specific knowledge about the parts of plants.

Whenever you come to a subheading as you are studying, first think of a question that you expect the material in the section to answer or that the subheading itself suggests to you. For example, the subheading *Roots* may raise this question in your mind: *How is the root important to the plant?* After formulating a question, read the section itself, keeping your question in mind so that you will be helped to understand and remember much of what the section says. Sometimes the first question you think of may not be a good one, but if that happens, you will soon think of a better question as you begin to read the section.

Suppose that your assignment is to study a chapter titled THE ROARING TWENTIES. In the discussion that follows that main heading, you find these subheadings: *Economics of the Era; Industrial Change; Prohibition, a Social Issue; Fashions and Life-Style.* The following questions would be good ones to keep in mind as you read the section that comes under each subheading:

1. *Was the country in a good economic position?*
2. *How was industry changing?*
3. *Why did some people favor prohibition?*
4. *How did fashions reflect the life-style?*

If you were researching information about GOLD, what questions could you develop from the following subheadings?

1. *Major Mine Locations*
2. *Uses of Gold*
3. *Determining Value*
4. *Importance in World Economics*

Often as you study, you will want to make notes that you can look over later to help you recall much of what the section says. In making such notes, be sure to do these things:

1. Make notes on only those points that appear to give answers to your questions.
2. Write enough in each note so that it will help you recall what the section said about the point to which the note refers.
3. Try to write each note in your own words, but make sure that it doesn't change the meaning that the section gives.
4. Do not write a note that you do not understand.

The following is the information given about a main heading, SKI-ING, in an article about winter sports. Obtain an overview of the information by reading the subheadings; then formulate a question for each section, write the question, and make notes that will help you remember the answer to your question.

Popularity of Skiing. Skiing became a popular sport in Norway in the mid-1800's. The first official competition recorded was held in Norway in 1862. At about the time skiing was growing in popularity in Scandinavian countries, it was brought to the United States. In 1904, the National Ski Association was formed in Michigan. The third winter Olympic Games at Lake Placid, New York, in 1932, helped increase the interest in skiing.

Today skiing is a very popular winter sport that is enjoyed by millions the world over. Skiing affords an excellent opportunity for people to enjoy the out-of-doors. Ski resorts can be found in mountain areas in many parts of the world.

Equipment. It is imperative that properly fitted and functioning equipment is used. Perhaps the most important pieces of equipment are the boots and the bindings. Boots may be made of leather or synthetic materials. They should fit snugly, particularly around the ankles and the heels. Bindings are of various designs, and most of them have built-in safety devices. These bindings are set to release the boot from the ski whenever any lateral or unusual motion of the boot occurs. Proper releases help the skier avoid serious accidents.

Skis may be made of metal, wood, or fiber glass. The length of the skis used by an individual depends on his or her height and weight and the type of skiing the person plans to do.

Tapered poles of aluminum, fiber glass, or wood, with baskets located slightly above the bottoms of the poles, are carried by the skier to aid in balancing, maneuvering, and increasing speed. The basket prevents the pole from sinking too deeply into the snow.

Warm, insulated clothing is necessary for comfort and to prevent frostbite. Thermal underclothing and "layered" clothing are preferred by skiers. Layers of clothing provide insulation against the cold. Gloves or mittens, caps, and goggles are essential pieces of equipment.

Types of Skiing. Downhill skiing and cross-country skiing are by far the most popular types of skiing for pleasure. Competitive skiing is growing in popularity and includes downhill racing, slalom, giant slalom, and ski jumping.

In downhill racing skiers start at the top of a slope and ski down the fastest way possible. Slalom is downhill racing against time between gates (pairs of bamboo poles with flags) that are placed strategically on a slope. Skiers must weave between the gates during a descent. Giant slalom is similar to slalom racing, but the course is much longer and the gates are farther apart.

To many ski jumping is the most fascinating of skiing events. Jumpers speed down an elevated trestle and then soar through the air for several hundred feet before landing on the slope below. In competition a jump is judged not only on the distance of the jump but also on the style and balance of the skier and the proximity of his skis to each other on landing.

If one of your questions was *What equipment is needed for skiing?* you might have written notes similar to the following:

1. Boots of leather or synthetic material. Must fit snugly.
2. Bindings with safety devices to protect skier.
3. Skis of metal, wood, or fiber glass.
4. Tapered steel, aluminum, or wooden poles with baskets.
5. Clothing — thermal and layered.
6. Gloves or mittens, caps, and goggles.

Do the notes that you made about each section answer the question you had formulated?

In addition to a strategy for studying printed material, effective study habits also include preparation for study. In order to study effectively, you must have a period of time in which you will be uninterrupted. You should have all necessary materials available, including books, paper, and pencils. You should give yourself enough time to do the job completely and not feel rushed by another commitment. The key to effective study is to avoid interrupting your train of thought once you have begun to work.

Discussion

Help your class answer these questions:

1. How can you quickly get an overview of information?
2. Why is an overview important?
3. What questions did you think of to keep in mind for reading the sections that go with the subheadings about GOLD on page 246?
4. What things should you be sure to do as you make notes about information that you want to remember?
5. What questions did you use for reading each section in the article about skiing? What was your answer to each question?
6. How should you prepare to study?

On your own

In an article about PHOTOGRAPHY you find the subheadings given below. What question might you expect the section under each subheading to answer? On a sheet of paper write a question for each subheading.

1. *Types of Cameras*
2. *Composing Pictures*
3. *Artificial Lighting*
4. *Developing Film*

As you study the following information, use the suggestions that this lesson has given. On a sheet of paper write 1) a question to keep in mind as you read the section that goes with each subheading and 2) notes to help you recall the information in each section.

The Origin of Acupuncture. For thousands of years the Chinese have practiced a method of medical treatment called acupuncture. While the exact origins of this practice are unknown, legend has it that a Chinese emperor long ago discovered that soldiers wounded by arrows recovered from illnesses in other parts of their bodies. About 2500 B.C. the first text on acupuncture described the two forces of energy within the body — *yin* (a negative force) and *yang* (a positive force). Internal illnesses were thought to result from an imbalance between the negative and positive forces in the body. Over the years acupuncture has been used to treat bodily malfunctions, such as asthma, headaches, and insomnia, but it is now most widely used as an anesthesia.

Acupuncture Method. The art of acupuncture is based on twelve meridians in the body, each associated with an organ, such as the heart, or with a bodily function, such as respiration. Each meridian is a pathway in which *yin* and *yang* flow. Along these meridians are points at which needles may be inserted to restore the balance of *yin* and *yang*. Originally there were thought to be about 300 points, but modern charts indicate more than 1,000 points where needles may be inserted.

Acceptance of Acupuncture. The Chinese claim some definite advantages to acupuncture anesthesia. It is safe, there is no change in the level of body fluids in a patient, and there are no postoperative effects, such as nausea. Acupuncture has gained some acceptance in England, France, Germany, and Russia. Medical personnel in the United States have generally rejected acupuncture because the insertion points do not seem to relate to what is known about the body's nervous system. The Chinese acknowledge that fact and can offer no explanation. They use acupuncture because they feel it works.

Checking your work

If you are asked to do so, read aloud the questions you wrote for the subheadings about PHOTOGRAPHY. Listen while others in your class read their questions. Do the same for the information about ACUPUNCTURE. Then compare the notes you made with those that your classmates made.

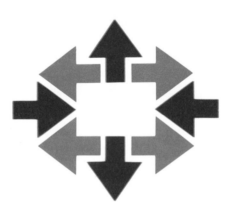

SANCHO

by J. Frank Dobie

In the mesquite (mĕs-kēt′) and white-brush country southward from San Antonio, Kerr had a little ranch on Esperanza (ĕs′pə-rän′zə) Creek. He owned several cow ponies and maybe forty cows and their offspring. Three or four acres of land, fenced in with brush and poles, grew corn, frijoles, watermelons, and calabazas[1] — except when a drought was on.

Kerr's wife was a Mexican named María. They had no children. She was clean, thrifty, cheerful, always making pets of animals.

Late in the winter of 1877, while riding along San Miguel Creek, Kerr found one of his cows dead in a bog-hole. Beside the cow was a scrawny, mud-plastered, black-and-white paint bull calf less than a week old. It was too weak to trot; perhaps other cattle had saved it from the coyotes. Kerr pitched his rope over its head, drew it up across the saddle in front of him, carried it home, and turned it over to María.

She had raised many dogie calves, also colts captured from mustang mares. The first thing she did now was to pour milk from a bottle down the orphan's throat. With warm water she washed the caked mud off its body. But hand-raising a calf is no end of trouble.

María called the dogie Sancho, or "Pet." She was especially fond of Sancho, and he grew to be especially fond of her.

She would give him the shucks wrapped around tamales (tə-mä′lēz) to hold them together while they are being steamed. Then she began treating him to whole tamales, which are made of ground corn rolled around a core of chopped-up meat. Sancho seemed to like the meat as well as the corn. As everybody who has eaten them knows, true Mexican tamales are well seasoned with pepper. Sancho seemed to like the seasoning.

In southern Texas the little *chiltipiquin* (chēl′tĭ-pĭ-kēn′) peppers, red when ripe, grow wild in low, shaded places. Cattle never eat them,

---

[1] **calabazas** (kä-lä-bä′säz), squash.

leaving them for the wild turkeys, mockingbirds, and blue quail to pick off. In the early fall, wild turkeys used to gorge on them so avidly that their flesh became too peppery for most people to eat. The tamale diet gave Sancho not only a taste but a passion for the little red peppers growing under trees and bushes along Esperanza Creek; in fact, he became a kind of *chiltipiquin* addict. He would hunt for the peppers.

Furthermore, the tamales gave him a tooth for corn on the ear. The summer after he became a yearling, he began breaking through the brush fence that enclosed Kerr's corn patch. A forked stick had to be tied around his neck to prevent his getting through the fence. He had been branded and turned into a steer, but he was as strong as any young bull. Like many other pets, he was something of a nuisance. When he could not steal corn or was not humored with tamales, he was enormously contented with grass, mixed in summertime with the sweet mesquite beans. Now and then María gave him a lump of the brown *piloncillo* (pē-lôn-sē′yō) sugar, from Mexico, that was used throughout the border country.

Every night Sancho came to the ranch pen to sleep. His bed ground was near a certain mesquite tree just outside the gate. He spent hours every summer day in the shade of this mesquite. When it rained and other cattle drifted off, hunting fresh pasturage, Sancho stayed at home and drank at the well. Sancho was strictly domestic.

In the spring of 1880 Sancho was three years old and past, white of horn, and as blocky in shape as any long-legged Texas steer ever grew. Kerr's ranch lay in a vast unfenced range grazed by the Shiner brothers, with headquarters on the Frio River. That spring they had a contract to deliver three herds of steers, each to number twenty-five hundred head, in Wyoming. Kerr was helping the Shiners gather cattle and, along with various other ranchers, sold them what steers he had.

Sancho was included. One day late in March the Shiners road-branded him **7 Z** and put him in the first herd headed north. The other herds were to follow two or three days apart.

It was late afternoon before the herd got its final trimming and was shaped up for the long drive. It was watered and eased out on a prairie slope to bed down. But Sancho had no disposition to lie down — there. He wanted to go back to that mesquite just outside the pen gate at the Kerr place on the Esperanza where he had without variation slept every night since he had been weaned. Perhaps his appetite called for an evening tamale. He stood and roamed about on the south side of the herd. A dozen times during the night the men on guard had to drive him back. As reliefs were changed, word passed to keep an eye on that paint steer on the lower side.

When the herd started on, next morning, Sancho was at the tail end of it, often stopping and looking back. It took constant attention from one of the drag drivers to keep him moving. By the time the second night arrived, every hand in the outfit knew Sancho by name and sight — the stubbornest and gentlest steer of the lot. About dark, one of the men pitched a loop over his horns and staked him to a bush. This saved bothering with his persistent efforts to walk off.

Daily, when the herd was halted to graze, spreading out like a fan, the other steers eating their way northward, Sancho invariably pointed himself south. In his lazy way he grabbed many a mouthful of grass while the herd was moving. Finally, in some brush up on the Llano (lăn'ō), after ten days of trailing, he dodged into freedom. The next day one of the point men with the second Shiner herd saw a big paint steer walking south, rode out, read the 7 Z road brand on his left side, rounded him in, and set him traveling north again. Sancho became the chief drag animal of this herd. Somewhere north of the Colorado there was a run one night, and when morning came, Sancho was missing. The other steers had held together; probably Sancho had not run at all. But he was picked up again, by the third Shiner herd, which was coming on behind.

He took his accustomed place in the drag and continued to require special driving. He picked up in weight. He chewed his cud peacefully and slept soundly, but whenever he looked southward, which was often, he raised his head as if memory and expectation were stirring. The boys were all personally acquainted with him, and every night one of them would stake him. He never lunged against the rope as a wild cow brute would.

One day the cattle balked and milled at a bank-full river. "Rope old Sancho and lead him in," the boss ordered, "and we'll point the other cattle after him." Sancho led like a horse. The herd followed. As soon as he was released, he dropped back to the rear. After this, however, he was always led to the front when there was high water to cross.

The rains came right that spring, and grass came early. By the time the slow-traveling Shiner herds got into No Man's Land, beyond Red River, they were putting on tallow every day, and the sand-hill plums were turning ripe. Pausing now and then to pick a little of the fruit, Sancho's driver saw the pet steer following his example. Learning to eat *chiltipiquíns* on the Esperanza had made him experimental in foods.

Meantime the cattle were trailing, trailing, every day and Sunday too, in the direction of the North Star. For five hundred miles across Texas, counting the windings to find water and keep out of breaks, they had come. After getting into the Indian Territory, they snailed on across the Wichita, the South Canadian, the

North Canadian, and the Cimarron. On into Kansas they trailed and across the Arkansas, around Dodge City, cowboy capital of the world, out of Kansas into Nebraska, over the wide, wide Platte, past the roaring cow town of Ogallala, up the North Platte, under the Black Hills, and then against the Big Horn Mountains. For two thousand miles, making ten or twelve miles a day, the Shiner herds trailed.

When, finally, the dogies reached their new home in Wyoming, Sancho was still halting every now and then to sniff southward for a whiff of the Mexican Gulf. The farther he got away from home, the less he seemed to like the change. He had never felt frost in September before. The Mexican peppers on the Esperanza were red ripe now.

The Wyoming outfit received the cattle. Then for a week the Texas men helped brand C R on their long sides before turning them loose on the new range. When Sancho's time came to be branded in the chute, one of the Texans yelled out, "There goes my pet. Stamp that C R brand on him

good and deep." Another drag man said, "The line riders had better learn his tracks and watch for them."

And now the Shiner men turned south, taking back with them their saddle horses and chuck wagons — and leaving Sancho behind. They made good time, but a blue norther was flapping their slickers when they turned the remuda loose on the Frio River. After the Cowboys' Christmas Ball most of them settled down for a few weeks of winter sleep.

Spring comes early down on the Esperanza. The mesquites were all in new leaf with that green so fresh and tender that the color seems to emanate into the sky. Bluebonnets, pale pink Mexican primroses, and red phlox would soon sprinkle every open flat and draw. The prickly pear was ready to be studded with waxy blossoms and the white brush to be heavy with its own perfume. The windmill grass — "rooster's foot," as the vaqueros[2] call it — was crowding the tallowweed out in places. It was time for the spring

[2] **vaqueros** (vä-kâr′ōz), cowboys or herdsmen.

cow hunts and the putting up of herds for the annual drive north. The Shiners were at work.

"We were close to Kerr's cabin on Esperanza Creek," John Rigby told me, "when I looked across a pear flat and saw something that made me rub my eyes. I was riding with Joe Shiner, and we both stopped our horses."

"Do you see what I see?" John Rigby asked.

"Yes, but before I say, I'm going to read the brand," Joe Shiner answered.

They rode over. "You can hang me for a horse thief," John Rigby used to tell, "if it wasn't that Sancho paint steer, four year old now, the Shiner 7 Z road brand and the Wyoming C R range brand both showing on him as plain as boxcar letters."

The men rode on down to Kerr's.

"Yes," Kerr said, "old Sancho got in about six weeks ago. His hoofs were worn mighty nigh down to the hair, but he wasn't lame. I thought María was going out of her senses, she was so glad to see him. She actually hugged him, and she cried, and then she began feeding him hot tamales. She's made a batch of them nearly every day since, just to pet that steer. When she's not feeding him tamales, she's giving him *piloncillo*."

Sancho was slicking off and seemed mighty contented. He was coming up every night and sleeping at the gate, María said. She was nervous over the prospect of losing her pet, but Joe Shiner said that if that steer loved his home enough to walk back to it all the way from Wyoming, he wasn't going to drive him off again, even if he was putting up another herd for the C R owners.

As far as I can find out, old Sancho lived right there on the Esperanza, now and then getting a tamale, tickling his palate with chili peppers in season, and generally staying fat on mesquite grass, until he died a natural death. He was one of the walking Texas longhorns.

DISCUSSION

1. How did Sancho happen to become a pet? For what foods did Sancho develop an unusual taste?
2. Why did Sancho become especially well known to the men in the cattle drive to Wyoming? How did Sancho help in the cattle drive?
3. When did the Shiner men start the long drive? When did they reach Wyoming? Approximately when did they return home?

4. How long did Kerr say Sancho had been home? What may have been the reasons for Sancho's arriving home several weeks later than the drivers?

5. Do you think the Shiner men had reason to be frustrated with Sancho? How do you think they actually felt about him? Why do you think that?

6. Do you think Sancho's taste for tamales and peppers was the main reason that he loved his home so much? What makes you think as you do?

7. Do you think Sancho was just an unusual animal, or would all animals behave as he did in a similar situation?

AUTHOR

Renowned as a collector of Texas folklore and historian of the Southwest, J(ames) Frank Dobie was born in 1888 on a small ranch in Live Oak County, Texas, not far from the Mexican border. After graduating from Southwestern University, he earned a master's degree at Columbia and for many years was a professor of English at the University of Texas in Austin.

In his early thirties, Mr. Dobie left teaching for a year in order to manage a quarter-million-acre ranch owned by his uncle. There he lived and worked with cowboys, and it was through this experience that he was first made aware of the wealth of fascinating Southwest folktales and traditions of the range. After he returned to teaching, he also began to edit the publications of the Texas Folklore Society, for which he served as secretary and editor for over twenty years. As an author, he recorded hundreds of tales and incidents in a lively and informal style of writing which soon made him well known. His many books include *The Longhorns,* in which "Sancho" appeared, *Coronado's Children, Up the Trail from Texas, A Vaquero of the Brush Country,* and *The Mustangs.* He also wrote numerous stories and articles for leading magazines.

Mr. Dobie's work brought him countless awards and honors. One of his honorary degrees, from England's Cambridge University, was accompanied by a citation written in Latin which read in part, *"De bobus longicornibus quod ille non cognovit, inutile est alliis cognoscere"* — "What he doesn't know about longhorn cattle isn't worth knowing."

PHARAOH

TREASURE

by Robert Kraske

Storing wealth in a vault to protect it against thieves started long before the twentieth century; just how long before, it is difficult to say.

About 2600 B.C., when King Cheops (kē′ŏps) directed his royal architect to build a great pyramid and to place his burial chamber in its center, he had good reason for his order. For centuries, robbers had broken into the tombs of his royal ancestors and had made off with the treasures they held. Despite guards and watchmen who patrolled the crypts, robbers still managed to violate them.

Pharaoh (fâr′ō) Cheops was a man of enormous vanity, but he was not naïve. He realized that tomb robbing amounted to a profession among many of the craftsmen who built the tombs — with an assist from high government officials who, for a share of the treasure, were quite willing to rearrange the patrols of guards for the convenience of the robbers. Pharaoh also realized that the curses his ancestors had placed on persons violating the tombs did not deter them. These thieves would even steal statues of the very gods they worshiped! Their greed, Pharaoh realized, was stronger than their fear.

Consequently, this mightiest of all pharaohs demanded a monument that not only would surpass the crypts of any of his ancestors but would be impenetrable to those jackals, the tomb robbers.

Located five miles southwest of Cairo, the Great Pyramid of Cheops stands today as the largest vault ever constructed to guard the wealth of one man. So cleverly was it designed that it took robbers four hundred years to find its secret entrance.

The Great Pyramid qualifies as one of the world's all-time engineering marvels. Built of two and one-quarter million blocks of limestone and granite, it covers a thirteen-acre tract of desert sand, an area equivalent to ten football fields.

When Cheops first looked upon his completed tomb, the Great Pyramid measured 481 feet to the tip of its capstone and 755 feet — about the length of two and a half city blocks — along each of its four sides. (But erosion and the pilferings of later tomb builders reduced these measurements to today's 450-foot height and 746-foot sides.)

Astonishing about a structure of this bulk is the precision with which the Great Pyramid was made. The largest stone edifice in the world, Cheops is a perfect square. Centuries before the compass was invented, its builders aligned its four sides almost exactly north, south, east, and west. In 1925 the Survey Department of the Egyptian government found a maximum error of only one twelfth of a degree. The limestone blocks were hewn to a thickness that varies only one hundredth of an inch over an area of thirty-five square feet. Despite their size, they fit together with a tolerance that is less than half the width of a human hair.

Cheops came into power about 2600 B.C. and immediately ordered construction on his monument to begin. During nine months of the year, four thousand laborers worked on this stone colossus. But during the three-month-long flood season, when cultivation of the rice fields was suspended, as many as a hundred thousand men worked at one time.

The laborers were separated into gangs of eighteen to twenty men. Their only tools were hand tools — copper and stone chisels, dolerite hammers, and bronze saws with jeweled cutting edges. To cut a block of limestone, they chipped slots in the stone on the quarry floor, then inserted wood wedges into the slots. Dousing the wedges with water, they waited until the wood expanded and split the stone. Then they pried the block loose. The average weight of these blocks was two and a half tons, but some weighed as much as fifteen tons.

Each block was carefully measured and marked for placement in the growing pile of stone. Gangs chiseled in marks to identify the quarry from which a block was cut. They also chiseled in the name of the crew, like "Vigorous Gang" or "Enduring Gang." At least one gang, unimpressed with their god-king and the glory of his monument, chiseled unflattering remarks into the stone, like "How drunk is the king."

The pyramid builders had no block and tackle to lift the blocks. They used only log levers, rope, and sheer muscle power to ease the blocks onto log rollers or wooden sledges. The brute strength of the laborers also hauled these huge dead-weight blocks up ramps of earth and stone and slid, nudged, and fitted them into their proper place on the pyramid.

To insure the integrity of the tomb, the king's architect planned the burial chamber in the heart of the pyramid, 140 feet above the desert, with an ingenious system for sealing it against intruders for all time. The sealing system worked like this:

A funeral procession of chanting priests carried the mummified king up the Grand Gallery and placed him in a granite sarcophagus in the 34- by 17-foot burial chamber. Then, while still in the heart of the Great Pyramid, workmen released three enormous limestone plugs. The plugs slid down the 153-foot-long Grand Gallery and into the ascending corridor leading to the gallery.

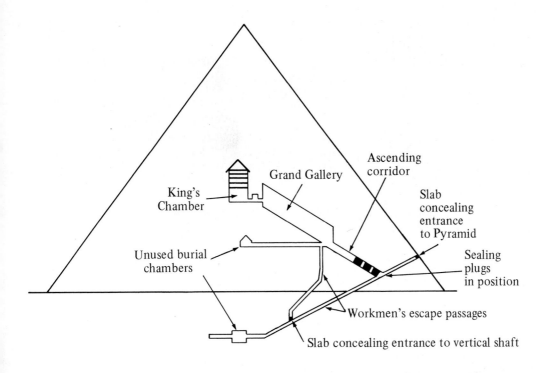

King's Chamber

Grand Gallery

Ascending corridor

Slab concealing entrance to Pyramid

Unused burial chambers

Sealing plugs in position

Workmen's escape passages

Slab concealing entrance to vertical shaft

With the huge blocks sealing the gallery from within, priests and workmen escaped down a shaft that connected with a corridor leading back up to the entrance in the outside wall of the pyramid. When the last priest stepped out of the pyramid, he closed a single stone slab on a pivot. This slab fit flush with the outer wall. When the slab was cemented shut, the entrance to the tomb was concealed in the sheer white-limestone wall. No one could detect the entrance slab from the thousands of other slabs that made up the Great Pyramid's north wall.

In the dark interior of the burial chamber, Cheops lay secure for all time, protected by a mass of stone that would intimidate the most arrogant and skillful of tomb robbers — or so everyone thought.

But hardly had the dust settled in the burial chamber when plots were hatched to rob the tomb. Perhaps it was inevitable. An entire population knew about the treasures that lay in the King's Chamber. Stonemasons, carpenters, water pourers, and thousands of other laborers had watched the tomb rise and knew its basic construction. They were quick to band together and make plans to get at this richest of prizes.

Unlike other tombs, however, which fell as soon as guards and officials could be safely bribed, Cheops stood secure against intruders for four centuries. The original laborers who were familiar with its design and the high priests who knew the location of its secret entrance had been long dead when robbers, chiseling into the north wall, broke into the corridor behind the slab that sealed the entrance. How they picked the precise spot to begin chiseling — whether it was by pure accident or through some knowledge of where the entrance was — is not known. But we can imagine their excitement as they raced down the passage, their cedarwood torches flickering in the darkness, then their cries of dismay as they saw the limestone plugs.

The royal architect would have been disappointed in what happened next. The plugs did not offer the deterrence he had counted on. The robbers began chiseling a long crawlway around them. Scenting treasure, they hammered feverishly on their copper chisels. Chips of stone flew. Sweat smarted their eyes. Then a chisel broke a hole in the stone. Dank air filled their nostrils — the Grand Gallery!

Now babbling and calling excitedly, they scrambled up the gallery and burst into the burial chamber. Their talk ceased as they held their torches high and gazed awe-struck at the polished red-granite walls of the King's Chamber.

What treasures did they find? What had Cheops brought with him into that chamber for aid and comfort in his journey into the afterlife?

The world will probably never know. Those unknown tomb robbers forty centuries ago made no inventory of their haul and, as far as is known, no records exist of the treasure that accompanied Cheops into his dark vault.

However, we can get a fair idea of the treasure the robbers found when we examine the treasure discovered in another tomb. The tomb of Pharaoh Tutankhamen (too′täng-kä′mən) was found intact only a half-century ago. Every other tomb in the Valley of the Kings had been plundered by 1000 B.C. Yet the tomb of King Tut remained undisturbed. An inscription carved into the rock over the entrance read, "Death will touch with his wings anyone who disturbs the pharaoh," but it's doubtful that Tut's curse had any effect on robbers.

Little is known about the boy-king Tutankhamen. The son-in-law of Queen Nefertiti, he began his reign about 1361 B.C. He was ten years old. He married a girl twelve years old and died at age nineteen.

Even his name was unknown to Egyptologists until 1906 when a goblet bearing his name was unearthed near Thebes in the Valley of the Kings. Later, when a British archaeologist named Howard Carter heard of the goblet, he took as his personal quest the discovery of the tomb of this mysterious king of Egypt's past.

Carter spent six years in the Valley of the Kings searching for the tomb. He crisscrossed the valley with trenches and once came within a few feet of the entrance. Then, on November 25, 1922, he found it. Holding a lantern, he stepped into the tomb. In the darkness, he saw "strange animals, statues, and gold — everywhere the glint of gold!"

The discovery of Tutankhamen's tomb was one of the most important archaeological finds of all time. For eight years after he opened the tomb, Carter worked with a crew of assistants to catalogue over two thousand objects buried with the boy-king. Among these objects were an ivory game board, a gilt chest of jewels, sacred objects such as scarabs and amulets, a chest of linens, two dismantled gilded chariots, a folding camp bed, a wood bust of Tutankhamen adorned with a necklace and earrings, a throne sheathed with gold and inlaid with colored-glass jewels and semiprecious stones, gold and iron daggers, alabaster vases that once held oil to groom the king, a six-foot-long gilded statue of a wooden lioness, a black varnished wood statue of Tut adorned with a gold collar, a gold armchair trimmed with ebony and ivory, royal scepters, and a toy box and paint set from Tut's childhood.

But the richest find was Tut's mummy itself. Carter found the king still wrapped in linen windings in the inner box of a series of boxes that fitted closely together, as Carter said, "like a nest of Chinese boxes. Each box or coffin was constructed in the shape of the king with a carving of his face wearing a crown. The four outer cases were made of gilded wood. Then came a sculptured stone sarcophagus. Next came three inlaid coffins, the innermost of which weighed over a ton of solid gold. The funeral mask on this box was of beaten gold encrusted with lapis lazuli, carnelian, and turquoise."

These treasures came from the tomb of a king who had neither the prestige nor the wealth of Egypt's mightiest pharaoh thirteen centuries

The funeral mask that covered the head and shoulders of Tutankhamen's mummy is of beaten gold inlaid with semiprecious stones and colored glass paste. Scholars consider the mask to be an exact likeness of the young pharaoh.

before. What fabulous treasure was buried with Cheops we can only surmise. It's unlikely, however, that a greater hoard of wealth has ever been found by robbers at one place and at one time.

In later centuries, bands of Persians, Romans, and Arabs attacked the Great Pyramid of Cheops. In their search for treasure, they used everything from battering-rams to gunpowder. But they found nothing. Those first unknown robbers had found a way into the greatest vault ever constructed by man and had taken every bit of the treasure.

DISCUSSION

1. For what purpose was the Great Pyramid of Cheops built?
2. Why is the Great Pyramid an engineering marvel?
3. How long did Cheops's tomb remain safe from robbers?
4. Why is it likely that the riches stolen from the Great Pyramid were far more valuable than those buried with King Tut?
5. Why do you think Cheops's order to begin work on his pyramid was given just as soon as he became pharaoh?
6. Judging from the construction of the Great Pyramid, in what branches of knowledge do you think the ancient Egyptians were far advanced?
7. Why do you think animals were not used as beasts of burden in building the pyramid?
8. Why were treasures buried with the pharaohs? Judging from the kinds of objects found in Tut's tomb, what do you think the pharaohs expected life after death to be like?
9. Did the power of religion and government in ancient Egypt depend on love or fear? Why do you think as you do?
10. In Egyptian society as a whole, what value was placed on human life? Why do you think that?

The Tree

by Olivia E. Coolidge

He never knew who his father had been, and he could not perfectly remember his mother. He slept in no special corner of his own, but just where he could, most frequently in the workshop where the gardening tools were repaired. Now and then he was issued a loincloth, and he usually had enough left of the old one to tie a strip around his head against the sun. He was the least of all the slaves in Pharaoh's garden, and he did not even have a name. The women and children laughed at his queer shape and called him Monkey. The overseers said, "You, there!" or laid on with a stick. The other gardeners simply ignored him or kicked him aside like a dog when he got in their way.

During a great part of the year he worked at buckets, lifting water until his hands, calloused as they were, would mark the rope with blood. His whole back was seamed with welts from many beatings; and it might have appeared a marvel, if any man had cared to wonder at it,

that he could endure so much and live so long. If he had been set to work in the more beautiful parts of the garden, he would have been driven harder and might have died, as others did, in a year or two. Fortunately even the overseers were ashamed of him and used to place him near the stinking rubbish pits outside the wall of the garden, or in other hidden places, where for hours together they did not need to come. This had saved him, while in time a very special pride of his own had grown within him. Alone of all the slaves of Pharaoh, he owned a tree.

Egypt was a poor land for trees. The floods destroyed them, and the hot, dry time, when the earth cracked open, withered them away. So precious were they that no man might cut one, even on his own land, without asking permission to do so. The best trees were all imported and grew in rich men's gardens. Pharaoh's came by ship from Lebanon, or up the Red Sea from distant Punt and over the desert, with a train of water carriers to moisten their roots. A collar of solid gold would not have bought one, yet this meanest of the slaves in the garden nursed one he had some right to call his own.

It happened, while this slave was still a lad and had not yet been put to the heaviest labor, that the glorious mind of Pharaoh had conceived of a lake especially created for the pleasure of his wife. A boat of the finest cedarwood inlaid with gold should ride on it, in which twenty girls were to row and sing in chorus to delight the queen. A gay painted summerhouse on the shore must look over the water at masses of green beneath the cliffs of the western desert, mysteriously purple in the shades of the setting sun. These beautiful thoughts Pharaoh proclaimed from his gold throne in his hall of audience, wearing the blue crown and holding the glittering symbols of his divinity. These commands the chief minister heard, groveling on the floor before his king and god as was proper. These he proclaimed in his turn to the Master of Pharaoh's Boats, the Steward of Pharaoh's Summerhouses, the Director of Pharaoh's Pleasures, and all such people as were thought worthy to hear the good news from his exalted lips. Next, these gave audience to lesser persons, and they to others. In a little time extra slaves were set to make mattocks or baskets for the carrying of earth, while droves of wretched laborers were being herded into boats in the delta to join with those stationed at Thebes on the glorious work.

That was a bad time, and the slave always remembered it with a shudder. Indeed, his twisted shape was mainly due to carrying those heavy loads before he was grown. Many died, for besides the labor, there was sickness that spread like wildfire through the wretched temporary barracks, where at night the men had scarcely room to stretch full length upon the floor. Soon there was a gravedigger gang, for such people were not worth the trouble of embalming. Crowds of new slaves came in every month and died like flies, while a few became seasoned, only to collapse at last under the incessant toil. First a vast basin had to be hollowed and the earth carried out in baskets to spread on the banks or farther away. There were great boulders in this soil, some of which fifty men could hardly drag up the bank and off into the desert. Besides the lake, a canal must be constructed to bring water and to let it flow out again across the land. An island was made in the middle and, on the western bank, a series of hummocks so that the trees might rise toward the cliffs as Pharaoh's beautiful thoughts had imagined them. Long before the banks were ready, trees arrived and were laid by the

hundreds in temporary trenches, while the head gardeners inspected their watering and cursed the delay.

It was over at last, and the mud barracks knocked down, the rubbish and filth of the slave camp tidied away. Quick-growing bushes had been planted by thousands to clothe the slopes with green while the trees were young. Forget-me-nots, celandine, and other wild-flowers had been set out in masses by the water. By next year all traces of man's miseries would be smothered in a great fairyland of blossom.

Gangs of slaves who were no longer needed had been sent to the quarries, a dreadful fate which this one escaped only because he was considered too ill. When he did not die after all, they sent him staggering down to the lake where men were planting in groups of five — two digging holes, two carrying water, and one doing the skilled work. The trees were by now in poor condition, and it was considered better to discard a doubtful one than to be blamed for planting those which did not grow. As a matter of course, the importers had

supplied twice as many as would be required. Dead ones were thrown on a heap, whence they disappeared with the connivance of the overseers, who understood that the men must do some sort of cooking now and again. It was with this idea in mind that the slave, tugging one night at the brush pile, found himself with a tree in his hands which he felt sure could yet live.

His first thought was to throw it back and find another. His second was to plunge his nose deep among its branches and enjoy the smell. It was a cypress, which he had never before seen closely, since he and his gang had been planting peach trees in clumps along the shore. It came into his mind that if he could plant it, he might take pleasure in passing it from time to time. Outside the high wall of the palace garden was a small space, half-concealed by the belt of flowering shrubs screening the rubbish pits. It was on the far side of the path and very private. Yet, he thought, I can find excuses for coming here. He went down to the lakeside to fetch a bucket so that he could plant exactly as he had seen the gardeners do.

Later on, when he was set to watering the garden, he remembered the little tree only now and again. After a few months, he forgot it completely until the next growing season came to remind him. The tree was still there and had bright little tips to its branches, which were more beautifully scented than ever before. For the very first time he felt a sense of possession and liked it. Nobody will beat me, he thought, if I root you up and throw you away. Reflecting thus that its tender growth was by his permission, he began to feel an anxious pride, as a man does in his child. He formed the habit of looking at it daily and giving it water, while he calculated its growth in a twelve-month or wondered how tall it would be in several years.

It was not until seven growing seasons had passed by that an incident taught him that his tree was no longer a child but had become a god. That year there was sickness among the slaves of the palace, as was often the case in the outbuildings where lower servants lived seven or eight to a room. One day when the slave came to ask for his daily rations, he found, not the hag who usually cooked for him, but a youngish, shabby girl.

It was the custom of the stewards in Pharaoh's household to give the slaves their supplies at about the time of the full moon. Each had his measure of oil, his portion of onions or salt fish, and his small sack of grain. This went to the wives, who ground and baked and doled out with careful planning so that the ration might last until the moon was full again. If a slave had no woman, he gave up his food to the wife of another, who paid herself as a matter of course by pilfering from his stock. The wretched hag who fed this slave not only starved him but daily made him the target of her shrill abuse. It had become a penance to fetch his bread, which was doled out in ever smaller portions as his dumb endurance made the woman bold.

The slave slouched up to the doorway and extended his hand, while the girl with a sullen scowl on her pinched face put into it his miserable allotment. She was expecting to shrink away and scream an answer when he bullied her, but to her surprise, he took it with a heavy sigh and turned away. Starvation was preferable to jeers, he knew.

He was halfway across the yard when the girl came running after him. "Here!" she said abruptly and slipped into his hand another piece of bread.

He twisted it between his fingers slowly as he thought things out. "You will be beaten," he mumbled after a moment, staring at it as if it were some strange delicacy from Pharaoh's kitchen.

The girl shrugged in her sulky fashion. "Not today," said she, half-ashamed of her impulse and angry at being seen in public with this twisted mockery of a man. "The woman is far too sick to care." With that, she turned around and ran away.

She had shown him kindness, and she had bothered to answer when he spoke, and besides all this, there was the bread. He puzzled over his feelings while he chewed it slowly, exploring each mouthful with caution for lumps too hard for his teeth. By midday, he had come to the conclusion that he would offer her something, though this was easier said than done, since he had not even a small clay amulet of his own. After a great deal more thinking, he went very reluctantly and broke a beautiful, scented branch off his tree.

Nothing was private in the slave quarters. Since morning the girl had already endured a good deal in the way of remarks about her handsome new lover. If he had brought her a posy from the marshes, she might have thrown it out indignantly and sent him about his business without delay. Unfortunately, the branch was far too queer a present, and she took it, screeching with laughter, from door to door. By nightfall, it was common knowledge that he had broken a piece off one of Pharaoh's valuable trees.

The story did not reach the overseer until morning, but when it did, he took his stick and went to investigate. Now and then flowers were picked before they were quite faded. It was even possible, when fruit was gathered, to look occasionally another way. Trees, however, were Pharaoh's pride and must never be damaged. Besides, the slave should not have been near them in the course of his work.

The inquiry started with a beating that very soon induced the slave to confess his sins. "It was only a tree by the rubbish pits," cried he.

"There is no tree by the rubbish pits," retorted the overseer and laid on harder.

"Suppose we make him show us," one of the men who held the slave suggested good-naturedly. "He is really too stupid to explain clearly where he has been."

They let him get up and lead the way miserably to the little space beneath the bushes and the wall.

"Why, there is a tree here after all!" exclaimed the overseer. "This is quite extraordinary. I must ask the head gardener where he would like it, as there is no use leaving it in a place like this." He went away with his men after pointing out to the slave his daily allotment of work.

All day long the slave struggled sullenly with the buckets, aching in every limb, brooding wretchedly.

By now the tree had become more to him than a possession; it was something that made him a man, not a beast, in his secret heart. When evening came, he gathered a handful of berries he had heard his fellow slaves say were poisonous. Some overseers who pressed their men too hard had died mysteriously, but the slave was far too humble for any such ideas. His thought was to lie out under the tree that night and kill himself.

It was peaceful close to the wall, protected by the bushes and hearing the scented branches of his tree rustling above his head. He felt comforted by the whispering sound and did not eat the berries. "I will not actually be moved," the tree seemed to be saying. "You had better wait."

By a miracle, the very next morning there was another overseer, a fierce new broom with an even larger stick. "Because the old one has the sickness," shouted he, "is not a reason for you to slacken in your work."

There were more blows that week than usual, but the slave did not mind them. When he heard the old one was actually dead, he felt a fierce joy mixed with awe. "There is a powerful god in my tree," he muttered. "How strange I did not know it until it killed this man!"

Time passed quietly thenceforth, until the tree had grown so tall that the slave was constantly frightened lest the gardeners notice it. Fortunately the queen perceived it first from her boat of cedarwood, in which the girls were singing softly as they rowed about. "As I look around this paradise," said she to Pharaoh, "it is that single cypress by the distant white wall which pleases me most greatly. How perfectly you have placed it at the end of the gap the canal makes between the trees!"

A man who is also a god does not expect in one short lifetime to think all of his wondrous thoughts himself but has to delegate to his servants many of the treasures of his mind. Thus Pharaoh was pleased to accept this as part of his own plan, and he readily answered, "I am particularly happy that it gives you pleasure because it is in such details that I best express the exquisite perfection of my taste. I will send a gold ring to the chief among my gardeners for his care in fulfilling my desires."

After this, the tree grew freely, and no one hindered it. If the slave was seen watering it from time to time, it was considered a part of his duty and occasioned no remark. The little space between the tree and the wall was now his lair, and in it he had even accumulated a few possessions. He had found a ragged old cloak for cold nights, had laid a soft bed of rushes, and had brought in pretty pebbles or flowers to please his tree.

Like all gods, the tree was quite capricious. A certain charm might be good for many days if repeated to it exactly; yet eventually the charm wore out after some fashion, and the slave would get into trouble until he had changed his spell. He took to asking people about spells and became quite learned in them, so that now and then he was called upon for magic when people were ill. This brought him presents, which he faithfully buried by the tree, keeping back nothing. Better still, it earned him gratitude. Old slaves were not very common among the lower servants, and his fellows began to feel curiously proud of him for living on. Even the overseers became friendly in time and seldom did more than whistle their sticks through the air. "This work is too much for you," said the latest one quite kindly as he found him struggling with the bucket. "We must give you something light, in the kitchen perhaps, where there will be scraps better suited to your toothless gums."

"I like — this work," protested the old man, gasping, but the overseer only laughed a little as he moved away.

He took his trouble to the tree that night as usual, but for the first time for many years it did not comfort him. "You are too young," he muttered into its branches, "and do not know what it feels like when your strength begins to fail." The tree answered nothing, for there was not the slightest breeze, and no combination of spells would seem to produce one. At last when dawn came, the slave saw that his god despised him in its youthful strength and had cast him off completely. He scattered his rushes into the pit, folded his cloak, buried the bright stones under a covering of earth, and went away.

He was not the slightest use in the kitchen, where the chattering dazed him and the stuffy heat of the fires gave him headaches all day long. People were always pushing him aside to get at things behind him. The head chef openly pitied himself for being saddled with a man who was queer in the head. They let him try to sweep the floor but then said he was too old to carry the rubbish and sent a boy to take it out to the pits. At night they kindly gave him a very warm corner near the embers of the hateful fire, where he lay feeling stifled and sickened by the heavy smell of fats.

After a while their patience wore thin with him, and they found him a nuisance. "Stop poking around!" yelled the head chef crossly one day as he was trying to sweep.

The old man tottered to a corner and sat down, with his hands to his bursting temples, groaning.

"Phew!" said the head baker, taking up one of the little fans which were used to keep the fire glowing and trying to cool off his face. "I really never felt heat anything like this before."

"It's just as bad outside," said a boy staggering in with water. "The sky is a gray-blue color, and there is a queer ring around the sun."

"It is the end of the world!" cried a young barbarian sharply.

"Nonsense!" retorted the head chef, feeling that it was his duty to set a tone for the kitchen. "Once in my father's time there was a flood in heaven, so that water poured out of it for hours, turned his house to mud, and washed it away. Frogs descended, he said, with the water, but in a few days they died and stank. This was a marvel that started with a queer ring around the sun."

A slave looked up from a duck that he was turning on a spit above the flame. "That is only rain," he said with scorn. "In Troy, we have it often." He never let the kitchen forget that his father was king of a few miserable huts somewhere by the ocean to the north.

"I suppose it rains crocodiles in Troy!" said someone scornfully. It was long ago established in the kitchen that every story about Troy was to be taken as untrue.

One of the baker's boys, who was bringing over a fresh batch of cakes for frying, chose this moment to faint dead away and fell with a clatter, dropping the dough from his tray and collapsing on top of it.

The head baker burst into a wail. "It wants but half an hour to Pharaoh's dinner!" cried he in dismay. "Bring me some more quickly! Old fool in the corner, come here and clean up this mess!" He bustled about, sweat streaming from his forehead, and harried his underlings.

In the confusion of preparing Pharaoh's dinner, the kitchen was a turmoil. Carvers clamored for the meat, decorators snatched at the breadstuffs, beautifully dressed waiters rushed in and out, swearing horribly at the kitchen servants. Everyone was slipping and sweating in the terrible heat. When the meal was over, the slaves all straggled into the courtyard without touching the scraps that were their usual food. Even the water boy, who was famous for his appetite, declared himself revolted by the very idea of eating anything. They were content to fan themselves, dip head or hands in water, and stare exhausted at the leaden sky.

The old man, his throbbing head clutched in his hands, tottered off around the corner. For the first time since he had come to the kitchen, nobody bothered to ask where in the world he thought he was going. He went along the familiar path by the gardeners' quarters, where a few wretched women and children

stared listlessly after him, and passed out of the small side gate leading to the pits.

The tree was taller than ever and looked as though its young pride felt no concern with stunted, elderly things. He did not even venture to address a spell to it but sat down quietly, happy at least that there was no stupid chattering out here. The tree stood silent, and there was no conversation between them, as there once had been. "I planted you," he did say reproachfully after a long time, but if it stirred at all in answer, it was far too near the top for him to see.

It was getting very dark, and he ought to go back to the stuffy kitchen, where he would have to parry endless questions about where he had been. Before he went, he would say one spell, the first and simplest he had uttered, when long ago the spirit of the tree had revealed itself by slaying the overseer who threatened it. He crawled back into his lair and fumbled in the loose earth about him for his offerings of pretty stones. Then he turned himself onto his back and said the words, looking straight up into the darkness of the branches. After a moment, with the tiniest of sighs, the tree began to answer him.

It answered with a whisper, a stirring, a lashing, a rumble, a flash, and a roar. It whipped and bent to the storm as the heavens were opened and the water streamed down, as if from the overflowing of some heavenly Nile. Roofs were blown off in the slave quarters, and mud walls melted down to shapeless lumps. Pools of water extinguished the fires all over the kitchen. In Pharaoh's quarters, the god's own bed was hastily moved from under a drip. People huddled together in the torrents, shivering and wailing, while the children shrieked at the lightning flashes, and men spoke of the end of the world.

It was a terrible time, and yet it was quickly over. In the steaming damp of the following day, mud walls were rising again. Children were gathering palm leaves for roofing. Painters and workmen were busy repairing the damage to the solider parts of the house. On the second day, things were so nearly in order that the gardeners could take out their men to pick up torn branches and cut off battered flowers.

The tree by the rubbish pits had blown over. "That is a pity," said the chief gardener, "for this tree was one which Pharaoh placed himself. We must find another for this spot, but meanwhile, be sure you save the wood."

"There is an old man here," exclaimed one of the slaves who was nearest. "The tree is lying across him, and I think he is dead."

"What an extraordinary thing!" said the chief gardener, peering through the branches. "Does anybody know who he is?" Nobody did. "Well, I suppose you two will have to bury him somewhere."

"By the by," said the head chef four or five days later, "what became of the old dodderer who used to sweep round here? Does anybody know where he has got to?" Nobody did.

DISCUSSION

1. Why were trees especially precious in ancient Egypt? How did the slave acquire his tree? What did he do with it?
2. How did the overseer find out about the slave's tree?
3. What first made the slave believe that there was a god in his tree?
4. What happened to assure the slave that the tree would remain by the rubbish pits?
5. Why did the slave eventually receive better treatment? Was his life much different because of it? What makes you think as you do?
6. On his last visit to the tree, why do you think the slave repeated his very first spell, the one he had said before the death of the overseer?
7. What caused the cypress tree to appear sometimes to answer the slave's remarks and at other times to remain silent? At the end of the story why do you think the tree began its answer with "the tiniest of sighs"? Why was it significant that the tree's final answer became more and more violent?
8. Do you think the slave's spell at the end of the story worked in exactly the way that he had wanted? What makes you think as you do?
9. Why was it appropriate that the slave and the tree should die together?
10. Why was the tree so important to the slave?

AUTHOR

Olivia E. Coolidge grew up near London where she was born in 1908, the daughter of a noted English historian and newspaper columnist, Sir Robert Ensor. In her early teens she came to share her father's great interest in the classics, and she had mastered both Latin and Greek before entering college. After graduating from Oxford University, she taught for several years in Germany and England before coming to the United States. Although her trip was intended only as a visit, she has remained in this country ever since. She was a teacher at private schools here for eight years before her marriage in 1946 to Archibald Cary Coolidge.

Mrs. Coolidge had long been interested in writing for young people but did not have the time that writing requires until her retirement from the teaching profession. Her first book, published in 1949, was *Greek Myths.* It reflects her classical background as do some of her later books: *The Trojan War, Roman People, Caesar's Gallic War, Men of Athens, Lives of Famous Romans,* and *The King of Men.* But she has also written about other times and peoples as indicated by such titles as *Egyptian Adventures, Churchill and the History of Two World Wars, Makers of the Red Revolution, Legends of the North,* and *Tales of the Crusades.*

Her writing has been widely acclaimed and has established her reputation as a distinguished biographer and historian. Mrs. Coolidge's books are based on careful and extensive research, and in her wide reading she looks particularly for meaningful details of daily life which she can use to help re-create the atmosphere of the period she is writing about. Her ability to make her characters and their world seem vivid and real is evident in ''The Tree,'' one of the stories from the collection entitled *Egyptian Adventures,* which describes life in Egypt three thousand years ago.

The Coolidges live in a house on the grounds of a boys' school in Bethesda, Maryland, where Mr. Coolidge teaches. They have four children, all married, and several grandchildren.

FROM THE BOOKSHELF

ANNA, *by E. M. Almedingen*
This story, based on the life of the author's great-grandmother, presents an authentic picture of country life in czarist Russia.

BALLERINA, *by Nada Curcija-Prodanovic*
Lana, a Yugoslavian girl in the State Ballet School, suffers a tragic accident that threatens her future as a dancer.

AMERICAN WOMEN IN SPORTS, *by Phyllis Hollander*
The talent, determination, speed, and grace shown by fifty-two well-known sports heroines prove that women do belong in sports.

ZOOS OF TODAY, *by James R. Johnson*
The author presents an informative discussion and interesting anecdotes about the pros and cons of keeping animals, the life of a zoo keeper, and some famous zoos past and present.

SPEAK ROUGHLY TO YOUR LITTLE BOY, *edited by Myra Cohn Livingston*
A gifted poet has made a collection of parodies that are fun to read and to compare with their originals.

FLAMBARDS, *by K. M. Peyton*
In spite of the conflicts she must face, orphaned Christina finds love on an English estate where horses seem more important than people.

THE TAMARACK TREE, *by Betty Underwood*
Caught up in the controversies of education for women and the anti-slavery movement in the early 1800's, Bernadette Savard has to decide what direction she wants her own life to take.

THE PIGMAN, *by Paul Zindel*
Their friendship with a lonely old man who collects china pigs ends in a tragedy that forces two teen-agers to examine their actions.

Prisms

Contents

Prisms

Irene Hunt

Ordeal in Spring

The Civil War has been under way for nearly two years, and
Jethro Creighton has sadly watched relatives and friends go off to
fight — his brothers Tom and John; his cousin Eb, who grew up with
him; and the local schoolmaster, Shad Yale, who is almost like a
brother. All are in their late teens or early twenties, but Jeth is Matt
and Ellen Creighton's youngest son and not old enough to enlist.
Besides, his father is too ill to work the southern Illinois farm, so it is
up to Jeth and his older sister, Jenny, to raise crops to feed not only
their parents and themselves but also their brother John's wife,
Nancy, and her two small children. In the following excerpt from
the book Across Five Aprils, young Jethro suddenly finds himself
overtaken by the war and thrust onto a battlefield of his own.

The deserters came in droves. The Point Prospect campground was said to be swarming with soldiers who made forays on chicken coops, pigpens, and smokehouses where winter meat was hung. In the spring and summer, vegetable gardens, cornfields, and fruit orchards were robbed. No one dared to approach the camp. Even the U.S. agents from the cities upstate appeared to be in no hurry for a visit; it was known that the deserters carried their arms and that they were desperate. For a neighbor to have recognized a face among them might well have been sufficient reason for getting a bullet between the eyes; these men meant to take no chances with an informer.

The stories varied; some said there were a hundred men at Point Prospect; others put the number at nearer five hundred. In the early months of '63, the theft of food was their only crime against the community; by March, however, a killing took place.

There was a man known as Hig Phillips down in the southern part of the county, and the story came out that he had hired a substitute to go to war for him. That in itself was not uncommon; many others in the county had taken advantage of this method of dodging the draft, which in the spring of '63 included men from twenty up to the age of forty-five. Three hundred dollars was what it took. That was a lot of money, but once the substitute was found and the three hundred dollars paid, a man could sit back comfortably and yawn at the war news if he chose.

There were men who were forced to take advantage of this system of substitute-hiring because of serious illness in the home or the dependency of their motherless children. There was, however, no reason why Hig Phillips should have avoided the draft except that he was a lazy bachelor much favored by his mother, that he was fond of good food and a comfortable bed, and that he had been known to adhere to the opinion that fools could do the fighting while men of intelligence and property might take pleasure in the prospect of a long and easy life. He was not generally admired for these views, but that fact bothered him hardly at all.

Hardly at all, that is, until one moonless night a band of young men visited him — men who knew what gangrenous wounds were like, what marches through cold rain or blistering heat meant, while hunger gnawed at their stomachs or weakness from typhus or dysentery brought agony to every step; men who had seen the dead piled high on smoking battlefields and had come to believe that the soldier of two years had done his share, that the burden should now fall upon other shoulders.

Although there were many who held Hig Phillips in contempt, his murder was an act of lawlessness that terrorized the county. People realized that anything could be expected from a mob of undisciplined desperadoes. Nancy now heeded Ellen's advice and closed her house completely, bringing her stock up to Matt's barn and keeping her children in the comparative safety of their grandfather's home. Jenny was no longer allowed to drive alone to Hidalgo for the mail. No one ventured far away from home after nightfall, and no one ever went to bed with the full confidence of security. The fury of the abolitionists and the Copperheads was now taken over by the deserters.

One night in February of '63, as the family sat around the open fire, a wagon clattered down the road from the north and stopped in front of the house. Opening the door, Jethro saw three young men jump down from the wagon and stride up to the porch.

"Is this the home of Matthew Creighton?" one of them asked. Jethro noticed the crispness of the man's voice — an upstate voice, he thought.

"Yes, sir, my father's right here. Will you come indoors?"

They came inside with a great clatter of heavy boots. Jenny stood, wide-eyed, beside her father's chair; Nancy and Ellen held the small boys tightly in their arms. Matt tried to rise.

"Stay seated, sir. We're here to ask you a few questions." The young man who spoke threw back his coat to show his uniform and insignia. "We are representatives of the Federal Registrars; we are charged with hunting down deserters from the United States Army."

"Will you take chairs, gentlemen?" Matt said evenly, but Jethro noticed the sudden paleness of his father's face.

"Thank you, no. We are here to inquire if this is the home of Ebenezer Carron, Seventeenth Illinois Infantry, Army of Tennessee."

"It is. This has bin Eb's home since he was a lad of ten or so."

"Have you seen him lately?"

"Why, no. Him and my son Thomas left together for the Army in August of '61. My own boy was kilt at Pittsburg Landing; we ain't heered from Eb but once since then."

"You know the penalty for shielding a deserter from the United States Army?"

"I do. Air you tellin' me that Eb is a deserter?"

"His commanding officer has reason to believe that he is and that he has been making his way toward this part of the state — we assume toward his home."

Matt lifted a shaking hand and covered his eyes. Jenny glanced at him anxiously and then suddenly blazed out at the questioner.

"We haven't seen Eb. He's not here, and I'll thank you not to worry my father with more of this talk. If you want to look through this house —"

"We do, miss — this house and all other buildings around here."

Jenny grasped the kerosene lamp with a firm hand. "Jeth, you come with me. We'll show these soldiers through the house; they can hunt outside for themselves."

Her anger made Jenny a very grand lady, Jethro thought. He had never seen her more beautiful than she was that night, with her cheeks flaming and her eyes large and black with mixed anger and fear.

The soldiers grinned a little at one another and followed her and Jethro up to the sleeping rooms in the loft first and then down again to the kitchen and pantry where Jenny took down the big key to the smokehouse and handed it to one of the men.

"We lock the smokehouse these nights. It's true there are deserters in these parts, and there's thievin' around everywhere. But we're not shieldin' anyone. Go look in the smokehouse for yourselves; go through the barn, the grainery, everywhere you think someone might be hidin'. After that I would say you'd best go down to the Point Prospect campground. The talk is that there are plenty of deserters there."

The Federal Registrars looked uncomfortable.

"Yes, we've heard," one of them muttered.

Jenny nodded. "It is easier to come to a house and upset a sick old man and womenfolk. Nobody in this neighborhood thinks it's very healthy to go down to Point Prospect, but you sounded so brave just now — I thought you might want to do your duty down there."

The man who had done the questioning bowed mockingly before Jenny.

"We'll see to our duty, miss, and if we find Ebenezer Carron, we'll take him back with us — and you too maybe." He turned to Jethro. "Will you get a lantern, young man, and light us out back?"

Jethro took down the lantern that hung on the outside wall of the kitchen and started down the path toward the barn. The soldiers searched the place thoroughly and then walked back to their wagon. One of them spoke sternly to Jethro on the way.

"If this man Ebenezer Carron turns up, you know what to do?"

"No, sir."

"Then you'd better listen. You get word to the Office of the Federal Registrars in Chicago right away, telling them where the man is or expects to be. You fail to report him, and you and your family will be up to your necks in trouble. Do you understand?"

Jethro nodded briefly. He was deeply antagonized by these men, but he knew they were simply carrying out a job assigned to them. Anyway, he was glad when the wagon carried them away — to the north. Evidently they were not going down to the deserters' camp at Point Prospect, not that night anyway.

There was an early spring that year. By the first of March the weather was warm, and the higher fields were dry enough for plowing. Jethro carried a rifle with him when he went down to John's place to work. It was always possible that he might bring down some kind of wild game for the table or that he would have need to defend himself against a desperate man.

The field he plowed that day in early March was bordered on the east by dense woods, and Jethro became conscious that each time he approached the woods side of the field, the sharp, harsh call of a wild turkey would sound out with a strange kind of insistence — almost as if some stupid bird demanded that he stop and listen. Once when he halted his team and walked a little distance toward the woods, the calls came furiously, one after the other; then when he returned to his team and moved toward the west, they stopped until he had made the round of the field.

After several repetitions of this pattern, Jethro tethered his team and, taking up his rifle, walked into the woods. His heart beat fast as he walked, and his slim, brown hand clutching the rifle was wet with sweat. A neighbor, Ed Turner, was giving him a day's help in the field across the road, but Jethro chose not to call him although he felt he was taking a dangerous chance.

He walked slowly and carefully, pausing now and then to listen. The calls stopped for a while, and he was half convinced that they had actually come from a wild bird. He made no move for a few minutes, and they began again, softer now and more certainly coming from the throat of a man.

Jethro stood quite still. "Hello," he called finally. "What is it you want of me?"

There was no answer. Then the call came again, softly, insistently, from a clump of trees, one of which was a tremendous old oak — long since hollowed out, first by lightning and then by decay.

Jethro walked closer, his gun raised, and after a minute the human voice which he had been half expecting to hear called out to him.

"Put yore gun down, Jeth; I ain't aimin' to hurt ye. I didn't dast take the chancet of Ed Turner hearin' me call to ye."

"Who is it?" Jethro asked. "Come out and let me see your face."

Then a skeleton came out from among the trees. It was the skeleton of a Union soldier, though the uniform it wore was so ragged and filthy it was difficult to identify. The sunken cheeks were covered with a thin scattering of fuzz; the hair was lank and matted. It fell over the skeleton's forehead and down into its eyes. The boy stared at it without speaking.

"Jeth, you've growed past all believin'. I've bin watchin' you from fur off, and I couldn't git over it — how you've growed."

Then Jethro realized who it was. "Eb," he exclaimed in a voice hardly above a whisper. "It's Eb, ain't it?"

There was utter despair in the soldier's voice.

"Yes," he said, "I reckon it's Eb — what there's left of him."

For a few seconds Jethro forgot the Federal Registrars and the fact that not only the word which preceded Eb but also his method of announcing himself gave credence to the suspicion that he was a deserter. But for those first few seconds Jethro could only remember that this was Eb, a part of the family, the boy who had been close to Tom, the soldier who would have more vivid stories to tell of the war than ever a newspaper would be able to publish. He held out his hand.

"Eb, it's good — it's so good to see you. Pa and Ma will be —" he stopped suddenly. He noticed that Eb ignored his outstretched hand.

"Yore pa and ma will be scairt — that's what you mean, ain't it? Scairt fer themselves and ashamed of me." He paused for a second and then added defiantly, "I deserted, you know; I up and left Ol' Abe's Army of the United States."

Jethro could only stare at his cousin; he could find no words.

"Desertin' ain't a purty word to you, is it? Well, I done it — I don't jest know why. We'd had another skirmish, and there was dead boys that we had to bury the next day — and we'd bin licked agin. All at oncet I knowed I couldn't stand it no longer, and I jest up and left.

Oncet a man has left, he's done fer. I've bin a long time gittin' home, and now that I'm here, it ain't no comfert."

"Eb, couldn't you just come up to the house and see them for a few hours or so? Couldn't you have a good meal and get cleaned up and tell the folks all you know about Tom?"

"I caint. I could git 'em into awful trouble. Besides, they would prob'ly jest as soon not set eyes on the likes of me agin."

"But, Eb, if you can't come up to the house, what *did* you come for?"

Eb's face showed quick anger. "I come because I couldn't help myself, that's why. *You* don't know what it's like. There be things that air too terr'ble to talk about — and you want to see the fields where you used to be happy, you want to smell the good air of old Illinois so much that you fergit — you go crazy fer an hour or so — and then you don't dare go back."

He shivered and leaned back against a tree trunk as if just talking had taken more strength than he had to spend.

"Have you been down to the Point Prospect camp, Eb?" Jethro asked after a while.

"A couple days. It's worse than the war down there, with fellers afraid and gittin' meaner as they git more afraid. I didn't come back to be with soldiers anyway. I'm sick of soldiers, livin' and dead; I'm sick of all of 'em." He threw himself down on a thick padding of dead leaves and motioned Jethro to do the same.

"I want ye to tell me about 'em, Jeth — Uncle Matt and Aunt Ellen, Jenny . . ."

"You knew Pa had a heart attack; he's not been himself since. Ma's tolerable, and Jenny's fine. We do the work of the farm together, Jenny and me."

"And John and Shad — where air they? They jined up, didn't they?"

"Yes, John's in Tennessee under a general named Rosecrans. And Shad's in the East with the Army of the Potomac."

"How did you git the word about Tom?" Eb asked.

"Dan Lawrence was home on sick leave. His pa brought him over; he told us all about it."

"I was at Pittsburg Landing too, but I didn't know about Tom — not fer two or three days. I wanted to write, but somehow I couldn't do it. Tom and me had bin in swimmin' the day before the Rebs su'prised us; we was both of us in good spirits then, laughin' and carryin' on like we done in the old days back home. Somehow all the spirit in me has bin gone ever since. I could stand things as long as I had Tom along with me."

He ran his hand across his eyes as if to shut out a picture or a memory. "Tell me about little Jenny; is she still in love with Shad Yale?"

"More than ever, I guess. She writes to him a lot; he sets great store by her letters."

"He ought to. A man needs a girl's nice letters when he's sufferin' with the homesick."

Jethro studied Eb's sunken cheeks and dull eyes.

"How do you manage to eat, Eb?"

"I don't do it reg'lar, that's shore. I live off the land — steal a little, shoot me a rabbit or squirrel and cook 'em over a low fire late at night. It ain't good eatin', but nothin's good these days like it used to be."

Jethro's insides twisted in sympathy. "Are you hungry now, Eb?"

"I'm allus hungry. Ye git used to it after a while."

"Nancy fixed me some grub to bring to the field with me; I'll go get it for you."

He ran to the fencerow where he had left two pieces of bread and the cuts from a particularly tender haunch of beef that Nancy had wrapped in a white cloth for him. Ordinarily he would have eaten the snack by midafternoon, but Eb's wild-turkey calls had made him forget it. He returned to Eb minutes later with the food and a jug of water.

They sat together in the shadows, while Eb ate with an appetite that was like a hungry animal's.

"Eb, I've got to tell you," Jethro said quietly after a while. "The soldiers that call themselves the Federal Registrars was at the house lookin' for you last month."

Eb seemed to shrink within himself. He looked at his hands carefully, as if he really cared about inspecting them, and his mouth worked in a strange, convulsive grimace. He wouldn't look at Jethro when he finally spoke.

"I was an awful fool — at least you got a chancet in battle — maybe it's one in a hunderd, but it's a chancet. This way, I got none. There's no place on this earth fer me to go. Even the camps of deserters don't want fellers as weak and sick as I am; they let me know that quick at Point Prospect. I'll either freeze or starve — or else be ketched. I'd give jest about anythin' if I could walk back to my old outfit and pitch into the fightin' agin. A soldier don't have to feel ashamed."

Jethro sat for a while trying to think of some way out of the situation; it appeared more hopeless the more he thought. He was frightened — for the despairing man in front of him, for himself, and for his family. When he finally spoke, he tried hard to sound reassuring, but the pounding of his heart made his voice shake.

"Well, you stay here till we can think of somethin', Eb. I'm goin' to get you some quilts and things from Nancy's place; I'll bring you what grub I can lay hands on — I can always get eggs and a chicken for you. I think you'd best eat all you can and rest for a spell; we'll think of what's to be done when once you get a little stronger."

Eb looked up then. "You all but fool me into believin' that somethin' *kin* be done, Jeth, but I know better. You ner no one else kin help me now — not even Ol' Abe hisself."

Ol' Abe. Mr. Lincoln. Mr. President.

"I ought to go back to work, Eb."

"I guess so." Eb looked at him with a suggestion of a smile. "I caint git used to it — you bein' big enough to handle a team alone. You seem almost a man these days, Jeth; even yore hair ain't quite as yaller and curly as it used to be."

Jethro turned away. "I'll bring you a quilt from Nancy's before I go in for the night," he said shortly.

He walked back to his waiting team; there was still time to plow a dozen furrows before sunset — and to think.

He had faced sorrow and fear; he had felt a terrible emptiness the day Shadrach and John went away. But he had never been faced with the responsibility of making a fearful decision like the one confronting him now.

The authority of the law loomed big in his mind; he remembered, "You and your family will be up to your necks in trouble." Loyalty to his brother Tom and the thousands who had fought to the last ditch at Pittsburg Landing, at Antietam, Fredericksburg, and all the other places that were adding length to the long list — how could loyalty to these men be true if one were going to harbor and give comfort to a man who simply said, "I quit."

But, on the other hand, how did one feel at night if he awoke and remembered, "I'm the one that sent my cousin to his death." Eb was not a hero, certainly — not now anyway. People scorned the likes of Eb; sure, so did Jethro himself, and yet —

"How do I know what I'd be like if I was sick and scared and hopeless; how does any man know that ain't been there? We got to remember that Eb has been in battles for two years; maybe he's been a hero in them battles, and maybe to go on bein' a hero in a war that has no end in sight is too much to ask.... Sure, deep down in me, I want Eb to get out, to leave me free of feelin' that I'm doin' wrong to give him grub, or takin' the risk of keepin' it a secret that he's here. Yes, it would leave me free if he'd just move on — but no, it wouldn't. I ain't goin' to be free even if he moves on; I can't set down to a table and forget that someone sick as Eb looks to be is livin' off the land, that he's livin' scared like a wild animal that's bein' hunted.

"But what's it goin' to be like if more and more soldiers quit and go into the woods and leave the fight-in' to them that won't quit? What do you say to yourself when you remember that you fed and helped someone like Eb and maybe you get a letter from the East that Shad is killed and you see Jenny grievin', or that John is killed and Nancy and her little boys is left all alone — how do you feel when things like that come up?

"Of course, right now I could say to Pa, 'I leave it up to you' — and then what could he do? Why, he'd be caught in the same trap I'm in now; I'd wriggle out of it and leave the decidin' to a sick old man; I'd put him in the spot where any way he decided would be bad — hurtful to a man's conscience. No, there ain't an answer that's any plainer to an old man than it is to me."

Jethro lay awake in his room that night and wrestled with his problem. He wondered if, after all, it wouldn't be better to ask his father's advice, but he decided against that almost immediately and as firmly as he had rejected the idea that afternoon. What about Ed Turner, staunch and level-headed neighbor? No, Ed had two sons in the army; it wouldn't do to lay this responsibility upon Ed's shoulders. He thought of Eb's words, "You ner no one else kin help me now — not even Ol' Abe hisself."

Ol' Abe. Mr. Lincoln. Mr. President. Not even Mr. Lincoln himself!

294

Jethro turned restlessly in his bed. What if one put it up to Mr. Lincoln? What if one said, "I will abide by the word of him who is highest in this land"? But wasn't that word already known? Wasn't the word from the highest in the land just this: turn in deserters or there will be terrible trouble for you and your family?

But Mr. Lincoln was a man who looked at problems from all sides. Mr. Lincoln was not a faraway man like General McClellan or Senator Sumner or Secretary of State Seward. Mr. Lincoln had plowed fields in Illinois; he had thought of the problems men came up against; he was not ready to say, "Everything on this side of the line is right, and everything on the other side is wrong."

But would one dare? A nobody, a boy on a southern Illinois farm — would he dare? Mr. Lincoln held the highest office in the land; what would he think? Would it vex him that a boy from southern Illinois could be so bold? And anyway, how could one say it? What manner of words could one use so as not to be too forward, too lacking in respect toward the President of the United States?

Jeth realized he was not going to be able to go to sleep. There was a candle in his room; there was some ink and an old pen. He got up in the quiet of the night, lighted his

candle, and began to write on a piece of rough lined paper.

The next morning he hid sandwiches inside his coat, and at the barn he picked up a few eggs from the nests up in the loft. He dug an apple out of the straw in the apple-cave; no one would question that — a boy needed something to munch on in midmorning.

Eb was feeling a little better that morning. The quilts Jethro had taken from Nancy's house had made the long night more comfortable; he had washed himself in the creek and looked refreshed.

"You've brung me a feast, Jeth," he said gratefully.

They sat together for a while and talked in low voices.

"I'll be gittin' out in a day or so, Jeth. I caint hev you takin' all this risk."

"If you could go back to the army, you would, wouldn't you, Eb?"

"You're askin' a man if he had a chancet to live, would he take it. But I've told you, Jeth — a deserter caint go back. I'll be hunted the rest of my days — but the rest of my days ain't goin' to be too many."

Jethro said nothing, but as he plowed that morning, he made up his mind to send the letter. It was a frightening thing to do, but if one did nothing — well, that was frightening too. He knew Eb was not really planning to leave -- Eb was a lost and frightened boy, and there was nowhere else to go. For Jethro there was nothing to do but send the letter.

The plowshares needed sharpening, Jethro told his father that noon. Hadn't he better drive over to Hidalgo and get that work done? He'd pick up the mail, too, for themselves and for Ed Turner. Was that all right with his father?

Matt seldom questioned Jethro's decisions. The boy was doing a man's work; he was due the dignity accorded to a man. Matt assented to the trip readily, and Jethro, with the letter in his pocket, drove off down the road, his heart pounding with excitement.

In Hidalgo the old man who took care of the mail glanced sharply at Jethro when he noticed the inscription on the envelope. But he was a silent man with problems of his own; as long as a letter was properly stamped and addressed, it was no affair of his. Privately he thought that some people were allowing their young ones to become a little forward, but that was their concern. He threw Jethro's letter in a big bag that would be taken by wagon down to Olney that evening.

The long wait for an answer was interminable. Jethro tossed at night and wondered: had he done an impudent thing, had he laid himself open to trouble, had he been a fool to think that a boy of his age might act without the advice of his elders? Sometimes he got up and walked about his narrow room.

Eb's often reiterated "I'll be goin' on soon, Jeth; I won't be a burden to you much longer" became like the whippoorwill's cry — always the same and never ending. Jethro closed his ears to it, but the tensions within him mounted, and the necessity of providing for Eb's needs in strictest secrecy became a task that seemed to grow in magnitude as the days went by.

"If I could be sure I'm doin' the right thing," he would say to himself, as he watched the dark earth fall away from his plowshares. "If I could feel really set up about doin' a fine thing, but I don't know. Maybe I'm doin' somethin' terrible wrong; maybe the next time they come, the Federal Registrars will take me."

The letter came one noon when they were all seated at dinner. As so often happened, it was Ed Turner who brought the mail out from town. Jenny ran to the door, eager for a letter from Shadrach; Nancy's eyes pleaded for word from John.

But Ed held only one large envelope, and that was addressed to Jethro in a small, cramped handwriting done in very black ink. The envelope was postmarked Washington, D.C.

"Looks like purty important mail you're gittin', Jethro," Ed said quietly. His eyes were full of puzzled concern.

Jethro's head swam. This was the showdown; now all the family, Ed Turner, and soon the neighborhood would know everything. In the few seconds that passed before he opened the envelope, he wished with all his heart that he had not meddled in the affairs of a country at war, that he had let Eb work out his own problems, that he, Jethro, were still a sheltered young boy who did the tasks his father set for him and shunned the idea that he dare think for himself. He looked at the faces around him, and they spun in a strange mist of color — black eyes and blue eyes, gray hair and gold and black, pink cheeks and pale ones and weather-beaten brown ones.

He read the letter through, word for word, and while he read, there wasn't a sound in the house beyond the slight rustle of the page in the shaking hand that held it. When he was through, he held the letter out to Jenny, with a long sigh.

"You can read it out loud, Jenny."

Jenny stared at him as if he were a stranger; then she shook her head.

"It's your letter, Jeth; you'd best do the readin'."

He didn't know whether he could or not — there was a great pounding in his ears, and his breath was short — but he ran his hand across his eyes and swallowed hard. After the first few words, his voice grew steady, and he read the letter through without faltering.

Washington, March 14 1863

To Master Jethro Creighton
Hidalgo, Illinois

Dear Jethro;

Mr. Hay has called my attention to your letter, knowing as he does the place in my affection for boys of your age and the interest I have in letters coming from my home state of Illinois.

The problem which you describe is one, among so many others, that has troubled both my waking thoughts and those that intrude upon my sleep. The gravity of that problem has become of far-reaching significance and is one in which the authority of military regulations, the decline of moral responsibility, and the question of ordinary human compassion are so involved as to present a situation in which a solution becomes agonizingly difficult.

I had, however, made a decision relative to this problem only a few days before receiving your letter. There will be much criticism of that decision, but you will understand when I say that if it be a wrong one, I have then erred on the side of mercy.

The conditions of that decision are as follows: all soldiers improperly absent from their posts, who will report at certain points designated by local recruit offices by April 1, will be restored to their respective regiments without punishment except for forfeiture of pay and allowances for the period of their absence.

This information you may relay to the young man in question, and I pray that the remorse and despair which he has known since the time of his desertion will bring his better self to the cause for which so many of his young compatriots have laid down their lives.

May God bless you for the earnestness with which you have tried to seek out what is right; may He guide both of us in that search during the days ahead of us.

Yours very sincerely and respectfully,

A. Lincoln

DISCUSSION

1. Why had Eb deserted? How did he feel about his desertion? What did Eb think would eventually happen to him?

2. Why did Jethro decide not to tell his father about Eb? What was the reason Jethro did not go to Ed Turner for advice?

3. What conflicting feelings did Jethro have which made the situation in which he found himself seem so hopeless?

4. To whom did Jethro finally turn for help with his problem? Before seeking that help, what arguments for and against writing the letter did Jethro weigh in his mind?

5. When the reply to his letter came, what solution did it provide to Jethro's problem?

6. What did Jenny's conversation with the Federal Registrars tell you about her?

7. Do you think Eb might desert again? Why do you think that?

8. Jethro worried that President Lincoln would think him bold and impudent for having written the letter. Judging from Lincoln's reply, what do you think his feelings about Jethro were?

9. As you read this story, did you have greater sympathy for Jethro or for Eb? Why?

10. President Lincoln expected that the decision he had made would be criticized. Why do you think some people would oppose his decision? Why would others favor it? How do you feel about his decision?

11. Have you ever been in a situation where you had to make a choice between solving a difficult problem by yourself or turning to another person for help? If so, tell how you handled the situation and what your feelings were.

AUTHOR

Irene Hunt was born in 1907 near Newton, Illinois, on a farm which had been in her family for generations. She was educated at the Universities of Illinois, Minnesota, and Colorado and was a teacher for a great many years. Good books have always held excitement for her, and she feels strongly that young readers can gain important insights through well-written stories. It is not surprising, therefore, that she eventually decided to try her hand at writing. Her first book, published when she was fifty-seven, was the widely acclaimed *Across Five Aprils.*

As the setting of *Across Five Aprils* Miss Hunt used the southern Illinois farm on which she grew up. For the historical background of her novel she did long and careful research, but many of the situations and episodes in the book were suggested by family records and letters and by the stories told to her by her grandfather, who had been a boy of nine at the outbreak of the Civil War. *Across Five Aprils* won numerous awards and was sole runner-up for the 1965 Newbery Medal.

Miss Hunt's second book, *Up a Road Slowly,* received the Newbery Medal for 1967. Although it is based in part on personal recollections, the story is mainly fiction. Other books she has written are *A Trail of Apple Blossoms* and *No Promises in the Wind.*

Recently Miss Hunt gave up her position as Director of Language Arts in the schools of Cicero, Illinois, in order to have more time for writing and for traveling. She now lives in North Riverside, Illinois, and among her hobbies are music, cooking, and refinishing old furniture.

LINCOLN MONUMENT: WASHINGTON

LET'S GO SEE OLD ABE
SITTING IN THE MARBLE AND THE MOONLIGHT,
SITTING LONELY IN THE MARBLE AND THE MOONLIGHT,
QUIET FOR TEN THOUSAND CENTURIES, OLD ABE.
QUIET FOR A MILLION, MILLION YEARS.

QUIET —

AND YET A VOICE FOREVER
AGAINST THE
TIMELESS WALLS
OF TIME —
OLD ABE.

LANGSTON HUGHES

TAKE A DEEP BREATH

by Arthur C. Clarke

A long time ago I discovered that people who've never left Earth have certain fixed ideas about conditions in space. Everyone "knows," for example, that a man dies instantly and horribly when exposed to the vacuum that exists beyond the atmosphere. You'll find numerous gory descriptions of exploded space travelers in the popular literature, and I won't spoil your appetite by repeating them here. Many of those tales, indeed, are basically true. I've pulled men back through the air lock who were very poor advertisements for space flight.

Yet, at the same time, there are exceptions to every rule — even this one. I should know, for I learned the hard way.

We were on the last stages of building Communications Satellite Two; all the main units had been joined together, the living quarters had been pressurized, and the station had been given the slow spin around its axis that had restored the unfamiliar sensation of weight. I say "slow," but at its rim our two-hundred-foot-diameter wheel was turning at thirty miles an hour. We had, of course, no sense of motion, but the centrifugal force caused by this spin gave us about half the weight we would have possessed on Earth. That was enough to stop things from drifting around, yet not enough to make us feel uncomfortably sluggish after our weeks with no weight at all.

Four of us were sleeping in the small cylindrical cabin known as Bunkhouse Number 6 on the night that it happened. The bunkhouse was at the very rim of the station; if you imagine a bicycle wheel, with a string of sausages replacing the tire, you have a good idea of the layout. Bunkhouse Number 6 was one of these sausages, and we were slumbering peacefully inside it.

I was awakened by a sudden jolt which was not violent enough to cause me alarm but which did make me sit up and wonder what had happened. Anything unusual in a space station demands instant attention, so I reached for the intercom switch by my bed. "Hello, Central," I called. "What was that?"

There was no reply; the line was dead.

Now thoroughly alarmed, I jumped out of bed — and had an even bigger shock. *There was no gravity.* I shot up to the ceiling before I was able to grab a stanchion and bring myself to a halt, at the cost of a sprained wrist.

It was impossible for the entire station to have suddenly stopped rotating. There was only one answer; the failure of the intercom and, as I quickly discovered, of the lighting circuit as well forced us to face the appalling truth. We were no longer part of the station; our little cabin had somehow come adrift and had been slung off into space like a raindrop falling on a spinning flywheel.

There were no windows through which we could look out, but we were not in complete darkness, for the battery-powered emergency lights had come on. All the main air vents had closed automatically when the pressure dropped. For the time being, we could live in our own private atmosphere, even though it was not being renewed. Unfortunately, a steady whistling told us that the air we did have was escaping through a leak somewhere in the cabin.

There was no way of telling what had happened to the rest of the station. For all we knew, the whole structure might have come to pieces, and all our colleagues might be dead or in the same predicament as we — drifting through space in leaking cans of air. Our one slim hope was the possibility that we were the only castaways, that the rest of the station was intact and had been able to send a rescue team to find us. After all, we were receding at no more than thirty miles an hour, and a rocket scooter could catch up to us in minutes.

It actually took an hour, though without the evidence of my watch I should never have believed that it was so short a time. We were now gasping for breath, and the gauge on our single emergency oxygen tank had dropped to one division above zero.

The banging on the wall seemed like a signal from another world. We banged back vigorously, and a moment later a muffled voice called to us through the wall. Someone outside was lying with his space-suit helmet pressed against the metal, and his shouted words were reaching us by direct conduction. Not as clear as radio — but it worked.

The oxygen gauge crept slowly down to zero while we had our council of war. We would be dead before we could be towed back to the station; yet the rescue ship was only a few feet away from us, with its air lock already open. Our little problem was to cross that few feet — *without* space suits.

We made our plans carefully, rehearsing our actions in the full knowledge that there could be no repeat performance. Then we each took a deep, final swig of oxygen, flushing out our lungs. When we were all ready, I banged on the wall to give the signal to our friends waiting outside.

There was a series of short, staccato raps as the power tools got to work on the thin hull. We clung tightly to the stanchions, as far away as possible from the point of entry, knowing just what would happen. When it came, it was so sudden that the mind couldn't record the sequence of events. The cabin seemed to explode, and a great wind tugged at me. The last trace of air gushed from my lungs, through my already-opened mouth. And then — utter silence, and the stars shining through the gaping hole that led to life.

Believe me, I didn't stop to analyze my sensations. I think — though I can never be sure that it wasn't imagination — that my eyes were smarting, and there was a tingling feeling all over my body. And I felt very cold, perhaps because evaporation was already starting from my skin.

The only thing I can be certain of is that uncanny silence. It is never completely quiet in a space station, for there is always the sound of machinery or air pumps. But this was the absolute silence of the empty void, where there is no trace of air to carry sound.

Almost at once we launched ourselves out through the shattered wall, into the full blast of the sun. I was instantly blinded — but that didn't matter, because the men waiting in space suits grabbed me as soon as I emerged and hustled me into the air lock. And there, sound slowly returned as the air rushed in, and we remembered we could breathe again. The entire rescue, they told us later, had lasted just twenty seconds . . .

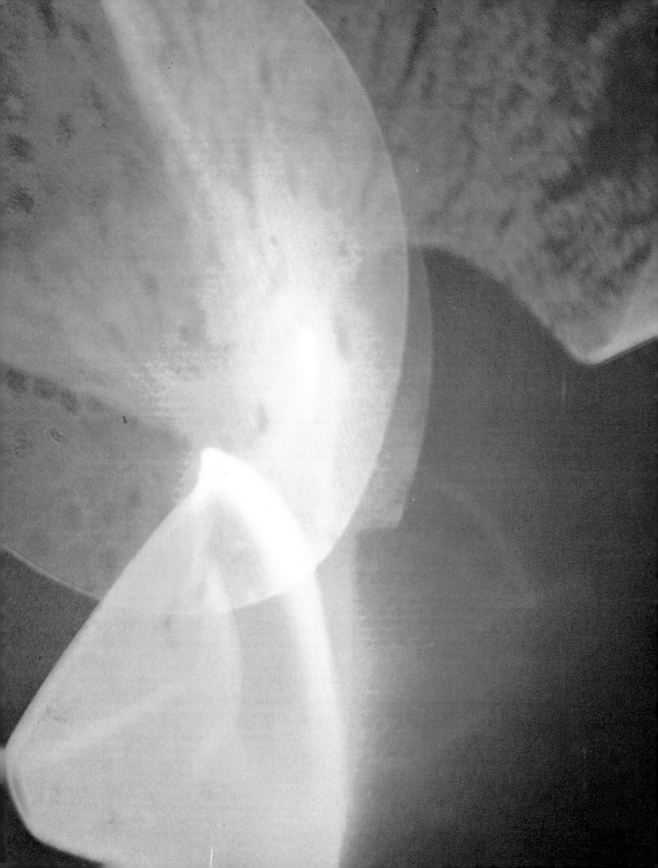

Well, we were the founding members of the Vacuum-Breathers' Club. Since then, at least a dozen other men have done the same thing, in similar emergencies. The record time in space is now two minutes; after that, the blood begins to form bubbles as it boils at body temperature, and those bubbles soon get to the heart.

In my case, there was only one aftereffect. For maybe a quarter of a minute I had been exposed to *real* sunlight, not the feeble stuff that filters down through the atmosphere of Earth. Breathing space didn't hurt me at all — but I got the worst dose of sunburn I've ever had in my life.

DISCUSSION

1. What was the reason Communications Satellite Two rotated? Why did it rotate at thirty miles per hour?
2. What three things convinced the narrator that his cabin had separated from the satellite?
3. Why was it impossible to rescue the men by towing them in the cabin back to the station?
4. Describe the rescue operation, and explain the purpose of the air lock.
5. Why do you think the men in the cabin had not been provided with space suits?
6. Before moving into the satellite cabin, the men had been weightless for several weeks. Where do you suppose they were living during those weeks and what were they doing?
7. Why do you think the narrator experienced a tingling feeling over all his body after the air rushed out of the cabin?
8. Do you think the near disaster was the result of an unavoidable accident or of poor planning on the part of those who designed and equipped the satellite? Give reasons for your answer. Can you think of precautions that you would take, if you were the commander of such a satellite, in order to insure the safety of the men? If so, what are they?

9. Do you think the events described in this story could actually happen? Why do you think as you do?
10. It took the rescuers an hour to reach the men, but to the narrator the period of waiting seemed very much longer. Have you ever been in a situation where you were worried or anxious about something and time passed unbelievably slowly? If so, describe the situation and your feelings.

AUTHOR

Arthur C. Clarke was born in Minehead, England, in 1917. Even as a child he was interested in science, and he constructed his first telescope at the age of thirteen. Not having money enough for college, in his late teens he became a government auditor. Because his job was not a demanding one, he had time to pursue his interest in science and to join the British Interplanetary Society, which was then a small group whose ideas were generally considered absurd.

While serving with the Royal Air Force during World War II, Mr. Clarke published numerous articles on electronics and also his first science-fiction stories. After the war, an ex-serviceman's grant enabled him to enroll at King's College from which he graduated in 1948 with First Class Honors in physics and mathematics. For two years he was an editor of the journal *Science Abstracts,* but since 1951 he has devoted most of his time to writing and to lecturing. When he is not traveling, he lives in Colombo on the island of Ceylon.

Mr. Clarke is one of the most successful and respected of today's writers of science fiction. Because of his scientific background, his writing has a sound factual basis which makes his fantasies seem believable to readers. Actually, however, nearly half of the more than forty books he has written are nonfiction works about space and underwater adventure. The sea is as fascinating to him as outer space, and skin diving and underwater photography are two of his main interests. Five million copies of his books have been sold in twenty languages, and he has contributed hundreds of articles and short stories to leading magazines.

The Greenwood Boys

by Willie Morris

Where did boys growing up in the 1940's find fun and excitement in a small Southern town? Here Willie Morris recalls a comical incident from his happy boyhood in Yazoo City, Mississippi.

There was something in the very air of a small town in the Deep South, something spooked-up and romantic, which did funny things to the imagination of its bright and resourceful boys. It had something to do with long and heavy afternoons with nothing doing, with rich slow evenings when the crickets scratched their legs and the frogs made delta music, with plain boredom, perhaps with an inherited tradition of making plots or playing practical jokes. I believe this hidden influence has something to do also with the Southern sense of fantasy and the absurd. We had to work our imaginations out on *something*, and the less austere, the better.

People rarely believe that a boy we knew ran all the way around a very large block in thirty seconds, hence breaking every track record in the world. Well, there is some truth to this story, but sometimes one has to lie to tell the truth, and I had better describe this event in a little more detail.

There was a pair of twins who lived in the town; their names were Paul and Pinky Posey. They looked so completely alike that at times even their parents could not tell them apart. They both had long red hair, they were identically bowlegged, they had the same floppy ears and squeaky voices, and they wore the same clothes, which usually consisted of blue jeans and white T-shirts, minus shoes. They even got warts in the same places at the same time. Paul was slightly more intelligent than Pinky, but that was not saying too much. The only way we could tell

310

them apart was that Pinky had four toes on his left foot, but seldom did anyone want to get close enough for a thorough examination.

One summer a group of five or six boys from Greenwood, a town about fifty miles up the river, came to Yazoo for a two-week visit with their rich relatives. They were extremely obnoxious visitors, and since Greenwood was a somewhat larger town, they lorded it over us, calling us country bumpkins and the like, and acting for all the world as if they were from Paris or London or Constantinople or the lost underwater island of Atlantis. I have met many snobs in my lifetime, but to date, these boys from Greenwood, Mississippi, still rank as the biggest.

One afternoon Spit McGee, Bubba Barrier, Billy Rhodes, and I were playing marbles in front of the Yazoo high school, just minding our own business, when the visitors from Greenwood walked by and decided to show us how superior they were. "Here come them Yankees from Greenwood," Spit said. "Wonder what they're gonna tell us *now?*" They proceeded to tell us how wide the main street was in their town and how big the houses were. "Why, the Yazoo River up there," one of them said, "is a lot cleaner than it is by the time it gets down here. Up there it's blue as can be. You can even see the gars wigglin' at the bottom. Down here it's all mud. You're gettin' all our dirt." They went on like this for a few minutes. Bubba and Spit and Billy Rhodes and I ignored them and concentrated on our marbles. Finally one of the Greenwood boys said, "And you see this big fellow right here? He can outrun anybody in this hick town." The object of this superlative was a tall hatchet-faced individual named Marsh. "That's true," Marsh said. "I can outrun anybody in town, and I can do it runnin' backwards!"

"Well, can you now?" Spit McGee suddenly exclaimed, jumping up from his game of marbles with such vengeance in his eye that I wondered what had gotten into him to break our icy silence in the face of the visitors' provocations. "Here's bettin' you five dollars and ten moonpies that we know somebody who can run around this-here block in thirty seconds, and it'll take your man at least three minutes to do it by Bubba Barrier's daddy's stopwatch."

"Thirty seconds to run around *this* block?" The leader of the Greenwood gang laughed. "That's impossible. Let's just walk around this-here block and see how big it is." So we all started from the front of the high school building, turned left on College Street, left on Calhoun, left again on Jackson, and a final left on Canal, arriving after a good eight or ten minutes' walk in front of the school again. It was not only a long block; it was the longest in town.

"Your man can't do it in thirty seconds," the Greenwood leader said.

"Ol' Marsh can do it in three minutes, though, and your man can't do it in five."

"Meet us right here in front of the school this time tomorrow," Spit McGee said, "and bring your five dollars and enough extra spendin' money for the moonpies."

"We'll be here," the boy said, "and we'll make you look mighty silly."

After they had left, we all turned on Spit. "Are you crazy?" Billy Rhodes shouted.

"Shut up!" Spit exclaimed. "Just leave it up to me. It's three thirty now. Y'all meet me right here at three tomorrow afternoon. Bubba, be sure and bring your daddy's stopwatch."

At three the next day, after a night of considerable worry, Bubba and Billy Rhodes and I showed up in front of the high school. There, on the front steps, was Spit McGee, and with him were Paul and Pinky Posey.

Spit was at fever pitch. "Bubba, you'll run the stopwatch. Paul, this here's the place you'll start runnin'. Pinky, you come with me. The rest of you don't do nothin' till I get back. And remember, Paul, once you turn the corner out of sight, you stay hid behind Mr. Frady's house till we come for you." With that, he and Pinky Posey started walking down the side-walk, in the opposite direction from the finish line for the race, and soon disappeared. Two or three minutes later Spit returned alone.

"Where's Pinky?" Billy Rhodes asked.

"He's hidin' in the shrubs in front of Miz Williams's house, just before he turns the corner for the home-stretch," Spit said mysteriously. It was just beginning to dawn on us what Spit was up to, but before we could question him as to particulars, we caught sight of the Greenwood boys coming our way.

"You mean this is the little twerp that can outrun Marsh?" The leader laughed when he saw Paul Posey, floppy ears and all, sitting on the steps of the school.

"Why, I could whip him *crawlin',*" Marsh said.

"We'll see about that," Spit said. "You run first," he added, pointing to the incorrigible Marsh. "Pick some-body from your side to run the stop-watch with Bubba Barrier so you'll know we ain't cheatin'."

Marsh lined up at the starting point, and when Spit shouted *Go,* he took off at a lightning pace. Soon he was out of sight and around the corner. We all sat nervously and waited. Billy Rhodes and I exchanged glances, while Paul Posey limbered up his bowlegs and did some exercises.

Finally, about two and a half min-utes later, the Greenwood runner came into sight at the opposite end of the block. "There he is!" our antago-nists yelled gleefully. "Man, can't he run?" Marsh approached the finish line, and as he did so, Bubba posted his time at three minutes, six seconds.

"Okay, Paul," Spit said. "Line up." Paul Posey went to the line, and with the shout *Go* he started out, legs churning, and disappeared around the first turn.

"That little twerp's so bowlegged he won't even finish," Marsh said.

"His bowlegs pick up steam after the first turn," Spit replied.

Now the Greenwood slickers sat down to wait for Paul's appearance around the final turn in the opposite direction three or four minutes hence. To their horror, in a mere ten seconds he appeared around that corner and headed toward the finish line.

"*Faster!*" Spit shouted. "*Speed it up!*" Billy Rhodes yelled. The redhead, his features contorted and weary, his hair waving in the breeze, raced in our direction and crossed the finish line. I counted four toes on the left foot.

"Thirty seconds even," Bubba judged, and the boy from Greenwood who had been checking the stopwatch, by now wordless and in a state of shock, agreed. As we all patted our man on the back, the Greenwood boys stood off by themselves, shaking their heads and whispering in astonishment.

"That'll be five dollars, plus fifty cents for ten moonpies," Spit said, extending his hand. Our enemies counted out the money and then departed, too defeated to offer their congratulations. They never had the gall to face us again.

When they were out of sight, Spit said, "Let's go." Considerably more respectful of Spit McGee than we had ever been, we turned the corner where Paul Posey had originally disappeared and walked to the back of Mr. Frady's house. Paul Posey was sitting nonchalantly on the back steps of the house. "Come on, Paul," Spit said. "Let's go eat some moonpies." Spit kept three dollars for himself and gave a dollar apiece to Paul and Pinky Posey.

DISCUSSION

1. Why were the boys from Greenwood unpopular?
2. What bet did Spit McGee make with the Greenwood boys? How did Spit manage to win the bet?
3. How does the opening paragraph of the story help to explain Spit McGee's thinking of his clever scheme?
4. Since it was Spit McGee who had made the bet and was responsible for trying to win it, why did the other Yazoo boys have "a night of considerable worry" before the race?

5. Why do you think the Greenwood boys' taunts were usually received by the Yazoo boys with "icy silence"? What do you suppose prompted Spit McGee to break that silence and propose the bet?

6. How long did it appear to take the Posey boy to run more than three-fourths of the way around the block? How long did it take Pinky Posey to run the homestretch? Why do you think the Greenwood boys did not become suspicious about the outcome of the race?

7. Do you feel that the Greenwood boys deserved the treatment they received? Why do you feel as you do?

8. What does the term "country bumpkin" mean? Who were called "country bumpkins" in this story? What does the term "city slicker" mean? Who could have been called "city slickers" in the story? Which group outsmarted the other? How would you explain the popularity of stories in which the "country bumpkin" or the underdog wins out?

AUTHOR

Born in 1934, Willie Morris left Yazoo City, Mississippi, at seventeen to attend the University of Texas. Following graduation, he studied at Oxford University as a Rhodes Scholar. When he returned from England in 1960, he went back to Texas and was the editor of a well-known newspaper, *The Texas Observer.* Several years later he moved with his wife and young son to New York City where he became editor in chief of *Harper's Magazine,* the oldest magazine in America.

"The Greenwood Boys" is an excerpt from Mr. Morris's book for young people, *Good Old Boy.* He is also the author of books for adults, and his stories and articles have appeared in various magazines.

BE KIND

. . . Be kind
To one who cannot prove
He was a boy
By pointing to a tree, a house or creek
And saying from behind a rutted cheek,
"It was this world I was born into.
My father carried off this hill on his shoe
Into the house.
My mother swept it out."

BILLY EDD WHEELER

THE HORSECATCHER

by Mari Sandoz

Young Elk slipped along just under the crest of the ridges. He moved as the wolf travels, where he would not be silhouetted against the sky and yet where he could search the wide slopes of prairie on both sides and vanish quickly in either direction if need be.

The young Indian was dressed to fade into the drying summer prairie, in a gray-figured calico trader's shirt, his braids wrapped in the calico too, his leggings and breechclout of deerskin, with sturdy Cheyenne moccasins and an extra pair tied to his back. He carried only a light bow and quiver, for around his waist was a thick coil of rope.

Cautiously the Cheyenne youth crept over a ridge to look at the small herds of wild horses dotting all the wide plain below him and as far westward as he could see. The closer ones grazed or stomped flies, the colts down sleeping or running in play, the far-off only small dark specks on the hazy summer prairie. As Young Elk looked from one herd

to another, searching, the horses suddenly swept together like dark leaves in a gust of wind and then spread over the plain, moving, running. They could not have seen him, he knew. It must have been a wolf, perhaps, or a dry-weather whirlwind or a rolling tumbleweed that frightened one horse to running, and so all went.

It must have been something small, perhaps only a rattlesnake's angry whirring, for the horses didn't run far. But they kept moving now, and Elk followed, edging in closer, creeping to one knoll after another, from weed to bush to washout, until he found the little herd he sought — mostly mares, gray and bay, with a black and a sorrel, and their colts. He was very careful now and swung around down a draw and ran to head them, so if he must follow a long time, he would not be in some far enemy country.

The young Indian kept well hidden, but in the excitement of this first chase afoot and alone, he ran too hard, without the judgment of a trained runner or the horse stalker's patience. Instead, his moccasins sang on the grass as though he could hope to outdistance any mustang before the next ridge. He ran until he was winded, and his side ached as from the hot thrust of a Kiowa lance. Torn with the pain, he recalled an old Cheyenne remedy. Stooping far over to his left side without bending a knee, he picked up a pebble, spit under it, and replaced the little white stone in its exact nest. He smiled to himself as the pain eased off.

With his side relieved a little, he decided to take a look over the next ridge. He wasn't far enough ahead of the little herd, his circling entirely too short, but he was pleased actually to see the colt that he had noticed two days ago on the way home with a party from a ceremonial. The colt was a very late one, just born then, and staggering to his feet; the mare, old and not worth a chase, Elk's father had said — not even the short chase required to capture such a poor one. But the wobbly black foal had fine long legs and on one side a white patch shaped like a bear reaching from the rump forward to the shoulder, a big white patch like a bear running, flat paws lifted in his hurry up the withers.

Now Elk had found the colt again, but already much stronger, playfully jumping and shying around the restless mares. He wished he had his brother Two Wolves along, and fast horses. They could easily catch the whole little bunch and be much safer than Elk alone, afoot. It was true that the horses were not worth the chase and the taming, particularly so far in dangerous country, yet Young Elk had been drawn to the new foal by something beyond the value for use or trade. Watching Bear Colt the day before yesterday, he had wanted, not to catch him, but to run beside him over prairie and hilltop in sun and in rain. There seemed something like a calling on the summer wind from the colt, a calling that made a gaiety and a softness within the breast of the young Cheyenne.

Overimpatient now that the colt was there before him, Elk started to crawl toward the resting horses. He moved carefully up along a low place, the grass as unstirred by his passing as from a snake's cautious glide. But he had no plan, even if he got close enough for an arrow. Either he had to tire the horses out or shoot the mare, if he could. Then the little foal would be easy to wear down by cutting across on him, as a wolf does a rabbit. But while Elk was trying to overcome his deep reluctance to any killing, a bird flew up from among the mares. It was the shining black bird that rides on horses and picks insects and nits out of the long, ensnaring manes. In return it was a good watcher, as

good a scout as any guarding a
Cheyenne village.

The bird burst into the air with a
sharp cry of alarm, and the horses
were off again, past the young Indian, the mares with their heads up,
manes and tails flying in a windy
cloud about them, their colts running at their flanks. Behind them
the stallion hurried the lagging old
mare, threatening to nip her rump if
the chase got hot. Her colt tried
hard to keep up, the clean white
side like a galloping bear.

Young Elk was angered by his
foolish impatience. But there was
nothing to do now except follow
out upon the open prairie where he
could be detected by enemies from
very far off, with nowhere to run.

For a while Elk made himself remember these enemies as he followed the little herd, slipping
through draws and gullies whenever he could. But he must keep the
horses moving, for therein lay his
vague hope of catching Bear Colt.
He must give them no rest and no
time to eat or to water night or day.
It would be hard, for man also liked
sleep, and Elk himself could sleep
as soundly as the badger in his
winter burrow. Unfortunately too,
an Indian needed to eat and drink
as much as the horses did, and the
little waterskin now bobbing at
Elk's belt and the bladder of pemmican that he had pilfered from his
mother's store would not last long.

Several times he tried to get the little herd headed back toward his home region, but the long runs around them always gave the horses a little rest. When he reappeared, the wily lead mare just swung out past him, and Young Elk had to run even harder to keep the herd from edging eastward to lower ground, where the creeks were not yet dry and where no lone pursuer could hope to keep them from watering.

By now, Elk was more than two sleeps of regular travel from where he had first found Bear Colt again, better than forty of the white man's miles. Surely the lead mare would be circling back northward soon, to her usual range. But, instead, she headed straight on, and all the young Indian could do was to try to stay close enough to keep the horses moving, keep them from feed or rest and particularly from water.

Around dusk the herd began to lag, and an excitement rose in Elk as he got his rope out to catch the little colt. But as he hurried to cut the distance, the rise of the late moon seemed to strengthen the horses, or perhaps it was the howling of the coyotes and wolves that echoed from ridge to ridge. Slowly the herd drew farther away, until they were only darkish blurs in the dusky moon. If they struck water, they could drink their fill before Elk could get there.

Elk was tired too, worn as a coyote that had been fleeing all day before a prairie fire; but as the moon hazed in a thin clouding, the hoofs ahead hurried faster, drawn by some far smell of water. Once more Elk had to run to scatter a cluster of dark shadows from a drying pond and do it without whoop or noise for enemy ears. But this time the herd did not start away, just watched a short distance off. Elk walked around the muddy bank to leave the disturbing man smell, yet the mares still tried to sneak in around him. He snatched the calico strips from his braids and tied them to rosebushes on the bank. But the horses still hung around in uneasy clots of darkness, always just out of reach of the Indian's rope; one trying to run around him on this side, one on the other, until he was driven to take the chance of a little fire. He threw together a narrow smudging row of twigs and leaves for a slow burning, one that would make little flame until he was well back in a dark draw, in case enemies were around.

Reluctantly, the mares started their faltering colts away from the smell of smoke, and once more Elk had to start too, stiff and worn out, when he could have been home asleep. He could have been deep in the soft bed robes instead of dozing as he ran over the dark, cactus-patched prairie, feeling ready to go down like a horse with a foot in a badger hole.

But the bear-marked colt drew Young Elk on, and he hoped that he was still following the right horses. As Elk hurried to keep the horses moving, he tried to detect the small dragging steps of a young colt; yet any would be worn and sleepy now, so he could only follow into the light of dawn. To keep himself awake as his worn moccasins felt out the rough ground, he began to talk softly to this Bear Colt, speaking the words to himself as in a dreaming.

"Let me catch you, tame you, care well for you," he murmured in his coaxing, gentling way. "We will have a softness in our breasts for each other. I will warm to the sight of you on the hillsides, and you will come to my call. If I am hurt, you will not leave me, and I shall pursue anyone who steals you to the ends of the horizon. We shall harm no living thing, but together we shall be one, a tall man-horse, or, better, a horse-man, for there will be much more of you, Bear Colt, my brother, than of me."

When the warm dawn cleared, the young Cheyenne found himself close to Bear Colt, the old mare a good whooping distance behind the straggling herd. The stallion, weary too, let her go to the failing colt, stumbling, but still too fast for the worn Elk. Once he took his rope down, but as though smelling the danger, the colt staggered on, growing stronger with the increasing day.

The sun rose and spread a shimmer of heat dance along the western horizon, crossed overhead, and still the young Indian plodded on, his legs really broken with fatigue, his feet bleeding from the cactus and brush and rock of the long chase. He was in strange country now: dry and gray, with little except snakes, lizards, and scrubby sagebrush. No sign of buffalo, not even an antelope running his curious semicircle or a rabbit hopping. By midafternoon Elk was still following the slow dust of the horses but more to be led out to water than to turn their direction or to do any capturing. There was little weight left in the water pouch, and since yesterday, he had been saving it for the suffering colt. For his own burning thirst he tried to work a pebble around in his mouth, but his stubborn tongue remained dry and swelling.

Then suddenly Young Elk had to realize that he was being trailed. Perhaps he had suspected it since he followed the faltering colt out on the bare, empty plain, with no draws, no gullies that might offer escape if enemies came. It was reckless, but the gaunted little foal had been going down every few steps, although still brave, springing up at every approach, still trying to overtake the old mare. Worn as the colt seemed, and taming, Young Elk was stumbling too, with shimmering heat burning his back and his eyes, his feet swollen and as awkward as stumps of wood.

There seemed to be no birds to fly up in warning, but Elk watched the sky for the eagle or the buzzard making a sudden turn. He finally saw something of the enemy himself — three Indians leading extra horses, coming along a far draw, very cautiously, perhaps unwilling to believe that one youth could be out here alone, afoot. He must be a decoy, a bait for an ambush.

Young Elk could not run now or even hope to hide. Besides, the colt was staggering and falling again, his legs crumpling; and this time Elk stood still and made his soft, gentling song in his parched throat. The gaunted colt clambered to his forelegs and then up; but instead of stumbling after the mare, he turned and came toward Elk, spraddle-legged, head down and swaying, the poor swollen tongue far out. He came to Elk as to one he had known a long time, as he had for two of his four days of life, his poor nose groping at the youth's clothing, trying to suck at the ragged shirttail. The young Indian laid his arm over the thin, bony neck and held the colt to him a moment, looking off the way the herd was straggling, knowing they must be following a

smell of water somewhere in the breaks standing bluish against the southwest. But behind him and his colt were the stalking men, and although the sun was lowering fast, the enemy would be upon them before dark, and by then the colt might die if he got no milk or even water. So Elk slipped his rope in a hackamore about the bony head and helped the colt into a little washout and dribbled the bit of water left in the skin pouch into his eager, uplifted mouth. Then he tied the sticks of legs together and laid the struggling colt out carefully, so he could not get his back downhill. Even the strongest horse can die in a few hours that way, Elk knew. Afterward, he looked carefully back over the empty plain before he slipped out to try to catch the loitering mare, plodding slowly after the rest now. He hurried almost to dropping and considered trying to halt her with an arrow; but he was not close enough for a sure shot with his little bow, and he would not wound her foolishly.

Then suddenly the three Indians were there but ahead of him, rising out of a canyon, riding for him across the sun-yellowed evening plain. Elk ran back toward the washout, for he must not let the Bear Colt die tied with a rope, die with his legs shamefully tied. It was a good white man's mile away, and only the thought of the colt got Young Elk there ahead of his enemies. He fell into the hole with tearing breath and red streaks before his eyes. The colt was alive and kicking feebly. Young Elk dug in under the bank, hacking at the soft earth with his knife as his pursuers stopped short of the washout, apparently still fearing a trap. They kept back and shot arrows into the hole, Kiowa and Comanche war arrows; and Elk returned several of them to hold the men away while he pushed the leg-tied colt into the hole and then backed in, too, as far as he could get.

By now the entire washout was in deep shadow, the arrow points glistening in the slanted sun as they came from both sides; and Elk knew that the warriors would certainly be in upon him with war clubs and knives before he could try to get away in the coming dusk. They would kill him; and then the colt, brave as the bear of courage on his side, would die, for no one would trouble with such a poor creature.

Angered by this thought, Young Elk set another of the arrows sticking around him to the bowstring, and then another and another, arcing them to fall near the washout, shooting fast, trying to make it seem there were several warriors here. At least the men up there wouldn't find him with their arrows like a porcupine's risen quills sticking foolishly unused all around him.

One arrow surely hit, for a man roared out an angry word, an angry Cheyenne word. It seemed they crept up around him in earnest now, for the arrows came in straighter. He squeezed in tight against the colt, the poor little creature sucking at his braid, at the torn cloth of his shirt, at his ear. It was so pitiful that the young Indian wanted to leap out, defy these enemies with his naked knife, kill them all to save the poor little spotted horse.

Then he heard more words from the fading light above him, awkward Kiowa words for "Give up!" and something perhaps intended as the same in Comanche and finally in clear Cheyenne. The sudden hope for Bear Colt made Young Elk reckless, made him forget that Cheyennes sometimes became part of the enemy both by capture and by marriage.

"I am Cheyenne!" Elk called out. "Of the Cut-finger People!"

There was a brief silence as of whispering and then a roar of laughter. "So you are a Cut-finger? More truly a crooked-tongue Kiowa son of a captive! Where is your party?"

"There is no party. I am alone — Young Elk, son of Elk River."

There was a snort of disbelief. "Elk River has then truly fathered a foolish one, to stray so far —"

"I was chasing a colt."

"Alone? Why should one not yet a warrior be permitted so far in enemy country?"

"It is our country too," Elk replied angrily; then he realized the danger of his hasty tongue. "It is true that the enemy — that others — are more often here," he had to admit in his fear for Bear Colt.

There was a mumbling in the dusk above to this, and finally one man crept nearer in the thickening dark before the moon's rise. He asked and answered many questions. He talked like a good Cheyenne, and because Young Elk had to get quick help for his colt, he finally let himself be coaxed out into the light of a little fire that the men shielded from the prairie with their blankets. He saw their faces, their accouterments. Plainly they were Cheyennes — three young men who had gone down southward afoot from Bent's Fort to locate some good horses, not mustangs but the larger ones, the Spanish horses of the Texas settlements.

"Our young friend is impatient with your long tongue," one of the men interrupted the speaker. "It seems he would say something."

Young Elk was hurt by the words that were spoken as of a boy; but he could not protest, not with the colt tied in the washout, perhaps already dead. They jumped down with a twist of burning sagebrush for light. The tough Bear Colt was alive, sucking at Elk's shirt as he untied the cramped legs. "It is this bear upon his side that I have been following," he tried to explain.

"The colt is a very poor and starving one to risk a life among enemies," the oldest of the Cheyennes said as he poured a little water over the blackened tongue and into the sucking mouth.

Young Elk made the sign of agreement as he drank sparingly and began to chew a little pemmican for the colt to suck, as he had heard could be done. And while he chewed, he moved his weary hand over the white bear patch, rubbing the sand away slowly, and more slowly, until he was asleep, bent over the colt. The three Cheyennes squatting around the tiny coals laughed a little, but gently.

DISCUSSION

1. Why did Young Elk seek out one particular herd?
2. Why did Elk keep circling the herd? What was Elk's purpose in keeping the herd moving?
3. Why was it dangerous for Elk to be so far out on the plain?
4. Why did the three warriors stop short of the washout instead of attacking immediately? Why did Elk shoot back the warriors' arrows as quickly as possible?
5. In what ways did Elk show his inexperience as a horsecatcher?
6. What did Elk do between the time he first sighted the warriors and the time they arrived near the washout? What does your answer suggest about the vastness and flatness of the plain?
7. Do you think Elk will be a good master? What passages or incidents in the story support your answer?
8. Do you think Elk was cruel to keep the horses from resting, eating, and drinking? Why do you think that?
9. Do you think Elk was foolish to risk his life in order to capture the colt? Why do you think as you do? Why do you think Elk had a special feeling for this particular colt?
10. Had Elk originally intended to go so far from home to capture the colt? How do you know? If Elk had been asked why he eventually went so far, what explanation might he have given? Have you ever been in a situation where you might have given the same explanation? If so, what were the circumstances?

AUTHOR

Mari Sandoz was born in Sheridan County in northwest Nebraska in 1901. Life was rugged in the Sand Hills cattle country, and as a youngster she not only was expected to do much of the housework but also was taught how to tend a trapline, catch minks and coyotes, and cure pelts. After winter blizzards she and her brother would dig the cattle out of enormous snow-drifts.

Her parents were Swiss immigrants, and she grew up speaking German and hearing French, Polish, and Czech as well as English, which she learned after she started school at the age of nine. When she had completed the eighth grade, she succeeded in passing a rural teachers' examination and for five years taught in rural schools in western Nebraska. Miss Sandoz later attended the University of Nebraska as a special student, but she did not graduate because she had not finished high school. At various times she was a proofreader, an editor, a researcher on Sioux Indians, and eventually director of research for the Nebraska State Historical Society. After 1935, writing became her principal occupation, but she was always interested in young people and especially young writers, and for many years she taught courses in the writing of short stories and novels.

Miss Sandoz said, "I began writing as soon as I learned to put letters together." A number of her early stories were published in the junior page of the Omaha *Daily News,* and her later stories and articles appeared in national magazines. Her first book was *Old Jules,* a biography of her hot-tempered, gun-toting pioneer father. It was published in 1935 and was awarded a $5,000 nonfiction prize by the Atlantic Monthly Press.

A colorful writer and a painstaking researcher, Miss Sandoz became one of America's leading regional historians. Today she is best known for her nonfiction and biographical works, and such books as *Old Jules, Crazy Horse,* and *Cheyenne Autumn* have been listed among the greatest stories written about the West. The selection you have just read is an excerpt from a short novel entitled *The Horsecatcher.* Other books Miss Sandoz wrote for young people are *The Battle of the Little Bighorn, Winter Thunder,* and *The Story Catcher.*

SKILL LESSON 5

EVALUATING AND JUDGING STATEMENTS

PART ONE

When you are reading informative material, you may come across STATEMENTS OF OPINION as well as STATEMENTS OF FACT. When informative material includes statements of opinion, it becomes necessary for you to recognize them as opinions. One way you can do this is through your own knowledge and experience. Which of these two statements is a statement of fact? Which is a statement of opinion?

1. Some apples are yellow.
2. Yellow apples are better than red apples.

Through your own experience you know that apples can be yellow. You can further verify sentence 1 by looking at different kinds of apples. A statement of opinion is not a fact that can be tested or verified. Sentence 2 is an example of a statement of opinion since it tells only how the writer feels about yellow apples and red apples.

Some statements of fact cannot be tested or verified through one's own knowledge and experience. Sometimes you must consult a reliable source, such as a dictionary or an encyclopedia, to test a statement of fact. The following sentences are statements of fact. Which one could be tested through personal knowledge and experience? Which one would have to be checked through some other source?

1. George Washington died in 1797.
2. This newspaper doesn't have any comics.

The first sentence states a fact that you would have to check by using a reference book. It happens that the statement is not true, but it is still a statement of fact, because it can be tested or verified. The second sentence is a statement of fact that you could easily check by looking through the pages of the newspaper.

Which of the following statements are fact and which are opinion?

1. We celebrate Independence Day on the fourth of July.
2. President Eisenhower was the thirty-second President of the United States.
3. The pollution problems of this country will be solved in the next twenty years.
4. Mr. Smith declared himself a candidate for Congress.
5. The Braves will win the series in four straight games.
6. You will never find a better bargain in suits than this one.
7. The mayor's speech was outstanding in every respect.
8. The mayor delivered his speech in just ten minutes.
9. This city would be a lot better off if there weren't so many speeding motorcycles.
10. There are many more motorcyclists in the city now than there were ten years ago.

Did you conclude that sentences 1, 2, 4, 8, and 10 are statements of fact? Sentences 3, 5, 6, 7, and 9 are statements of opinion not only because they express how the writers feel about certain things but also because there would be no easy way to test or verify those statements.

How could you test or verify each statement of fact (sentences 1, 2, 4, 8, and 10) — through your own knowledge and experience or by consulting reliable source materials?

Sometimes writers mix facts and opinions together, and it may be difficult for you to distinguish between the two. Consider, for example, the following paragraph:

1. A government spokesman today announced the latest figures on the cost of living. 2. As he had predicted earlier, the figures

remained very close to the figures announced in early summer. 3. However, it is generally felt that the figures should be going down, not just remaining the same. 4. The next figures are to be released at the end of the year. 5. If the figures at that time are no lower, the President will surely impose price controls. 6. Some members of Congress have expressed concern about the figures. 7. They, and probably others, are certain to demand price controls, should the cost-of-living figures remain high.

The writer starts out by stating certain facts that could be tested or verified — *that a government spokesman announced the latest cost-of-living figures, that they were very close to those announced earlier, and that the spokesman had predicted that the figures would remain about the same.* In the third sentence the writer is expressing an opinion. No explanation of *it is generally felt* is given in the paragraph and no explanation of *who* or *how many* feel that way. The third statement in the paragraph, then, is not one that could be easily verified, if at all. The fourth statement is again one of fact. It would be easy to find out if a decision has been made to *release new figures at the end of the year.* The fifth statement reverts to opinion. Unless the President has announced that he will impose price controls under certain conditions, there is no way of knowing that he will. This is pure opinion on the part of the writer. The sixth statement is one that could be tested or verified. It is a statement of fact, although the word *some* is not very exact. Again the seventh sentence reverts to opinion. It would be impossible for anyone to predict that certain members of Congress would demand price controls under the conditions set forth. Other factors may influence the situation. The writer is merely expressing what he *thinks* will happen. The word *probably* is a word that often signals a statement of opinion, further evidence that the final sentence is opinion, not fact.

Not all statements of opinion are lacking in value. In fact, there are times when the opinions of knowledgeable people can be very helpful. For example, if you were planning a trip to Mexico, the opinions of someone who has traveled in that country many times could help you know such things as what kind of clothing to take, what the most interesting places to visit are, and the names of some good but inexpensive restaurants. Gardeners often rely on the opinions of experts when they make decisions about the planting of trees, flowers, or vegetables in certain kinds of soils. You yourself would probably not be wrong in accepting the opinion of the librarian in deciding on which book about a particular subject would be most interesting and helpful. In the areas of advertising, newspaper accounts, and political speeches, however, you should read with some thought to statements of fact and statements of opinion in terms of accepting or rejecting what the writer is presenting.

Discussion

Help your class answer these questions:

1. How is a statement of opinion different from a statement of fact?
2. What are two ways in which you can test or verify a statement of fact?
3. Which way of testing or verifying a statement of fact did you decide on for sentences 1, 2, 4, 8, and 10 on page 331?
4. How may statements of opinion be helpful?

PART TWO

Although part of a statement may contain a fact, in the other part of the sentence the writer may make an assumption that is not correct on the basis of the fact. In the sentence "It's getting cloudy, so it's surely going to rain," a fact is stated: "It's getting cloudy." On the basis of that fact an assumption is made: "it's surely going to rain." From your own experience, does it always rain when it gets cloudy? Haven't you seen many cloudy days when no rain fell?

A statement that takes things for granted is an ASSUMPTION. It is something that is accepted as being true whether it is true or not.

Read the sentences below carefully. What assumption is made in each sentence?

1. Since I took so long with the test, I know I did not do well.
2. The dance will be a failure because we don't have money for a live band.

In sentence 1 the first part is a statement of fact. The second part makes an assumption based on the statement of fact. But is the assumption correct? Do you always do poorly on a test that takes a long time? Are tests that take a long time always difficult?

In sentence 2 the statement of fact follows the assumption. Before you accept the assumption as true, you might ask yourself some questions. Haven't you been to successful dances where the music was on records or tapes? Is a live band the most important ingredient for a successful dance?

In the two sentences you have just examined, the words *since* and *because* were clues to the inclusion of assumptions in the sentences. In the following sentence the word *since* or *because* does not appear, but there is still an assumption based on a fact. Can you decide what the assumption is?

Bill's good looks won him the medal.

It may well be true that Bill is a good-looking young man. But the suggestion that *he won the medal because of his good looks* may well be an assumption. If the contest involved talent or physical ability of some kind, then it is doubtful that Bill's looks had anything to do with his winning.

Identify the assumption in each of the following sentences:

1. Mr. Markson does not know how to speak French, so he should not open a travel agency.
2. Because one of the players was hurt, we lost the game.
3. The painters won't be finished for three more weeks since they were a week late in starting the job.
4. This book will certainly be a bore since it doesn't have any pictures.
5. Bob's fight in the hallway got him a low grade in math.

Sometimes a writer uses words and expressions that are vague and have no definite connections with the subject of the material. By using VAGUE EXPRESSIONS, the writer hopes to convince the reader of something. In the following paragraph pay particular attention to the italicized words and groups of words.

The status in life that any person can attain *knows no bounds.* Through *hard work* and *untiring efforts* one can *climb the ladder of success.* A *willingness to sacrifice* and a *dedication to ideals* can lead to a *fruitful, wholesome* life that brings many *rewards.*

The effect of words and expressions, such as *knows no bounds, climb the ladder of success, fruitful,* and *wholesome,* in the paragraph could lead the reader to an incorrect conclusion. Apparently the writer is trying to indicate the characteristics needed for one to attain success in life. Because the statements are partially true, you may be tempted to agree with the writer. You should ask yourself, however, if these are the only factors necessary for success. What is meant by *hard work?* What are *untiring efforts?* What does *dedication to ideals* really mean? Such expressions are vague and mean very little in the context of the paragraph.

Can you find vague expressions in the following paragraph?

The Craddock is a luxury car, and its purchase means an investment in mechanical excellence. This mechanized marvel will not only elevate your standard of living but also your standard of driving. Elaborately engineered suspension systems afford comfort that is unsurpassed. The Craddock is the ultimate in transportation.

Advertising materials and political speeches make much use of assumptions and vague expressions. The use of them, however, is not limited to just those two areas. They may be found in many kinds of reading matter. You should learn to recognize assumptions and vague expressions and to question their validity whenever you see them in your reading.

Discussion

Help your class answer these questions:
1. What is an assumption?
2. What clue words do you often find in statements that contain assumptions?
3. What assumption is made in each of sentences 1–5 on page 334?
4. What are some examples of vague expressions?
5. What vague expressions did you find in the paragraph about the Craddock car on page 335?

On your own

Number a sheet of paper from 1 to 5. Beside each numeral write either *statement of fact* or *statement of opinion* for the sentence that goes with that numeral.

1. A leash law should be put into effect in this town.
2. The telephone was invented exactly one hundred years ago.
3. There were five bands in the parade this morning.
4. The Blue Sox will without a doubt win the all-star game.
5. Paxton soap gets clothes cleaner than any other soap.

Continue numbering your paper with the numerals 6–10. Beside the correct numeral write the part of each sentence that is an assumption.

6. You will catch a cold because you got your feet wet.
7. Since I have been your representative for two terms, I am best qualified to serve you again.
8. Sally must be a good student since she often takes books home.
9. Sherri's illness will cost us the game.
10. Because it has a new formula, Trifle soap is the best soap.

Checking your work

If you are asked to do so, read one or more of your answers aloud. For each statement of fact in sentences 1–5, tell how you would test or verify each fact. If there are two parts in the sentences that contain assumptions, be sure you understand which part states a fact and which part makes an assumption.

You Can't Trust a Mother Elephant

by Leonard Lee Rue III

When I photograph wildlife, I always try to get as close to my subjects as possible.

On one occasion I was photographing elephants in one of East Africa's parks, where the law says you cannot leave your vehicle to approach wildlife but you can drive off the road to get closer.

My driver and I found a herd of four cows and six young. One baby elephant couldn't have been over a week old — the smallest elephant I'd ever seen.

Cow elephants always defend their calves, especially when they're too young to move fast. As we approached, the cows gathered in a protective circle.

We must have crossed that invisible safety line the baby's mother had drawn, for suddenly she charged. With ears fanned out, trunk rolled up, and head tilted forward, she thundered toward us, venting screams of rage.

But the charge was a bluff. After coming at us for about a hundred feet, the cow stopped, and with much headshaking and earwaving, she walked backward to rejoin the herd.

Well, we circled them several times, taking photos, always trying to edge in closer. Every time we crossed that imaginary line, the cow lunged toward us. Her first eight or nine charges always ended the same way. She would go a hundred feet at full speed, we would retreat, and she would turn back to the herd with threatening gestures.

On the last charge — and by this time we were pretty blasé — we drove off, stopped, and took the car out of gear, waiting for *her* to stop and retreat. She did not.

Fortunately my driver didn't panic. He engaged gears smoothly, and we started up. I was standing up through the open roof, hanging on with one hand, taking pictures with the other.

The cow chased us for about nine hundred feet, bellowing and screaming. The last photo I took shows the cow just five feet behind us. Luckily, charging elephants keep their trunks rolled up out of the way. If she had ever extended her trunk, she could have flipped our Land Rover with ease.

Finally, either satisfied that she had made her point or not sure what she would do with us if she caught us — I had some pretty vivid ideas about it myself — she stopped. This time we did not. If she had had enough, so had we. That was one time I was almost too close to my subject.

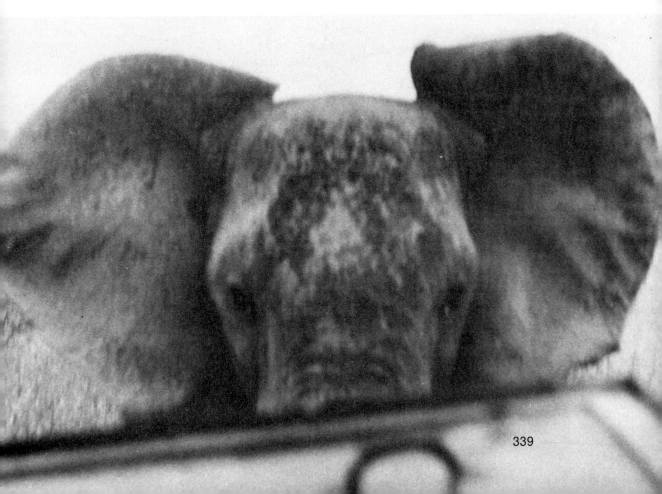

339

The Kelp Forest

by Carl L. Biemiller

The range was not the entire world. But it was more than 80 per cent of it, and all water. The nuclear war had long since melted much of the polar ice caps. Whole sections of continents were long gone. The range was life. It supplied many of the raw materials of civilization for the hive cities. Those cities lay burrowed deep in North and South America, Asia, Africa, Europe, and Australia. Where England had been was part of the open range. And the range was a global warehouse which also stored man's equipment for survival.

Kim Rockwell, Marine Warden Third Class, was working a small portion of it, and that was not pleasant at the moment. But it was better than being in the cities. He was lucky to be in the sea at all. And even bright Wardens Third Class do not get fancy range jobs. Not when

they are seventeen. He could take some pride in himself, however. The International Marine Council screened only the best of the youth candidates chosen by the Career Boards for Underwater Cadet and Warden Training.

He had worked hard ever since he left the Municipal Nursery where all children were graded for future places in society. He had studied the science of the sea eight hours a day for more than ten years. And he even had studied at night when the hypnosleep machines turned his dreams into classrooms to add more knowledge.

The seas had also changed in the two centuries since the man-made suns seared earth with radioactive death. The old knowledge about oceans and ocean life was still on the library shelves, the microfilms, the tape records buried before the war. But the life forms within the depths, even the character of some waters themselves, had altered during the trial of heat and radiation. Winds, waves, and currents were different from those recorded in the past. There were wardens of commander grade who argued that the rotation of the earth, and maybe its orbit around the sun, had altered.

Kim was cruising the kelp forest. It was spooky today. The sky, some one hundred and fifty feet above at the sea surface, was overcast and dull gray. But even on the brightest days the forest was dark and moody, its light dimmed by the giant, floating fronds of the huge algae and the thicketlike stipes, or stems, of the ancient crop. The water was full of bouncing spores. They pinged off his itchy gill suit.

The silico-membrane suit was not only skintight but was quite literally skin, with an inner lining of pore-penetrating follicles of hairs. They reached beneath Kim's own tawny hide to his blood stream to supply him with oxygen directly from the water and to remove the carbon dioxide from his system at the same time. Kim's lungs were working on exercise alone. He was breathing like a fish. But the gill suit itched. The darkness and the hailstorm of spores annoyed him.

He kicked his swim fins and glided, trying to decide whether the gathering darkness made the light from the equipment pack on his chest necessary. That keel-shaped pack held working tools, communications devices, lunch pellets, and a small drug gun powerful enough to paralyze the motor muscles and nerves of all but the largest of the sea predators likely to appear in the forest.

There had been a forest of kelp, giant algae, along the southern California coast of North America for centuries. Men had harvested it since the nineteenth century, mostly for food and drugs. But in the generations since the nuclear war, the changed sea had altered the forest. Its plants grew to weird immensities with stipes as thick as ancient earth tree trunks and with fronds, or leaves, as large as great floating tents.

Men still harvested the kelp for the substance called algin, which made a gluelike jelly that both preserved food shipped from the sea and made containers for it which, like rubbery missiles, could be shot through the compressed-air, food-freight tubes to the cities inland. More important, men mined the forest.

The great plants absorbed vast amounts of minerals through their fronds: cobalt, iron, nickel, lead, tin, zinc. The minerals obtained after processing were reasonably pure too. They were not like the crazy, unstable, radioactive isotopes from the mines of land. And they were vital to man.

It was Kim's job and the work of many other wardens to make the kelp flourish, to record its progress, to aid in its harvest. He worked by day, as did the plants which used their chlorophyll and sunlight energy to grow and also to store their minerals.

At night he slept in a pressurized silicate bubble anchored eighty feet down on the bottom. He breathed compressed air from the bubble's own units or fresh air valved in from a snorkel tube fastened to a tank buoy, which also marked the bubble's location on the sea surface. It was home, where he could peel off the gill suit and rub algin lotion on his skin to remove the day's tickles. The bubble was hot shower baths, hot meals, and a bed. It was an office where sonar devices pinged and radar and TV spied on his sector of the forest. It was a toy laboratory, a place where temperature charts were kept, salinity and sea chemical tests recorded. It was his house three months out of four. The fourth was a leave month, usually spent in the onshore headquarters compound that was miles south in Baja California.

His patrol buddy, co-custodian of Sector 12 Forest Area 80, the five square miles of their joint responsibility, was Toby Lee. She was a year older than Kim, but he ranked her by one month in the same grade, Warden Third Class. He had the uneasy feeling that she knew more about the work than he did, however. She came from a long line of fishery and sea-farm experts. She was Japanese. If the history books were right, the nation of her ancestors, now only a single tiny island, had been taking 90 per cent of its proteins from the sea for a thousand years.

Right now Toby was missing, and the forest gloom was deepening. By normal routine she shouldn't be too far away, but it was easy enough to remain unseen in the kelp lanes.

Kim picked up the warbler snapped to the top of his chest pack and spoke into it. The sound waves pulsed far and fast through the water.

"Toby. Come in, Toby. Time to knock off, time to swim home."

The receiving units on the rim of his goggle mask trilled faintly.

"Whose home?" they chittered in soprano sonics.

Twelve feet of bottle-nosed *Tursiops* (tûr'sē-ŏps'), a dolphin weighing half a ton, slipped between kelp stipes and grinned at him.

"If there's anything I hate, it's a big joker," said Kim through the warbler. "I'm worried, Pudge. I can't raise Toby. She ought to be working within a few hundred yards of here at this time of day. We're not far from the bubble. Want to take a look for me?"

The sleek mammal slipped out of sight with one surge of fluked tail. The sound in Kim's mask receivers

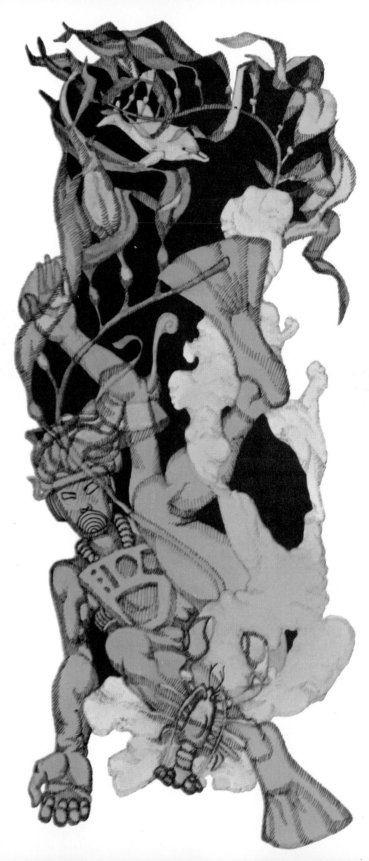

whined up the auditory range beyond his hearing as the dolphin beamed on its own echo-location mechanism.

For the millionth time as he swam in its general wake, Kim appreciated the aquatic miracle that was the dolphin and the intelligence long inherent in its brain capacity — always physically larger than man's. Communication with it, perfected originally through sonic codes, had evolved over years of in-sea team-work into something near direct mental contact, a direct exchange of thoughts.

The pelagic, or open-sea range, herds, which supplied meat and leather to the burrow cities of the wasted continents, could not be handled without dolphin help. And the bay-area food-shark complexes, even estuarial sea farms, could not be efficient without their assistance. Without their affection and friend-ship, the subsea continental shelves and deep slopes, even the sea sur-faces, would destroy men with loneliness, if not with other perils.

Pudge and an equally sizable fe-male named Peggy worked this sec-tor with Kim and Toby although they were on call for many duties when needed anywhere.

Kim's receivers vibrated.

"Trouble here," reported Pudge. "Found her, but she's unconscious. Am taking her to her bubble. Meet us there. Don't try to join us here. Poison water!"

Kim swam, every muscle straining as alarm gave him extra strength. He wished he had taken one of the water-ejection jet sleds on patrol that morning. He steadied his thinking.

"Can you give me an idea of her condition?" he warbled. "Any apparent suit rips or wounds?" Already warden discipline and warden training had freed his mind for emergency action.

"Think drowned" was the answer. "Water this area stained odd brown, similar to blood. No suit rips. No wounds."

In Kim's mind there was a clear, if fleeting, picture of this patient cetacean (sī-tā'shən), his teeth gently but firmly holding Toby's underarm and shoulder, moving swiftly toward the bubble.

"How's your own air?" Kim piped. Then, before the answer, he said, "Leave her at the bubble. When you surface, see if the stain goes all the way to the surface, and check the wave action up there, the wind too."

Without losing a stroke, he reached into his chest pack for the compact, fist-sized communicator and began his report to base. It was a report that would be picked up and recorded by every picket bubble in the forest as well as the headquarters compound in Baja.

Kim found Toby half lifted into the open-water hatch leading into the bottom level of the bubble where Pudge had placed her. In one swoop he was hoisting her into breathable air on the grilled deck below the living area. Then he lifted her gently through the hatch to the main bubble floor.

Her body was cold and faintly tinged with a purple cast. She was not breathing. He found a medical blanket, set it to full heat, and wrapped her slight form within it. He threw his mask off, gulped deeply, and began mouth-to-mouth artificial respiration, not yet wishing to use the high-oxygen drug injection directly into the blood stream until the lungs were partially active. He worked steadily, patiently, with a paced rhythm as the minutes passed.

Others worked too. Back at Baja, headquarter wardens passed quiet orders along the bubble network. Men from the next nearest Forest Area in Sector 12 took tool-laden water jet sleds and left their patrol range for Kim's. A picket hovercraft, riding herd on the whale range some fifty miles east of the kelp belt, streaked off post, picked up a doctor from a mother ship, and whizzed for Kim's marker buoy.

Kim never knew just when he had begun to concentrate on the fact that Toby's trouble might not be caused by a lack of oxygen, that the dolphin's thought about drowning might not be right. He knew that Toby was not responding to artificial respiration. And she should have been. He didn't know how long he had been working on her when the thought of poison passed through his mind.

Poison water, the dolphin had reported. The intelligent mammal was never wrong about changes in the sea. But what kind of poison? What kind of natural taint in this section of the Pacific coastline? He kept right on working, forcing air into Toby's lungs, but he searched his mind back through old lessons, old studies, as he worked.

The sea was full of life forms, many that could be detected and studied only through a microscope. They were the drifters called plankters. They were plant plankton and animal plankton. They were food for other tiny forms of life. Indeed, some of them were food for the largest animals and fishes in the sea, some types of whales, for instance. Among them, these primitive organisms too small to see with the naked eye, were certain forms called dinoflagellates (dī'nō-flăj'ə-līts). These microscopic organisms had characteristics of both plants and animals.

They had another characteristic too, Kim remembered suddenly. Sometimes they multiplied. They flowered and turned poisonous. The flowering, according to the old books, caused "red tides." Then marine creatures — tidewater fish, crabs, mussels, eels, and others — died by the millions.

Pudge had reported that the sea around Toby was stained brown, like old blood. Could Toby have taken in dinoflagellate poison through the gill suit? If so, it would have blocked her heart action, frozen her muscle action.

He made his decision. He acted upon it. He left Toby and stumbled to the well-stocked medical kit, half wondering why he still had swim fins on his feet. He found the hypo needle and sought among the carefully labeled stimulants for the ampoule marked adrenalin. He fixed the hypo and made the injection. His fingers were still trembling when Commander Tod Torrance's voice reached into the bubble. Kim felt very old, very tired, but he made his report.

Kim left Toby in the blanket as he placed her on her bunk. He settled beside her on his knees, and awkwardly but effectively, he applied pressure and release to her rib cage.

Then her chest fluttered. He could feel her tremble. He bent his mouth to hers and began again the respiratory process. He felt her shake as though something inside her were trying to get out. Her eyes opened and looked through him into nothing.

The communications console spoke.

"This is Doctor Felipe Baguio. We're right above you. Sea is calm. Wind no force at all. We're lowering a pressure capsule to your bottom hatch. The dolphin is steadying the cable to you. I'm coming down on a weighted dive. Give me a reading on your bubble pressure so I can stabilize the capsule for the patient."

Kim gave him the figures automatically.

"It's dark up here, so I'll be a few minutes," said Dr. Baguio. Kim had not noticed the cold light come on from the silicate bubble walls as it did automatically each day when the surface above met nightfall. The people from Area 81 must be coming in on laser light units to cut the muck outside.

There was noise from the seahatch deck below. He left Toby and looked down. The doctor, his wet suit dripping, was slipping out of a small tank harness and dropping a weight belt, which fell with a *chunk*.

Dr. Baguio was deft and sure as he examined Toby Lee. He talked to himself as much as he talked to Kim. "Toxic all right. Poison right to the entire motor system. Some kind of an alkaloid with a nitrogen base. There's an antidote for something like this in your kit made right from your garden of kelp. But how would you know? Stimulant was right too, but there's a better one in the kit too. How would you know? She's a hospital job. Have to watch brain damage."

"Will she be all right?" asked Kim.

"Think so. Don't really know. As soon as I do, you'll know."

With the two men from Area 81 helping, they placed a drowsing Toby into the pressure capsule and sealed her there. Such capsules had their own buoyancy attachments and could pop directly to the surface for immediate pickup. This one would attach to the flat hull of the picket hovercraft and be zoomed to the base hospital at Baja within minutes.

"So long," said the little doctor cheerfully. "Glad there wasn't anything messy down here like shark attack. Make your own report to headquarters, Rockwell. I'll make mine on the way. Suggest you use shield suits and air tanks if you're going to work bad water. Gill suits would put the stuff right into your blood stream. I'm off."

The doctor slipped into his gear, pushed through the lower hatch, and vanished.

Kim turned to face the wardens from Area 81. They introduced themselves. Although their names and voices were familiar to Kim, their persons were not. Changing shifts, different duty hours, varied leave times, did not make for many close acquaintances within forest sectors. But the bond of common work, shared danger, and the dependence of each upon another made them closer than the families in the old history books once were.

Tuktu Barnes was wide and stocky, with a deep chest and a vast spread of shoulder muscles. He came from the North, from McKinley City, deep within the Alaskan mountain ranges, and had taken his training there. He had served a brief apprenticeship in the Bering Sea before his transfer to the kelp forest. Many generations ago Tuktu's ancestors had been Eskimos. He was a specialist, or going to be, in nutrients, the foods of the plants, mammals, and fishes, the foods of mollusks. He would someday help man enrich the many "desert" areas of the range — to support useful life which would, in turn, support the cities.

Genright Selsor, who was Tuktu's patrol buddy, was slender and somehow angular. He was relaxed, genial, and black as the night within the abysses of the sea. He had been schooled in the great burrow city that lay safe and busy under the plateau of ancient Ethiopia. He too had served a short apprenticeship in-sea off the coast of southwest Africa before transfer. The Service did move its people, as it would move Kim. Selsor hoped, someday, to be one of the great oceanographic chemists.

Kim moved to the instrument console, adjusted the radar controls, and began a 360-degree sweep. His visitors peeked at the screen with him. Kelp stipes. Moving blips in the north-south fish lanes.

There were two blips, fair sized, almost motionless directly above the bubble and only about three feet from the surface of the sea.

"I know them," said Genright. "Pudge and Peggy. They sure are good to Tuktu and me."

Kim made a very slight control change. There was a straight line of light, broken with an indentation, and in front of it, fanning into the darkness, was a pale blur, a phantom of cloud.

"That's shoreline," he said, "and something coming from it which fades away into the sea. Take a good look, Selsor. You want to be a chemist. Is that a chemical cloud or a physical one?"

"Whatever it is, it's an active radar-wave conductor," said Genright.

"Of course," said Kim, "of course, of course . . ."

He snapped open the communicator to Baja headquarters, using the bubble network channel so the whole forest could hear. "Rockwell reporting to base," he said.

"All right, Rockwell, let's hear it," said Commander Torrance.

"Barnes and Selsor are with me, sir," Kim said. "I am not taking them out until first light. Suggest, sir, that all forest bubbles make a scan of the coastline at intersect Coordinates Forty and One-eighty South and, if base thinks justified, that some overflight be made in the area. The scope here picked up sort of a cloud showing, sir. It might indicate something flowing from land to sea which might have changed the water elements, maybe causing a poison area. It's only an idea, sir."

"We'll check," said the commander. "Meanwhile, all bubbles make scan and report. Rockwell, Barnes, and Selsor, we'll get additional men into your present area as needed. But I expect a complete check from you as soon as possible. You'll be glad to know that Lee is responding to care."

"Thank you, sir," said Kim.

"Out," said Baja base to the network.

There was only one light in the forest in the morning. It was comprised of different degrees of shadow. It was almost always dark under the canopy of kelp fronds, which hid millions of the smaller fish from the greater ones which preyed upon them. Sometimes there seemed to be more light near the bottom where moray eels, rock fishes, brittle stars, abalones, and lobsters watched an endless parade of life from their own hidey-holes. Even the huge holdfasts, root structures, of the kelp stipes teemed with life, most of it microscopic in size, some of it dangerous to the valuable kelp crop.

Kim noticed that the sea urchins were getting out of hand again despite constant efforts to get rid of them. Urchins, those walking pincushions of living spines, ate the key, or primary, stipe of a plant, leaving it to float free and die.

He thought about bringing the sea-otter packs back for a week or so. The sea otters, tame and joyful beasts whose gleaming pelts once caused wars in long-past centuries, loved urchins. They loved them for breakfast, lunch, and dinner. The otter herdsmen moved them about the forest from time to time to grow fat while controlling pests.

The forest was a jungle all right. It was a nursery and a slaughterhouse too, where wandering giants of the sea often cruised, seeking easy food. It felt restless that morning. He didn't know about Tuktu or Genright, but Kim felt a vast uneasiness, an itch of trouble. For no definite reason, he felt wary, extra alert.

They had not yet found tainted water although the dolphins were making wide-ranging casts. And they too were moving with some speed, using sleds, stopping only to take water samples and to examine darker sections of the forest for dead fish. They checked the clusters of tiny life forms which attached themselves to kelp fronds and filtered their food from the water. They would die first from poison.

There was normal movement in the fish lanes, the traffic of grazing fish which had to be kept from the kelp as much as possible, and bigger fish pursuing the grazers. All of them, however, were impelled by their own sensory urges through the lanes.

The lanes were two parallel lines of small nuclear power packs spaced at intervals some three hundred feet apart. The distance between the lines was about one hundred yards, the "highway" down which the fish swam. The packs emitted sound waves geared to an unpleasant frequency which formed, in a sense, a barrier on either side of the "highway." Since everything in the sea is, in some measure, sensitive to sonic impulses which guide much of fish movement, the fish stayed in the "middle of the street." They moved rapidly when chased either by the dolphins or other creatures seeking snacks.

The power packs also served another purpose. They could be controlled to produce heat which caused thermal, or heat, currents to rise from the sea floor. Thus the rich food, or nutrients, in the sediments of the bottom rose to feed plankton which in turn fed the fish which ate plankton. Plankton eaters, like herring, sardines, and anchovies, swimming down the "highway," literally swam in a never-ending chain of roadside restaurants.

Pudge and Peggy arrived in a boil of water from their own speed. Pudge wore a crown of kelp stipes that he had torn off in passage. He looked like a grin wearing a wig, and he nuzzled and bumped Kim into a slow somersault, almost shifting the compact tank from his shield suit. He was glad to see Kim. He always

was. He didn't need code or trills to say so. Kim could feel the cetacean's thought, and he sensed that Tuktu could also. Tuktu might have told him that a couple of million years' worth of Eskimos had talked to fish, whales, seals, foxes, and a lot of other wild things as well.

If Pudge looked silly, Peggy was ridiculous. She was a bigger creature than the male dolphin, maybe fifteen feet in length and thicker through the girth. She had slammed through something that left a dab of phosphorescent slime on her dorsal fin and around her mouth. Her grin was green, and it glowed. Her dorsal fin looked like some strange plant growing from her spine. She too nuzzled Kim and spun him into a slow turn.

"Report, report, you lumps," said Kim. "Did you find bad water? Did you see dead fish? What about the sea?"

The dolphins had ranged far, into and past the areas adjacent to Kim's own. The surface sea was quiet, winds gentle. There was no bad water that they had found. There were no dead fish except some they had eaten. A killer whale of great size had skirted the seaside of the forest, swimming fast to the south. They had given it room and hidden even though the killer whale was their own first cousin. There were boats in the sky headed for the area. That was all. Yet, added Pudge, to him the entire range along the coast seemed alert and waiting for something.

"Let's check in to base," said Genright.

Kim snapped on the communicator. "Rockwell here, sir, together with Barnes and Selsor, the Area 80 Patrol . . ."

"Come in, Rockwell, we've been expecting you. This is Lieutenant Rang."

"We have found no poison water, sir," said Kim. "Dolphins have covered two areas beyond us to the north and indicate no altered sea. Forest seems normal, sir. But dolphins reported surface craft approaching this vicinity. Any findings at base, sir, about cause of tainted water?"

"Rockwell," said the lieutenant from Baja, "Commander Torrance asked me to tell you that he and investigation crew were into the coast early. They found remains of an old atomic desalinization plant from the days when fresh water was first made from salt. The walls which held the old coolant system for the pile had burst from age. What liquid was left ran off over a hard-baked surface into the sea. There wasn't too much of it apparently, but it poisoned a small area of the sea with radioactive plankton. The commander thought dinoflagellates too. He commended you."

"Thank you, sir," said Kim.

"Don't interrupt, Warden Three. The dolphin report of craft in your vicinity is correct. It is early in the season, but rather than risk even the slightest danger to the kelp, the commander has ordered harvest crews to cut crop. Barnes and Selsor will return with you to bubble where you will all stand by to assist at Harvest Master's orders. That is all for now."

They pointed the sleds for Bubble 80 and moved through the patrol alleys in the gently waving, swaying, dancing stipes.

As they rode their jet sleds, Kim wondered about his edginess. The forest didn't feel right to him. Was it because there might still be a patch of poison water wandering among the kelp?

"Let's move a bit nearer bottom," suggested Kim. "Might make a little better time. These shield suits and tanks slow us some despite the sleds. And I think we could use some lights. Okay?"

"Good idea," warbled Genright.

Kim hesitated. "This may sound silly," he said, "but it will only take a second. I want something a bit bigger than a hand light. Let me get out the laser, and I just might grab a drug gun too."

"Jumpy?" asked Genright.

"Some," said Kim evenly.

"Me too," said Tuktu suddenly.

They rummaged with equipment clips on the sleds, and went on, spraying radiance throughout the lanes. Some sizable scallops swam by, ejecting water from their shells, which they clapped like hands for motion. The sudden light had them looking for darkness. Green and red sea anemones, more like bloated flowers than living creatures, flexed nervously on the bottom.

Tuktu saw it first. His warbler squeaked. Kim automatically set his communicator to full send and receive. Genright named it.

"Giant squid!"

A single press of a stud on the laser light Kim carried made it both a light and a tight-beam heat ray capable of boring through rock.

"Tuktu! Genright! Split!" he commanded. "Separate!" He spoke into his communicator. "Giant squid," he reported. "Suggest any surface craft lift from water."

There was a hiss and a boil of tiny bubbles as Kim's laser beam lanced ahead into what seemed a wall of great grasping arms and tentacles.

Tuktu's sled peeled off to the right, banging against kelp stipes. Genright's turned left down a fish lane. Kim angled his toward the surface in an effort to rise above the monster.

He heard Tuktu's voice burble like flute music.

"This thing's forever," it said. "It must be a hundred yards long!"

Kim kept his thumb on the firing stud as he angled upward, trying for the great squid's eye. A coil of rubbery arm, round as a barrel, tipped his sled and sent it spinning away from him. He held hard to the laser

and dived for the bottom. The arm drew the entire sled into a writhing nest of flesh. Kim swam desperately for one of the huge, igloolike holdfasts which anchored the kelp plants.

From the corner of his eye he saw a blinding streak of light, then another. Tuktu and Genright, from somewhere down the length of the monster, were firing into the bulk.

There was a smother of bubbles and a heaving swell of water as if the ocean were suffering some internal storm. There was a brittle crackling. He could hear Tuktu again. Oddly enough, the voice sounded cool, almost amused.

"This thing's tearing down more kelp than they'll harvest."

It was hard to see in the light-streaked water, but clearly the squid had turned direction. Kim fired again and again into the mass. Three quarters of the creature were arms and tentacles. It would take luck to find head, eyes, and nerve centers.

There was a high-pitched warble, tilting off the edge of sound into a scream.

As Kim watched in horror, he saw a great curved arm come into view. It carried the limp body of Genright. Unconsciously, Kim noted that the young warden's tank and mask seemed to be intact. But Genright's body was rag-flopping, inert. Kim swam directly into the tangle of deadly flesh.

"Tuktu!" he warbled without thinking. "It's got Genright. I'm making a try for him."

There was no answer.

Then there was and, with it, new courage.

Boring through the kelp, swiftly and as directly as aimed missiles and just as relentless, came the dolphins. They homed on the great squid's mantle, their jaws scissoring for the attack. Generations of their cetacean ancestors, particularly their cousins, the whales, had fed upon squid and, because of their diet, had borne the scars of arms dappled with toothed suckers.

There was a single thud of impact. Pudge and Peggy struck simultaneously, driving their weight into the prey. There were tons in collision.

From the edge of his vision, Kim sensed other forms behind the dolphins. Dimly he knew that they must be divers coming from the harvest fleet on the surface with new help. And in the new light that they brought with them, he saw Genright's body float loose as the giant arm released it. Immediately he swam for it.

The world turned black. The massive struggle vanished. The giant squid spewed forth tons of the inky, ebon fluid concealed within its body for use as a last, desperate escape cover. An acre of the kelp forest became night. Kim reached Genright. He found a grip on a tank

strap attached to his shield suit and held on.

Something reached out of the darkness and struck a blow. Kim felt his head snap into his shoulders. And that was the last he felt. But the squid arm that had flicked from the inky cloud to deal that blow curled back upon itself. It slowly settled to the bottom.

Kim opened his eyes and looked at the little brown-faced doctor he had last seen in the bubble with Toby Lee, Dr. Felipe Baguio. But something was funny. The doctor had two faces. Tuktu was standing beside him. He had two faces as well.

"Genright?" Kim asked through stiff lips.

"Regenerating room," said Tuktu, "for a new arm."

"You're fine," added the doctor. "We got you both up in a hurry, and too fast for the capsule, so you had to go back under pressure. That process is now complete. If you can't move, don't worry. I've got you in a stiff gelatin cast."

Kim could almost feel his mind begin to work.

Genright and a new arm, he thought. There were many creatures in the sea with the power to grow new appendages for those lost in combat or by accident. Long study of those creatures over the years had made some of the process available to man. All sea hospitals kept spare parts in their body banks — arms, legs, and also vital organs. Regeneration was a fact and almost always successful.

"Toby?" he asked.

"So maybe Genright will have a white arm," said Tuktu. "But thanks to you, he and Toby will be around for a long time." He grinned. "You didn't ask how I was," he continued, "and Pudge and Peggy are busy below."

Kim smiled. Suddenly he was very sleepy. He slept.

DISCUSSION

1. How had the nuclear war changed the world physically? How long after the war does this story take place?

2. What was Kim's job, and how had he prepared for it? How did the kelp in Kim's time differ from that of the twentieth century? What were its uses in Kim's time? What were other important products of the range?

3. What happened to Toby Lee? What had poisoned a small area of the sea?

4. In what specific ways did Pudge and Peggy help Kim in this story? What had made it possible to train dolphins to assist in the work of the range? How did the wardens and the dolphins communicate?

5. What happened to Kim and Genright in their battle with the giant squid? What medical treatment did each receive afterward?

6. In Kim's time, how were children raised? What evidence from the story supports your answer? Do you think Kim and his coworkers were free to choose their lifework? What makes you think that?

7. Which do you think had greater importance, the range or the hive cities? Why? What do you think life may have been like in the hive cities?

8. From what different parts of the world did Kim and his coworkers come? What do their origins suggest to you about the way in which the world was being governed in Kim's time?

9. How did scientific knowledge in Kim's time compare with that of today?

10. What aspects of Kim's life appeal to you? What aspects would you not like? Would you exchange your way of life for his? Why or why not?

11. In this fictional account, Kim remembers various things he has read in the "old history books" about the twentieth century. What events and accomplishments of the present century do you think will in fact seem important to people living two hundred years from now?

AUTHOR

Carl L. Biemiller, a newspaperman and magazine editor, was born in 1912. He has been assistant publisher of the Camden *Courier-Post* and the Philadelphia *Daily News* and executive editor of *Holiday* magazine. "The Kelp Forest" is an excerpt from his book *The Hydronauts*, which was published in 1970 and praised as an outstanding science-fiction novel. Mr. Biemiller has long been fascinated by the oceans and makes his home on the New Jersey shore. He and his wife have four grown sons.

CAT AND THE WEATHER

Cat takes a look at the weather:
snow;
puts a paw on the sill;
his perch is piled, is a pillow.

Shape of his pad appears:
will it dig? No,
not like sand,
like his fur almost.

But licked, not liked:
too cold.
Insects are flying, fainting down.
He'll try

to bat one against the pane.
They have no body and no buzz,
and now his feet are wet;
it's a puzzle.

Shakes each leg,
then shakes his skin
to get the white flies off;
looks for his tail,

tells it to come on in
by the radiator.
World's turned queer
somehow: all white,

no smell. Well, here
inside it's still familiar.
He'll go to sleep until
it puts itself right.

MAY SWENSON

The Eighth Wonder of the World

About twenty-two centuries ago, a poet named Antipater (ăn-tĭp′ə-tər) drew up a list of the Seven Wonders of the World. Antipater was a Greek who lived in the city of Sidon (sīd′n), then a Phoenician port and now part of the country of Lebanon. His list of Seven Wonders included the most marvelous structures he knew.

Most of the Wonders were in Greece or had been built or designed by Greeks. The only exceptions were the Pyramids of Egypt and the Hanging Gardens of Babylon. The other five Wonders were the statue of Zeus at Olympia, the temple of the goddess Artemis (är′tə-mĭs) at Ephesus (ĕf′ə-səs), the Mausoleum, or great tomb, at Halicarnassus (hăl′ə-kär-năs′əs), the Colossus of Rhodes, and the Pharos (fâr′ŏs′), or lighthouse, of Alexandria.

All of them were truly wonderful. But Antipater left one Wonder off his list, because neither he nor any other Greek had ever heard of it. This Eighth Wonder of the World was brand-new. It had been finished in 214 B.C. It was a wall, a snakelike line of stone and brick and mud that stretched for an incredible distance across the northern border of China.

And where was China? You could have gone up and down the length and breadth of Greece, asking the wisest men, and none of them could

by Robert Silverberg

have told you. Perhaps a few had heard merchants' tales of a land somewhere in the country of the sunrise, east of Egypt, east of Persia, far, far beyond the boundaries of civilization. They might have heard stories of a place that manufactured fine silk robes and other costly treasures.

No man of Greece had ever actually been to that distant, dreamlike sunrise land. So Antipater and his countrymen knew nothing of China's miraculous, wonderful Great Wall. It was not on the list of Wonders of the World. The Greeks of 200 B.C. looked smugly around at their own little corner of the universe. They pointed to a region that ran from Egypt in the East to Rome in the West and said, "This is the known world! This is civilization! All else is outer darkness! All else is barbarism!"

Out in the darkness, the Chinese would have laughed at such proud claims. For their civilization was much older than that of the Greeks. At a time when the Greeks clothed themselves in the rough skins of animals and lived in crude, savage huts, the Chinese already had hundreds of years of art and culture behind them. Now the Greeks talked about the Seven Wonders of the World — but the Chinese had created an Eighth Wonder, the Great Wall.

Why was such a wall wonderful? What was special about the Great Wall of China? Was it made of shimmering marble? Was it inlaid with gold and precious stones? No. It was and is a barrier of ordinary stone, common brick, plain mud. Why, then, was it a Wonder of the World?

The Great Wall is big. It is so big that the mind has trouble imagining its vastness. It is the biggest single structure ever made by man.

How big is big?

The Great Wall of China runs a zigzag course for some 1,850 miles across China. That's just the *original* Great Wall, the one that was finished in 214 B.C. Later, Chinese rulers tacked three hundred miles to the western end of the Wall. Much later, four hundred miles were added at the eastern end. There are more than a thousand miles of inner walls. There are some useless loops and spurs where the engineers got lost and built in the wrong direction. All told, the Great Wall of China has been measured at 3,930 miles in length.

Let's forget about the extra loops and zigzags and stick to that original figure of 1,850 miles. Try to imagine what it really means to say that a wall runs such a distance. Suppose we got into a car in Los Angeles and began to drive eastward across the country. We'd pass through the cactus-strewn Mojave Desert and on into Arizona, and in a couple of days we'd be near the Grand Canyon. Then we'd enter Colorado, and our car would make its way over the mighty Rockies. Kansas would be next. Hour after hour, we'd see nothing but endless fields of wheat, ripening in the hot sun. A sign would tell us that we had left Kansas behind and were now in Missouri. At last we would halt in the city of St. Louis, on the banks of the Mississippi River.

From the Pacific to the Mississippi — quite a drive! It's about nineteen hundred miles: roughly the length of the Great Wall of China.

Pretend, now, that that stupendous Wall ran alongside the road as we made our drive — not just a line of telephone poles but a massive bulwark, thick and strong, twenty or thirty feet high and fifteen feet wide. Through the baking desert, over the tops of the sky-piercing mountains, across the broad plains, the Great Wall would be our companion for mile after mile after mile.

How big is big? If we put the Great Wall down at the eastern end of the country, it would run from New York to Kansas. If we started it at Rome, it would wriggle across Europe to the shores of Portugal.

The Wall contains enough stone and brick to form a barrier eight feet high and three feet thick right around the world at the equator — twenty-five thousand miles. In 1793, when ambassadors from Great Britain visited China, they measured the Wall and declared that it contained more material than all the buildings of their native land.

It is a monster of stone. It lies across China like a gigantic serpent. It sprawls over valleys, up the steep mountainsides, through the thirsty deserts. It dances upon the summits of towering peaks, reaching for the highest pinnacles. It stretches on and on, numbing the eye, a grayish-blue streak, a ribbon in the distance, striking toward the horizon.

The Seven Wonders of the World that Antipater listed have met with harsh fates. The proud statues have long since toppled, the lighthouse of Alexandria lies under the waters of its harbor, the Hanging Gardens of Babylon have crumbled into mud. Of Antipater's Seven Wonders, only Egypt's Pyramids survive at all.

But the Great Wall remains. After twenty-two centuries it still sweeps across thousands of miles of China. What we have today is not the original Great Wall, of course. Over the centuries battalions of men have labored to repair and rebuild the Wall, keeping it strong. Most of the present Great Wall goes back only five hundred years, though it follows the ancient route laid down by the first builders.

One man gave the order for the Wall to be built. He was a Chinese emperor, a strange, cruel, brilliant man. He wanted to create a boundary to divide civilized China from the territory of the wild men to the north. He gave the word, and all China toiled to raise his barrier. Millions of men slaved to build the Wall. Thousands died. They brought together enough stone to build *thirty* Great Pyramids of Egypt, and they strung a fabulous line of wall across unthinkable distances.

The Great Wall was meant to keep the barbarians out. It didn't. They came through the Wall and over the Wall anyway. In time, they conquered China. Then it was their turn to rebuild the Great Wall, to keep other invaders from doing the same thing. The story of the Great Wall through the ages is one of constant invasion.

Today that fantastic Great Wall, that unbelievable serpent of stone, that Eighth Wonder of the World, is a kind of giant museum piece.

DISCUSSION

1. When was the original portion of the Great Wall completed?
2. Which civilization was older, the Greek or the Chinese?
3. What is remarkable about the Great Wall? The length of the original Wall is about the same as the distance between what two American cities? How does the amount of stone used to build the Wall compare with the amount used for the Great Pyramid?

4. What do you think made the Seven Wonders seem so marvelous to Antipater and other Greeks? If they had known about the Great Wall, would they have included it in their list of Wonders? Why do you think as you do?

5. Why were the ancient Greeks unaware that the Wall existed? The world known to the Greeks was confined to the lands around what body of water?

6. Do you think the Wall was built for a good purpose? Why do you think that? How well did it serve its purpose? What lesson could the nations of the world learn from the Great Wall?

AUTHOR

Robert Silverberg was born and grew up in New York City. As a child he spent much of his time reading and was especially interested in stories about the fantastic and the improbable. By the age of nine he had read most of the books of mythology and fantasy in his local library, and he then began reading science fiction. He first started to write when he was thirteen, and by the time he was eighteen, his writing was nearly professional. His first science-fiction novel, *Revolt on Alpha C,* was published while he was still in college. Since graduating from Columbia University in 1956, he has been a full-time author.

Mr. Silverberg's writing has brought him many awards and honors, and he is the author of more than a hundred books and about six hundred stories and articles. Some are written under his own name, but others are written under various pen names, such as Walker Chapman or Calvin M. Knox. Most of his early books and stories were science fiction, but he has also written a great deal of nonfiction on a wide range of subjects. Among his recent science-fiction works are *Time of the Great Freeze, Planet of Death,* and *Across a Billion Years.* His latest nonfiction books include *The Man Who Found Nineveh, The Morning of Mankind,* and *The Long Rampart,* from which "The Eighth Wonder of the World" is taken.

Edward H. Schafer and The Editors of TIME-LIFE BOOKS

CHINESE:

Synonym for

SUPERIOR

In spite of the excellence of the purely scientific discoveries made in ancient China, her greatest contribution to humanity was technological — the work of her artisans and technicians.

Four Chinese technological inventions of Han[1] and medieval times laid the whole basis for the European exploration and colonization of the world: the compass became the tool of the pioneering seafarers of Portugal, Holland, and England; gunpowder enabled Europeans to subdue the lands they found; paper and printing made possible the widespread knowledge of ideas and decrees.

By Han times, the Chinese had made compasses — spoons of lodestone, a naturally magnetic iron ore — that rotated freely on a polished board. The floating needle, magnetized by rubbing it with lodestone, was probably not invented before the T'ang[2] period. Neither device was used for anything more scientific than to locate the most favorable site for a building or a tomb, however, until the eleventh century, when the compass was finally applied to navigation. It may have reached Europe through the Arabs.

Gunpowder, to the medieval Chinese, was simply an aid to aes-

---

[1] Han (hän), a Chinese dynasty, 206 B.C.–A.D. 221.

[2] T'ang (täng), a Chinese dynasty, A.D. 618–907.

thetic pleasure. They had learned how to combine potassium nitrate with the proper proportions of charcoal and sulfur to make an explosive by the seventh century A.D. But they used it only in displays of fireworks to illuminate great court and public celebrations: "fire trees," "flame flowers," and "peach blossoms" of gunpowder exploded in the sunset skies over the capital of the empire. Apparently the Chinese did not use gunpowder in warfare, even as a simple incendiary substance for fire arrows, until the eleventh century.

The invention of the first paper, which was made from tree bark, hemp, old rags, and fishing nets, is attributed to one Ts'ai Lun (tsĭ′ lŏon′) in A.D. 105, but actual samples of earlier rag paper have been found. From the second century on, paper was used as a substitute for the silk cloth on which important and elegant messages had always been written. The crude pulp was strengthened with starch, sized with gypsum, coated with gelatin, stained in handsome colors — yellow was a favorite — and even polished. This whole complex technology was transmitted to western Asia in the eighth century. By the ninth century, paper had everywhere replaced the traditional papyrus from Egypt. Ultimately a new European industry was devoted to the manufacture of paper, and the parchment of medieval Christian monks became a thing of the past.

Printing from woodblocks is believed to have begun in the seventh century, though the earliest surviving printed book is a later one, a sacred Buddhist scroll from the eighth century A.D. The art developed from several techniques that were used between the fourth and seventh centuries: the stamping of textile patterns, the impressions of seals — both secular and religious — and the common practice of taking ink rubbings from stone engravings. These forerunners of printing were used mainly for religious purposes.

The material used in woodblock printing was usually pear or jujube wood, cut to the size of two book pages and smoothed and softened with paste. The matter to be printed was written on a two-page sheet of thin, transparent paper. This was spread carefully over the woodblock and rubbed so that the ink adhered to the paste. Then the woodblock cutter carved around the transferred written characters so that they stood out, raised in high relief. The printer brushed ink on the block and pressed blank sheets onto it to make the prints.

The early invention of printing provided a means for the wide distribution in China of the sort of materials that were available in the rest of the world only in manuscript and hence could be read by only a few. The spread of the art of printing, like that of making gunpowder, seems to have followed the far-ranging

Above: Fifteenth-century lacquer cabinet. *Private Collection.*

Below: THE IRONERS, detail from a twelfth-century painting on silk entitled LADIES PREPARING NEWLY WOVEN SILK. *Courtesy Museum of Fine Arts, Boston.*

Sixteenth-century porcelain pot with a fish symbolizing wealth and domestic harmony. *Courtesy of the Fogg Art Museum, Harvard University. Bequest of Samuel C. Davis.*

Mongol conquests of Europe in the fourteenth century.

In addition to these inventions, which profoundly altered the course of world history, Chinese technology produced many significant but less dramatic innovations. Some of these were also adopted by Europeans; others were developed independently, but much later.

The wheelbarrow was a Chinese invention of the third century B.C., not known until centuries afterward in Europe; so also was the breast collar and harness that enabled domestic animals to pull heavy loads. Chinese technicians were the first to undertake deep borehole drilling — holes two thousand feet deep were drilled in the salt mines of the province of Szechwan (sŭ'chwän') in the first century A.D. The world's first suspension bridges supported by ingeniously woven bamboo cables, as well as the earliest known segmental-arch bridges, were built in China between the third and the seventh centuries A.D.

The ancestor of the modern Great Wall, which became the Eighth Wonder of the World, was constructed by the Ch'in emperor Shih Huang Ti (shǐr' hwäng' tē') in the third century B.C. The first important canals were built soon afterward, and gradually a vast network was developed. By the eighth century A.D. it was possible to float a cargo from the Yangtze River in the south to the Yellow River in the north without reloading it.

First to discover the value of lacquer, a natural varnish obtained from a relative of the sumac, the Chinese used it to paint images on Bronze Age buildings and to preserve and decorate wooden articles, leather shoes, and silk hats. Sometimes it was improved by the addition of gold dust, mother-of-pearl, and red pigments. In the early centuries of our era, handsome Buddhist images were made by pressing lacquer-soaked cloths over clay models; and in medieval times, marvelously designed actors' masks, representing the faces of supernatural beings, were made in the same way.

Other innovations were the domestication of the silkworm and the complex process of reeling silk filaments from cocoons. For many centuries only the Chinese knew how to control the life cycle of the silkworms, feeding them with the leaves of white mulberry and killing whole generations before they could rupture their cocoons. The Chinese were also the sole possessors of the techniques for reeling off the long, undamaged, resilient filaments and twisting them into threads of great strength. Drawlooms were developed in China to weave these threads into richly ornamented damask.

Articles made of porcelain, also a Chinese invention, became the envy of the world in early medieval times. The Chinese had made fine pottery vessels since the Stone Age, but making porcelain required the addition to the clay of a mineral called feldspar. At first they merely applied feldspar as a glaze on the surface, but by T'ang times they had learned that the mineral could be added to the clay — before the vessels were molded — and the mixture fired at a higher temperature to produce porcelain. Shards of the renowned T'ang porcelains have been found as far away as Mesopotamia and Africa.

These and other products of early China became so well known for their excellence that, by medieval times, the word for "Chinese" became a synonym for "superior" in many Asian languages. A distinguished ninth-century Arab author wrote that while the Turks were the greatest soldiers and the Persians the best kings, the Chinese were preeminent among all craftsmen.

RUBY CAT

by Carroll B. Colby

A famous jewel thief who was known by the name of Klaus Gudden arrived in Germany in 1894. He had with him two fabulous matched rubies. The jewels had originally been the eyes of a statue in a Korean temple. That was in about A.D. 165. Then they were stolen from the statue. In 1560 they were acquired by the sultan of the Ottoman Empire. He in turn gave them to a lady. The rubies cost her her life, for a thief killed her to get them. Later they belonged to Louis XV, who gave them to Madame de Pompadour. She eventually sold them to a Russian nobleman. How Gudden came by them will probably never be known.

In any event, as soon as he appeared in Berlin, the police began searching for him. He was caught, and as he tried to escape, he was shot and killed. But the jewels were not found. A few years later, a gem expert named Graves attempted to find out what had happened to them, for they couldn't have vanished into thin air. Undoubtedly Gudden had hidden them on the chance that he could return for them later.

Mr. Graves learned that when the police set their dragnet, Gudden was trapped in a certain block in Berlin. He had been unable to leave that block for several days. Searching for clues in that limited area, Graves discovered that Gudden had visited a little ceramic shop on the very day that he had been killed.

This shop specialized in clay cats, and Gudden had picked up one that had just been removed from the kiln. After looking it over for several minutes, he asked the owner to set that cat aside for him until he returned for it. He scratched an X on the bottom and left orders that that particular cat was not to be sold to anyone else.

When the shop owner learned that his strange customer had been killed, he included the cat in a shipment with dozens of others just like it.

Graves traced the shipment to America, but there the trail branched out in a hundred directions. The cats had been sold all over the country, and it was impossible to trace them all.

Somewhere one of those cats may hold within its clay body a half-million dollars in rubies. Eight inches high, it lies with its tail wrapped around its body and forepaws. It was originally yellow, but by now it must be darker and cracked and chipped with age. The faint X on the bottom may no longer be visible. But the years will not have damaged the fortune it guards.

BILLY BEANS
Lived Here

by Jean McCord

For the rest of her life, Ellie knew that every single solitary time she ever saw a white pigeon, she would think of her brother! She would be forced to think of her brother, sometimes thinking of him dead, which he was; most times remembering him alive and happy and working hard, and free.

FREE! The one in the family who had risen above their way of life. The one who shucked off bitterness and anger and would not allow a shred of meanness near him.

He had freed himself and was teaching Ellie to be free, when ... but here, if Ellie's thoughts came wandering near the accident, little things in her head started dancing around ... the way gnats do ... of a summer evening. They hurt the backs of her eyes and made her clench her fists until the fingernails bit. And unless she quickly rushed around, did something to divert it, a gob of bitterness, the very thing that Billy had abhorred, rose up and choked within her throat.

But Time was slowly probing long fingers of forgetfulness into her brain.

Now the summer was almost over.

The family had moved away from that place, that hopeless farm they had been living on. The things that had filled her life were gone. The things that Billy had been and done were no more. Even her memories of him, she realized, were growing blurred, melting, running away. She could scarcely ... straining her mind to remember what he looked like, she couldn't. She was scared; desperately she dug like a hunted gopher into her belongings for a couple of old pictures.

She blew the dust away and peered closely, and yes, he was in there! He had really lived and walked on the earth and been laughing and smiling. And yes, she remembered now how his thick and shaggy hair had looked like straw piled on his head. And though he was sixteen, four years older, there had been only an inch difference in their heights.

She remembered clearly now. . . . They had just moved out onto the old Oliver place when he came home one day, swinging into the yard with his usual jaunty, fast-moving walk and carrying a small cardboard box under one arm.

"Look here," he said proudly, coming into the kitchen and setting the box carefully on the table. "I helped old Mr. Woody clean out his pigeon loft. He gave me these."

Lifting a top flap, he reached into the box and gently withdrew a small white bird. All the little kids in the family crowded round, pushing and jostling, each putting out a finger to touch or stroke the soft white feathers.

"Well, just what you aim to do with 'em, Billy?" his mother asked from the sink where she stood cleaning and cutting up carrots for their soup pot.

The three little boys and Ellie swung their eyes from the bird up to Billy's mouth for the reply.

"Thought I'd raise 'em up," he said slowly. "There's money in pigeons. You know, squabs. Raise 'em for restaurants, things like that. These here are homers, though. Let 'em grow, train 'em right, and they always come straight back to their loft." He smiled down at the little boys. "Can't ever get lost. How'd you like to be like that?"

"Well," his mother said. "Well, Billy . . ." And she waved her knife through the air in a futile gesture.

It was plain she didn't think much of the idea.

"You wait, Ma," he promised. "They won't be no trouble to no one, and I'll feed them myself."

He picked up the box.

"Come along, Towhead." Hooking an elbow round Ellie's neck, almost choking her, he dragged her outside, but she liked it. She hung on to his arm and made him swing her off the ground. He was awfully strong for his age, Ellie thought.

She liked this one brother of hers better than anybody else in the world. There were other brothers in the family. Besides the three little boys there were Flinty and Brady and Pete. But the older brothers were different; they paid her no attention. They did things alone, and if they had money of their own, they spent it any way it pleased them. They took silly, giggling, lipsticked girls to the movies.

When Billy made a dollar or two, he gave half to his mother. With the rest he'd get things that were desperately needed then, maybe a part for the ancient, dying car they had traveled in all over the country. If there was any money left, he sometimes grabbed Ellie and they took in a movie too. They liked the same things, cowboy movies and cowboy songs. At least Billy liked them, and whatever he liked was good enough for Ellie.

Right now, if he wanted to raise birds, she'd stand behind him.

She'd even help him, if he wanted her to.

"Figured I'd put 'em up in the old barn," Billy was saying as he released her.

"Here." He handed her the box to carry. She felt proud and big inside that he trusted her so much.

They pushed open the sagging, warped doors and went inside the dark and musty barn.

It was a huge building, at least fifty years old. Once it had been sturdy and well built, but the weight of time was crushing it. Strong winds had tested themselves against its sides, and the west wind had won, forcing it to lean in and away.

At one end was a loft, built of big timbers, a ladder leading to it. It was filled with dust-layered junk — boxes of outmoded clothing, bits of harness, pieces of broken tools, the thousand and one things that accumulate around a farm, too broken to use, too good to throw away.

Within a week the two of them had thrown down the junk, only keeping emptied crates to make nesting boxes with, for they had big plans of things to come.

"With these two, Sis, we have all we need for a start," Billy stated, strong authority in his voice. "We'll get four, five hatchings from them in a year, and soon the little ones will be nesting and give us more. Before you know it, we'll have the best-sized pigeon loft in the state."

"And you said I get to name these," she reminded. "If I help."

"Sure. What'll it be?"

"Thought I'd call one 'Christy' and one 'John.' Which is which?"

He laughed. "I don't know. Never thought to ask old man Woody how to tell the ladies from the gentlemen. But whoever lays the eggs is 'Christy.' O.K.?"

They swept the loft over and over, always able to raise a cloud of dust which choked and made them sneeze.

Finally Billy went out somewhere and brought home a load of straw in the old car. They spread it deep on the floor and put layers in all the nesting boxes. By now they had thirty-seven boxes lined up, sitting open and empty, waiting for Christy and John to get busy.

Their father looked on the venture with a jaundiced eye. "Foolishness, Bill. Git all tied up with stuff like that, won't have time for reg'lar things."

"Like what, Pop?"

"Takin' a little job here, a little work there. Make some money, not spend it on pidjuns!"

"Yeah. I know what you mean, Pop."

It was a joke in the family, among them all, that the old man spent more effort digging up little jobs for his kids to do for pennies than he ever would working any deal for himself. As for himself, he didn't believe in full-time jobs.

"Ties a man down too much. Can't make a million theta'way" was his ever-ready comment.

The older boys, and lately even Billy and Ellie, referred to the old man among themselves as the "Millionaire."

Billy agreed to whatever the old man said, then went right on with what he had in mind. He had learned it was the most effective way. Offer no opposition. Swerve a little from an outlined course. But hold fast and tight to his own idea.

It left the old man feeling pacified but slightly puzzled.

Billy was in high school, taking all the courses he could, but he still kept going at numerous small jobs. Every weekend found him laboring at some cleanup job or grocery delivery or helping out at a trucking place or organizing the junk that the small fry in the family collected. To sell or make something out of, Billy said. He was making avid collectors of them all, right down to the baby of the family, four-year-old Jim Dandy. Nothing was too small to escape Jim Dandy's notice, though sometimes he mistakenly contributed things like shiny stones or broken beetles to the common stockpile.

Since the old Oliver place sat outside the line of city limits, no restrictions gave the Beans family any law trouble. The older boys hauled home wrecked metal junk heaps, one after another, victims of the savage accidents that occurred up and down the fast-paced highway. They meant to salvage the still-usable parts to sell, or use, in case they ever had a use for them, but somehow other matters claimed their attention, so the wrecks lay scattered around the yard in rotting, rusting piles. Still, they did make very fine things for the little kids to play in.

Just before the end of school, Billy had said, "I've got a run this weekend, Sis, a long haul. The dispatcher at the truck company is letting me take out a big job alone." He carefully closed the cage door.

"Can I come with this time, Billy?" Ellie asked softly.

He thought for a long moment before he answered, "I think ya better not. It's a long, tough haul. Besides, ya got school, and I won't be in till late Monday morning. Got to miss some school myself."

"Well," she sighed resignedly. "Well, it's finals week anyway."

"There ya are. Ya know ya can't come with when ya got exams comin' up."

They worked together, cleaning cages. Ellie fixed two crates to carry birds in. This would be a good training flight for them, over four hundred miles, and the birds could always use the practice. If one bird came in with a good time, they decided they might even risk the entry fee and enter him in one of the local races.

Then it was suppertime, and they left the barn loft. Billy carried the two light wicker crates, holding fifteen racing birds.

"Where're ya goin', Bill?" asked the Millionaire.

"Over the mountains. Be back on Monday."

"Git good pay for it, will you?"

"Good enough." Billy glanced at the old man. What fancy money-making scheme was he going to propose?

But the old man said only, "Well, do be careful 'bout thet downgrade. Shift yer gears low before you come over the top. It drops down in a hurry."

"Sure. Thanks, Pop." He shoved back from the table. Reaching out, he tweaked Ellie's nose. "Good luck in yer exam Monday."

Something black and fearful twisted down through Ellie's stomach, starting at the tip of her nose.

"Billy!" she cried, running out the back door after him. "Please! Let me come with!"

He stooped for the bird crates. "Now, Sis. Exams. Remember?"

"But I can make them up," she pleaded desperately.

He patted her arm. "Next week. Then you'll be through school. Free all summer." Seeing the unreconciled look in her eye, he said persuasively, "They're goin' to let me take a Salt Lake run soon. You can come on that, and I'll even let ya drive across the desert."

And with that promise, she let him go, holding her right arm high in silent farewell.

All that night Ellie tossed fitfully on her cot, the bottom half of which she shared with Jim Dandy. Several times the little boy in his sleep protested at her movements, which twisted the blankets off him. Each time, Ellie woke up sharply and, reaching down, gently covered him again.

In the gray, cold light before dawn, she finally arose and, tucking the little boy up firmly, dressed and went to the kitchen. Searching in the breadbox, she saw a new loaf of bread and the heel of an old one, dried hard.

"Good for the teeth," she told herself and took the hard crust.

She stood in the middle of the room a moment, listening to the sounds of the sleepers in their beds. Around her, in the kitchen was a breath-holding silence, only her heartbeat sounding in it, and the dim shadowy forms of tables and chairs, cupboards and stove, waiting for the life of the day.

She stepped quietly outside, and there on the northeastern edge of the world was the tip of a cold and pale sun. The weeds left cool, wet streaks on her legs where she tramped through them going to the barn. She climbed to the loft.

The birds huddled in near darkness, but her coming awoke them, and they stretched their wings and called softly to each other. Dangling her legs over the edge of the floor, she nibbled her bread, noticing for the first time that stale bread tasted sweeter than new bread if you chewed it long enough.

Ellie was only halfway through the bread when the birds began to arrive. The first one that came in startled her. She watched open-mouthed as it broke through the hanging wire trap and came into its own box. Then, while she was still puzzling over it, the others began to come home. Finally they came in a rush, too fast to count accurately, but she knew at least twelve birds had come in. Billy had taken out fifteen; he had told her that he would release them from their baskets at six o'clock sharp. The earliest she had expected any one of them back was noontime. Yet she knew it wasn't even six yet. It was closer to five. AND THE BIRDS WERE COMING IN! The pit of her stomach was sick and burning, and something seemed to be squeezing her throat where she had swallowed the bread. In that moment she knew for sure what had happened.

Rushing down the ladder, she burst into the house and her parents' bedroom.

"Ma!" she screamed. "Ma! Wake up, Ma!"

Her mother lifted her head, her gray hair straggling down around her temples and her eyes not yet focused.

"Ma!" Ellie threw herself down on her knees beside her. "Ma! Something's happened to Billy. The birds are in! It's only five o'clock!"

Mrs. Beans dropped her head back heavily onto her hard mattress. Then she waved her hand limply to drive her daughter away. "Stop . . . foolishness, Ellie. Just . . . something . . ." Almost immediately she was deeply asleep again, her mouth halfway open and her cheeks caved in.

Ellie's father rose on one elbow, his fingers digging into his eyes.

"Ellie," he said plaintively, "ifen you can't sleep, the rest of us would like to."

She rose slowly to her feet, staring down at them. "Fools!" she cried; then bursting into a sobbing scream, "Oh, fools!"

She ran away from them all then, up into the hills behind the house

because she could not bear to be there, to hear the words confirming what she knew was true. Somewhere on the highway a fatal thing had happened! Ellie fought to keep away the swarm of sights that jostled for attention in her brain. Billy, tired and weary even before he had left, had drowsed a moment at the wheel . . . or a car . . . some other truck . . . had smashed head-on . . . or a tire blew, at high speed . . .

She knuckled her eyes until big red shapes flared and replaced the image of the truck crashing, the crates bouncing, bursting, the birds swifting out, the birds speeding home.

Later in the day, when the hills were hot and dry and a shimmering heat haze bent the house and the old outbuildings into crazy shapes, she slowly picked her way through the tall dead grasses. When Ellie reached their dusty yard, she could hear her mother sobbing, muffled because her apron was thrown over her head. Ellie dragged her feet, trying to hold them back, but they took her through the door and into the kitchen.

Her father stood there, with both hands shoved in his pockets and his head hunched low. Jim Dandy was clutching his mother's skirts, howling lustily in fright.

Automatically Ellie bent down and picked him up, carrying him upstairs to the bedroom. When she

had soothed him into sleep, she returned to the kitchen.

"He is dead, isn't he?" she demanded fiercely.

Her mother's louder outburst of sobbing and her father's shifting his weight from foot to foot answered her.

"The downgrade," her father said, his jaw working. "I warned the boy. I said, 'Go easy.' The Highway Patrol claims his brakes burned out." He hunched his shoulders. "Shouldn't ha' been usin' brakes nohow!"

"You shut up!" Ellie's mother screamed. "My good boy is gone! Don't you blame him now!"

By squeezing something in her head, Ellie closed her ears. She moved around the kitchen, fixing a bite to eat for them. And by another effort of will, she managed not to think about it. By dropping down the secret partition, the wall in her brain that separated the outside life from the things inside her head, she had just enough sense left to move herself around from one chore to another like a mechanical doll.

The birds came home, but Billy never did. The company he worked for gave him a funeral. Not a big funeral nor a grand one but satisfactory. And his fellow workers sent a big wreath of pretty pink roses in a horseshoe shape.

378

Ellie went with her folks and sat down in back.

"He's up there," she told herself, "in that gray box." But some great doubt, nesting inside her chest, refused to believe it. She knew she was expected to cry, as her folks were doing. Even big old lazy Brady was snuffling in a kerchief. But though she tried hard, squeezing her eyes painfully tight, no tears came. She tried pinching her leg, and it hurt bad. But no tears. And she couldn't even think of Billy. Instead, she kept seeing the birds coming in, wheeling gracefully round and round, big wagon-wheel circles.

The minister was talking, out where they went with Billy's gray box. She could see his mouth working, but all she heard in her ears was a soft, gentle cooing. And her eyes saw the place around her, a flat, treeless, barren section of graveyard, newly opened. Her mind saw nothing; at least not then. Later on, it grew and swelled to a rubbery, undulating picture in her brain.

When they went home, she climbed up to the loft, and the pigeons' cooing was soft and real in her ears. Somewhere, quite near, Billy slouched back on an upended crate, and he was very real and accepting and certainly not dead.

She found herself spending most of her time up there, doing nothing.

Sitting on a sagging crate, listening to the birds cooing. She still took care of the birds daily; watering, feeding. There was a hundred-pound sack of mixed grains in one corner. She wondered vaguely what she would feed when that ran out, but she didn't really give any worry-thought to it. Somehow it seemed too vague a trouble and too far away.

At dusk her mother called, piercing the silent gloom of evening.

"Ellie! You, Ellie!"

Her mother never spoke a thing in a normal voice. Every word she uttered came out a whining complaint, even if it was only a statement on the weather. And truly she had much to complain about. There had never been enough food to make the rounds of every plate. It was difficult to scrape things together. Every meal was a separate ordeal.

How many trips had Ellie made, trudging to the store, for a single loaf of bread or a few cents' worth of potatoes? She would never be able to count them! Yet, somehow, if their mother had been more cheerful, Ellie thought dully, the thing that had them in its tightening grip might have been forced to hold off just a little. There was still hope, perhaps seeded in the little boys . . .

But their mother would not hope! Ellie thought about her older brothers. Brady, who tried working a few times, got into trouble, and quit for good. Now his time was spent hanging around the pool halls in town or slouching outside on the sidewalk.

Flinty and Pete both grew crankier every day. They snarled at the whole family; mostly they snarled at each other. And sometimes there were fierce flare-ups out behind the house when in seconds they would be at each other's throats; then gouging, kicking, kneeing fights down in the dust of the yard, till they both lay racked in exhaustion.

But Billy had been different. Billy had made her a promise. "Look, kid," he'd tried to tell her up in the barn, the soft pigeon sounds punctuating each of his words. "All life isn't like ours. What I mean is, well, we're poor and all that, but there are other things. I know there are, and I'm findin' out about 'em all the time. Life isn't all money, like the old Millionaire thinks it is, and it isn't just raisin' kids, tryin' to feed 'em more all the time, like Ma thinks it is. I can't tell ya what life really is, for you and me, 'cause I don't know yet. I can only tell ya what it ain't. It ain't what Brady and Flint and Pete think, chasin' girls all the time. And it ain't being unhappy all the time like Ma is, or walkin' around in a dream all the time like Pa.

"For you and me, anyway, it's somethin' all different, Ellie, maybe like books and pictures and music and a little more money, all rolled together. I kinda think it's goin' to be somethin' we can do and be proud in and that means somethin'. Anyway, when I find out more about it, I'll tell ya right away."

She had been squatting on her heels, the edge of her cotton dress dragging in the straw. She looked around at their tiers of boxes, filling up now with the new birds, and the old hens, sitting on more nests, hatching out more and more pigeons for them.

"Ain't our birds goin' to make us rich, Bill?" she had asked timidly. "I thought when we got to selling them, they'd bring in plenty."

"No!" He'd made a quick rasping sound that didn't quite sound like a laugh. "We ain't goin' to make no money off 'em. They eat up more than they can ever bring in."

"But you said, last summer . . ."

"I know! I know! But now we own ninety-two birds. And how many have we sold in a year? Just six!" Then he said softly, "And two of those I traded for corn."

"Well, why are we . . ." Her voice had trailed off in a plaintive sound.

"Why are we keepin' them?" He sighed. "Spendin' money on their feed and time on their care? I ain't sure, but I think it's cause they're Beauty. Can't you feel it, Sis, inside you, when we open the cote and let them all out? They swirl up in the

sky like a . . . a scarf, a white scarf, or maybe a white flag; and then they sweep back and forth, wavin' through the air till we call them in."

Sometime near the end of August the whole Beans family moved away, off the decaying farm and clear to the other side of town.

"Be better for us all," the old Millionaire said. "We ain't gittin' ahead in the world, way we should." His wild dreams were growing, feeding on the fruit of their adversity, it seemed. His swollen schemes of millions, millions, leaped and twisted from the endless stream of his mouth.

"Makes no nevermind to me," Ellie muttered when her mother told her.

She had spent the whole summer huddled up in the loft, missing more than half her meals. Consequently, she was skinnier than the old black scarecrow that flapped out in a barren field, guarding nothing. Time didn't flow past and around her anymore. It stood suffocatingly still, wrapping her in a cloak of sodden grayness in which nothing happened, because anything that could happen, of importance, already had. The only thing she'd noticed in the last two months that puzzled her, and of course there was no one around to explain the Why of it, was that a certain stick of sunlight falling through a knothole in the barn had changed its angle.

They moved away then, no one caring much whether they did or not. They had to leave all the birds behind because, of course, there was no place to keep them in a house in town.

"There's no more feed anyway," Ellie said.

"Well, now," her father said, "those-there birds had it good long enough. They kin jus git out and rustle for themselfs."

"Sure," Ellie said and firmly refused to think of cats and rats and boys with BB guns.

It didn't happen till after they had left the farm, abandoning the white birds and the sagging heaps of dead cars and the remaining small pile of salvage that Billy had not had time to turn in.

Then a new worry got inside of Ellie's head. It bored up from her mouth, tasting like that red ant she had once accidentally eaten, and though she swallowed and swallowed, she couldn't get rid of the fiery feeling. She walked long miles every day, turning her eyes this way and that on the new part of town. It walked right along, beside her, outside her, inside her. And the worry grew. It outwalked her, swelling, expanding, like the windy old Millionaire's dream of countless piles of money. Then the thought became a gray thing which, if she allowed it to, could double her over and twist her insides in cramps. There were tears, too, which had never been shed, and these would come surging into her head, making her whole face swell up; but they wouldn't come out, and she felt like a balloon, blown full up, just ready to explode.

And the worst thought, the one that hurt as if a devil had thrust a hot fork into her heart and twisted it, was the absolute certain knowledge that if she had been along that night, just sitting there beside him in the truck, surely the accident would never have happened. Yes, surely this one thing was the worst. If only she'd been along ... this thought said itself over and over in her head ten thousand times, till now it had grown into a sore spot like a canker, raw and painful, never getting any better. It wasn't exactly that she blamed herself for the accident — she was twelve years old and knew the difference between what one did and what one thought he did — but only that if she had really insisted that night, had maybe stowed away or something, her being there ... her presence ... might have *prevented* it!

Finally the day came when she absolutely knew she had to do something. She somehow had to change one fact. THERE WAS NO MEMORIAL! There was nothing around even to show he'd once been part of their family. No one mentioned his name anymore. The little boys had quit asking for him. Jim Dandy had put a puzzled frown on his pale face when she'd whispered in his ear, "Billy! Billy!" She shook him till he cried.

She formed her resolution lying stretched out flat in bed one night, staring at a jagged crack cavorting on the ceiling. Suddenly the whole thing came alive and leaped right out at her. She wondered in excitement why she hadn't thought of it before. It was the perfect, simple answer. It only needed a little money. "Two dollars would do it," she thought.

At dawn, in the quiet strangeness of this new house, she rose and dressed carefully. She tiptoed into Pete and Brady's room and picked up the first pair of pants heaped on the floor. The pockets clinked softly, satisfactorily.

Very slowly, she walked downtown, touching each tree on the street as she passed. The morning breeze blew against her hot forehead and into her open mouth. She felt a little singing noise inside her head, and it was a good feeling. She waited outside the hardware store till it opened, patiently leaning against the wall, sliding one foot up and down on it.

Then, with her heavy burden and a coiled rope which she slung over one bony shoulder, she started walking out to the old farm. Most of the morning was gone when she got there. The sun was yellow-bright and hot overhead. But she had more time than she needed.

She didn't go near the empty house where both the front and back doors swung creakingly on broken hinges. Someone, boys most likely, had stoned out all the windows. Instead, she walked around it, keeping her eyes riveted on the side of the barn, the big, wind-tilted barn with boards that were plenty good yet.

Climbing once more up into the loft — and then never again, she knew — she pulled up her rope that she had tied to a five-gallon bucket. Her eyes looked quickly around the loft, though she didn't want them to and tried to prevent it. There were no birds.

She climbed out the small window of the pigeon trap and eased her way onto the roof, the rope tied to her wrist so it wouldn't drop.

Then, with a fierceness and determination born of a grinding desperation, she began her memorial. In big, black, dripping letters, six feet tall, she painted out his name. "BILLY BEANS," it said, bigger than life, clear across the shingled roof of the barn. She slid and jumped to the ground, half of her five gallons of black paint still left. Standing on an old pigeon crate, she wrote on the side of the barn fifty feet long, "LIVED HERE."

She threw her sticky paintbrush aside and jumped back to view her work. Too close. Running now, panting, fearful, as if she were leaving something horrible behind like a monster in a nightmare, her weak and rubbery legs bore her to a ditch beside the highway. At a safe distance she tumbled down into the weeds and lay there sobbing, dryly at first; and then like a spring that is released from pressure, the tears sprang up. They washed down her face, cleansing, purging, and they had been the sickness inside all the time.

Through the film over her eyes, two small watery windows, she saw her work standing out boldly, as it would even from a distance. And everyone, no matter who, passing by, would see and wonder and remember! The stark black words would paint themselves upon each traveler's brain.

The wind might blow, and the barn might lean and someday fall, but as long as these marked and branded people lived, those four black words would live ... within their brains.

DISCUSSION

1. Of her four older brothers, why did Ellie like Billy best? What project did Billy and Ellie undertake together?
2. Why did Billy keep the pigeons even after he found he was not going to make any money from them?
3. Why was life so difficult for Ellie's family? Why was her mother always complaining? Why did the older children among themselves refer to their father as the "Millionaire"?
4. Long before the Highway Patrol notified her parents, how did Ellie know what had happened to Billy? After trying unsuccessfully to rouse her mother and father, why did she run off into the hills?
5. Why did it become so important to Ellie that there be a memorial to Billy?
6. Why do you think Ellie shed no tears at Billy's funeral? When she had written the memorial on the barn, why was she finally able to cry?
7. After the funeral, why did Ellie spend most of the summer up in the barn loft? How do you think Ellie felt about having to leave the pigeons behind when her family moved?

8. The thought that hurt Ellie most was that if she had gone on the trip with Billy, the accident would not have happened. Do you think that she could have prevented the accident if she had been with him? Why do you think that?

9. Ellie thought of Billy as "free," and from him she was learning to be free. What did the word *free* mean to Ellie?

10. What kind of boy was Billy? In what ways was he quite different from his parents? How well do you think Billy's parents understood him?

11. What had Billy expected his future and Ellie's to be like? Do you think his dreams were in vain? Why do you think that?

12. If Ellie could have afforded a stone monument for Billy, would it have satisfied her more than the one she made? Why do you feel as you do?

AUTHOR

Jean McCord's life has been one of changing scenes and varied occupations. She was born in Hayward, Wisconsin, but she moved so frequently as a youngster that she had attended sixteen different schools before completing high school at the age of fifteen. That she was successful in gaining an education in the face of great odds she credits to her love of books and her desire for knowledge. In 1946 Miss McCord graduated from the University of California, where she majored in biology. Her scientific training equipped her for positions she has held in hospital and research laboratories, but she estimates that over the years she has worked at more than forty other occupations.

Miss McCord now makes her home in California, but she continues to enjoy changes of scene and travels widely. She tries to devote about half her time to writing, and many of her stories are based on incidents in her own adolescence or on experiences of young people she has known. Two collections of her short stories have been published: *Deep Where the Octopi Lie,* which includes "Billy Beans Lived Here," and *Bitter Is the Hawk's Path.*

Skier

He swings down like the flourish of a pen
Signing a signature in white on white.

The silence of his skis reciprocates
The silence of the world around him.

Wind is his one competitor
In the cool winding and unwinding down.

On incandescent feet he falls
Unfalling, trailing white foam, white fire.

Robert Francis

How the Educated Bulldog Said Too Much

by Carl Carmer

Indiana corn is said by those who know (and *who* should know as well as Indianians?) to grow faster and have a better flavor than any other kind. I don't quite know whether or not to believe a farmer of French descent who lived near Vincennes who said that he almost laughed himself to death when he was sowing corn because the sprouts came up from the seeds so fast that they tickled his feet. He said he went to the house to call his hired man, and when he came out, the corn had already eared at a height of about thirty feet. He sent the hired man climbing up a stalk after the ears, and by the time he'd got up thirty feet, the corn was growing so fast the ear was thirty feet higher. The hired man climbed on up and finally got so high he was out of sight. The farmer said he hollered to him to start back, and he said he'd been trying to, but the corn was growing faster than he could come down, and he was getting higher all the time. He never did get down, and the farmer never saw him again. This particular stalk, the farmer said, happened to be popcorn, and when the ears got up so close to the sun, the heat was so great that all the kernels popped and fell all over his hayfield. He said a mule that was standing hitched to a hayrake in that field mistook all those white popcorn kernels for a June snowstorm and just naturally lay down and froze to death.

This same farmer had a son of whose ability he was very proud, and the son had a bulldog. When the boy was eighteen years old, the farmer sent him way across the state to Earlham College to get an education. The boy took the bulldog along for company. After the boy and the dog had been at Earlham a month or so, the old man received a letter from his son.

This is what the boy wrote:

"Father, an astonishing thing has happened. The bulldog has begun to talk. Moreover, he seems to have a fairly good mind. I'd like to make a suggestion to you. If we educated the bulldog along with me here at Earlham, we'd have at the end of four years not only the one talking bulldog in the world but the one and only talking bulldog with a college education. We could exhibit him then all over Indiana, charge admission, and make a lot of money. If you agree with me, Father, just send me double the usual amount of money for books, laboratory fees, incidentals, and miscellaneous. It will be a mighty good investment."

So for four years the farmer sent his son double the usual amount for the usual items, and finally the day came when his son and the remarkable bulldog were to return home with their college degrees. The boy wrote that the bulldog had made an outstanding record at Earlham and had taken honors in two subjects. He said that he and the dog would travel by train to Vincennes and then hire a boat to take them downriver to the farm.

The old man got very excited on the day they were due to arrive, and he waited anxiously on the bank as the little boat approached. When the boy jumped ashore, his father clasped him in his arms — and then he looked about him and said, "And where's our educated bulldog?"

"Well, Father," said the boy, "it was as I said. The bulldog graduated with honors, and then we both took the train for Vincennes. When we got there, I hired a boat to bring us here. And on the way down, I said to the bulldog, 'Isn't it wonderful, in less than an hour, now, we'll be back with my father.'

" 'What, that stupid, uneducated old ignoramus?' said the bulldog, and, Father, it made me so angry to hear him speak so insultingly of you that I kicked him overboard. He couldn't swim a stroke, and so he was drowned."

Well, that's the story — sworn to as gospel truth by a lot of respectable Indianians — so I guess it must be so. They say that the father was convinced it was true, praised his son for being so loyal to his old dad, and gave him a homecoming party that night at the farmhouse that folks remember to this day.

SKILL LESSON 6

UNDERSTANDING AND FOLLOWING DIRECTIONS

In school and out you are constantly faced with directions. How well you accomplish certain tasks may very well depend on your ability to understand and to follow directions.

When you are helping your mother unpack the groceries after a trip to the supermarket, she may very well give you a direction like this: "Put the hamburger in the refrigerator and not in the freezer because I want to use it tonight." Unless you understand and follow that direction, your evening meal may be delayed.

In school you may be told, "Read only pages 73 to 78 and answer only questions 1 to 4." Failure to follow those directions correctly might result in wasted time and effort or in inadequate preparation for class work.

If you are following a set of directions, it is very likely that the order in which you do the directions is important. In a recipe, for example, if you are told to "heat the butter first," it probably means that you are going to need melted butter shortly, perhaps to combine with another ingredient. Of a more serious nature, the first direction for replacing a tube in a television set might read, "First disconnect the plug from the electrical outlet." Following that direction could save you from the possibility of receiving an electrical shock.

Consider the importance of order in the following directions for replacing broken glass in a special type of aluminum storm window:

1. Loosen tension screws on the inside runners.
2. Remove rubber stripping in frame.

3. Take out any pieces of broken glass.
4. Fit stripping around new glass.
5. Insert glass and stripping in frame.
6. Tighten tension screws.

Could the rubber stripping be removed easily without first loosening the tension screws? Could the glass and rubber stripping be inserted in the frame if the screws were not loosened? It appears that it would be a difficult if not an impossible job to replace the glass without having followed the first direction.

Following directions in the proper order is important, but so is understanding the reason for each direction. In the directions you just read, why was it necessary to remove the rubber stripping? Why did the directions tell you to take out any pieces of broken glass? Why did the last direction tell you to tighten the tension screws?

Look at the map below. Suppose someone stops you at the corner of City Limit Drive and Main Street and asks you how to get to the National Bank. What directions would you give him?

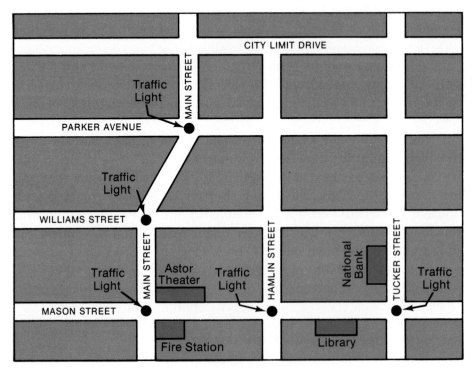

Your directions do not have to agree in wording with someone else's, but they should agree in basic information, such as beginning direction of travel, changes in direction of travel, traffic lights, and attention to certain buildings and other landmarks. Later in this lesson you will have a chance to check your directions with those of your classmates.

How do you read a set of directions? First you should read the directions rather quickly to determine how difficult they are and also to find out what materials you will need. After your first reading of the following directions for making a mosaic of foodstuffs, decide whether you could obtain the required materials and whether the directions are clear and easy to follow.

MATERIALS NEEDED:

A piece of plywood or scrap lumber; a pencil; glue; a brush; shellac; different kinds of beans; rice; dried split peas; sunflower seeds; salt and pepper; ground coffee or tea leaves.

STEPS TO FOLLOW:

1. Draw a design on the plywood or lumber.
2. Study your supply of foodstuffs and decide which will be used for what part of your design.
3. Cover a small area of your design with glue.
4. Place in the glue whichever foodstuff you have decided to start with, fitting the pieces carefully together.
5. Continue adding other foodstuffs until you have completed the design.
6. For the background (the part outside the design) use either salt and pepper, ground coffee, or tea leaves, and apply small pinches of the material to the glue.
7. Let the picture dry overnight.
8. To protect the picture, apply a coat of shellac with a brush.

After your first quick reading of directions, you read them a second time, this time slowly, to be sure you understand the order of the directions and the reason for each direction. After your second reading

of the directions for making a mosaic of foodstuffs, answer the following questions:

1. *Why does step number 3 come just before step number 4?*
2. *Why does step number 6 come after you have completed filling in the design?*
3. *For what reason is step number 2 important?*
4. *What is the purpose of step number 7?*

The third thing you do in following directions is to gather whatever materials are needed and then read each step carefully as you do what it tells you.

The directions for carrying out a science experiment for making salt crystals are given below. Read the directions through rather quickly to get an overview of the directions and the materials. Then read the directions slowly, making sure you understand not only each direction but also the reason for it. Finally, read the directions a third time, again slowly, almost as if you were actually doing the experiment.

MATERIALS NEEDED:

water
salt
a glass
some string
a pencil

PROCEDURE:

1. Boil enough water to fill the glass.
2. While the water is still boiling, add to it one half cup of salt.
3. Stir the salt and water until much of the salt has dissolved.
4. Remove the pan from the heat so it will stop boiling.
5. Let the pan sit until the undissolved salt has settled to the bottom.
6. Pour only the clear solution into a glass.
7. Tie one end of a short piece of string to the middle of the pencil.

8. Place the pencil across the top of the glass with the string immersed in the solution. Make sure the string is hanging straight.
9. Put the glass in a place where it will not be disturbed and where the liquid can cool.
10. Look at the string a few hours later. When the liquid has cooled sufficiently, you will find that salt crystals have formed on the string.

Answer the following questions about the directions you just read for making salt crystals:

1. *What purpose did the pencil serve in the experiment?*
2. *Why is it necessary to do step number 4 before step number 5?*
3. *Why is step number 5 important? How does it affect what is done in step number 6?*
4. *Why is the string tied to the* middle *of the pencil?*
5. *If, in step number ten, you find that salt crystals have not yet formed when you look at the string, what should you do?*

Many of the directions that you have to follow are in the textbooks and other books that you use in school. In a language workbook you may find directions similar to the following. As you read the directions and the paragraph, think about what you would do in following the directions correctly.

The following paragraphs contain a number of errors. Underline once each word that should begin with a capital letter. Underline twice each word that is misspelled. Draw a circle around each incorrect punctuation mark. Draw an x in each space where a punctuation mark is needed.

Why do leaves change color and fall in the autumn. Chlorophyll keeps leaves green all summer, but toward the end of sumer shorter days and less sunligt cause the chlorophyll to fade. When this happens, leaves change in color from green to yellow red and orange.

A layer of cells forms on the stem below a leaf, cutting off water from the leaf and helping to break down the chlorophyll further. as the layer of cells tightens its hold on a leaf stem, it weakens the connection of leaf to twig. A breeze or sudden rain brakes the connection, and the leaf flutters to the ground.

Mathematics textbooks often have directions that you must read slowly and follow carefully. The following directions are for a written exercise on sets and subsets. Think about the steps and how you would follow them to complete the exercise correctly.

Each set in the column at the left is a subset of one of the sets in the column at the right. Number a sheet of paper from 1 to 10. Match each set in the left column with a set in the right column. Write the letter for the correct set beside the number of the set it matches. You will not use all the sets listed in the second column.

1. {bears}	A	= {vegetables}
2. {shirts}	B	= {musical instruments}
3. {roses}	C	= {streets}
4. {Peter, David, John}	D	= {trees}
5. {guitars}	E	= {states}
6. {elms}	F	= {nuts}
7. {Kansas}	G	= {clothes}
8. {hamburger}	H	= {colors}
9. {string beans}	I	= {meat}
10. {walnuts}	J	= {radio stations}
	K	= {first names}
	L	= {animals}
	M	= {reference aids}
	N	= {flowers}

A social studies text may have directions that require careful reading and thought if you are to understand the steps and the order in which to do them. As you study these directions, try to picture what the finished chart would look like.

Make a chart of information about the thirteen original states. On a sheet of paper draw horizontal rules that divide it into three equal parts. At the left side of your paper use these headings to label the three parts: New England States; Middle States; Southern States. Across the top of your paper write these headings: Name of State; Date Admitted to Union; Principal City. In the appropriate part of your chart number and list each state. Fill in the other information called for.

Discussion

Help your class answer these questions:

1. What are some examples of directions that you sometimes follow outside of school?
2. Why is the order in which you follow directions sometimes so important?
3. Why is it important that you understand the reason for each step in a set of directions?
4. How many times should you read a set of directions when you are actually making something or performing an experiment? What is your reading rate for each time you read the directions?
5. What are some examples of directions that you sometimes need to follow in school?
6. What were your answers to the questions on page 394 about the directions involving the aluminum storm windows?
7. What directions did you decide on that go with the map on page 394?
8. What were your answers to the questions on page 396 about the directions for making a mosaic of foodstuffs?
9. What were your answers to the questions on page 397 about the directions for the science experiment?

On your own

The directions for making a bacon pancake are given below. Use the procedure for following directions suggested in this lesson as you study the recipe.

INGREDIENTS:

3 strips of bacon pepper
1 cup of flour   3 eggs
2 tablespoons of sugar   2 cups of milk
½ teaspoon of salt   ½ pint of light cream

COOKING INSTRUCTIONS:

1. Cut bacon into ½-inch squares.
2. In a 9-inch frying pan cook bacon until it is crisp.
3. Do not pour off bacon drippings.
4. Combine flour, sugar, salt, and pinch of pepper.
5. Combine eggs, milk, and cream, and beat lightly.
6. Combine dry and liquid ingredients. Mix until smooth.
7. Pour mixture over bacon and drippings.
8. Bake in 375° oven 30 minutes or until it is golden brown.
9. Cut in wedges and serve.
10. Topping may be maple syrup, jam, or sour cream.

Number a sheet of paper and write answers to the following questions about the directions:

1. In what kind of order are the ingredients listed?
2. In what kind of order are the cooking instructions listed?
3. What is the reason for step number 1?
4. What is the purpose of the second part of step number 6?

Checking your work

If you are asked to do so, read aloud one or more of your answers. Make sure you understand reasons for the order of the ingredients and the order of the cooking instructions. Be sure you understand the correct answers to the other questions.

Gifts of the INDIAN

by C. Fayne Porter

Americans today have something of a reputation for being impressed by statistics concerning money, so try this one: the United States is, of course, the world's leading agricultural nation, but more than half of the cash farm crop of this country comes from products the Indian developed! This makes him certainly the greatest of the Stone Age farmers.

Today's domestic tillers of the soil realize about three billion dollars annually from corn, the most valuable crop grown in the United States. Corn has been called the greatest natural resource of our country, and a bumper corn crop will equal the total value of all wheat, potatoes, barley, rye, rice, tobacco, beans, and sweet potatoes grown yearly. Science is still puzzled as to how the Indians ever developed it in the first place, because no wild corn has ever been found; it is by now so thoroughly domesticated that it has lost the power of self-propagation in an untended state. It grows only where man plants it and is totally helpless without man's care. Other cereal grains thrive by themselves, but not corn; its origin is shrouded in mystery. Scientists have improved corn, true, *but all of the main types now grown were developed by the time of Columbus.* (This includes popcorn. It was often served sweetened with maple sugar.)

And let's add the Irish potato, one of the world's most widely grown vegetables. Irish it is not; it came first from the high plateau country of Peru and Bolivia. The world embraced it, and its total production of over eight billion bushels yearly makes it an easy winner on the world scene; its annual value surpasses that of all the gold and silver mined yearly throughout the world. While we're on the subject of potatoes, add the sweet potato and some types of yams as of American origin — the three from different families and representing different kinds of domesticated vegetables.

To this list add tomatoes, the leading crop canned in the United States

CORN DANCE *by George Catlin*

today; tobacco, base of a billion-dollar-a-year industry, plus the related uses of nicotine in insecticide and medicine; table beans, both the dry (kidneys and limas) and the string beans or green beans; the castor bean used for medicinal castor oil and a wide variety of commercial needs; the peanut, and its vast range of by-products; pumpkins and the related squash families; the green or bell peppers and the red chili pepper (not the black table variety, however); pineapples; avocados; eggplant; wild rice; cassava (from which our tapioca comes); native grape strains; strawberries; blackberries; raspberries — and on and on the list might go.

Then, too, quite an industry has been built around what the Indians of South America once called *cahuchi* (the weeping tree). The Indians would make cuts in the bark and gather the "tears" from this tree, which would be compressed into balls and used as toys and playthings. Today we know "the weeping tree" as the rubber tree, and the rubber industry is a giant one: in the United States alone, rubber and rubber-goods production is in the five-billion-dollar-a-year class.

Where would the scientific study of biology and medicine be without the prolific and ubiquitous guinea pig, domesticated by the South American aborigines? In the field of medicine, consider curare, quinine, cocaine, cascara, arnica, petrolatum, ipecac, and wintergreen, a few of the curative

BALL PLAY OF THE CHOCTAWS *by George Catlin*

substances understood and utilized by the Indians. So skillful were the Indians in the knowledge of natural remedies that in 1952 a scholar could write "... in the four hundred years that the European physicians and botanists have been analyzing and examining the flora of America, they have not yet discovered a medicinal herb not known to the Indians."

In fact, the Indians whom the first settlers found had a far better conception of what constituted good health and how to maintain it than did the settlers themselves. They were a scrupulously clean people, unlike the Europeans who first came to their shores. Columbus took back the news of how often the Indians bathed, and one of the first dictates set down by Queen Isabella of Spain was to the point, if misdirected: "They are not to bathe as frequently as hitherto."

Columbus took back another idea which he got from the Arawaks, one which would become synonymous with ships that sail the sea and the men who sail them. That idea also concerned a tree, called the *hamaca,* whose bark was used to make a swinging bed, hung by vine ropes between two supports. This, of course, became the hammock, beloved of old sailors and do-it-yourself gardeners.

American soldiers who coursed over the world in World War II were greeted by small fry (and some fry not so small) in the most remote and inaccessible corners of the earth with the same classic query: "Got any gum,

Yank?" Chewing gum, along with cigarettes and chocolate candy, became the wampum for Yanks everywhere. Cigarettes were of American Indian origin, as was chocolate — and chewing gum. The Indians used numerous tree gums for chewing as well as the Central American chicle, which is the "chewy" base of all gum made today.

The white comers to the New World found themselves in an environment and in a land so foreign to them as to be almost incomprehensible. There was only one way in which the white man could survive, and that was by emulating the Indian, who knew and understood the land and its ways. So the newcomers took nearly all that the Indian had to offer — they took his means of transportation like the canoe and the snowshoe, they took his buckskin dress for life on the frontier, and they took his foods like cornbread and persimmon bread and hominy and succotash and the corn tortilla of the Southwestern Pueblo dwellers. As an interesting aside here, all the poor starving Pilgrims at Plymouth Rock, with centuries of supposedly superior occidental learning behind them, refused to eat the plentiful clams of that area because they thought them to be poisonous. We can thank the Wampanoags of Massachusetts for introducing the Pilgrims to the fine old Indian tradition of the clambake.

They took, too, the Indian's names for the rich and varied land upon which he lived. Probably in every county in the United States today (exclusive of Hawaii) there is an Indian place-name — of a stream or a mountain or a city — whispering of the time when another people lived and worked and played here. The sonorous roll of the old Indian names is indelibly stamped into the fabric of the land — Mississippi and Monongahela, Narragansett and Natchez, Savannah and Seattle, Tishomingo and Taos, Winnemucca and Wichita —and half of our fifty states bear names which stem from Indian words.

All of these things we have talked about thus far have been tangible. Still unanswered is the question: What kind of people were those Indians? They came from widely varied backgrounds, and any statement would have to be a very general one. The Indians represented over two hundred and fifty different tribes in the United States alone, speaking a hodge-podge of languages and possessing widely divergent customs and cultures and habits.

Most revealing of the Indians' day-to-day life and attitude is a statement by one of the great early students of the plains tribes of this country. That man was George Catlin, who traveled among them and lived among them in the period from 1830–1836. Catlin was a gifted artist; he captured on canvas many of the important leaders and many of the little-known ceremonies among better than two score of the plains tribes from the Canadian

WHITE CLOUD *by George Catlin*

COMANCHE VILLAGE *by George Catlin*

MOVING CAMP *by George Catlin*

border southward into the territory then held by Mexico. The presentation of the Indians as they were was his life's work, and when he published his *Last Rambles Amongst the Indians of the Rocky Mountains and the Andes* (1867), he could say:

I love a people who have always made me welcome to the best they had . . . who are honest without laws, who have no jails and no poorhouse . . . who never take the name of God in vain . . . who worship God without a Bible, and I believe that God loves them also . . . who are free from religious animosities . . . who have never raised a hand against me, or stolen my property, where there was no law to punish either . . . who never fought a battle with white men except on their own ground . . . and oh! how I love a people who don't live for the love of money.

DISCUSSION

1. Approximately what per cent of the income from farm crops in the United States comes from products developed by the American Indians? Name some common foods that the Indians developed.
2. What product used by the South American Indians became the basis of a leading American industry?
3. What else besides foods did the settlers adopt from the Indians in order to survive in the New World?
4. Why do you think George Catlin decided to devote his life to "the presentation of the Indians as they were"?
5. Look again at the quotation at the end of the article. In praising the Indians, Catlin was, by comparison, criticizing certain white men. Of whom was he being critical and why? What did Catlin mean when he said that the Indians "never fought a battle with white men except on their own ground"?
6. What is meant by the opening words of the article, "Americans today have something of a reputation for being impressed by statistics concerning money"? Is the statement a fair one? Why or why not? Why do you think the author began with these words?
7. Why is it appropriate that the author ended his article with Catlin's statement about "people who don't live for the love of money"?

The MYSTERIES of the CABALA

by Isaac Bashevis Singer

*In Warsaw, Poland, in the early
1900's, a young Jewish boy makes
a sobering discovery.*

Everyone knew us on Kroch-malna Street. My friend Mendel and I walked there every day for hours, my hand on his shoulder, his on mine. We were so preoccupied telling each other stories that we stumbled into baskets of fruits and vegetables belonging to the market women, who shouted after us, "Are you blind or something, you slobs?"

I was lean, white-skinned, with a scrawny neck, blue eyes, fiery red hair. My sidelocks were always flying as if in a wind; my gaberdine often went unbuttoned, its pockets loaded with storybooks I rented two for a penny. Not only could I read a page of the Talmud by my-self, I kept on trying my father's volumes of the Cabala, still without understanding much. On the end pages of these books I would draw, with colored pencils, six-winged angels, animals with two heads and with eyes in their tails, demons with horns, snouts, snakes' bodies, calves' feet. In the evening, when I stood on our balcony, I stared up into the star-studded sky and brooded about what there was be-fore the creation of the world. At home everybody said I was growing up to be a crazy philosopher, like that professor in Germany who pondered and philosophized for years, arriving at the conclusion

that a man should walk with his head down and his feet up.

My friend Mendel was the son of a coal porter. Every few weeks his father brought a huge basket of coal for our stoves, and my mother gave him a kopeck. Mendel was taller than I, dark like a gypsy, his hair so black it had a bluish tinge. He had a short nose, a chin with a split in the middle, and slanting eyes like a Tartar's. He wore a tattered gaberdine and torn boots. His family lived in one room at 13 Krochmalna Street. His mother, blind in one eye, dealt in crockery in a stall behind the markets.

We both had the same passion: inventing stories. We never got tired of listening to each other's tales. That late afternoon in summer, as we passed Yanash's bazaar, Mendel halted. He had a secret to tell me: It was not true his father was a coal porter. That was only a disguise. Actually he was richer than any Rothschild.[1] His family had a palace in the forest and a castle on the sea, full of gold and diamonds. I asked him how they had become so rich, and Mendel said, "Swear by your fringed garment, Isaac, you will never tell anyone."

I swore.

"Let's split a straw."

We picked up a straw and, each taking an end, tore it between us as a bond. In Mendel's Tartar eyes a dreamy smile appeared, and he opened a mouth of extremely white teeth, just like a gypsy's. He said, "My father is a robber."

A shiver ran down my back. "Who does he rob?"

"He digs tunnels into banks and drags out their gold. He hides in the forest, waiting to ambush merchants. He wears a gun and a sword. He is a sorcerer, too, and he enters trunks of trees, even though no one can see any opening."

"So why does he have to be a porter?" I asked.

"So the police won't find out . . ."

Mendel told me that his father did not operate single-handed. He was the chief of twelve hundred thieves, whom he sent all over the world to rob people and bring back the booty. Some sailed the seas and attacked ships; others held up caravans in the desert. And when he, Mendel, became bar mitzvah,[2] he would also become a robber and would marry a princess from the other side of the River Sambation. She was already waiting for Mendel to come to the palace and wed her. She had golden hair falling to her ankles and wore golden slippers on her feet. To keep her from running away, Mendel's father had bound her to a pillar with a chain.

---

[1] Rothschild, a wealthy Jewish family of European bankers.

[2] bar mitzvah, a boy who has reached the age at which he is considered an adult and a full member of the Jewish community.

410

"Why does she want to run away?" I asked.

"Because she is yearning for her mother."

I knew it was all lies and even realized which storybooks the different parts came from, but his story enchanted me all the same. We were standing near the fish market, where carp, pike, and chub swam in tubs of water. It was Thursday, and women were buying fish for the Sabbath. A blind beggar wearing dark glasses, with a cottony gray beard, plucked chords on a mandolin while he sang a heart-rending song about the sinking of the *Titanic*. On his shoulder was a parrot, picking at its feathers with its beak. The beggar's wife, young and as agile as a dancer, collected alms in a tambourine. Over the Wola section, the sun was setting, larger than usual, as yellow as gold. Farther out lay a huge, sulphur-yellow cloud, blazing like a fiery river upon a bed of glowing coals. It made me think of the River of Fire in Gehenna (gĭ-hĕn′ə), where the wicked are punished.

Mendel and I, even though we were best friends, were also silently engaged in a struggle. He was envious of me because my father was a rabbi and because we lived in an apartment which had two rooms, a kitchen, and a balcony. He was always trying to prove that he was the stronger, cleverer, and more learned one. Now I was trying to

invent a story just as wonderful as Mendel's, or even more wonderful. Abruptly I said, "I also have a secret I've never told you."

Mendel's Tartar eyes filled with mockery. "What's your secret?"

"Swear you won't tell anyone."

Mendel swore with a false smile and a look that almost seemed to be winking at someone unseen.

I said, "I know the Cabala!"

Mendel's eyes narrowed into slits. "You? How could you know it?"

"My father taught it to me."

"Is it allowed — to teach a boy the Cabala?"

"I'm different from other boys."

"Ah, well! . . . So what did you learn?"

"I can create pigeons. I can make wine flow from the wall. I can recite a spell and fly up in the air."

"What else?"

"I can take seven-mile steps."

"What else?"

"I can turn invisible. And I can change pebbles into pearls."

Mendel began to twist one of his sidelocks. Just as mine were disheveled, his were twirled tightly like two little horns.

"If that's so, you could have more money than the richest man in the world."

"Yes. True."

"So why haven't you got it?"

"One is not allowed to make use of the Cabala. It's very dangerous. There is one spell that if you utter it, the sky turns red like fire, the sea begins to churn, and the waves rise until they touch the clouds. All the animals drown; all the buildings collapse; an abyss opens, and the whole world becomes black as midnight."

"How does that spell go?"

"Do you want me to destroy the world?"

"Nnnn . . . no."

"When I'm older, I will get permission from the prophet Elijah to fly to the Holy Land. And there I will live in a ruin and bring the Messiah."

Mendel bent his head. He picked up a piece of paper from the sidewalk and began to fold it into a bird. I expected him to ask many more questions, but he remained stubbornly silent. All at once I felt that in my ambition I had overdone it; it was Mendel's fault. He had driven me to try to make myself too great. My own words had frightened me. One is not allowed to play games with the Cabala. Terrible nightmares might invade my sleep. I said, "Mendel, I want to go home."

"Let's go."

We moved toward the gate that led to Mirowski Street, no longer walking with our arms about each other's shoulders, but a little apart. Instead of drawing us closer, our talk had separated us. But why? I suddenly noticed how ragged Mendel's clothes were. The toe of his left boot had opened like a mouth,

and the nails stuck up like teeth. We came out on Mirowski Street, which was littered with horse dung, straw off farmers' carts, rotten fruit thrown out by the fruit merchants. Between the two city markets stood a building where ice was manufactured. Though it was still day outside, the electric lights were burning inside. Wheels turned rapidly; leather conveyor belts flowed; signals lit up and extinguished themselves. Not a single person was to be seen. Uncanny noises came from in there. Under our feet, through grates, we could see into cellars where tanks full of water were turning to ice. For quite a while Mendel and I stood there gawking; then we moved on. I asked suddenly, "Who feeds her?"

Mendel seemed to wake up. "What are you talking about?"

"I mean the girl with the golden slippers."

"There are maidservants there."

Not far from the second market, I saw two coins, two copper six-groschen (grō'shən) pieces that lay side by side as if someone had placed them on the sidewalk. I bent down and picked them up. Mendel, having seen them too, cried out, "Partners!"

I gave him one immediately, though at the same time I thought that if it had been he who had picked them up, he would not have given me one. Mendel looked at the coin from every angle, and then he said, "If you can turn pebbles into pearls, what do you want a six-groschen for?"

I would have liked to ask him: And if your father is such a rich robber, what do you want a six-groschen for? But something held me back. I was suddenly aware how yellowish his skin was and what high cheekbones he had. Something in that face spoke to me, but what it was saying I couldn't grasp. The lobes of his ears were attached to his cheeks; the wings of his nostrils rose and fell like a horse's. The corners of his mouth curled with envy, and his black eyes scorned me. He asked, "What are you going to buy with your money? Candy?"

"I'll give it to charity," I said.

"Here — here's a poor man."

In the middle of the sidewalk, on a board with little wheels, sat half a man; he looked as if he had been sawed across the middle. Both hands gripped pieces of wood padded with cloth, on which he leaned. He wore his cap visor over his eyes, and a torn jacket. On his neck hung a cup to throw alms in. I knew very well what could be bought for six groschen — colored pencils, story-books, halvah³ — but some pride ordered me not to hesitate. Stretching my arm out, I tossed the coin in the

---

³ **halvah** (häl-vä′), a candy made of honey and sesame seeds.

cup. The cripple, as if afraid I might change my mind and ask for it back, rolled away so quickly that he almost knocked somebody over.

Mendel's eyebrows came together. "When do you study the Cabala? At night?"

"After midnight."

"So what's going on in heaven?"

I lifted my eyes to the sky and it was red, with black and blue streaks across the middle, as if a storm were coming. Two birds flapped up, screeching, calling each other. The moon had come out. Only a minute ago it had been day. Now night had fallen. The women at the street stands were cleaning up their merchandise. A man with a long stick was walking from one lamppost to the next, lighting the gas flames. I wanted to answer Mendel but couldn't think what to say. I was ashamed of my pretending, as though I were suddenly a grownup. I said, "Mendel, enough of these lies."

"What's the matter, huh?"

"I don't study the Cabala, and your father is not a robber."

Mendel stopped. "Why are you so angry? Because you gave your six-groschen to the beggar?"

"I'm not angry. If you have a palace in the forest, you don't carry coals all day long for Haim Leib. And you haven't got a girl with golden slippers. It's all a fairy story."

"So you want to quarrel? Don't think just because your father is a rabbi I'm going to flatter you. Maybe I have lied, but you'll never know the truth."

"What is there to know? You made it all up."

"I'll become a bandit, a real one."

"They will roast you in Gehenna."

"Let them roast me. I'm in love!"

I looked at him, shocked. "You're lying again."

"No, it's the truth. If not, may God strike me dead on the spot."

I knew Mendel would not swear such an oath in vain. I felt cold, as if someone with icy fingers had touched my ribs. "With a girl?"

"What else? She lives in our courtyard. We'll get engaged. We'll go to my brother's in America."

"Aren't you ashamed? . . ."

"Jacob also was in love. He kissed Rachel. It is written in the Bible."

"Girl-chaser!"

And I began to run. Mendel screamed something after me, and I even imagined that he was pursuing me. I ran until I reached the Radzymin study house. Near the door Mendel's father was praying, a tall, lean man with a sharp Adam's apple, a bent back, and a face that was coal black, like a chimney sweep's. His loins were girded with a rope. He shook, leaned forward, and beat his chest. I imagined he must be asking God's forgiveness for the blasphemies of his son.

At the east wall stood my father in a velvet gaberdine, wearing a broad-brimmed hat and a white sash about his waist. His head touched the wall as he swayed back and forth. A single candle burned in the Menorah.[4] No, I did not yet know the Cabala. But I knew that everything that was happening to me tonight was filled with its mysteries. I felt a deep sadness such as I had never felt before. When my father had finished praying, I said, "Papa, I have to talk to you."

At my serious tone, my father looked at me out of his blue eyes. "What's the matter?"

"Papa, I want you to teach me the Cabala."

"So that's it? At your age it is forbidden to study the Cabala. It is written that these mysteries should not be divulged to a man before he is thirty."

"Papa, I want it now."

My father clutched his red beard. "What's your hurry? You can be a decent man without the Cabala."

"Papa, can one destroy the world with a holy spell?"

"The ancient saints could do everything. And we can do nothing. Come, let's go home."

---

[4] **Menorah** (mə-nôr′ə), a candlestick, usually having seven branches, that is used in Jewish religious ceremonies.

We moved toward the gate, where Rebecca, the baker's daughter, stood with baskets full of fresh rolls, bread, bagels warm from the oven. Women were picking over the baked goods, and the crusts crackled. My father and I walked out into the street, where the gas lamps cast a yellow glow. Between two chimneys spouting smoke and sparks hung a large, blood-red moon.

"Is it true that people live there?" I asked.

My father was silent for a while. "What makes you think so? Nothing is known. Cabala is only for strong brains. When weak little brains are immersed in the Cabala, one can easily fall into insanity."

My father's words frightened me. I felt myself close to madness.

He said, "You are still a boy. When, God willing, you grow up, get married, have more sense, then you will find out what you can do."

"I'm not going to get married."

"What else? Stay a bachelor? It is written, 'He created it not in vain. He formed it to be inhabited.' You will grow up, be matched with a girl, and get engaged."

"What girl?"

"Who can know in advance?"

At that moment I realized why I was so sad. The street was full of girls, but I didn't know who was going to be my betrothed. She, the one destined for me, didn't know

either. It could be that we both bought candy in the same store, that we passed each other, looked at each other, not knowing that we were going to be man and wife. I began to look among the crowd. The street was full of girls my age, some a little younger, some older. One walked and licked an ice-cream cone. Another one nibbled cheesecake at Esther's candy store, holding it between her thumb and middle finger, with her pinky lifted up elegantly. A girl carrying books and notebooks under her arm, with red ribbons in her braids, a pleated skirt and a black apron, had black-stockinged legs that looked like a doll's. The streets were full of the aroma of fresh bagels, of breezes coming from the Vistula River and the Praga forest. Around the street-lamps a myriad of winged crea-tures whirled — moths, butterflies, gnats — deceived by the light into believing night was day. I looked at the upper floors, where girls stood on balconies, gazed out of win-dows. They were talking, singing, laughing. I listened to the noise of sewing machines, to a gramophone playing. Behind a window I saw the dark shadow of a girl. I imag-ined she was staring at me through the mesh of the curtain. I said to my father, "Papa, can you find out from the Cabala who you are going to get engaged to?"

My father stopped. "What do you have to know for? They know in heaven, and that is enough."

For a while we walked in silence. Then my father asked, "Son, what has happened to you?"

All the lampposts became bent and all the lights foggy as my eyes filled with tears. "Papa, I don't know."

"You are growing up, my son. That is what is happening to you."

And my father suddenly did something he had never done be-fore — he bent down and kissed my forehead.

DISCUSSION

1. What pastime interested both Mendel and Isaac? Why did the two boys try to outdo each other with their stories?

2. What secret did Mendel reveal about his father? What secret did Isaac tell Mendel? Why did Isaac later regret having invented his story? When Isaac asked his father to teach him the Cabala, what did his father say?

3. What did Mendel reveal that came as a shock to Isaac? Why did Isaac at first not believe him? How do you know that what Mendel told him made a great impression on Isaac?

4. Where did Isaac find his father and Mendel's? Describe the appearance of the two men.

5. How did Isaac's father explain the boy's feeling so puzzled and sad?

6. Judging from the conversation about it in the story, what do you think the Cabala is?

7. Before each boy revealed his secret, why do you think he made the other swear not to tell it? After the boys had exchanged stories, why did Isaac feel that their talk had separated them rather than drawing them closer?

8. Long after Mendel had told his story, why do you suppose Isaac asked him who fed the girl with the golden slippers?

9. How did the relationship between the two boys change after the finding of the six-groschen pieces? In your opinion, what were Mendel's feelings that Isaac sensed but was not quite able to grasp? Why did Isaac give the six-groschen piece to the beggar?

10. When Isaac asked his father questions about destroying the world with a spell and about people living on the moon, do you think he was satisfied with the way in which his father answered him? Why or why not? Do you think Isaac really expected that his father would be able to answer the questions? Why do you think that?

11. Do you think that the rabbi had been an unloving father? Why do you think as you do? Do you think that Isaac had ever doubted his father's love for him? Why do you think that?

12. In Isaac's later life, do you suppose he became more interested or less interested in the mysteries of the Cabala? Why do you think as you do?
13. It is obvious from the story that Isaac's family would choose the girl he would marry. How would you feel about having a marriage arranged for you in this way?

AUTHOR

Born in 1904 in Radzymin, Poland, Isaac Bashevis Singer moved with his family to Warsaw at the age of four. His father and both his grandfathers were rabbis, and he himself studied for several years at a Warsaw rabbinical seminary. Eventually, however, he decided to give up his religious studies and to become a writer like his older brother.

Mr. Singer began his career as a journalist in Poland, but in 1935 he came to the United States and settled in New York City. There he joined the staff of the *Jewish Daily Forward,* a Yiddish newspaper in which most of his stories and novels originally appeared. His works have been reprinted in Yiddish newspapers throughout the world and have been translated into fifteen languages for publication in book form and in magazines.

The adult books Mr. Singer has written during the past forty years have received many awards and have brought him recognition as an exceptional storyteller. He is the most popular and perhaps the greatest living Yiddish writer. Although he started writing books for young people only a few years ago, these too have been highly praised. Three of his books for children were runners-up for the Newbery Medal in 1967, 1968, and 1969. "The Mysteries of the Cabala" is a chapter from *A Day of Pleasure,* a book for young adults which received the 1969 National Book Award.

Mr. Singer became a United States citizen in 1943 and now lives with his wife in an apartment on New York's West Side.

FROM THE BOOKSHELF

THE LOCH NESS MONSTER, *by Elwood Baumann*

From earliest times attempts have been made to track the monster that supposedly inhabits Scotland's Loch Ness. The attempts still go on, now with the help of airplanes, submarines, and sonar equipment.

FAST BREAK, *by Curtis Bishop*

When Sam's new friend, a Mexican boy, has to return to Mexico, Riverside High's chances for a basketball championship seem ruined.

ALL THE DARK PLACES, *by J. Allan Bosworth*

Peter was so fascinated by Preacher's End cave that he was foolhardy enough to enter its dark, silent depths alone.

THE YEAR OF THE THREE-LEGGED DEER, *by Eth Clifford*

It should have been the beginning of a happy life on the Indian frontier for Jesse Benton, his Indian wife, and their two children, but the hate and prejudice of a few men brought unexpected challenges.

THE RESTLESS GHOST: THREE STORIES, *by Leon Garfield*

These three stories, set in the eighteenth century, are about a ghost that takes the place of a real boy, two highly unsuited shipmates, and a simpleton who averts a mutiny and wins his lady's hand.

THE TOMBS OF ATUAN, *by Ursula K. Le Guin*

Arha, young high priestess of the tombs, must choose between light and dark in a moment of crisis for herself, for Ged, the wizard of Earthsea, and for Earthsea itself.

YANKEE DOODLE BOY: A YOUNG SOLDIER'S ADVENTURES IN THE AMERICAN REVOLUTION TOLD BY HIMSELF, *by Joseph P. Martin*

This firsthand account of the experiences of a fifteen-year-old soldier in the Continental Army, which was first published in 1830, has now been republished for young readers.

Tapestry

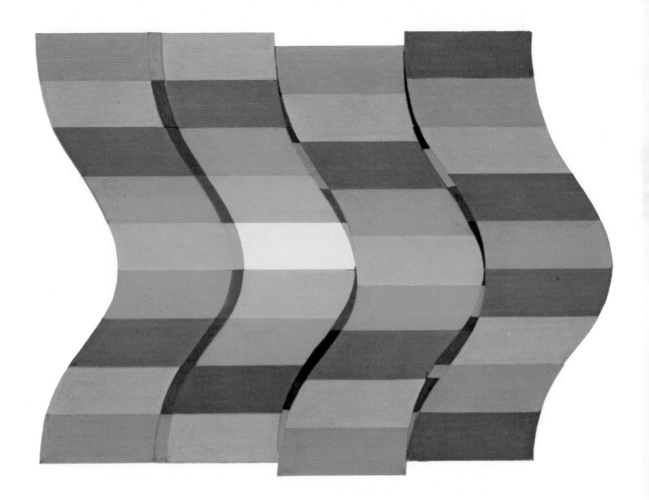

Contents

422

Tapestry

Oak Island

by Edmund Burke

The canoe slipped quietly across the water, the three boys paddling it swiftly and smoothly toward their target. The sky, dull and dark with the approach of autumn, was harsh overhead, and as they skirted islet after islet, they remembered that all these islands and the bay in which they lay were haunted. Old men said the dog of the devil had chosen Mahone Bay as his special territory, chosen it and held it.

Actually the three boys didn't really care. In this late summer of 1795, their work was finished, and they were off on a camping trip. Anthony Vaughan, Daniel McInnis, and Jack Smith, Nova Scotians all, were heading for Oak Island, the only island in Mahone Bay to boast a tree, the only one of 365 which really amounted to anything. They drove the bow of the canoe onto the beach of a cove and stepped out. Camping gear and food stowed to one side, they pulled the canoe completely free of the water.

With the afternoon ahead of them, they set out on a leisurely exploration of the island. They pushed around a swamp, climbed one or two small hills, and then crossed an old trail. Eagerly, looking for something they couldn't name, they began to follow. It led toward the center of the island, rising steadily as it went, until finally the boys found themselves on top of what was probably the largest hill on the island. There, just on the crest and obviously at the end of the trail, stood an old oak tree, hoary with age, mossy and storm battered. The three, clustering at its base, stared upward and noticed that high on its side one limb had been partly sawed off.

As far as any of them knew, no one lived on Oak Island, and no one ever had. The sawed-off branch hung above, a wooden question mark. Dan McInnis, the lightest of the three, began his preparations and with the help of his two companions started the ascent. He got up without trouble and carefully made his way onto the branch. As far as he could see, the stub was about four feet long. He edged out carefully, tensing himself, dreading the sound of cracking wood. The stub held, and suddenly he was within inches of the end. Under his hands, spread out to hold him, were deep marks, grooves in the wood, cut as though by block and tackle. Dan McInnis leaned forward and looked down.

His companions were standing looking up, their faces turned toward him. He was about to call down when he noticed something odd, something strange, about the ground beneath. Vaughan and Smith were in the middle of a big circle, a circle that stood out plainly from where he sat. Yet Dan could remember nothing of the sort when he'd been down there. He backed slowly until he reached the massive trunk and then hastily slid and fell to the ground. While his mystified companions watched, he bent down and began to trace the outline of the circle he'd seen.

That night around the campfire the three talked over their find.

Nova Scotia was full of tales of pirates and buccaneers, tales of dead men and ghosts, of slaughtered prisoners and buried treasure. The three had heard them all, and it seemed no more than reasonable that they had stumbled upon the site of one of the fabled caches. The circle, so plain from above, was hard to see from ground level, but they'd measured it roughly. Thirteen feet it was, just about right for the burial of a treasure chest. They'd come camping with just the faintest hope of finding adventure. It looked as though their dreams might have been fulfilled. Tomorrow they'd start to dig. The treasure couldn't be far below the surface, and its finding would be a fitting climax to their camping trip.

The three boys were so sure they'd stumbled on something of value that they did indeed set about digging the very next morning. They'd been back to the mainland and laid in a stock of food to supplement their camping supplies as well as tools for the job in hand. And so they dug, young strong muscles dislodging the soil as rapidly as possible. Their campsite was nearby, and they asked for nothing more.

The big hole went down and down, spade depth by spade depth. Two feet, three feet, four feet, five feet — arms used to scythe, hoe, and ax pushed the tools; hard, callous hands blistered with strain, but still they dug.

At ten feet they found something, something tangible, proof men had indeed dug there before. The three boys found themselves standing on a rough platform of oak planks, stretching solidly across the hole. Now, suddenly, there was an urgency in their digging, a haste that pushed them on in spite of aching arms and raw-palmed hands. They tore at the sides, ripping the planks out — and still there was nothing. There was a council of war then, to decide whether or not they should dig farther. The conclusion was both obvious and foregone — no one would dig ten feet down in the hard island soil to bury a platform of oak planks unless there was something to hide. They voted to go on digging.

For the rest of that autumn they dug. They made it down just below the twenty-foot mark, working in shifts. At twenty feet they found another layer of oak planking, as solid as the first. That was the only thing they found to give them hope, but it was enough.

So it went — for seven years. The three boys grew up and became men. Smith and McInnis married and brought their wives out to the island, farming a little, trapping a little — and always digging. Each time they reached another ten feet down into the dark, hard soil of the island, they'd find another layer of planking, as regularly as clockwork. The digging had long since ceased to be easy — now they were moving each spadeful, each bucketful, to the surface with a hand-operated hoist, trimming the sides and waiting for the day. The big hole had a name now. They called it the "Money Hole," and people on the mainland laughed and secretly wanted to join them.

In 1803 Jack Smith's wife became pregnant, and he took her ashore to Truro to a doctor. While she and her husband waited for the birth of the child, they talked to the doctor, John Lynds, and he asked them about the digging. Something in the way Jack Smith talked must have been contagious, because he aroused Dr. Lynds's interest in the idea. The next year, backed by some of his friends in Truro, Dr. Lynds formed the Oak Island Treasure Company. The three original finders were members, but now there was money, money to buy tools and to hire more men. That was all they needed, more men and more tools.

Many hands made light work, and the pit dropped deeper and deeper. The hole was larger now, to accommodate the workmen, and every ten feet a fresh layer of planks appeared. The three boys had not been wrong. At eighty feet below the surface, something new intruded itself — just below the planks was a three-inch layer of charcoal, completely covering the thirteen-foot circle. If that wasn't mystery enough in itself, they had no sooner dug through the charcoal than they uncovered a layer of something unknown to them, a total mystery.

It was a natural fiber, that much was indisputable, but no one on the island could identify it further. Hastily a sample was dispatched to the mainland, and the entire crew waited for the result. When it came, they were no closer to a solution of the mystery — in fact, if anything, they were more confused. They'd found a six-inch layer of the outer fiber from coconut shells. A quick glance at a map will show just how far Nova Scotia is from any source of coconuts. A single shell might have floated there, but not enough to fill an area of over 130 square feet to a depth of six inches. If there had ever been any question, the fiber answered it — the Money Hole was definitely man-made.

The coconut was a spur, if one had been needed, and the men dug even harder. At ninety feet they found yet another mystery, this time a three-inch layer of ship's putty. It was as though the makers

had been determined to baffle and confuse anyone who dared to delve behind them. The final confusion arose when, just beneath the putty, the excavators uncovered a flat stone.

Measuring some three feet long and perhaps fifteen or sixteen inches wide, it was thin and covered with fine markings. No one was able to decipher them, and Jack Smith took the stone off to his cabin. For many years it formed part of the Smith fireplace, but it was later transferred to the mainland. The last trace of it was in 1928, when someone remembered, vaguely, having seen it used as a doorstop in a Halifax office.

Just below the stone, and at the end of a week's work, someone pushed a rod down into the floor of the pit. It pushed through the soil quite easily and then, as expected, struck wood at the hundred-foot mark. The listening men thought they could hear a dull booming sound under their feet, and if it hadn't been quite so late, they'd have gone on digging. As it was, Saturday night had come, and they went ashore thinking of Monday and the few feet of earth which lay between them and their goal.

When Monday morning came, curious eyes watched the progress of the small fleet of boats that ferried the workers back to their task. On Oak Island the men almost ran up the long, now well-worn trail to the Money Hole — and there they halted, their mouths agape.

At their feet was the hole, but now it was nearly full of water. Sounding lines proved that a solid body of water, just over sixty feet deep, lay between them and their target. It was a blow that would have totally discouraged most men, but Dr. Lynds approached the matter logically. He knew of the existence, on the island, of several fresh-water springs. To him it was obvious that Saturday's probe with the rod had broken into the course of one of them — with the resulting flood. Now it was simply a matter of driving a parallel shaft close to the Money Hole and, from it, a gallery which would come in below the spring.

Lynds's logic was excellent — as far as it went — and he succeeded in selling the idea to his fellow stockholders. What he seems to have overlooked in his thinking was the fact that the original builders or diggers of the Money Hole would have had to go through the spring, if his assessment of the situation was correct. It would be highly unlikely that the spring had come into existence, completely and fortuitously, after the original hole had been dug.

The fact remains, however, that work was begun on the matching hole and continued to a depth of nearly 110 feet. The working level was now well below that of the first excavation, and there was no sign of water. It seemed safe to drive their horizontal shaft now, over beneath the site of the "spring." They didn't get far — the water nearly drowned two of the diggers, and when it finished rising, it was on a level with that in the first hole. It took less than an hour for weeks of digging to be completely submerged. With that second flood, the hopes of the first Oak Island Treasure Company were ended, flooded out, as it were, by the force of the water.

In 1849 a second company was formed, again with the name of the Oak Island Treasure Company. Jack Smith and Daniel McInnis were dead by then, but Anthony Vaughan led the hopefuls to the site himself. Dr. Lynds was a member of the second company. His faith had stood the test of the years, and he was quite willing to invest money in the new scheme. The rest of the members of the syndicate were hardheaded businessmen, and before they put any great amount of money into the venture, they were determined to know what it was, exactly, that they were after. They hired an itinerant coal miner named James Pitalbo to help them in answering that vital question. Pitalbo had invented a device that permitted sampling the subsoil without the necessity of digging a shaft. His gadget was a bit which turned on the end of a free shaft; the shaft itself was pushed around by a horse, and once in position, it bored its way deeper into the ground, sampling anything it encountered. By pulling it at any level, it was possible to tell just exactly what was down there.

Pitalbo and his device were installed on Oak Island, and a platform was built right across the first pit, above the water line. Before an excited crowd of spectators and speculators, Pitalbo began operations. Each time he brought up one of his primitive cores, a group of the investors examined it carefully. At one hundred feet the pod, or bit, revealed the oak planking which had been sounded so many years before. After a few more turns there were samples of oak, which appeared to form a layer five inches through. Then suddenly the bit went into empty air, an open space a foot deep. After that came another layer of oak, this time four inches through. Finally there was a layer of loose material which steadfastly refused to permit sampling. Each time Pitalbo put the bit down, it spun reluctantly, indicating that something was there, but nothing came up. He had drawn it up once when Dr. Lynds noticed a bright bit of color adhering to its side. Eagerly the men grasped at it — three tiny links of gold were clinging to the clay. The fragment passed from hand to hand as men's eyes lighted with gold fever. In the meantime,

canny James Pitalbo dropped the bit again, took another sample, and began to examine his core.

Out of the corner of one eye, a member of the syndicate saw Pitalbo pocket something from the core. He told Dr. Lynds what he had seen, and the doctor demanded that Pitalbo give them what he had found. The miner protested strongly and then promised to show everyone his find the next day, when there was to be an official meeting attended by all members of the company.

Unfortunately, during the night Pitalbo decamped. Taking a small boat, he rowed to the mainland, leaving his equipment behind him. He disappeared from the area completely for several months, only to return to Cape Breton Island later in the summer. There, in various places, he announced his intention of returning to Oak Island the following year — to begin his own search. He hinted that the Oak Island Treasure Company had no more claim than he, but he steadfastly refused to say what it was he had found. That winter, he was killed in a mine accident, and as far as anyone knows, he took with him to his grave the secret of what he had found on the bit.

In the meantime, the members of the company were by no means discouraged. Although Pitalbo — and his clue — were gone, the vital equipment was still there, and the men soon learned to use it. Day after day they probed through the water, through the earth, measuring, checking, measuring, and rechecking. In the end they came to the conclusion that there were two layers of loose material that could not be sampled. The first measured either twenty or twenty-two inches through and was immediately followed by eight inches of oak, then another twenty-two inches of loose stuff, and finally four more inches of oak. Logical deductions based on these figures saw two ship's chests, stacked one on top of the other — and, of course, filled with treasure. The chests were located roughly in the middle of the old thirteen-foot circle. There had been three gold links — and no further proof was needed.

The work began in earnest then, a second matching hole being dug just ten feet away from the original Money Hole. At a depth of 110 feet they stopped and tried once more to drive a secondary shaft toward the first digging. And once again the water poured in, filling the pit as fast as it had the others.

It was only then that someone finally abandoned the preconceived notion of a spring and began to interpret the regular, matching rise and fall of the water level in all three pits for what it was. It might, they conceded, be the result of the tide. At just that point one of the workmen fell into the first hole and came up with his mouth full of salt water. They were battling, not a fresh-water spring, but the sea itself.

Dr. Lynds had been wrong, and he was perfectly willing to admit it, but now he suddenly remembered a point which he'd noted when the boys first brought him to the island. The beach at Smith's Cove had been smooth, not with a natural smoothness but, rather, with an almost artificial quality. Perhaps the sea was entering at the cove.

Once more the members of the company took heed of the doctor's words and, moving the entire crew down to the beach in the cove, began to dig there. Dr. Lynds's memory had served him well, for under the 150-foot beach (which they patiently dug up, foot by foot) they found evidence that men had been there before them. Beneath the surface sand they found a firm layer of gravel, which in turn was succeeded by a stratum of boulders. At first the boulders seemed to lie haphazardly, but closer examination showed that they formed a huge, irregular pattern which allowed the tidal floods to move freely through. Beneath the boulders was a layer of eelgrass, one of the more common aquatic plants of the region, but obviously cut and laid in position by plan. And beneath the eelgrass was a massive layer of coconut fiber, tons and tons of the tropical material.

Finally, beneath the big coconut mat were a series of five stone-lined channels, leading from the sea back toward the location of the Money Hole.

At some point in time, someone with a thorough working knowledge of engineering and hydrodynamics had built a highly ingenious system which would ensure a constant flow of water inland from the sea. Although the tide would ordinarily have affected its working, the coconut fiber and the eelgrass formed a perfect sponge which would empty itself when the tide was out. The whole project was so well conceived and so well executed that to the members of the company it seemed impossible that they would ever be able to drain the Money Hole. They had no pumps which could possibly cope with the sea, and in actual fact, in 1850 it is doubtful that such pumps were even in existence. There remained only one course which might allow them to reach the golden goal — they must stop the sea before it reached the cove. With the last of their money they began to build a cofferdam offshore. Built high enough and strong enough, it would block the tide, and eventually they might be able to drain the Hole. A sudden storm, rising in the bay, smashed the cofferdam before it was completed, and the second Oak Island Treasure Company was out of business.

Sand

Gravel

Boulders

Eelgrass

Tide channel

Coconut fiber

Still, the legend grew, as treasure legends do, and in 1893 a third company was formed by Frederick Blair. Astute and intelligent, Blair marshaled his resources carefully, sending advance crews in to build cookhouses and bunkhouses. Then he hired over one hundred laborers and engaged the services of a firm of mining engineers as consultants.

Using a three-inch pipe, Blair sank a two-and-a-half-inch drill. The engineers on the project reasoned that water pressure, plus the disturbances created by the now many shafts, both vertical and horizontal, might easily have displaced the treasure. But the drill struck something at 125 feet. There were bits of iron and bits of wood in the stuff brought up, and the driller in charge swore on oath that the drill had pierced what "appeared to be chests and coins." There is a big question mark here, for iron and oak may indicate chests, but there is no proof of coins. Whether the master driller knew more than he told must remain one of the minor mysteries, like that of James Pitalbo.

Blair was pleased with the results of the drilling but far from satisfied, and he ordered the bore to be sunk farther. At 153 feet the men met one of the greatest surprises of all — a tough layer that reacted like solid stone. The drill finally bit through it, and when the core was surfaced, it looked exactly like concrete. The core was immediately shipped to England for analysis by a well-known firm of chemists in London. In the meantime, operations on the island continued. Having pierced the "concrete," the drill dropped free for seven feet and then met another layer like the first.

The London report was succinct, but although it clarified one question, it posed many others. According to A. Boake Roberts & Co. Ltd., the material in question was cement and had been set there by men. From the report and from the on-site drilling, Blair established, to his own satisfaction at least, that deep in the ground was a concrete chamber, with a roof three feet in thickness, which was seven feet high and which had a floor as thick as its roof. From parallel drilling he even established the other dimension of the chamber, stating that it was five feet wide.

Blair and his partners had made a great deal of progress, but unluckily for them, funds were beginning to run short. In a final effort, Blair decided to find out exactly where the water from the Money Hole went on its return to the sea. Stationing men all along the shore of Smith's Cove and the immediate shoreline, he dropped a strong red dye into the pit itself. The men waited for hours, each watching his sector for the telltale stain, yet there was nothing. Acting on a hunch, Blair sent more men out, this time to the other side of the island. Sure enough, the red stain was marking the sea on the other side of Oak Island from Smith's Cove. It was no longer a question of one intricate maze of artificial waterways, but of two, one on the north shore, one on the south. And after the previous experiences with one set, it seemed unlikely that the newly discovered channels could be blocked. Resignedly, Blair closed down his operations; his cash and credit were both exhausted.

Four years later, a four-man party tried again. This time the treasure hunters were Frederick Childs, Albert Gallatin, Duncan Harris, and Franklin Delano Roosevelt, who was later to become President of the United States. At his mother's house near New Brunswick, young Roosevelt had heard the story of the Money Hole and persuaded his friends to join him in a holiday lark. They raised some money and brought a big drill to Oak Island. It had a maximum reach of about 150 feet and on several occasions touched that depth. Each time, the cores showed the same result, confirmed by analysts at New York's Columbia University. Down there, under the Money Hole, was manmade rocklike material. The earlier report from London had been amply confirmed.

Other expeditions have tried their hands at the game, but they have met with no more success than their predecessors.

Sometimes, though, you wonder just how much gold, if any, is buried in that mysterious pit. As far as anyone knows, the only "haul" in the 170-odd years that have elapsed since the three boys began digging has been three small gold links. Perhaps Pitalbo found something — but what? The biggest single question which Oak Island poses, apart from whether or not there's any real treasure there, is that of its origin.

Three main ideas and a fourth wild one have been put forward to account for the "cache." One is simply that it is pirate loot, buried against the time when the owners would be free to come and reclaim their property. A second advances the idea that it is the site of the long-lost French crown jewels. Various researchers and scholars have said that when Louis XVI and Marie Antoinette were captured at Varennes, one of the ladies of the court made her escape, carrying the jewels. Further research has located traces of a Frenchwoman in Lonsburg, Nova Scotia, who might or might not have been this same lady. At any rate, no trace of the jewels has ever been found. The third idea, put forth in 1930, is that there is no treasure involved but that the Money Hole is all that remains of a Viking colony on the site. More fantastic is the fourth idea, proposed by a Nebraskan in 1953. In a privately printed book called *The Oak Island Enigma,* one Thomas Pennell Leary stated his theory that the site contains all the original works and manuscripts of Sir Francis Bacon, including, of course, those which he wrote under the pseudonym "William Shakespeare."

Mr. Leary's idea is so far-fetched and so lacking in proof that it is almost funny. Equally, the Viking idea warrants little more than a passing glance. There is nothing about Oak Island and its Money Hole which fits in with anything we know about the Vikings or their way of living.

If we forget those two guesses, we are left with only two possibilities — the pirate idea or the romantic notion that the French crown jewels are hidden there beneath the old oak tree. Before you take sides and subscribe to either, let's look back at the evidence.

At some date prior to 1795 a party landed on the island, unobserved by anyone from the nearby coastal villages, and began what amounted to a major engineering project. It would be a big job with today's modern equipment; in those days it must have been little short of monumental. These unknown persons dug a hole thirteen feet in diameter which went down to a known depth of some 160 feet. At the bottom they built what we assume to be a concrete chamber seven feet high and five feet wide, with sides which were three feet thick. Approximately sixty feet above, during the course of refilling their hole, they deposited two oak chests, one on top of the other. Just above the chests they placed a flat stone slab and, immediately atop the stone, a thick layer of ship's putty. Above that were a layer of coconut-fiber matting and then a layer of charcoal. They placed solid oak platforms across the hole at ten-foot intervals until they reached the surface. The spaces between oak platforms were, of course, filled with soil.

While this enormous project was going on, and timed so that the work must have coincided, they also built an intricate system of artificial waterways leading in from the sea on either side. In order to maintain and utilize the flow of tidal water, the waterways had to be constructed at sea level, so that when they reached the Money Hole, they were nearly ninety feet below the surface of the ground. This meant that these channels had to be cut for a total distance of a half mile at roughly that depth, allowing for variations in the island's surface. On the Smith's Cove side at least (the other side has never been excavated), the work involved the use of some several tons of coconut-fiber matting, to make the tidal sponge, as well as enough eelgrass to form a foot-thick mattress extending over a distance of 150 feet.

There must have been a large working party, one with a minimum of twenty workmen. At their head there would have been at least one person with a sound and thorough knowledge of engineering theory and practice, a man or men capable of planning and carrying out the entire operation. There must, in addition, have been one or more ships of considerable tonnage. If there was only one, it must have made several trips, for the sheer bulk of the coconut fiber would have more than made cargo for the average ship of the period prior to 1795. Finally, there must have been a considerable amount of cement available in order to pour the hidden chamber. Above all, we must imagine that of all the men involved, none ever told the story and that each man was content to keep his own counsel and carry the secret to his grave. If only one of them had talked, the story would have leaked, and while the treasure might still be there, it would not remain so fascinating a mystery.

The idea that Oak Island contains the French crown jewels is a romantic one but hard, in the light of the known facts, to believe. Could one lady, even with an escort of cavaliers, make her way from France to Nova Scotia and then hire the necessary men and buy the requisite materials to undertake the project? Even if she'd been able to do so without attracting attention

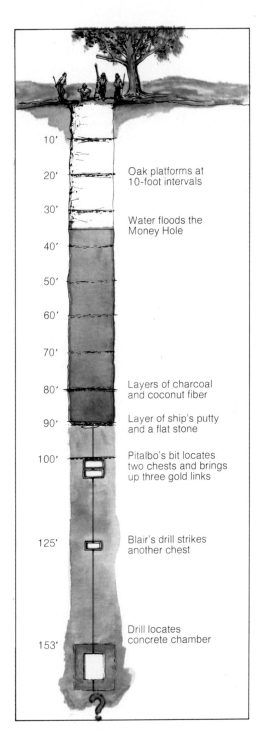

10'
20' — Oak platforms at 10-foot intervals
30' — Water floods the Money Hole
40'
50'
60'
70'
80' — Layers of charcoal and coconut fiber
90' — Layer of ship's putty and a flat stone
100' — Pitalbo's bit locates two chests and brings up three gold links
125' — Blair's drill strikes another chest
153' — Drill locates concrete chamber

from government, local or otherwise, wouldn't some of the hired hands have talked or at least speculated aloud? Even if, at the end of the work, she'd personally disposed of them all by poison or something equally deadly, they'd have been missed. And moreover, where would she or her employees have found that coconut matting?

Finally, of course, there's the pirate idea, and for once it seems the most likely answer. Most of the researchers into Oak Island have felt that it was the repository for the treasure of the famous Captain William Kidd. There is, however, no proof that Kidd, his officers, or men would have had the necessary technical knowledge to undertake the involved engineering and construction on which the mystery is founded. Nor is there evidence that Kidd's crews were so loyal as to carry the secret to their graves.

If we must accept the pirate story, it makes far more sense to think of ships coming to Oak Island, the crews swarming ashore to do the work, and then the ships sailing away again. Somewhere out on the broad Atlantic a sudden storm arises, and the ships with their crews sink without a trace.

No matter how you look at it, no matter which educated guess you believe in, Oak Island still stands, rather remote, rather bleak, and seemingly full of mystery forever. Someday soon perhaps we'll read that someone has gone down to the bottom of the Money Hole with a metal detector and actually found the treasure chests. Then perhaps we'll know what's there and — even more interesting — who put it there.

DISCUSSION

1. Who first attempted to solve the mystery of Oak Island and when?
2. What different kinds of materials have been found in the Money Hole?
3. On what did searchers base their deductions about the existence of treasure chests and a concrete chamber?
4. What system had the original builders designed for insuring a constant flow of water inland from the sea? How was the sea responsible for putting three of the treasure companies out of business?

5. What theories have been advanced to explain the origin of the Money Hole? Which of them does the author think most likely? What are the author's arguments against the other three theories?
6. Can you think of any reason for placing oak-plank platforms at ten-foot intervals in the Money Hole? If so, what is it?
7. What do you think the "three tiny links of gold" might have been that were brought up with Pitalbo's sampling bit? Why do you think Pitalbo chose to disappear rather than show what he found on his next sampling?
8. What do the builders' tremendous efforts in constructing the Money Hole suggest to you about the value of whatever was buried there? How do you think the builders expected to be able to recover their treasure?
9. Do you think something is still buried in the Money Hole? Why do you think as you do?
10. Do you agree with the author's analysis of the four theories about the Money Hole? Why or why not? Can you think of any other possible explanation? If so, what is it?
11. Why do you think men have been willing to put so much time and money into trying to solve the mystery of Oak Island? Would you be interested in attempting to solve the mystery? If so, how would you go about it?
12. In your opinion, what is the most amazing aspect of the Oak Island mystery? Why?

Searching for Summer

by Joan Aiken

Lily wore yellow on her wedding day. In the nineties people put a lot of faith in omens and believed that if a bride's dress was yellow, her married life would be blessed with a bit of sunshine.

It was years since the bombs had been banned, but still the cloud never lifted. Whitish gray, day after day, sometimes darkening to a weeping slate-color, or, at the end of an evening, turning to smoky copper, the sky endlessly, secretively brooded.

Old people began their stories with the classic, fairy-tale opening: "Long, long ago, when I was a liddle un, in the days when the sky was blue . . ." and children, listening, chuckled among themselves at the absurd thought, because *blue*, imagine it! How could the sky ever have been *blue*? You might as well say, "In the days when the grass was pink."

Stars, rainbows, and all other such heavenly side shows had been permanently withdrawn, and if the radio announced that there was a blink of sunshine in such and such a place, where the cloud belt had

thinned for half an hour, cars and buses would pour in that direction for days in an unavailing search for warmth and light.

After the wedding, when all the relations were standing on the church porch, with Lily shivering prettily in her buttercup nylon, her father prodded the dour and withered grass — although it was August, the leaves were hardly out yet — and said, "Well, Tom, what are you aiming to do now, eh?"

"Going to find a bit of sun and have our honeymoon in it," said Tom. There was a general laugh from the wedding party.

"Don't get sunburned," shrilled Aunt Nancy.

"Better start off Bournemouth way. Paper said they had a half hour of sun last Wednesday week," Uncle Arthur weighed in heavily.

"We'll come back brown as — as this grass," said Tom, and ignoring the good-natured teasing from their respective families, the two young people mounted on their scooter, which stood ready at the churchyard wall, and chugged away in a shower of golden confetti. When they were

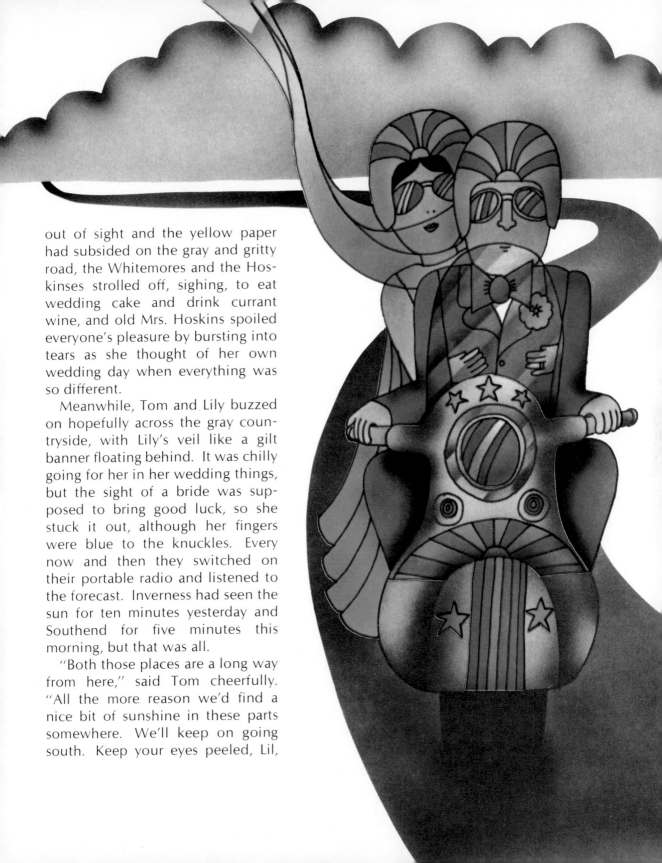

out of sight and the yellow paper had subsided on the gray and gritty road, the Whitemores and the Hoskinses strolled off, sighing, to eat wedding cake and drink currant wine, and old Mrs. Hoskins spoiled everyone's pleasure by bursting into tears as she thought of her own wedding day when everything was so different.

Meanwhile, Tom and Lily buzzed on hopefully across the gray countryside, with Lily's veil like a gilt banner floating behind. It was chilly going for her in her wedding things, but the sight of a bride was supposed to bring good luck, so she stuck it out, although her fingers were blue to the knuckles. Every now and then they switched on their portable radio and listened to the forecast. Inverness had seen the sun for ten minutes yesterday and Southend for five minutes this morning, but that was all.

"Both those places are a long way from here," said Tom cheerfully. "All the more reason we'd find a nice bit of sunshine in these parts somewhere. We'll keep on going south. Keep your eyes peeled, Lil, and tell me if you see a blink of sun on those hills ahead."

But they came to the hills and passed them, and a new range shouldered up ahead and then slid away behind, and still there was no flicker or patch of sunshine to be seen anywhere in the gray, winter-ridden landscape. Lily began to get discouraged, so they stopped for a cup of tea at a drive-in.

"Seen the sun lately, mate?" Tom asked the proprietor.

He laughed shortly. "Notice any buses or trucks around here? Last time I saw the sun was two years ago September; came out just in time for the wife's birthday."

"It's stars I'd like to see," Lily said, looking wistfully at her dust-colored tea. "Ever so pretty they must be."

"Well, better be getting on, I suppose," said Tom, but he had lost some of his bounce and confidence. Every place they passed through looked nastier than the last, partly on account of the dismal light, partly because people had given up bothering to take a pride in their boroughs. And then, just as they were entering a village called Molesworth, the dimmest, drabbest, most insignificant huddle of houses they had come to yet, the engine coughed and died on them.

"Can't see what's wrong," said Tom after a prolonged survey.

"What'll we do, Tom?" Lily asked.

"Have to stop here for the night, s'pose." Tom was short-tempered with frustration. "Look, there's a garage just up the road. We can push the bike there, and they'll tell us if there's a pub where we can stay. It's nearly six anyway."

They had taken the bike to the garage and the man there was just telling them that the only pub in the village was the Rising Sun, where Mr. Noakes might be able to give them a room, when a bus pulled up in front of the petrol pumps.

"Look," the garage owner said, "there's Mr. Noakes just getting out of the bus now. Sid!" he called.

But Mr. Noakes was not able to come to them at once. Two old people were climbing slowly out of the bus ahead of him: a blind man with a white stick and a withered, frail old lady in a black satin dress and hat. "Careful now, George," she was saying, "mind ee be careful with my son William."

"I'm being careful, Mrs. Hatching," the conductor said patiently as he almost lifted the unsteady old pair off the bus platform. The driver had stopped his engine, and everyone on the bus was taking a mild and sympathetic interest except for Mr. Noakes, just behind, who was cursing irritably at the delay. When the two old people were on the narrow pavement, the conductor saw that they were going to have trouble with a bicycle that was propped against the curb just ahead of them; he picked it up and stood holding it until they had passed the line of petrol pumps and were going slowly off along a path across the fields. Then, grinning, he put it back, jumped hurriedly into the bus, and rang his bell.

"Old nuisances," Mr. Noakes said furiously. "Wasting public time. Every week that palaver goes on, taking the old man to Midwick Hospital Outpatients and back again. I know what *I'd* do with 'em. Put to sleep, that sort ought to be."

Mr. Noakes was a very repulsive-looking man, but when he heard that Tom and Lily wanted a room for the night, he changed completely and gave them a look that was full of false goodwill. He was a big, red-faced man with wet, full lips, bulging pale-gray bloodshot eyes, and a crop of stiff, greasy black hair. He wore tennis shoes.

"Honeymooners, eh?" he said, looking sentimentally at Lily's pale prettiness and giving her a tremendous pinch on her arm. Disengaging herself as politely as she could, she stooped and picked up something from the pavement. They followed Mr. Noakes glumly up the street to the Rising Sun.

While they were eating their baked beans, Mr. Noakes stood over their table, grimacing at them. Lily unwisely confided to him that they were looking for a bit of sunshine. Mr. Noakes's laughter nearly shook down the ramshackle building.

"Sunshine! That's a good un! Hear that, Mother?" he bawled to his wife. "They're looking for a bit of sunshine. Heh-heh-heh-heh-heh-heh! Why," he said, banging on the table till the baked beans leaped about, "if I could find a bit of sunshine near here, permanent bit that is, dja know what I'd do?"

The young people looked at him inquiringly across the bread and margarine.

"Lido, trailer site, country club, holiday camp — you wouldn't know the place. Land around here is dirt cheap; I'd buy up the lot. Nothing but woods. I'd advertise — I'd have people flocking to this little dump from all over the country. But what a hope, what a hope, eh? Well, feeling better? Enjoyed your tea?"

Tom and Lily stood up. "I'd like to go for a bit of a walk, Tom," Lily said. "Look, I picked up that old lady's bag on the pavement. I didn't notice it till we'd done talking to Mr. Noakes, and by then she was out of sight. Should we take it back to her?"

"Good idea," said Tom. "Do you know where she lives, Mr. Noakes?"

"Who, old Ma Hatching? Sure I know. She lives in the wood. But you don't want to go taking her bag back, not this time o' the evening you don't. Let her worry. She'll come asking for it in the morning."

"She walked so slowly," said Lily, holding the bag gently in her hands. It was very old, made of black velvet on two ring handles and embroidered with beaded roses. "I think we ought to take it to her, don't you, Tom?"

"Oh, very well, very well, have it your own way," Mr. Noakes said, winking at Tom. "Take that path by the garage; you can't go wrong. I've never been there meself, but they live somewhere in that wood back o' the village. You'll find it soon enough."

They found the path soon enough but not the cottage. Under the lowering sky they walked forward endlessly among trees that carried only tiny and rudimentary leaves, wizened and poverty-stricken. Lily was still wearing her wedding sandals, which had begun to blister her. She held on to Tom's arm, biting her lip with the pain, and he looked down miserably at her bent brown head; everything had turned out so differently from what he had planned.

By the time they reached the cottage, Lily could hardly bear to put her left foot to the ground, and Tom was gentling her along. "It can't be much farther now, and they'll be sure to have a bandage. I'll tie it up, and you can have a sit-down. Maybe they'll give us a cup of tea. We could borrow an old pair of socks or something . . ." Hardly noticing the cottage garden, beyond a vague impression of rows of runner beans, they made for the clematis-grown porch and knocked. There was a brass lion's head on the door, carefully polished.

"Eh, me dear!" It was the old lady, old Mrs. Hatching, who opened the door, and her exclamation was a long-drawn gasp of pleasure and astonishment. "Eh, me dear! 'Tis the pretty bride. See'd ye s'arternoon as we was coming from hospital."

"Who be?" shouted a voice from inside.

"Come in, come in, me dears. My son William'll be glad to hear company; he can't see, poor soul, nor has this thirty year, ah, and a pretty sight he's losing this minute —"

"We brought back your bag," Tom said, putting it in her hands, "and we wondered if you'd have a bit of plaster you could kindly let us have. My wife's hurt her foot —"

My wife. Even in the midst of Mrs. Hatching's voluble welcome the strangeness of these words struck the two young people. They fell quiet, each of them pondering, while Mrs. Hatching thanked and commiserated, all in a breath, and asked them to take a seat on the sofa and fetched a basin of water from the scullery. William from his seat in the chimney corner demanded to know what it was all about.

"Wot be doing? Wot be doing, Mother?"

" 'Tis a bride, all in's finery," she shrilled back at him, "an's blistered her foot, poor heart." Keeping up a running commentary for William's benefit, she bound up the foot, every now and then exclaiming to herself in wonder over the fineness of Lily's wedding dress, which lay in yellow nylon swathes around the chair. "There, me dear. Now us'll have a cup of tea, eh? Proper thirsty you'm fare to be, walking all the way to here this hot day."

Hot day? Tom and Lily stared at each other and then around the room. Then it was true; it was not their imagination that a great dusty golden square of sunshine lay on the fireplace wall, where the brass pendulum of the clock at every swing blinked into sudden brilliance? That the blazing geraniums on the windowsill housed a drove of murmuring bees? That through the window the gleam of linen, hung in the sun to whiten, suddenly dazzled their eyes?

"The sun? Is it really the sun?" Tom said almost doubtfully.

"And why not?" Mrs. Hatching demanded. "How else'll beans set, tell me that? Fine thing if sun were to stop shining." Chuckling to herself, she set out a Crown Derby tea set, gorgeously colored in red and gold, and a baking of saffron buns. Then she sat down and, drinking her own tea, began to question the two of them about where they had come from, where they were going. The tea was tawny and hot and sweet; the clock's tick was like a bird chirping; every now and then a log settled in the grate. Lily looked sleepily around the little room, so rich and peaceful, and thought, "I wish we were staying here. I wish we

needn't go back to that horrible pub . . ." She leaned against Tom's comforting arm.

"Look at the sky," she whispered to him. "Out there between the geraniums. Blue!"

"And ee'll come up and see my spare bedroom, won't ee now?" Mrs. Hatching said, breaking off the thread of her questions — which indeed was not a thread but merely a savoring of her pleasure and astonishment at this unlooked-for visit. "Bide here, why don't ee? Mid as well. The lil un's fair wore out. Us'll do for ee better 'n rangy old Noakes, proper old scoundrel 'e be. Won't us, William?"

"Ah," William said appreciatively. "I'll sing ee some o' my songs."

A sight of the spare room settled any doubts. The great white bed, huge as a prairie, built up with layer upon solid layer of mattress, blanket, and quilt, almost filled the little shadowy room in which it stood. Brass rails shone in the green dimness. "Isn't it quiet?" Lily whispered. Mrs. Hatching, silent for the moment, stood looking at them proudly, her bright eyes slowly moving from face to face. Once her hand fondled the yellow brass knob, as if it might have been a baby's downy head.

And so, almost without any words, the matter was decided.

Three days later, they remembered that they must go back to the

village and collect the scooter, which must be mended by now.

They had been helping old William pick a basketful of beans. Tom had taken his shirt off, and the sun gleamed on his brown back; Lily was wearing an old cotton print which Mrs. Hatching, with much chuckling, had shortened to fit her.

It was amazing how deftly, in spite of his blindness, William moved among the beans, feeling through the rough, rustling leaves for the stiffness of concealed pods. He found twice as many as Tom and Lily, but then they, even on the third day, were still stopping every other minute to exclaim over the blueness of the sky. At night they sat on the back doorstep while Mrs. Hatching clucked inside as she dished the supper, "Star-struck ee'll be! Come along in, do-ee, before soup's cold; stars niver run away yet, as I do know.''

"Can we get anything for you in the village?" Lily asked, but Mrs. Hatching shook her head.

"Baker's bread and suchlike's no use but to cripple thee's innardses wi' colic. I been living here these eighty year wi'out troubling doctors, and I'm not about to begin now." She waved to them and stood watching as they walked into the wood, thin and frail beyond belief, but wiry, indomitable, her black eyes full of zest. Then she turned to scream menacingly at a couple of pullets who had strayed and were scratching among the potatoes.

Almost at once they noticed, as they followed the path, that the sky was clouded over.

"It *is* only there on that one spot," Lily said in wonder. "All the time. And they've never even noticed that the sun doesn't shine in other places."

"That's how it must have been all over the world, once," Tom said.

At the garage they found their scooter ready and waiting. They were about to start back when they ran into Mr. Noakes.

"Well, well, well, well, *well!*" he shouted, glaring at them with ferocious good humor. "How many wells make a river, eh? And where did you slip off to? Here's me and the missus was just going to tell the police to have the rivers dragged. But hullo, hul*lo*, what's this? Brown, eh? Suntan? Scrumptious," he said, looking at Lily and giving her another tremendous pinch. "Where'd you get it, eh? That wasn't all got in half an hour, *I* know. Come on, this means money to you and me; tell us the big secret. Remember what I said — land around these parts is dirt cheap."

Tom and Lily looked at each other in horror. They thought of the cottage, the bees humming among the runner beans, the sunlight glinting on the red-and-gold teacups. At night, when they had lain in the

445

huge sagging bed, stars had shone through the window, and the whole wood was as quiet as the inside of a shell.

"Oh, we've been miles from here," Tom lied hurriedly. "We ran into a friend, and he took us right away beyond Brinsley." And as Mr. Noakes still looked suspicious and unsatisfied, Tom did the only thing possible. "We're going back there now," he said. "The sunbathing's grand." And opening the throttle, he let the scooter go. They waved at Mr. Noakes and chugged off toward the gray hills that lay to the north.

They wondered how long Mrs. Hatching would keep tea hot for them.

"My wedding dress," Lily said sadly. "It's on our bed."

"Never mind, you won't need it again," Tom comforted her.

At least, he thought, they had left the golden place undisturbed. Mr. Noakes never went into the wood. And they had done what they intended; they had found the sun. Now they, too, would be able to tell their grandchildren, when beginning a story, "Long, long ago, when we were young, in the days when the sky was blue . . ."

DISCUSSION

1. How did Tom and Lily travel on their wedding trip? Where were they going?
2. Why had the sun and stars all but disappeared?
3. Why did Tom and Lily stop at the drab village of Molesworth?
4. Why did Tom and Lily go to the Hatchings' cottage? What made the young couple decide to stay with the Hatchings?
5. Why did Tom and Lily go back to the village? Why could they not return again to the Hatchings' cottage?
6. When and where does the story take place? What clues in the story support your answer?
7. Was Mrs. Hatching aware that the sun shone only around her cottage? On what specific passages do you base your answer?
8. If Lily and Tom had told Mr. Noakes about the sunshine, do you think the area would have become as popular as he indicated? Why do you think as you do?

9. If you had been in Tom and Lily's position, would you have told Mr. Noakes about the sunshine? Why or why not?

10. How do Mr. Noakes and Mrs. Hatching contrast in character? Which of Mr. Noakes's traits may also have been traits of the individuals responsible for the disappearance of the sun? How might the old saying "One bad apple can spoil the barrel" be applied to people like Mr. Noakes?

11. What details of the story make it a fantasy? What are some details included by the author to make the characters and events seem real and true to life?

AUTHOR

At the age of five, Joan Aiken spent her month's allowance on a large blue notebook and started filling it with stories and poems. She still has the notebook, and she has been writing ever since because, as she says, "Writing is just the family trade." Daughter of poet Conrad Aiken and sister of two professional writers, she is perhaps best known for her mystery-thrillers for both adults and young people.

Joan Aiken was born in England. When she was seventeen, she wrote down some of the fairy tales she had invented to amuse her younger brother, and they were broadcast on the Children's Hour of the British Broadcasting Corporation. At about the same time, she wrote a full-length children's novel and entered it in a competition. She was not the winner, but several years later she rewrote the novel, and it was published in the United States as *The Kingdom and the Cave.* Many of her children's stories are considered modern classics. One of her own favorites, *The Wolves of Willoughby Chase,* won the Lewis Carroll Shelf Award in 1965. *The Whispering Mountain* received the Manchester Guardian Award for Children's Literature in 1969 and was runner-up for the Carnegie Medal the same year.

A widow and the mother of two grown children, Joan Aiken now lives in Sussex, England. There she devotes herself to writing, but she also takes time to enjoy such hobbies as gardening, painting, and collecting nineteenth-century children's literature. On her frequent walks in the English countryside, she often discovers haunting places that she later writes about in her books.

A Garland
of Precepts

Though a seeker since my birth,
Here is all I've learned on earth,
This the gist of what I know:
Give advice and buy a foe.
Random truths are all I find
Stuck like burs about my mind.
Salve a blister. Burn a letter.
Do not wash a cashmere sweater.
Tell a tale but seldom twice.
Give a stone before advice.

Pressed for rules and verities,
All I recollect are these:
Feed a cold and starve a fever.
Argue with no true believer.
Think-too-long is never-act.
Scratch a myth and find a fact.
Stitch in time saves twenty stitches.
Give the rich, to please them, riches.
Give to love your hearth and hall.
But do not give advice at all.

PHYLLIS McGINLEY

SKILL LESSON 7

FIGURATIVE LANGUAGE

Writers often use colorful words and expressions to make their writing more interesting and to help you form pictures in your mind. They may use sensory words, words that particularly appeal to your five senses, and they may make comparisons that arouse your imagination and communicate ideas forcefully. Language that states things indirectly, that arouses your feelings and imagination, and that helps you form mental pictures is called FIGURATIVE LANGUAGE.

What pictures do the following examples of figurative language call to your mind?

1. The instant the bell sounded, Tim shot out of the classroom.
2. Suddenly a fierce light blazed in the darkness.
3. Sally's smile lighted up the room.

In sentence 1 the writer could have used the word *hurried* to tell how Tim left the classroom. But by using the word *shot,* he is helping you picture more clearly the action described. Of course he is not really saying that Tim left the classroom the way a bullet leaves a gun, but he is communicating in a forceful way the idea of great speed.

By using the word *fierce* to describe the light and the word *blazed* to indicate something about its action, the writer of sentence 2 is expecting you to "see" a blinding flash of light in what was complete darkness. He could have written *Suddenly a strong light shone in the darkness,* but that would not have aroused your imagination or painted such a sharp and dramatic picture as sentence 2 did.

In sentence 3 the writer is not really saying that Sally's smile increased the illumination in the room. What he is suggesting is that the atmosphere became warmer and probably more friendly.

SENSORY WORDS

Ideas that writers communicate are often forcefully expressed through their appeal to the senses. Words like *sour* and *tart* appeal to the sense of taste; *clang* and *clatter* would be identified with the sense of hearing. To which of the five senses — sight, hearing, touch, taste, and smell — would each of these words most likely appeal?

1. chimed	6. velvety
2. bland	7. squawky
3. majestic	8. mirage
4. scorched	9. gingery
5. silky	10. perfumed

Each of the following sentences makes a strong appeal to at least one of the five senses. Which one would you suggest for each sentence?

1. The wind tugged at my hair.
2. John's expression froze as he looked at the spoonful of medicine.
3. The grass was jeweled with dew.
4. The old car coughed and sputtered.
5. The boys bolted into the house when I took the hot, steaming pie out of the oven.

The poem "Hockey" on page 220 contains lines that describe sensory impressions: "The air bites to the center of warmth and flesh"; "The puck swims, skims, veers"; "The air is sharp, steel-sharp"; "Sticks click and snap like teeth." To which of the five senses does each of those expressions primarily appeal?

The following examples of figurative language that contain sensory words are taken from selections you read earlier. The page on which each example appears is given after the example so that you may refer to it, if you wish. Most of the examples appeal primarily to one sense,

but there are some that could appeal to more than one. Decide on the sense or senses to which each one appeals.

1. Chopin's waltzes just spring out of her fingertips . . . (page 21)
2. Hardly able to wait while it [a grouse] cooked, he tore at the hot meat, sizzling juice down his chin . . . (page 98)
3. The breaker gave me all the tossing of a bucking bronco. (page 197)
4. Nothing but the towering Himalayas, thrusting miles high on all sides, stretching in awesome grandeur from horizon to horizon, each pinnacle tipped with immense banners of snow plumes, streaming out in the wind, vivid against the darkly blue sky. (page 209)
5. . . . the peculiar gritty sound of crampons biting into packed snow . . . (pages 213–214)
6. . . . Ed sucked in a sharp, lung-piercing breath. (page 214)
7. . . . tickling his palate with chili peppers in season . . . (page 256)
8. Dank air filled their nostrils — the Grand Gallery! (page 262)
9. . . . his moccasins sang on the grass . . . (page 319)
10. . . . his side ached as from the hot thrust of a Kiowa lance. (page 319)
11. He threw together a narrow smudging row of twigs and leaves for a slow burning . . . (page 322)
12. . . . the image of the truck crashing, the crates bouncing, bursting, the birds swifting out, the birds speeding home. (page 378)

SIMILES

You often use comparisons to describe people, things, and actions. Comparisons like *cold as ice, warm as toast, playful as a kitten,* and *swift as lightning* are common to the everyday language of most people. The word *as* appeared in each of the comparisons you just read. The word *like* is also often used in comparisons. Common comparisons that contain *like* include *swam like a fish, looked like a tiger,* and *worked like a beaver.* A comparison that contains the word *as* or *like* is called a *simile.* The two things that are being compared in a simile are basically quite different, but in one respect, that which the writer is pointing out, they are alike. The comparison *Judi is as pretty as Karen* is not really a simile since one girl is being compared to another girl. The comparison *Judi is as pretty as a bouquet of spring flowers* is a simile since two things *(Judi* and the *bouquet of spring flowers)* are not really alike at all except in the one way that the writer is suggesting.

Writers use similes too, particularly when they want you to picture clearly what they are describing. In the selection "Owl Quartet" you read, "Like three little gnomes they [the owls] toured the room." In order for you to get a clear picture of how the owls moved, the writer compared their movement to that of gnomes, little creatures that sway slightly as they waddle along.

In the selection "The Eighth Wonder of the World" you read this sentence: "It [the Great Wall] lies across China like a gigantic serpent." That comparison certainly gives a clear picture of a wall that winds over the land and up and down hills, sometimes even doubling back on itself much in the way that a serpent does but, of course, on a much larger scale.

The selection "Billy Beans Lived Here" contains this comparison: ". . . she had just enough sense left to move herself around from one chore to another like a mechanical doll." What two things are being compared? What action is involved? Can you see that action clearly once you think of how a mechanical doll moves?

You find many similes in poetry since so often the writer of the poem is trying to get you to look at something in quite a different way from what you are accustomed to. What comparison is being made in these lines from the poem "Skier"?

He swings down like the flourish of a pen
Signing a signature in white on white.

You know that skiers sometimes wind around in great curves as they descend a slope. You know, too, that some people write their signatures in big, bold strokes with strong loops and curves. It is in this way that the writer is suggesting that you think of the pattern left by a skier on a snowy slope. How could the "signature" of the skier be "white on white"?

The following examples of similes are from selections that you have read in this book. The page for each example is given so that you may refer to more of the example, if you wish. For each example decide on what two things are being compared and how that comparison is helpful in your understanding of the passage or in helping to create a picture.

1. They [the owls] waited . . . meanwhile swaying their heads like pendulums to focus their eyes. (page 64)
2. Her [the bat's] high sharp cries
   Like shining needlepoints of sound
   Go out into the night . . . (page 120)
3. They [the ponies] bow shyly as wet swans. (page 170)
4. He looked unhappily at the two little old ladies, bright as crickets for all their sober, small-town dresses . . . (page 180)
5. Brilliant birds perched on overhanging limbs like noisy flowers. (page 231)
6. They [the lights] like a skyful of stars snared in a net and brought to earth. (page 234)
7. . . . our little cabin had somehow come adrift and had been slung off into space like a raindrop falling on a spinning flywheel. (page 305)
8. They [the pigeons] swirl up in the sky like a . . . a scarf, a white scarf, or maybe a white flag . . . (pages 380–382)

METAPHORS

Another common comparison used often in speech and in writing is the *metaphor*. A metaphor is in some ways like a simile; however, a metaphor makes a comparison without the use of the word *as* or *like*. A simile is expressed this way: *From atop the tall building the people looked like scurrying ants;* a metaphor would make the same comparison this way: *From atop the tall building the people were ants, scurrying here and there.* As with a simile, a metaphor compares unlike things, unlike in all but the one way the writer is suggesting.

In "I Meet Money" you read this sentence: "Dinner was a night-mare." That comparison is a metaphor in which the writer is suggesting that the dinner was an unpleasant experience in much the same way a nightmare is.

In "Another Kind of Courage" Mr. Golding said, "A painting by Goya, that's who you are, Joey . . ." In that metaphor Mr. Golding was comparing Joey to a painting by the Spanish painter Goya, noted for his striking portraits.

Not all metaphors state comparisons that directly, as you will see in this metaphor, taken from the selection "Sancho": "After getting into the Indian territory, they [the cattle] snailed on across the Wichita, the South Canadian . . ." The writer used the word *snailed* to suggest the very slow movement of the cattle across the Wichita and the South Canadian Rivers, much in the manner of the movement of a snail.

What is being compared in each of the following metaphors? How does the comparison help you understand or picture more clearly what is happening?

1. The shoreward-bound torrents of water ground overhead, making all the racket of a string of freight cars roaring over a trestle. (page 193)
2. The drumming of the water under the board had become a madman's tattoo. (page 197)
3. Then a skeleton [Eb] came out from among the trees. (page 289)
4. It [the Great Wall] is a monster of stone. (page 361)
5. . . . I think it's cause they're [the pigeons] Beauty. (page 380)
6. It [a new worry] walked right along, beside her, outside her, inside her. (page 382)

You have been examining examples of figurative language, language that evokes images and arouses feelings. You have learned that a writer uses sensory words — words that appeal to the five senses — when he wants to help you "experience" the events, situations, or conditions he is describing. You have learned about similes and metaphors — the language of comparisons, which a writer uses when he wants to convey effective impressions and vivid images. Figurative language is often language of insights, language of beauty, but its main function, like the function of all good writing, is to increase your understanding and enjoyment of what you read.

Discussion

Help your class answer these questions:

1. What is figurative language?
2. What are some examples of sensory words?
3. To which sense does each of the five sentences on page 451 primarily appeal?
4. To which sense or senses does each of the twelve examples on page 452 appeal?
5. What is a simile? How does a metaphor differ from a simile?
6. What comparisons are being made in the eight examples on page 454?
7. What are the answers to the two questions that precede the six examples on page 455?

On your own

The following examples of figurative language containing sensory words are taken from selections you read earlier. Number a paper from 1 to 6 and write beside each number the sense to which that example primarily appeals.

1. . . . with the sensation of a freezing knife plunging deeply into his chest . . . (page 216)
2. The banks were lined with huge trees, thick and twisted with lianas, making a screen and a mystery of what lay behind. (page 231)
3. . . . he chewed it slowly, exploring each mouthful with caution for lumps too hard for his teeth. (page 271)
4. . . . the sharp, harsh call of a wild turkey would sound out with a strange kind of insistence . . . (page 289)
5. . . . with rich slow evenings when the crickets scratched their legs and the frogs made delta music. (page 310)
6. The streets were full of the aroma of fresh bagels, of breezes coming from the Vistula River and the Praga forest. (page 417)

Decide whether each of these examples of figurative language is a simile or a metaphor. Number your paper from 7 to 14. Beside each number write *simile* or *metaphor* to indicate what kind of comparison is being made in each example.

7. Walter had as much sentiment as a rattlesnake . . . (page 189)
8. The cone has become the Volkswagen of the ice-cream world. (page 177)
9. It [the Great Wall] stretches on and on . . . a ribbon in the distance, striking toward the horizon. (page 361)
10. In the deep snowy creases of the mountain, the ponds lay like patches of black glass . . . (page 87)
11. Eb's often reiterated "I'll be goin' on soon, Jeth; I won't be a burden to you much longer" became like the whippoorwill's cry — always the same and never ending. (page 297)
12. Through the film over her eyes, two small watery windows . . . (page 386)
13. . . . the long humps of water peaking into ridges that marched like animated foothills. (page 193)
14. The sawed-off branch hung above, a wooden question mark. (page 425)

Checking your work

If you are asked to do so, give your answer to one or more of the examples of figurative language. For each simile and metaphor be sure you understand what two things are being compared. The number in parentheses tells you on which page you will find the example.

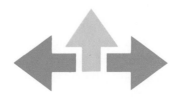

Dr. Dan

by Louis Haber

"SEWED UP HIS HEART" shouted the headline of the Chicago *Daily Inter-Ocean.* History had just been made. In a time when few surgeons dared to operate on the abdomen, let alone on the heart, Dr. Daniel Hale Williams had successfully operated on a dying man who had been stabbed in the heart. The man not only survived but lived for fifty years afterward. It was the first time in the history of medicine that this kind of surgery was attempted, and it was performed successfully! What was the background of this great pioneering surgeon?

Born in Hollidaysburg, Pennsylvania, on January 18, 1856, Dan was the fifth of a family of seven children. His father . . . , very active in the abolitionist cause, was a prominent member of the Equal Rights League. . . .

At the age of forty-seven Dan's father died of consumption, leaving his wife and seven children in financial difficulties. Dan, who was ten years old at the time, was apprenticed to a shoemaker in Baltimore, and his mother left Pennsylvania and went to Rockford, Illinois. Unhappy with his lot, Dan managed to run away and rejoin his mother in Illinois. A few months later, however, his mother returned east without him. Left on his own, Dan worked on lake steamers and learned the barber's trade. When his oldest sister, Sally, wrote asking him to join her in Edgerton, Wisconsin, Dan jumped at the chance. Opportunities for the Negro were greater in the West than in the South, and he soon opened his own barbershop in Edgerton at the age of seventeen. But Janesville, a few miles away, had schools, an opera house, and flourishing industries, so Sally and Dan moved there, and Dan got a job in the barbershop of Harry Anderson. After

Dan's sister married and left Janesville, Anderson took Dan into his home and treated him as one of the family.

Dan began to attend Haire's Classical Academy, which was the equivalent of a present-day high school. After graduating, he clerked and read the law in a lawyer's office for about one year, no doubt influenced by his older brother, who was already a successful practicing lawyer. However, Dan soon realized that the law was not for him.

In Janesville everybody stood in awe of Dr. Henry Palmer, a local physician. Dr. Palmer was an excellent surgeon who had been the director of the largest military hospital during the Civil War and Surgeon General of Wisconsin for ten years. News of Dr. Palmer's exciting work was often in the local newspaper, and when Dan read of it, he was determined that medicine was going to be his life's work. At the age of twenty-two he became an apprentice in Dr. Palmer's office. He stayed there for two years, reading medicine, learning to practice, and scrubbing up the office at the end of the day.

In those days it was customary for a person to open his own private practice of medicine at the end of two years of apprenticeship in a doctor's office. Few physicians at that time had gone to medical college. Dan, however, under Dr. Palmer's influence, was determined to obtain the best medical training available. In 1880, with a one-hundred-dollar bank loan in his pocket, Dan went off to Chicago Medical College (later to become Northwestern University Medical School). At that time, Chicago Medical College was one of the best medical schools in the country and had the "heroically high standard" of an eighteen-month course. Although standards were very high, laboratory work was virtually nonexistent, and the staff lectured, and operated also, in stiff collars and black swallowtails. Dan graduated from medical school in 1883 and opened an office at Thirty-first Street and Michigan Avenue in Chicago.

Dan Williams's true place in medicine must be measured against the background of his times. A new era in surgery began in the eighties. As a graduate in 1883, he belonged to a group of young men not bound by the prejudices of the previous generation and receptive to new thoughts and practices in surgery. A revolution was taking place in this field because of the work of Louis Pasteur in France and Joseph Lister in England. In the late seventies, Pasteur had laid the foundations of bacteriology. He had proven the relationship between certain microorganisms and specific diseases. He set forth his "Germ Theory of Disease" that was to sweep the medical world. Lister applied Pasteur's theory and revolutionized surgery by demonstrating the effectiveness of antiseptics (germ-killing chemicals) in the treatment of wounds. A furor was created, although it was difficult for the doctrine of antisepsis to gain acceptance among the older men of that day.

Many explanations of disease were offered before Pasteur. It was thought that illness was caused by demons inhabiting the body. The art of healing was dominated by superstition, witchcraft, and misinformation. Surgery was practiced by barbers. It was held that a sick person was filled with bad blood and for a cure should be bled. In many cases, patients who should have been given blood had blood taken from them instead. More patients died from the treatment than from the disease.

It remained for Pasteur to prove that disease was caused by harmful microorganisms, or germs, within the body. His work was to result in the virtual elimination of many diseases caused by germs. This knowledge was just beginning to be known in Williams's day. Abdominal and chest surgery was rarely if ever attempted because, even if successful, the infection that invariably followed caused the death of the patient.

When Williams began to practice medicine, Pasteur's germ theory of disease, Lister's antiseptic surgery, and the availability of anesthetics opened new vistas for the surgeon, and Williams was in a position to take advantage of these advances. Operations could be attempted now that were previously out of the question.

460

461

In his practice of medicine, "Dr. Dan," as his patients and friends came to call him, turned more and more to surgery. In those days operations in private homes were common. Not only did people distrust hospitals but Negroes could not gain admission except in the city's charity wards, where they were either neglected or used for experimentation. Furthermore, Negro doctors could not get hospital appointments because of racial prejudice and, therefore, could not get their patients into hospitals. It was even impossible for Negro women to get training as nurses since training schools would not accept them.

Most of Williams's first operations took place in the kitchens and dining rooms of patients' homes. In each case he applied Lister's principles of antiseptic surgery conscientiously and meticulously. He scrubbed the entire room with soap and water. He then sprayed carbolic acid, a strong germ killer, all over the room and followed that by sterilizing all the instruments to be used in the operation in a wash-boiler filled with steam. Hands and clothing were also included in the cleaning and sterilizing process. His results were excellent. Infection, the feared and dangerous aftermath of surgery, was avoided.

Soon Dr. Dan's reputation as a successful surgeon spread, and he was appointed to the surgical staff of the South Side Dispensary in Chicago. He also became clinical instructor and demonstrator in anatomy at the Chicago Medical College, where one of his students was Charlie Mayo of the famous Mayo brothers. Later still, he became surgeon to the City Railway Company, a position never previously held by a Negro physician. His appointment to the Illinois State Board of Health in 1889 was indicative of the kind of recognition he was shown. While the position carried no salary, it carried tremendous prestige.

It was a cold, wintry day in 1890. Dr. Dan was sitting in the warm, comfortable parlor of his friend, the Reverend Louis Reynolds, pastor of St. Stephen's African Methodist Church. The Reverend Mr. Reynolds had just asked him to use his influence to have Reynolds's sister admitted to a training course for nurses in one of the Chicago hospitals normally closed to all Negro applicants. Williams thought for a moment and then said, "No, I don't think I'll try to get your sister into one of these training courses. We'll do something better. We'll start a hospital of our own, and we'll train dozens and dozens of nurses." He went on, "There must be a hospital for Negroes but not a Negro hospital." Williams had been thinking of it for some time. He was well established in private practice by 1890 and was famed for his surgical skill, but still, as a Negro, he lacked a hospital appointment. This lack, and his indignation that all Negro patients were thrown into the city's charity wards, made him determined to start a new kind of hospital — one to be owned, staffed, and managed by blacks and whites together. Here Negro sick and poor would receive the best of care; ambitious young Negro doctors would have their chance; and young black women, not admitted to white schools, would be trained for the nursing the times demanded.

Williams threw himself into this new effort with enthusiasm. He formed committees of black and white people. He spoke at churches, street corners, club meetings, and anywhere else he was permitted to speak. He got the cooperation of many people, rich and poor, black and white. The idea of a hospital run by Negroes, where Negroes would be received on an equal basis, was very appealing to the black community.

On January 23, 1891, medical history was made. The first interracial hospital in the United States was founded. Articles of incorporation were drawn up in the name of the Provident Hospital and Training School Association. The trustees, executive committee, and finance committee were all black. The hospital itself opened its doors in May, 1891 — a three-story building at Twenty-ninth Street and Dearborn, with room for twelve beds. The first year, out of 175 applicants for nurse training, Dr. Dan accepted seven, the sister of the Reverend Mr. Reynolds among them. All were high-school graduates. The training period was for eighteen months.

The staff of Provident Hospital was made up of Negro and white doctors carefully selected for their qualifications. At the end of the first year, of 189 sick and injured treated at the Provident Hospital, twenty-three had improved, three had not, twenty-two had died, and 141 had recovered entirely — a remarkable record when only desperate cases were taken to a hospital. However, the economic depression of 1893 began to threaten Provident's existence. At that time help came in the form of Frederick Douglass, one of the most important Negro leaders in the country. It was the year of the Chicago World's Fair, and Douglass came as the Haitian commissioner. At the Fair he urged Negroes to contribute to Provident Hospital, the type of interracial organization of which he highly approved. Money began to come in, and things became easier for the hospital after the Fair.

July 9, 1893, was a hot and humid day in Chicago, and tempers were short. A fight in a saloon ended in the stabbing of a young Negro expressman, James Cornish. He was rushed to Provident Hospital with a one-inch knife wound in the chest near the heart. The call went out for Dr. Dan. By the time he arrived, Cornish had collapsed from loss of blood and shock, and it was obvious that he would soon die if nothing was done. But what could be done? Opening the chest cavity in those days was an

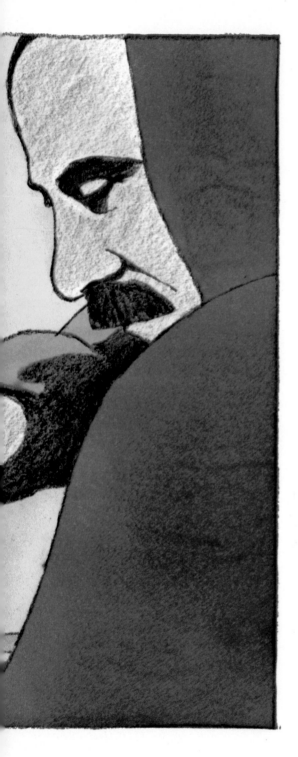

invitation to death. Nobody would have criticized Williams for following the standard treatment in this case of "absolute rest, cold, and opium," after which the patient invariably died. Why should he risk his surgical reputation? If he did not operate and the patient died, nobody would blame him. If he did operate and the patient died, he would be condemned by the medical profession. X rays had not as yet been discovered to help him, blood transfusions were unknown at that time, sulfa drugs and antibiotics to fight infection were also unknown. What to do? The patient was sinking. Dr. Dan decided to operate.

Six physicians — four white and two black — witnessed the operation. Dr. Dan worked swiftly. He opened the chest cavity and saw that the knife used in the stabbing had penetrated the heart about one tenth of an inch and had cut the pericardium, or sac surrounding the heart, one and one-quarter inches in length. He decided that the heart muscle did not need any suturing, or sewing up, but he did suture the pericardium. The atmosphere was tense as he worked and continued to be so until he finally closed up the wound. It was a daring operation — the first time a surgeon had entered the chest cavity. Would it work? Would the dread infection set in and kill the patient? On August 30, fifty-one days after Cornish had entered the hospital a dying man, he was discharged completely recovered.

He lived for fifty years afterward and died in 1943, having outlived his surgeon by twelve years!

Although Dr. Dan did not make an official report of this operation until three and a half years later, the newspaper headlines sent the news around the world. Williams was acclaimed as the first man in the world to "sew up the heart." Of course his great contribution was successful entrance of the chest and surgical exploration of the heart. His aseptic surgery was so perfect that no sign of infection appeared in the patient after the operation. The results were miraculous when one considers that Williams had very few of the advantages which modern surgeons have today in performing their open-heart surgery and heart transplants.

The world will remember Dr. Williams as a great American surgeon accorded top rank by his contemporary colleagues, white and black; as the founder of Provident Hospital, the first interracial hospital in the United States and forerunner of a hundred such institutions; as the first surgeon in the world to enter the chest cavity successfully; as the one who introduced the training of Negro nurses and interns in the United States; as a charter member of the American College of Surgeons; and, finally, as a founder and first vice-president of the National Medical Association.

DISCUSSION

1. How did Daniel Hale Williams begin his medical training? Why did he not follow the custom of his time and start to practice medicine as soon as he had finished his apprenticeship?
2. What two men were chiefly responsible for the revolution in medicine that took place a few years before Dr. Dan became a surgeon? What contribution did each of them make? What effect did their work have on Dr. Dan's methods and success as a surgeon?
3. Why was the founding of Provident Hospital a milestone in medical history? In what ways did the hospital benefit Negroes?
4. How was Frederick Douglass of help to Dr. Dan?
5. Why do you think Dr. Dan was determined that the hospital he founded should be owned, staffed, and managed by blacks and whites together?

6. How would you compare Dr. Dan's medical training with a doctor's training today?

7. Why do you think only desperate cases were taken to a hospital in the early 1890's?

8. What personal qualities did Dr. Dan exhibit in deciding to perform the first open-heart surgery?

9. Although it was unjust and unfortunate that Dr. Dan was denied the use of hospitals in his early practice of surgery, what advantages may there have been in his performing operations in patients' homes?

10. Reread the final paragraph in which the author lists six of Dr. Dan's accomplishments. Which do you think was the greatest? Why?

AUTHOR

Louis Haber has had a long and distinguished career in the teaching of science and holds degrees in both science and education. He has contributed articles to numerous science magazines and has collaborated on college textbooks. His work has also included research for the U.S. Office of Education. ''Dr. Dan'' is an excerpt from *Black Pioneers of Science and Invention,* the first book that Dr. Haber has written for young readers.

At present Dr. Haber is an adjunct professor of physical science at Pace College in New York City and chairman of the science department at Woodlands High School in Hartsdale, New York.

Hair has been a cause of fury since history began. If one generation accepts long hair, the next insists it must be short; if young rebels wear beards, those who come next revolt against beards; if women sweep their hair high, younger women challenge conformity by combing it down. Always there have been some people who have tried to tell others how to wear their hair. Sometimes with rage, and sometimes with laughter, we have been getting into each other's hair for at least five thousand years.

An Upward Trend

by Bill Severn

Madame de Pompadour started a new trend in France in the mid-eighteenth century by arranging her hair "in a hundred entrancing ways . . . till the court nearly went mad attempting to imitate her inimitable coiffures." She gave hair one of its enduring fashions, the style of dressing it without a part, combed straight back from the forehead and worn high at the front. But for the eighteenth century's women, that was just the foundation they built upon. Taking off from where the pompadour began, they padded, puffed, stuffed, and swept false hair up over wire frames until the towers of the previous generation were dwarfed by ranges of hair "that rivaled the Alps."

Artists mocked, writers ridiculed, and furious males wrote angry letters to the newspapers, but the hair-raising women made it evident that there were still more fantastic heights for their hair to climb. Taking a cue from the Macaronis,[1] the ladies soon outdid them. Hairdressers for women flourished, most of them men who apparently were dedicated to turning women's hair into upside-down wastebaskets stuffed with almost any trash that came to hand.

---

[1] **Macaronis,** young London dandies who went to outlandish extremes in the wigs and clothing they wore.

Bushels of cotton wool, shreds of rope, horsehair, bran, or straw were used for stuffing, mounded upon felt pads or cap wigs, with the natural hair brought up over the wire frames and masses of false hair added. Then the whole thing was cemented with a paste that hardened, and the outer shell was greased and floured with powder, decorated with gauze, tulle, pearls, and jewels. Creating a headdress was a problem in engineering that required a full day's time.

Once the structure was built, it remained undisturbed for from two to nine weeks. Some women slept with their necks on wooden supports to preserve their artificial "heads." The top-heavy oval of trash, which made a woman up to three feet taller than she really was, also caused the rebuilding of some homes to raise ceilings and widen doorways. Even so, women sometimes had to enter rooms on their knees and kneel on the floors of sedan chairs and carriages or else change the carriages, too, so that they were open-topped to accommodate the hair.

Another French lady, Louis XVI's frivolous and arrogant Queen Marie Antoinette, promoted the fashion of attaching ostrich plumes, some of them four feet high, to heads, and the ballrooms of London and Paris soon became "forests of waving feathers." She also amused herself by playing at farming at her summer palace, and that started ladies hanging carrots, onions, and other fresh vegetables on their hair. One day the queen hummed a tune from a favorite opera, and a few days later her ladies appeared with model stage settings for scenes from the opera on their heads.

When the French ship *La Belle Poule* won a victory over the English warship *Arethusa*, Frenchwomen celebrated the event by re-creating the battle on seas of hair, with model ships, fully rigged and manned with toy sailors. Others took to creating hairdos that formed the backdrop for scenes from novels, plays, poems, happenings in the news, events in history, fields of sheep and shepherds, models of the city of Paris, landscapes, mountains, windmills, and waterfalls.

The craze spread to England and so shocked some men that they stopped criticizing each other's hair to turn their full fury against feminine head whims representing small zoos with caged lions and tigers of blown glass, aviaries with miniature swans and peacocks,

and such varied things as drowned chickens, mad dogs, cupids, nymphs, the solar system in movement, and balloon ascensions. One mourning widow had her husband's tombstone, in miniature, erected in her hair; another outdid her with a model hearse drawn by six white horses.

Marie Antoinette suddenly switched directions, after losing most of her own hair during an illness, and helped lower hair again. The high constructed headdress was replaced with masses of curls that hung to the shoulders or with frizzed and bushy hair that one writer of the time criticized as "absolutely a lion's mane."

The French Revolution eventually cost the queen not only her hair but her head, and the threat of the guillotine also subdued the hair styles of other aristocratic ladies, even those in England who were far removed from such an act of final criticism. It was not a time for the noble and wealthy to call attention to the extravagance of hair. Women, like men, ended the century with shorter, more natural hair.

DISCUSSION

1. Why does the author compare eighteenth-century hairdos to wastebaskets?
2. What interesting hairdos appeared in Marie Antoinette's time?
3. What caused a drastic change in hair styles in France and England toward the end of the eighteenth century?
4. Compare and contrast present-day reactions to hair styles with reactions to eighteenth-century styles.
5. Why is a certain hair style called a pompadour? In what way was the pompadour "just the foundation" upon which eighteenth-century hairdos were built?
6. Why do you think aristocratic ladies in England were afraid to continue extravagant hair styles during the French Revolution?
7. What do you think caused the ladies of the eighteenth century to indulge in such outlandish hair styles?
8. Reread the introduction to this article. If the ideas expressed there are correct, what hair styles would you predict for the time when your children reach your present age? How do you think you will react to them?
9. Do you think that eighteenth-century men were justified in criticizing ladies' hair styles of that time? Why do you think that? Is present-day criticism of hair styles justified? Why or why not?

AUTHOR

Bill Severn is the author of many entertaining books and has written hundreds of short stories and articles for more than seventy magazines. Three of his most popular books are *Packs of Fun: 101 Unusual Things to Do with Playing Cards and to Know About Them; Rope Roundup: The Lore and Craft of Rope and Roping;* and *Magic and Magicians.*

Mr. Severn and his wife, Sue, are co-authors of several books and are currently working together on biographies for a series entitled *Men Who Might Have Been Presidents.*

Mr. Severn's hobbies are magic, American history, and book collecting. He and his wife live in Great Barrington, Massachusetts.

The Mound in the Cedar Grove

by Allan W. Eckert

The boy had been in the woods since before dawn, and he was well armed: not with gun and ammunition but with camera and film, with thick sketch pad and a pocketful of pencils. He walked slowly, frequently stopping and letting his eyes search the ground and trees and shrubbery ahead of him. Less than fifty feet from the tree where a wounded owl was perched, he stopped and sat on the ground for ten or fifteen minutes while he made a series of quick sketches of a fern frond that was half-unrolled.

When he began walking again, his eyes were on the ground, searching for something else to sketch, and he was soon directly beneath the big owl's perch without even suspecting the bird's existence — that is, until he saw the pellets.

At first he thought they were raccoon droppings, and he knelt for a closer look. But when he identified them an instant later, his heart leaped, and at once he looked upward and saw the huge bird, leaning against the trunk of the cedar with its eyes closed, only seven feet over his head.

A wild but controlled excitement blossomed in the boy, and his fingers trembled badly as he readied his camera, fearing that at any instant the big bird would fly off before the image of it was preserved on film. It was by far the closest he had ever come to a wild great horned owl, and his cup of happiness was brimming at such good fortune.

The light was poor at best here in the copse, but there was enough for some reasonably good shots, and he

473

took them swiftly, inwardly fuming at the loud click each time the shutter snapped and expecting at any moment to see the bird open its eyes and take wing. He snapped pictures from beneath and from all sides, and when his roll of film was used up, he quietly laid his camera to one side and got out his pencils and then did a whole series of rapid sketches, marveling all the while at the immense good fortune that had befallen him, not only in coming upon such a bird but in having it sit still for him for such a length of time.

But when he had worked feverishly there for an hour and the bird had still neither moved nor opened its eyes, a perplexed frown furrowed his brow. He took a stance a dozen feet from the tree, pad braced well and pencil poised to catch that moment of awakening, the initial opening of the wings, the swiveling of the head, the opening of the great orb eyes. And then he called aloud, "Hey!"

The bird did not move, and surprised, he called again, more loudly, "Hey, owl. Wake up! Move!"

There was no response, and for the first time the youth sensed something seriously wrong. He laid down his sketching equipment, walked to the cedar tree, and slapped the trunk so hard that his fingers stung. Still there was no reaction from the owl.

The boy scanned the surrounding area, and his glance fell upon a long, thin dead branch. He went to it quickly, picked it up, and broke off the smaller twigs projecting from it until he had a slender pole ten feet in length in his hand.

Gently he raised it and touched the very tip of it to the bird's breast, and when this failed to rouse it, he tapped slightly harder. The bird moved then, but not voluntarily. It tipped backward slightly, balanced precariously for a moment, and then tumbled to the ground.

The great horned owl was dead.

Mouth agape, the boy simply stared for a long while, not believing what his eyes were witnessing. And then a flood of questions filled his mind. Why? How? Did it die there? Did someone put it there? Was it poisoned? Was it somebody's elaborate idea of a way to trick him?

One of the owl's eyelids had been pulled open with the fall, and already there was a distinct glaze over the iris and pupil. The boy tossed his stick aside and dropped to his knees beside the bird and carefully put his hands under it and picked it up. It was not as heavy as he had expected, and he turned it over slowly, inspecting it.

The blood had only begun coagulating, and it stained his hands. He sought its source and found it, and then he found several other places where shotgun pellets had entered, and then all at once his vision swam and tears started to course down his cheeks.

He put the bird on the ground and wiped his eyes with the back of his hand, suddenly ashamed of his tears

and fearful that someone would see him and make fun of him. But a deep sadness welled within him, and his lower lip trembled again as he studied the carcass before him, so noble even in death. And along with the sadness came an anger at anyone who could so senselessly, so needlessly, destroy such a magnificent wild creature. A bitterness he had seldom known created a bad taste in his mouth, and he momentarily lived a little fantasy in which he encountered the person who had done this and made him everlastingly sorry for the wretched deed.

He stayed in the cedar copse most of the morning, at first making a dozen good close-up sketches of the bird or parts of it. He sketched the head, the beak, individual feathers, and toes. He studied the coloration carefully and made notes of the subtle changes of color where they occurred, and finally, when he had done as much as he could in this respect, he opened his pocketknife and very carefully began to skin the bird.

Although he had never killed a bird and never intended to, he had at his home an impressive collection of study skins. Most of them were songbirds — wrens and robins, larks and thrashers, vireos and warblers — but there were a good many others among them; a few hawks and a screech owl, several species of woodpeckers, a shrike, a bobwhite quail, red-winged and rusty blackbirds, and of course grackles and starlings and sparrows.

All of these were birds that he had found dead. The majority had been killed by autos; others he had discovered beside the railroad tracks. Still others he had picked up, especially after severe spring or autumn storms, at the base of a thousand-foot-high television tower not very far from his home.

Each of these birds he had skinned with great care, always dusting the inner side of the skin with a combination of alum and arsenic powders to prevent insect damage, then padding the body cavity with cotton batting and placing a label on the foot which bore the date and place of discovery along with the common and Latin names of the species and the sex.

These skins were an invaluable aid to him in his art, for only through minute study of them was he able to detect and emulate in his oil paintings and watercolors the subtle nuances of hue and shading in the plumage. And yet, even though he needed them badly, it never failed to distress him to skin out such a bird, and with unfaltering regularity the thought came to him while he was in the process of skinning one that he wished the bird could suddenly come to life, unharmed, and dart away from his hand to the freedom of the wilds in which it was hatched.

Because he worked with slow care, it took him over two hours to complete the skinning of this great horned owl, but he had done an excellent job, especially in those areas where the skinning was made particularly difficult by the lead pellets' having torn the flesh. When he was finished, he tore three sheets of sketch paper from his pad and taped them together, edge to edge, with transparent tape from the roll he had long ago made it a habit to carry in his pocket for emergency repair of accidentally torn sketches. He now had a large cylinder of paper, and one end of this he sealed together with more tape. Careful not to disrupt the plumage, he then placed the owl headfirst into the open end of the paper cylinder and sealed it behind the bird.

Satisfied that his newest specimen was now relatively safe from accidental damage, he turned his attention to the carcass. Once again he sketched, and this time it was the muscle structure of the bird that he drew, for this too would prove of value to him in properly shaping further great horned owls he might paint.

When he had finished, he laid his equipment aside and used his pocketknife to dig a hole in the soft loam beneath the tree in which the bird had died. Into this he placed the carcass and covered it, tamping down the soil firmly so that it would be less likely to be unearthed by any scavengers. He then walked down to the lakeshore, thirty yards distant, rinsed his hands and knife, and found a large round stone which he carried back and planted solidly atop the center of the little grave.

When he left the cedar grove, there was little indication that he had ever been there at all: a small mound of freshly packed earth, a small boulder, a discarded stick . . .

DISCUSSION

1. What made the boy suspect that something was wrong with the owl? What had caused the death of the owl?
2. How did the boy react when he discovered that the owl was dead?
3. What had the boy done with other dead birds he had found? Why?
4. What use did the boy make of the owl's carcass before burying it? Why?
5. How would you describe the boy in terms of interests, hobbies, and talents?
6. How do you think the boy felt about nature and wildlife? What details in the story support your answer?

7. What do you think the boy might eventually decide on as his life-work? Why do you think that?

8. Why was the boy's collection of study skins limited to birds that he had found dead? If the boy had wanted to kill other birds in order to have a greater variety of skins, do you think he would have been justified in doing so? Why do you think that?

9. How do some people's views about killing wildlife differ from those of the boy in the story? What views do you hold and why?

10. Some people would argue that because the owl itself was a bird of prey, the boy was being unduly emotional about the fact that the owl had been shot. What is your opinion?

AUTHOR

Allan W. Eckert became a full-time free-lance magazine writer in 1960. Before that, he worked at many jobs, including chemist's assistant, private detective, truck driver, cook, fireman, illustrator, newspaper reporter, and postman. As a young man, he spent several years hitchhiking around the country, living off the land, and learning about nature through firsthand observation. Nature and writing have always been his two major interests.

Mr. Eckert has had more than two hundred articles published in national magazines. His books include *The Great Auk, The Silent Sky,* and *Wild Season,* from which "The Mound in the Cedar Grove" is taken.

Born in Buffalo, New York, Mr. Eckert was educated at Ohio State University and the University of Dayton. He now lives in Dayton, Ohio, with his wife and children.

Open Season

by Will Stanton

I keep having this nightmare. I dream I'm on an island with nothing to eat but canned corned beef. I turn the key, and the little metal strip starts getting narrower. And narrower. I turn it slower — and slower — and it gets narrower — and narrower — and snap! This isn't so bad as nightmares go. The only trouble is, the same thing happens when I'm awake.

With sardines it works the other way. As you roll up the lid, it keeps getting bigger and bigger until it swallows the key. Fortunately, sardines are small and slippery, so you can get most of them out anyway.

The greatest friend the packaging industry has is the sporting instinct of the American people. If you can't improve a product, make it harder to get at. If this sounds like an exaggeration, have you tried unwrapping a new shirt lately? How about a lampshade? Okay then.

Take something as simple as a bag. I'm talking about the big ones that hold things such as dog food and lawn conditioner and so on. They are fastened across the top with some braided strings under which is a note saying that if you will pull the red string, or the green string, the whole top will open like magic. If you believe that, you will believe anything. Your best bet is to put the bag in a washtub and cut it in half like a watermelon.

Milk cartons come in several styles, the most challenging being the one that comes to a peak. For the purposes of this exercise I am going to ask you to think of it as a little roof. What you're supposed to do is separate the sides so it splits along the rooftree, allowing the gable to come out and form a spout. You will find, however, that the gable has been glued to the inside of the roof and it has to be torn loose,

480

leaving you with a crooked spout or no spout. This is particularly true of buttermilk cartons. To many people buttermilk can be unsettling at its best, and when it spurts out the side, running down the glass and across the counter top and into the drawer, it is anything but at its best.

To a layman the philosophy of packaging is a mystery. Light bulbs and eggs are enclosed in some of the flimsiest cardboard modern science can produce. You can crush an egg carton by putting your mail on it. On the other hand, a steel chisel designed for cutting metal comes well protected by shatterproof plastic. The plastic-bubble-on-cardboard design is popular for this sort of purchase. If you want to open one, don't waste your time on the plastic — you can't dent it. Try to hack or peel away the cardboard from the back. And don't throw away any of those curled-up scraps because they contain the instructions and the guarantee.

Or take aspirin. You have a choice of the handy tin or the economy bottle. The tin is designed on the "Press here" or reverse-mousetrap principle. It's convenient for carrying in your pocket, and if you press hard enough on the red dot, the thing will spring open, scattering aspirin everywhere. The bottle has a top that comes off easily enough,

but then you find a layer of cotton that has been tamped in like the wadding in a shotgun shell. Getting it out is going to require special equipment, and my experience has been that when you really need aspirin, it's no time to fool around with tweezers.

Vitamins are tricky too. You manage to tear off the outside covering, and you think you're home free. You're not. There's still a heavy-duty plastic cover that keeps you from getting at the cap. Anybody who can get this off without help doesn't need vitamins.

The powdered-sugar and macaroni people favor the thumbnail opening. At the top of the package there is a semicircle with simulated perforations around the edge. Underneath, they have printed a little joke which says, "Press thumbnail here." Unless you have the thumbnail of a Fu Manchu, all you're going to do is cave in the side of the box — and there goes the old ball game. Better plan something else for supper. For the simple fact is that for any kind of opening purpose, the thumbnail has become obsolete.

Food processors have a special knack for raising false hopes in their customers. Ready-sliced cheese, for instance — this sounds great. Open the package and slap together half a dozen sandwiches in a couple of minutes. Now, it's true that they do slice the cheese, just as they say. But what they don't tell you is that after they slice it, they send it through a laminating mill where it is pressed back together like plywood. I guess that's not such a good comparison because the last time I bought plywood, it got left in the rain, and when I wanted to use it, the layers had come apart like — well, I started to say like cheese, but I can see that's not going to clarify anything.

They also put out cheese wrapped in ordinary tinfoil. Don't let this fool you — nothing is ever as simple as it sounds. After it's wrapped, they send it through a special crinkling machine which permanently blends the cheese with the wrapper. And if you've never bitten down on a piece of foil with a metal filling, you don't know what snappy cheese is.

Where is it going to end? The time may come when our cities with their tall buildings and broad avenues will be empty. Our fur-clad descendants will be crouched over fires, gnawing on roots and bones while the fruits of our civilization lie all about them — only a thumbnail away.

Winter Morning

This smoky winter morning —
do not despise the green jewel shining among the twigs
because it is a traffic light.

Charles Reznikoff

SUSANA
and the
SHEPHERD

by Margaret Craven

All the passengers on the big transcontinental plane were interested in the young Basque (băsk) who occupied the rear seat. He was good-looking, with dark eyes and a proud, inscrutable face, tagged on the jacket with a check badge like a piece of luggage because he couldn't speak an English word.

"He's a sheepherder from the Spanish Pyrenees," the stewardess replied to an inquiry. "The California Range Association is flying over many of them. Usually three or four come together. He's the first to come alone."

Several of the passengers tried to be friendly, but the young Basque only stared at them, too bewildered and confused to smile, and finally a blond, who had traveled in Spain, said she'd draw him out. She'd toss a little Spanish at him. She'd just go over and give him the good old American *bienvenida.*[1]

---

[1] bienvenida (byān-bā-nē'thä), welcome.

So she went and spoke to him, and the young Basque just fixed upon her a pair of scornful, suspicious eyes and ignored her.

"Do you know what I think?" said the defeated blond to the stewardess. "I think his mother warned him to have nothing to do with American women. They'd eat him alive." And she was wrong; it was his grandmother who had warned him.

"Oh, he's a strange one," the stewardess told the navigator. "They're all silent, but this one wouldn't talk even if he knew how. I hope somebody meets him in San Francisco. I have strict orders not to turn him loose unless he's met."

The navigator was wiser. "He's from some small village, probably," he said. "Never seen a big city. Never been in a plane. If he's afraid, it's the kind of fear only the brave know. Otherwise he wouldn't be crossing an ocean and a continent to herd sheep for a stranger in a land he doesn't know. Let him alone. He's a kid with a dream."

And after that, across the plains and the mountains, the boy sat undisturbed, holding his dream, and his was the old dream many Basque boys have held in their hearts. Their land was not big or rich enough to support all. By custom, a family's land was left to the eldest son. The younger ones, therefore, must emigrate; their only hope of keeping the land they loved was to leave it — and come back rich.

It was possible. From his own village in the province of Navarra several had done it. Felipe (fä-lē′pä) had done it. He had herded sheep for six years in a place called Nevada. In all that time he had learned no more than fifty English words and been to town twice and spent not one coin on drink, smokes, or girls. He had come back with twelve thousand dollars — a fabulous fortune — and he had bought himself a band of fine sheep and married the prettiest girl in the village.

Many had come back, and more had not. Whenever American tourists came to the remote villages of the Pyrenees, some Basque father, prodded by his wife, said slowly, "If you have been to California, is it possible you know our son, Carlos (kär′lôs)?" Or Fermín (fĕr-mēn′). Or Esteban (ĕs-tä′bän). But they never did.

He, Juan Varra (hwän vä′rä), was going to be one of the lucky ones. He had made up his mind. The American consul at Bilbao (bĭl-bä′ō), where he had gone for his sheepherder's examination, had praised him. The doctor who had given him his physical had spoken about his strength. And while he had waited the long months for the completion of his papers, the priest had strengthened him.

No Basque had ever been remembered for his words, the priest had said — only for deeds and for courage. And if the ignorant thought he had a mist in his head like the mists of the mountains he loved, what of it? The thing to do was to be strong.

Yet when it was almost time to land, the boy found it hard to be strong. He reminded himself that an unknown *Americano* had paid hundreds of dollars for his passage, sight unseen, and why? Because he knew — as who does not — that for two thousand years the Basques have been famous for their skill with sheep.

He thought hard on *la abuelita* (lä ä-vwä-lē′tä), his little grandmother. How confidently she had smiled at him as she had prepared his favorite omelet for his last supper at home. With no teeth, she had looked like a little old baby, and he vowed now that with his first wages he would send her enough money to buy a set of shiny white store teeth,

485

so she could walk through the village head high and smiling.

Also he thought of his little brother, who had begged to come along, who must emigrate, too, when he was older. He must set him an example. He must not fail.

Then the plane landed. The passengers began to file out slowly. He followed them. Surely El Cid (ĕl sĭd), the bravest knight in all Christendom, never went forth to battle more staunchly than Juan Varra left that plane, the little stewardess at his heels, praying fervently somebody would meet him and ready to grab his jacket tails if no one did.

He was the last to pass the gate, and as he stepped through, he saw the most beautiful sight possible to any Basque far from home. He saw another Basque. He saw a browned face, no longer young, which was smiling and showing some splendid gold teeth. And the voice was speaking his own dialect, and it said, "Welcome, Juan Varra, and are the girls still as pretty in Navarra?" And this was Ancelito (än-sä-lē′tō), thirty years from home and as much a Basque as ever.

Ancelito collected his luggage and led him to the pickup truck. When they left the confusion of the city and were driving through the great wide green Sacramento Valley, Ancelito dropped pleasantries and began to speak so seriously in Spanish that Juan knew he must remember every word.

Now in early May the alfilaria was already dry. The corkscrew spirals on the wild grass that can work their way into the sheep's hides had already formed. It was vital, therefore, that the sheep be moved at once from the low range. Separated into bands, sheared, and branded, they had been driven to a central campsite, the trailer houses of the herders accompanying them. At the campsite, freight cars waited. The rich *Americano* who owned the sheep had rented a whole train, and at this very moment he was supervising the loading of the sheep bands into the cars. Tonight the train would carry the sheep across the great mountains into Nevada, where the long summer drive would begin at dawn.

Usually, said Ancelito, a boy from the homeland was kept on the valley ranch for several weeks to accustom him to the strange American ways. But now they were desperate for herders. Last year they had lost two older men from heart attacks. The camp tender had found them at eight thousand feet, stiff in their blankets. It would be necessary for Juan Varra to go to Nevada and to start out at dawn with a band of two thousand sheep. Every other day a camp tender would bring him supplies and tell him where to find water. He would have a burro, of course, and a dog which Ancelito himself had trained.

"There is nothing to fear," Ancelito told him gravely. "The dog will know what you do not."

The boy said with dignity, "I have no fear."

Ancelito questioned him carefully, and in response the boy told him, shyly and briefly, a little of his dream. After four hours' driving, they came at last to the campsite.

In the trailer house Juan Varra ate a quick meal while Ancelito checked the clothes and the bedding he'd need. Then through the dark they walked to the train.

"You will go in the caboose," said Ancelito. "You will sleep better, and tomorrow you will need that sleep. I will go by truck with the others and see you at daybreak."

Once, at night in his bunk, the boy woke and felt the train moving under him and the cold air on his cheek, and he could hear the hard pull of the engine, and he knew that they were crossing the mountains. When he woke again, it was to the smell of coffee and the touch of a trainman's hand on his shoulder. He put on his shoes and his jacket and drank two cups of coffee. When he left the caboose, he stepped out into the clear dawn and such a sight as he had never seen.

Already the sheep were being spilled out into the sage, one band at a time, its loaded burro, herder, and dog waiting to drive it away.

Because he was new, his band was the last. Then it, too, was spilled into the sage, and his burro and dog and a sheep tender drove the band away from the tracks as Ancelito motioned him to wait.

The train moved on, the boy waiting by the truck while Ancelito talked earnestly to the *Americano* who owned the sheep, and though they spoke English and the boy could not understand a word, he knew the *Americano* was worried.

"Andy, I'm scared to death to send him out. Can he do it?"

"Yes. He's used to hardship. He is not an American boy. He does not put his manhood in a car that can go ninety miles an hour. It is in himself."

"I know. He'll have the inbred willingness to endure."

"He has something else. He has a dream."

"All right. Let him go."

Then Ancelito gave the boy his directions and told him where he would find water. The owner shook his hand.

Juan ran into the sage and took the crook from the tender, and he gave the old signal to the dog with a lift of his hand, and he was off and on his own. He did not permit himself to look back for some moments. When he did so, it was as if the truck, the men, and the other bands of sheep had never existed, so quickly had the land taken them. And it was unlike any land he had ever seen and vaster than any he had ever imagined.

The sage and the green buck-brush stretched as endlessly as eternity, broken only by a few small yellow sunflowers and an occasional pine. There were no friendly villages, no small white houses with cheerful red-tiled roofs, nothing but mountains which did not stand up proudly as mountains should but lay rolling beneath his shoes.

He could scarcely bear to look at the sheep, so great was his disappointment. How ugly they were with their strange snub-nosed faces. The factory-made crook was awkward to his hand and so long that he was sure he would never be able to trip a ewe neatly by her hind feet. The Australian shepherd was unlike any dog he had known.

But the burro was the same. It trudged along with the sheep, carrying his supplies, topped by his big square bedroll. And the sheep baaed like sheep. The lambs frolicked like the lambs at home. And the dog let the sheep scatter only so far, rounding in the strays.

He counted the black sheep — the markers — carefully. There were twenty-one. He counted the bell-wethers. At the nooning-up he would unpack the burro, check his supplies, and repack in his own precise way. He would make a fire and set a pot of beans to simmer and cook himself a meal of ham and eggs. And this night, when the coyotes yapped and the dog answered them, prowling the bed

grounds, thoughts of home would creep into his head, and he would begin the long battle against loneliness. And he swore now, by all the lady saints and the gentlemen saints in the entire heaven, that he would fight it each night until he won.

It took him six weeks. He had no calendar and no watch, and he needed neither. Each day followed the familiar pattern. He was up before daybreak, building his fire beneath the heavy U-shaped iron, brewing his coffee. When the burro was packed, the daily trek began, the sheep scattering over a mile, the boy following, his beat-up .30-30 in a sling on his back, the dog alert to every sound of his voice, every movement of his hands.

Each nooning-up Juan cooked his meal while the sheep lay in the sage, chewing their cuds. And every other day the sheep tender came bumping through the buckbrush in his four-wheel-drive truck, bringing fresh meat and food, even water if necessary, and an eight-pound round loaf of white Basque bread which he had baked in a long pit. The sheep tender was a Basque also, but he had been too long alone. He had lost his dream. He could not talk easily to anyone, and when he spoke, it was always of some café in some valley town where he could fill himself up on red wine, poured from a goatskin, and eat prodigiously.

Sometimes on the rainy nights when the coyotes cried, the boy was so homesick for his land and his people that it was an agony within him, and he rose shaken and white. He dreamed one night of his *abuelita,* smiling and showing her toothless gums, and when he awoke, his cheeks were wet, and though never for an instant did he admit it was from anything but rain leaking into his little tent, after that he felt better.

Gradually the sheep did not seem quite so snub-nosed and ugly. They became the familiar sheep. He knew them, and a few too well — especially the cantankerous ewe with the twin lambs which he called *la bruja* (lä br$\overline{oo}$'hä), the witch.

He grew very fond of his burro, and he loved the Australian shepherd dog as deeply as a man can love a friend.

Then the six weeks were over, and with his band he took the old trail toward the higher mountains, the little burro leading the way because it knew it well. They reached the river, followed and forded it into the great national forest, traveling twenty miles in three days into the juniper range.

They were in the juniper forest a week, working their way up to the ponderosa and the sugar pines, and here the boy's loneliness finally left him.

Often he saw deer browsing at dawn and dusk, a doe keeping herself carefully between him and her fawn. Once, in the early evening, when the sheep had settled for the night, he came on a mother bear, scolding, slapping, and cuffing her two cubs to hurry them out of his way. Even the birds were a delight, the mountain bluebirds and jays, the sapsuckers and the black-and-yellow orioles. Here he was no longer a boy far from home. He was a Basque herder at his best, responsible and resourceful, like a soldier at some lonely outpost.

The tender's truck could not follow them now. The *Americano* who owned the sheep had established two cabins at seventy-five hundred feet from which several tenders took supplies to the various sheep bands by pack mule. And when Juan saw Ancelito riding through the trees leading a mule, he laughed aloud and was startled by the sound of his own voice.

The mule was a walking grocery store. Its pack bags were heavy with flour sacks, each of them fat with supplies.

Then for the first time Juan Varra was afraid. He was so afraid he wanted to bolt like *la bruja,* the witch ewe. On the mule bringing up the rear was a girl.

Ancelito dismounted. Had it gone well? ... Yes.... Had he been lonely? ... No — perhaps a very little at first. And as he spoke, not once did the boy glance at the girl.

It was only Susana, said Ancelito; and she was his daughter, come to the cabins for a few days, as he had promised her. She was quite harmless. As women go, she was no trouble. She would get the noon meal for them while they unpacked the supplies.

And she did. While the boy and Ancelito unpacked the supplies and discussed the best sites for the bed grounds and the danger of bears, Juan could hear the girl moving at the fire.

When the meal was ready and they sat down for slabs of jack cheese, ham and eggs, fresh bread and coffee, he was forced to look at her. Her feet were as big as a boy's. Her legs were encased in thick blue cotton pants like a boy's. Her top half was submerged in a shirt like a boy's. Her hair was drawn tight to the back of her head and hung in a thick brush, suitable only for a horse's tail. Furthermore, she did not look up at him from under her lashes and touch him with the briefest of cool, sweet glances to tell him she saw every single thing about him and found it good. She looked straight at him, and boldly, as one boy takes the measure of another.

He did not direct one word to her. When the meal was over and Ancelito and his daughter were mounted and leaving, he cast an "*Adiós*" (ä-thyôs') into the air, which she could take to include her if she wished.

"Is he alive?" Susana asked her father when the mules had started.

"Yes."

"Is he stupid?"

"No. He is silent. He is a Basque. I am a Basque."

"When you came to this country, you were not like that."

"I was exactly like that. He is afraid of you. But do not worry. I have told him you are harmless."

"Father, you didn't."

"But certainly. It would do you no good to make eyes at this one. He has a dream. He will save his money. He will go back to his village a *millonario* (mē-yō-nä'rē-ō) and marry the most beautiful girl in all Navarra. Now, if you were as wise as your mother —"

"*Papacito* (pä-pä-sē'tō)," said Susana slowly, "are the girls so pretty in Navarra?"

And Ancelito smiled at her and said, "Beyond description."

The voices carried back to the boy in the high, clear air, and though they were in English, he did not miss the scorn in the girl's voice. That night among the supplies he found that Ancelito had left him a beginner's Spanish-English reader.

Love may need no words, but resentment can use several. The next day Juan Varra opened the first crack in the dark tomb in which he was determined to bury himself for six years. He began to learn to read English.

Two days later, when the grocery mule came through the trees, the boy put on his most proud and silent Basque face, lest the girl think he was glad to see her. But it was not Ancelito and Susana who followed the mule. It was the dull camp tender who had lost his dream.

Juan did not admit to disappointment. He had no time to think of girls. The bears were troublesome. One old killer bear followed the sheep band, killing a ewe each night, and the boy tracked him and shot him. In all, he killed four bears.

In July the rams were brought in, and in August all the sheep bands were driven to a mountain valley, where the ewes were culled, the lambs separated into the fats and the feeders. On the way back to the high range with his reassembled band, Juan passed his first campers, and they were friendly. A little boy chased the lambs and couldn't catch them. The father and mother smiled at Juan and made him a present of a kitten. After that, the cat followed along with the sheep, and though Juan told himself he kept her only to protect his food from the chipmunks, he carried her under his jacket in the thunderstorms and let her sleep at the foot of his bedroll.

Then, in October, the long drive was done. The sheep were carried by two- and three-decker trucks down from the mountains to the low delta to browse on the corn stubble. The burro was left behind, for a cook wagon carried supplies. Just before Christmas the bands were driven to the home ranch to wait for the lambing, and it was here, in a neat white house, that Ancelito, the foreman, lived with Susana. The boy did not ask for her.

"Am I rich yet?" he asked Ancelito anxiously.

"In this country you are poor as a thin mouse," said Ancelito. "But at home already you can buy the finest house in the village."

It was Ancelito who helped him send money to his *abuelita* for her new store teeth and presents for the family. It was Ancelito who got from town the clothes Juan needed. After that, he spent nothing, and each month the *Americano* who owned the sheep deposited his wages in a savings account in his name. When, at Christmas, the other herders left the trailer houses and drove to town for a fine celebration, he did not go. And when he was working with the sheep near the white house and saw something soft and obviously feminine fluttering on the clothesline in the rear, he looked the other way, so tight was the dream still within him.

Right after Christmas the drop band was collected in a big open field, and lambing began. Four hundred lambs were born each night, the boy working out in the cold, helping the young ewes that were having trouble with their firstborn, turning the lambs. One early morning the *Americano* was helping put each ewe and her new lamb into a portable *chiquero* (chē-kā'rō), or pen, so she would claim her lamb, and he watched the boy work.

"He is wonderful," he said. "He will save twenty-five per cent more lambs. . . . Andy, we must keep this one."

"Yes, I have thought of it," said Ancelito.

The last night of the lambing, through no fault of his own, the boy lost two little lambs. This, to a Basque herder, is cause for heartbreak, not just for sadness. Ancelito took him to the white house for food and comfort, and there in the warm kitchen waited Susana.

Gone were the boy's shoes, the pants, and the horse's tail. She was as shy as a forest creature and as sweet as any young girl in Navarra on her saint's day. She was the daughter of a Basque, and she, too, could be silent. Without a word, she put the coffeepot before them and plates of ham and eggs. Then she left them, turning at the door.

"I am so sorry, Juan." And for an instant her glance touched his cheek and was gone.

He did not see her again, because this was the busy time — lamb tails to be docked, new sheep bands to be formed, the ewes to be sheared and branded. Then the winter was gone, and May here again, and the sheep driven to the campsite to go by train to Nevada. And the first year was over, and the cycle began again.

Now repetition had replaced newness, making the second year even lonelier than the first. In the buckbrush, loneliness became an entity, pressing constantly upon him. The boy talked aloud sometimes to the cat and the burro. The dog, of course, was his abiding friend.

Rarely the camp tender brought him letters from home. Those from his *abuelita* and his little brother were the same. They loved him; they missed him. But the letter from his elder brother, who was head of the family, held a new tone. How fortunate Juan was to be in that land where everyone was rich and all was easy. How hard it was to be the one who was left behind. Oh, he must not stay away too long. If he worked harder and was given a raise — if he saved all beyond the barest necessities, five years might be enough, or even four.

In the juniper forest one June day he heard a strange little whimpering, crying sound and came on a lone fawn. He longed to make a pet of it, to keep it with him, as the herders did sometimes. But he could not bear to take it from its mother, to teach it to be unafraid of man, to notch its ear so that when some hunter shot it, he would know that once it had had too good a friend in man. It reminded him of the girl.

Then again he had driven the sheep band into the ponderosa and sugar pines of the high range, and he was home in the mountains.

When the grocery mule came through the trees, Ancelito was with it but not Susana. This time the boy asked for her.

"And how is your daughter?" he asked formally, and Ancelito said she was well. She was going to school this summer. She was educating her head.

"It is that she does not wish a husband?" the boy asked slowly, and Ancelito said that, like all girls, she hoped to find one. But in this country it was the custom for many girls to help their husbands get started. Suppose Susana should marry a man who wished to possess a sheep band of his very own. What a fine thing if she could help him. Did Juan know that the sheepman chosen as the year's best in all California was the son of a Basque whose father had come first as a herder? No doubt his wife helped him, as his mother had helped his father. It was one of those strange American ways.

Several times this year the forest ranger came by at nooning-up and shared his meal. And once a party of mountaineers coming out from a climb passed by and hailed him. He had picked up enough English to say a few words now, but he was alone so much that the sound of a voice always startled him and filled him with uneasiness, because it broke the quiet monotony in which he lived.

Then at last it was fall, and the sheep were back on the delta, working their way toward the home ranch.

"How rich am I now?" he asked Ancelito.

After taking out his pencil and doing a bit of figuring, Ancelito replied gravely, "In this country you have a modest savings, but in Navarra you are a man of some means. All your relatives are trying to borrow money."

When the sheep band neared the home ranch, the boy watched eagerly for Susana to come home for the holidays from the school she attended, forty miles distant. And one afternoon just before Christmas, while he was working in the big field where the drop band was to be collected for the lambing, he saw her arrive, and the sight filled him with horror.

There was a loud and sudden roar, and into the ranch road from the highway bounced a small, open, ancient and rattletrap car, Susana at the wheel, her legs in jeans, her hair streaming behind her in a horse tail.

"She goes back and forth to school this way," said Ancelito calmly. "Scares the sheep. It is amazing what an *Americana* will do to educate her head and get ready to help her husband."

It was cold during this year's lambing, and again Juan worked each night in the big open field with the ewes. Late one night twin lambs lost their mother, arriving in this world so weak that in the morning he and Ancelito carried them to the house and bedded them in the warmth of the kitchen stove.

When the boy had finished working with the lambs and stood up, ready to return to the field, he saw that Susana was watching him quietly, sweet and feminine as she had been when she had prepared breakfast the year before.

"You had a good year, Juan?" she asked in Spanish.

"Sí."

"You were lonely?"

"A Basque is never lonely."

"See, *papacito,* he is afraid of me."

"I am afraid of no one."

"He is afraid of me. He is like the others. He learns nothing. He gives nothing. All he sees in this country

is money. All he wants to do is grab. He is stupid, *papacito.* He is more stupid than the sheep."

The boy followed Ancelito back to the field.

"She likes you," said Ancelito complacently. "If she did not like you, she would not be so *furiosa.*"

One day from the fields Juan saw the little rattletrap car take off down the road, and he knew Susana had gone back to school. He put her resolutely from his mind, and the months slipped by until the sheep bands were driven to the campsite and the second year was done.

The third year was as like the second as the second had been like the first — the loneliness and the constant movement of the sheep, the nooning-up and the bedding-down, and the watchful eye never forgetting to count bellwethers and black sheep. The coyotes yapped in the night, and the bears came in the night, and there were the cat, the dog, and the burro. Only the details were different and the girl's scornful words, and the thought of the girl was constantly in his mind.

In October, two days before the sheep bands were to leave the mountains, an early blizzard caught them, the snow falling so fast and heavily that they could not be driven out in time. The boy built a fire of green wood so that much smoke would rise to guide the camp tender, and Ancelito saw it and came with horses and men to trample and pack the snow so the sheep could move.

"Am I rich now?" Juan asked, sitting beside Ancelito in the truck on their way down to the delta.

"You are not quite a *millonario*," said Ancelito. "You have a little more than five thousand dollars. In your village it would be a very large sum." He spoke sadly.

"My work has not been good?" asked the boy. "The *Americano* is not satisfied?"

"He is much pleased. This morning when the sheep were safe from the blizzard, I called Susana and asked her to tell him. She says there are many letters for you. When a Basque family takes thus to pen, the news must be bad."

They rode in silence, not over to the corn stubble this time but to the white house, and when they went into the kitchen, Susana handed his letters to the boy, her eyes big and worried.

They left him to read them alone, and when they returned to the kitchen, he was sitting quietly, the letters spread on the table before him, his face stricken. He did not look up.

"My *abuelita* is dead," he said, and when Ancelito tried to comfort him, he made no response, and when Susana set hot coffee before him, he did not thank her. He was silent as only a Basque can be silent.

"Shall I tell you what is wrong?" asked Ancelito. "Shall I tell you how I know?"

The boy did not answer.

"When I came to this country," said Ancelito, "I spent ten years alone with the sheep. I had a dream also. I thought only of my people and of the day I would return to them. When I did so, I could not stand it. I had forgotten such poverty. Things were bad in my village. Everyone was poor and I was rich, and between us was a wall of jealousy I could not tear down or climb over."

The boy did not look up.

"Have you not seen the wall in these letters? Is not your elder brother resentful? Does he not complain of your good fortune?"

The boy was silent.

"I bought my parents the finest house in the village! I paid sixty American dollars for it. I gave them money to care for them, and I came back here where I shall never be rich. It is a friendly country. This is what matters."

"*Papacito,* it is useless!" cried Susana. "He is so stupid! Can you believe it? He does not know we love him of truth. He does not know you feel to him as a man to his own son. Let him save and go back. Let him be rich and miserable. Let him marry the most beautiful girl in all of Navarra. What do I care?"

Then the boy looked up. "Is it possible to bring my little brother to this country?" he asked slowly.

"It would take time, but it certainly is possible. He could live here with us. He could go to school. Susana could teach him to speak English."

"Is it possible Susana could teach me also? Could she teach me to tell her in English that in the mountains, when I am alone with the sheep, I do not think of any girl in Navarra? I think of her."

"This she would do gladly."

"Then if I have lost my dream, I can replace it with another. And if I do not return, it is nothing. I am a Basque," said the boy proudly, "and a Basque cannot lose his homeland, because he takes it with him always."

DISCUSSION

1. What Basque custom made it necessary for Juan to leave his home? What was his purpose in coming to America?
2. What were Juan's responsibilities as a sheepherder?
3. What did Juan find most difficult about his first few weeks in the mountains?
4. When Susana and her father brought him supplies, what were Juan's reactions to the girl?
5. What do you think Ancelito meant when he said of Juan, "He does not put his manhood in a car that can go ninety miles an hour. It is in himself"?
6. Explain the statement, "Love may need no words, but resentment can use several." How does the statement apply to Juan's feelings about Susana early in the story?
7. How did the letter Juan received from his older brother differ from those he received from his grandmother and his younger brother? How do you think the older brother really felt about Juan? What makes you think that? How would you explain the older brother's feelings?
8. At the end of the story, with what dream do you think Juan planned to replace his lost dream?

9. Do you think Juan's decision not to return to Navarra was a wise one? Why do you think that?

10. In coming to America and, later, in deciding to remain here, do you think Juan acted selfishly? Why do you think as you do?

11. Did Ancelito seem to have a good understanding of both Susana and Juan? Why do you think as you do? In what ways did Ancelito help the boy and girl to understand each other?

12. What did Juan mean when he said that "a Basque cannot lose his homeland, because he takes it with him always"? If you and your family had to move to another country, do you think you would continue to look on America as your homeland? Why do you think that?

AUTHOR

Margaret Craven was born in Helena, Montana, and graduated with honors from Stanford University. She has lived in California since finishing college and at present makes her home in Sacramento.

After working for several years on a newspaper, Miss Craven became a professional writer, and her stories have appeared in various leading magazines. Her background material for "Susana and the Shepherd" was acquired from a friend who, like the *Americano* in the story, brought young Basques to this country as herders for his sheep bands.

The Glorious Fourth

by John and Katherine Bakeless

The war with England had already begun. George Washington had been appointed commander of the colonial army; patriots had fought the redcoats at places like Lexington and Ticonderoga. The spirit of independence was in the air. Only one grave final step remained to be taken — the formal and official declaration of independence by the Continental Congress.

The scene was now set for independence. No matter how much they might protest they were only loyal Britons demanding only the rights of Englishmen, the colonists had refused to pay British taxes, they had driven out British governors, they had been shooting British soldiers, and they had taken over the government. No wonder Samuel Adams asked, "Is not America already independent? Why then not declare it?"

The Virginia delegates in Congress took their time about complying with the instructions which that state had sent them. The resolution for independence that they were to present had to be carefully thought out and carefully worded. It was June 7, 1776, before Richard Henry Lee, senior member of the Virginia delegation, rose to propose it.

John Adams promptly seconded Lee's resolution. The two had probably fixed that little matter up beforehand. They knew well enough that this public cooperation of a Massachusetts Yankee democrat and a Virginian aristocrat would serve as a strong hint to the central Atlantic colonies that the most important New England colony and the most important Southern colony were working together to support independence.

The delegates would also know that if the largest New England colony and the largest Southern colony felt that way, the rest of New England and the South would probably join them.

After it had heard the resolution, Congress did not rush matters. It decided to resolve itself into a "committee of the whole" to discuss what Richard Henry Lee had proposed. Legislative bodies frequently do that to make discussion easier and freer than it is under strict parliamentary procedure.

On June 10, 1776, the committee of the whole reported to Congress, and there was a more formal discussion of the resolution. Among those who argued against independence were John Dickinson, James Wilson, and Robert R. Livingston. They felt sure that the middle colonies were not yet ready for so bold a move.

But there was one strong argument for not delaying the declaration of independence. The colonists would soon reach the end of their resources. They badly needed foreign arms, foreign soldiers, and foreign money. The only countries that might possibly give such help were England's enemies, France and Spain. Both had fought the British not many years before. Though no longer at war, both were still hostile to Great Britain. Both would be glad to do anything they could to cause the British trouble. Either one might be willing to supply arms, money, or soldiers. If America declared herself an independent nation, France and Spain might be willing to recognize her independence and aid her against Great Britain. But they certainly would not go openly to the aid of American rebels who admitted they were still subjects of King George. (In the end, France provided all three necessities and Spain went to war with Great Britain, which assisted the colonies even if there was no formal American alliance with Spain as there was with France.)

After debating till seven o'clock in the evening of Saturday, June 8, Congress decided to go back into a committee of the whole on June 10. Following this second day of discussion, Congress decided to postpone any decision for three weeks, which meant until July 1. It seemed likely that the central colonies, which were still hesitating at the thought of complete independence, would soon change their minds.

Though Congress postponed the vote and though there was certainly some hesitation, the delegates appointed a committee of five to decide on the wording of a future Declaration of Independence — in case Congress should ever pass it. Four members of this committee, Thomas Jefferson, Benjamin Franklin, John Adams, and Roger Sherman, favored independence. The fifth member, Robert R. Livingston, still had his doubts. In fact, he did not vote for the Declaration when it was finally submitted to Congress, and he never signed it. Livingston was so doubtful about the whole thing that he left Philadelphia before the committee had finished revising the Declaration.

The rest of the committee had no doubt about independence at all. As soon as they met, they assigned Thomas Jefferson to write the first draft. Jefferson had been very silent during the debates since he did not care for public speaking. John Adams later said, "During the whole time I sat with him in Congress, I never heard him utter three sentences together." But Jefferson was already known as one of the best writers in North America, or, as John Adams put it, he had "a happy talent of composition."

Jefferson wrote the Declaration of Independence in the simple lodgings he had rented for himself — a parlor and a bedroom in the house of Jacob Graff, Jr., a Philadelphia bricklayer. Richard Henry Lee, though he had offered the original resolution for independence, had nothing to do with writing the Declaration that made his resolution effective.

Many years afterward, when John Adams and Thomas Jefferson were both old men and both ex-Presidents, John Adams thought he remembered that the committee had made Jefferson and himself a committee of two to write the first draft. Adams was perfectly sincere when he said this, and a warm friend of Jefferson's, whom he greatly admired, but he was very, very old and was apparently

confused. There is no doubt that Thomas Jefferson did write the Declaration of Independence, though the committee, especially Adams and Franklin, suggested certain verbal changes, and Congress eventually made some very important changes of its own.

Jefferson in later years had his own notes, made at the time, to prove his authorship; and the earliest draft of the Declaration now known (Jefferson may have torn up a good many sheets of paper while he was at work) is in his handwriting. Adams had no such record, only a very old man's memory of things long, long ago.

There is no reason for thinking that Roger Sherman did any of the drafting. If he did, it was very little. And Robert R. Livingston probably had as little to do with the Declaration as possible. Benjamin Franklin, who admired the Declaration of Independence as a literary production so much that he said he wished he had written it himself, wrote in a few changes in his own handwriting. A few others appear to be changes by John Adams; and Thomas Jefferson made some last-minute changes himself. All these alterations can easily be noted in the original manuscript, which still survives.

The committee were able to lay their approved form of Jefferson's draft before Congress on June 28, 1776. Congress merely received it formally and ordered it "laid on the table." For the moment, nothing

could be done about a *declaration* of independence since Congress had not yet voted in favor of independence. Richard Henry Lee's resolution had also been "lying on the table" ever since he had introduced it.

On July 2, however, Congress voted in favor of Lee's resolution and thus put itself on record as favoring independence. Congress went right on, that same day, to begin discussion of the exact wording of the Declaration. Thomas Jefferson's draft was now minutely scrutinized, line by line.

It was not very pleasant for Thomas Jefferson. His friend John Adams spoke vigorously in favor of the text of the Declaration as the committee had submitted it. But, as usually happens, everybody else thought he knew exactly how to improve the manuscript; and, as also always happens, everybody had a different way of doing it. Jefferson, having done his best, had nothing whatever to say. He listened in unhappy silence.

Franklin, sitting beside him and seeing his annoyance, tried to comfort him with a funny story. (Franklin was a little like Lincoln in one respect: He always had a joke or a story to tell, especially when a touch of humor might relieve a delicate or difficult situation.)

While the other delegates were slashing various words, sentences, and whole sections of Jefferson's draft, Franklin told him about a hatter who asked a friend to write a sign advertising the hatter's business. The sign, as written, read: "John Thomson, Hatter, Makes and Sells Hats for Ready Money." On it was also a picture of a hat. Then the man's friends began to make suggestions. One wanted the word "Hatter" removed, because the words "Sells Hats" implied he was a hatter anyway. Another thought the word "Makes" ought to be cut out. You can't sell a hat until it is made, he pointed out. Another struck out the words "for Ready Money." Another said: "Sells Hats? Why, no one would expect you to give them away!" Another thought the word "Hats" was needless. The picture was enough. In the end, all that was left of the original sign was the man's name and the picture!

Congress continued its discussion all day on July 3 and on into July 4, 1776, which was to become the most famous date in American history. The vote was taken by states — or rather, by colonies, for the colonies did not become states until they had formally proclaimed their independence. Each had only one vote, no matter how many delegates it had sent. The delegates from each had to agree among themselves how they would cast the vote for their colony.

Secretary Thomson called the roll, from North to South, beginning with New Hampshire and ending with Georgia. Twelve colonies had voted in favor of independence, and only twelve now voted for the text of the Declaration. In each case, the New York delegates abstained from voting because their Provincial Congress had instructed them to take no action, either for or against independence.

The Declaration of Independence was at first signed only by John Hancock, as president of Congress, and Charles Thomson, as secretary. When all the revision was finished, the actual paper of Thomas Jefferson's draft was pretty well scratched up, and Congress ordered that the whole Declaration be written in a clear copy and engrossed on parchment for signing.

There was no formal proclamation of America's independence on July 4, and it is very doubtful that the Liberty Bell rang at all that day. Congress had some other business to handle, and it went right ahead. It ordered the Declaration printed and also ordered printed copies sent to Washington's army, to all state assemblies, and to various churches.

Even though the Declaration of Independence was published in the Philadelphia *Evening Post* on July 6, it was not officially proclaimed until July 8. Behind Independence Hall stood a large platform built for a Philadelphia astronomer, David Rittenhouse, to use in his observations. Here, on the eighth, the people gathered, while Colonel John Nixon, of the Committee of Safety, read the Declaration of Independence publicly and officially for the first time, though everyone must have known for several days what Congress had done.

Post riders saddled their horses and rode off through the states in every direction, carrying printed copies of the Declaration, spreading the news as they went, and sometimes pausing to let the Declaration be publicly read before riding on.

People are likely to imagine that as soon as the Declaration was adopted on July 4, 1776, the delegates went up, one by one, and affixed their signatures. That was quite impossible. All that Congress had, at the moment, was Jefferson's draft, much corrected and scribbled upon with all the changes Congress had made. The signed Declaration of Independence, now displayed in the National Archives in Washington, is a copy of Jefferson's manuscript as changed by Congress, beautifully engrossed on parchment by a skilled professional penman.

It was not formally signed by the delegates until August 2, 1776. That is probably when John Hancock, affixing his usual big, bold signature, remarked that King George would have no trouble reading it — though he could have said the same thing when he signed Jefferson's draft, as amended. There is also a story that when Charles Carroll signed, someone remarked that there were so many Charles Carrolls in Maryland, no one would know which one it was. Then, the story goes, Carroll seized his pen and added "of Carrollton" so that there could be no possible doubt who the signer was. But many of Charles Carroll's signatures have survived, and they show that he often added "of Carrollton" for this reason.

There was a certain solemnity as the signatures were affixed. All the signers knew that if the American army won and America became free, they would be national heroes. They also knew that if America lost, most of them would be executed as traitors. There would be no doubt about their treason. There were their signatures on the Declaration — enough to hang them, without other evidence. Indeed, if America had lost the Revolutionary War, the signers of the Declaration of Independence would have been fortunate to get off with hanging. The legal penalty for treason was still hanging, drawing, and quartering.

Thinking of this, one individual remarked that, after the signing, there must be complete cooperation for victory: "We must all hang together."

"Yes," replied Benjamin Franklin, who loved his little joke, even if it was a rather grim one. "We must all hang together or we shall all hang separately."

To make sure they were in earnest as patriots, new delegates elected to Congress continued to sign the Declaration of Independence when they took their seats, even if they had not been members when it was passed. This continued at least as late as November, 1776.

That is the story of the Declaration of Independence, to which our country owes its freedom and two hundred years of successful democratic living.

By July 3, 1776, John Adams was certain that Congress would eventually adopt Jefferson's Declaration. In the two following paragraphs from a letter written to his wife on that date, Adams expressed his personal feelings about the Declaration and the way future generations of Americans should celebrate Independence Day.

I am apt to believe that it will be celebrated by succeeding generations as the great anniversary festival. It ought to be commemorated as the day of deliverance by solemn acts of devotion to God Almighty. It ought to be solemnized with pomp and parade, with shows, games, sports, guns, bells, bonfires, and illuminations, from one end of this continent to the other, from this time forward for evermore.

You will think me transported with enthusiasm, but I am not. I am well aware of the toil and blood and treasure that it will cost us to maintain this Declaration and support and defend these States. Yet, through all the gloom, I can see the rays of ravishing light and glory. I can see that the end is more than worth all the means. And that posterity will triumph in that day's transaction, even although we should rue it, which I trust in God we shall not.

DISCUSSION

1. Which two colonies took the lead in trying to persuade the Continental Congress to declare independence from England?
2. How was the Declaration of Independence prepared for consideration by the Congress? What did Congress have to do before any action could be taken on the Declaration?
3. Why was there a delay between the adoption and the actual signing of the Declaration?
4. Which specific colonies were hesitant about declaring independence?
5. What did Samuel Adams mean by the words, "Is not America already independent?"
6. Why do you think Congress delayed so many weeks before voting in favor of Lee's resolution for independence?

7. Why was the signing of the Declaration of Independence a courageous act for each of the delegates? In what way do you think having delegates sign the Declaration served to strengthen the colonies?
8. Do you think John Adams would approve of the way in which the Fourth of July is celebrated today? Why do you think that?
9. What is a traitor? What is a hero? What did the signers of the Declaration think would determine whether they had acted as traitors or as heroes? Is the difference between the two always determined in this way? Why do you think as you do?

AUTHORS

John and Katherine Bakeless are historians and biographers who, together and independently, have written many books. "The Glorious Fourth" is an excerpt from their book *Signers of the Declaration.* They are co-authors of two other books for young readers, *They Saw America First* and *Spies of the Revolution.*

The Bakelesses grew up in Bloomsburg, Pennsylvania, and both of them attended the State Normal School there. As children, they had little to do with each other, but John Bakeless says, "Matters changed when I was in college." They were married a few years after graduation.

Colonel Bakeless, who served for thirty-five years with the U.S. Army, has also been a news correspondent, editor, teacher, and lecturer. He holds three university degrees, including a Ph.D. from Harvard. Among the books he has written are *Turncoats, Traitors and Heroes* and *Adventures of Lewis and Clark.*

Katherine Bakeless is an accomplished musician. She studied at the Peabody Conservatory in Baltimore and with well-known musicians in the United States and Europe, and she has taught music in several schools. She is the author of a number of plays and has also written books about the lives of great composers.

The Bakelesses now live in Seymour, Connecticut.

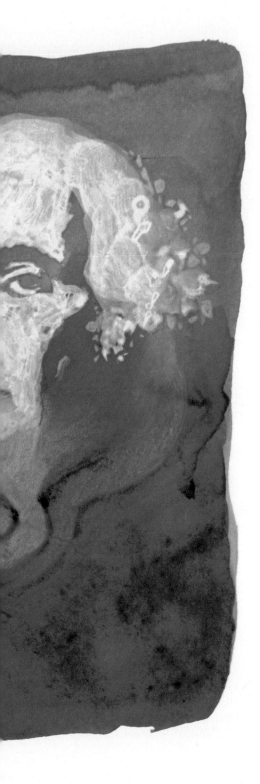

Prophecy in Flame

Grandfather wrote from Valley Forge,
"My dear, I miss you; times are harder;
The cheeses sent from home received,
A fine addition to our larder."

Grandfather wrote, "The volunteers
Are leaving — going home for haying;
We lose militia day by day;
But still a few of us are staying."

Grandfather wrote, "Last night I gave
My blanket to a soldier who
Was wrapped in rags; Phoebe, my dear,
The nights are cold. I dream of you."

Grandfather wrote, "That grand old man
Who bears us up seems not to tire;
I speak of General Washington,
Who last night shared with us his fire."

Grandfather dipped his quill and wrote,
Sanded and sealed his letter; sent it
Off with a splash of sealing wax,
Thinking of her for whom he meant it,

Nor dreamed that soldiers hungering here
Would feed a nation's new desire,
And men unborn would warm themselves
At that same small, fierce-flickering fire.

FRANCES MINTURN HOWARD

SKILL LESSON 8

IDENTIFYING THE THEME OF A STORY

Like most people you probably enjoy good mystery stories and good Westerns on television. Both kinds of stories often involve crime and justice. In fact they often have a similar message, such as *Crime does not pay*. The message that the writer of a story wants to share with you is called the THEME of the story. The theme of a story is usually a general message or truth, such as *Crime does not pay,* that can be applied to many stories. The theme develops from the characters (the persons or things that are in the story) and the plot (the events that take place in the story). Sometimes even the setting is important to the theme of a story, as in a story where someone is battling against the elements.

In the story "Larceny and Old Lace" you will recall that Florence Usher foiled the plans of Harry Gordon by taking the framed photograph that contained certain microfilmed documents. In the story "The Three Garridebs" Killer Evans tried to recover a counterfeiter's outfit but only succeeded in wounding Dr. Watson and in being captured by Sherlock Holmes. The theme of both stories is concerned with crime and justice. How would you state the theme of the two stories?

Just as *Crime does not pay* is a common theme, there are a number of other themes that you will find occurring over and over in stories. These themes may be stated in slightly different ways, but they frequently evolve from the various situations that are listed at the top of the following page.

1. People battling the elements.
2. The struggle of moral strength against brute strength.
3. Solving a problem through an understanding of self and others.
4. Success in performing a seemingly impossible task.
5. The need to adapt to a new environment.
6. The search of an individual for fame, love, or success.
7. Taking great risks to solve a problem or to fulfill a desire.

Courage and bravery are the bases for the themes of many stories. In the following write-up of a television play, courage and the will to survive have much to do with the theme. How would you state the theme of the story?

While exploring the vast wilderness of the Rocky Mountains, Jess and Hal realized, as the sun began to set, that they were hopelessly lost. Their food and water had been exhausted during the day. How the two young men managed to stay alive until their rescue five days later makes a gripping story of courage and determination.

The theme might be stated as: *Survival in the wilderness demands courage and determination* or *To survive in the wilderness a person must turn a hostile setting into a friendly one.* You may have stated the theme somewhat differently, but courage and survival are important to the theme.

In the following summary of a story, what qualities must Sandra have had to bring about the change in attitude of her friends? How would you state the theme of the story?

All the evidence pointed to the fact that Sandra Thompson was the last to be in the room where the successful businessman, J. T. Winston, kept his jewels and other valuables. Sandra used the room to tutor young Todd Winston. When it was discovered that the jewels were missing, Sandra maintained her innocence despite

the fact that most of her friends did not believe her. An accident on a nearby highway months after the robbery seemed to vindicate Sandra, but her friends remained unconvinced. The years that followed were filled with heartbreak and loneliness until at last the jewels were recovered, and Sandra was able to persuade her friends of her innocence.

Themes that revolve around love can be either sad or happy. In the story "Billy Beans Lived Here" the love of a sister for her brother forms the basis for the theme of the story. On page 373 you read "She liked this one brother of hers better than anybody else in the world." At another point in the story you read the following paragraphs:

He patted her arm. "Next week. Then you'll be through school. Free all summer." Seeing the unreconciled look in her eye, he said persuasively, "They're goin' to let me take a Salt Lake run soon. You can come on that, and I'll even let ya drive across the desert."

And with that promise, she let him go, holding her right arm high in silent farewell.

Earlier you learned that the theme of a story develops from the characters and plot. Who were the main characters in "Billy Beans Lived Here"? Were they rich or poor? People often have monuments or tombstones erected in memory of a dead relative. Why was this probably not so in the case of Billy Beans? What was Ellie's monument to her brother? What do you think is the theme of the story?

Theme is only one important element in a story. Plot, character, and setting are also important elements in a story. Theme is sometimes difficult to detect in a story, since it is the underlying meaning in the work and is not usually directly expressed. Analyzing the characters, how they act, asking why they behave in such a way, and taking into account setting and plot can lead to the identification of the theme of a story.

An analysis of the story elements in "A Cup of Tea" helps in identifying the theme:

Setting. The setting is the place and time of a story. The setting of "A Cup of Tea" is London during World War II in the 1940's, at a time when the city was being bombed heavily.

Characters. The characters in the story are Bill and Julie, two homeless teen-agers trying to survive the horrors of war.

Plot. The plot of a story is the series of events or actions that take place in the story. In the story "A Cup of Tea" Bill and Julie go to Bill's home to collect some things and to see if his aunt has returned. Near the house they pass a notice about an unexploded bomb and then see the bomb in the backyard. Julie feels uncomfortable. On page 5 you read: "I don't like it," she said. "Let's go." Although Bill doesn't admit it, he is frightened, too, but tries to act in a brave manner. Bill has his shave and both have tea. Then they leave the house. Sometime later the bomb explodes, wrecking a number of houses.

Theme. Courage would certainly appear to be at the center of the theme of the story "A Cup of Tea." Both Bill and Julie displayed courage to some extent. Which one displayed greater courage? If you think of courage in terms of Bill, you might decide that the theme of the story is something like *A great longing to live as normally as possible under difficult circumstances sometimes causes a person to take great risks.* Julie's friendship with Bill was so strong that she was willing to go into the house with the unexploded bomb, even though she, much more than he, understood the great risk they were taking. The theme of the story in terms of Julie might be *A strong feeling of affection toward someone else sometimes causes a person to take unnecessary risks.*

A humorous story may have a theme too. In "The Good-Luck Frog" Stacy's charm, a metal frog, first interfered with the sensor lens of the computer and caused Stacy to receive a low score for an almost perfect dive. It later shorted the entire computer, causing Stacy to receive an unbelievably high score and with it the championship. It seems unlikely that a simple metal object (the frog) could so completely disrupt the workings of a man-made marvel (the computer). And yet it did so in this story. Does that give you a clue as to what the theme of the story may be? Think about what the theme may be before you read further.

The theme of "The Good-Luck Frog" centers around certain accidental *circumstances* (the frog's being placed above one of the sensor lenses and later on top of the computer) and man's scientific *inventiveness* (the computer). With that in mind you would probably conclude that the theme is something like *Accidental circumstances sometimes defeat even the greatest products of man's inventiveness.*

"The Good-Luck Frog" may be said to have a secondary theme. Remember that Stacy felt that her good-luck charm (the metal frog) had helped her make it into the finals. With the charm lost, she feared facing her three dives in the finals. But by the time Dave got the frog back to Stacy, she had already made her first dive, and it was a very good one. Does that suggest anything to you about Stacy's need for a charm in order to dive well? The secondary theme of "The Good-Luck Frog" might be stated as *The successful performance of a task depends more on a person's ability than on luck.*

Usually there is no particular theme in nonfiction material since most of the time it presents information without the need for a plot. In "That Legendary Ride," however, which recounts Duke Kahanamoku's longest surfing ride, there is a theme. It might be expressed several ways in terms of the successful performance of a task, one way being *A firm belief in oneself can lead to success in the performance of a seemingly impossible task.*

In another nonfiction selection that you read earlier, "I Meet Money," there is a theme that centers on the need to adapt to a new environment and the problems that sometimes arise from having to do so. The theme of "I Meet Money" could be expressed as *A person may have to overcome problems when he tries to adapt to a new environment.*

Identifying the theme of a selection can help in your understanding of the basic meaning of the selection. Most stories and some nonfiction selections have themes. Careful thought to the characters, the plot, and the setting can be helpful to you in identifying the theme of a selection.

Discussion

Help your class answer these questions:
1. What is meant by the *theme* of a story?
2. What are other important story elements?
3. What did you decide is the theme of the story "Larceny and Old Lace"? Of the story "The Three Garridebs"?
4. What is the theme of the story summary about Sandra Thompson on pages 513–514?
5. What is the theme of the story "Billy Beans Lived Here"?

On your own

On a sheet of paper number and write your answer to each of the following questions:

1. In the story "Raymond's Run" Squeaky won the race and in the process learned something about understanding herself and others. Think about the plot and the characters. What is the theme of the story?
2. The story "The Green River Skinner" tells of hardships that Rue endured at the hands of both men and nature. The theme probably has something to do with strength and survival. How would you state the theme of the story?
3. Sancho in the story of the same name completes an almost impossible task, that of getting back to his home in Texas all the way from Wyoming. Does that suggest a theme for the story? How would you express the theme?

4. In the story "The Horsecatcher" Young Elk wants something very much and risks his life in order to get it. Does that suggest what the theme of the story is? How would you express the theme of the story?

Checking your work

If you are asked to do so, read aloud one or more of your answers. Listen as others give their answers. The wording of your answers need not be exactly the same as that of your classmates, but you should agree in general on the themes of the stories. You may need to discuss evidence in the stories that supports or discredits answers.

Let's hear it for the aeronaut,
who did it on hot air

by K. C. Tessendorf

To our Apollo-oriented generation, it seems surprising that in the eighteenth century, when Louis XVI and Marie Antoinette held court at the Palace of Versailles (věr-sī'), men were already drifting about the atmosphere at altitudes ranging toward twenty thousand feet. These were the aeronauts — the toast of their age. Their craft were great bags of hot air or hydrogen.

The brothers Montgolfier (mŏnt-gŏl'fē-ā), from a family of French papermakers, first demonstrated the flight of a hot-air balloon on June 5, 1783. The superior utility of hydrogen was known, but paper and cloth were too porous to contain the gas. Professor Jacques Charles (zhäk shärl), however, fashioned a rubber-lined silk balloon capable of restraining hydrogen and wafted it aloft before a tremendous crowd in the Champ de Mars (shäm' də märs') at Paris that same summer. Zooming to a great altitude, it tore, and the gaily colored, fluttering remnant descended upon frightened and bewildered peasantry at a small village near the present Parisian airfield of Le Bourget (lə boor-zhā'). "The affrighted inhabitants ran together," said a commentator, and believing that it was the skin of a monstrous animal, "they attacked it with stones, pitchforks, and flails."

The next balloon — made by the Montgolfiers — rose from the courtyard of Versailles with the royal couple in attendance. To see if higher airs would support life, a sheep, a cock, and a duck were sent along. This animal kingdom survived an ascent of some eight minutes. Now it was time for man.

The king held conservative views about human survival in the air and yielded only to the extent of being willing to allow criminals under death sentence to go up — with a pardon should they survive. This stipulation inflamed an associate of the Montgolfiers who was bucking hard to be first man in inner space. So he made a deal with the Marquis d'Arlandes (mär-kē' där-länd'),

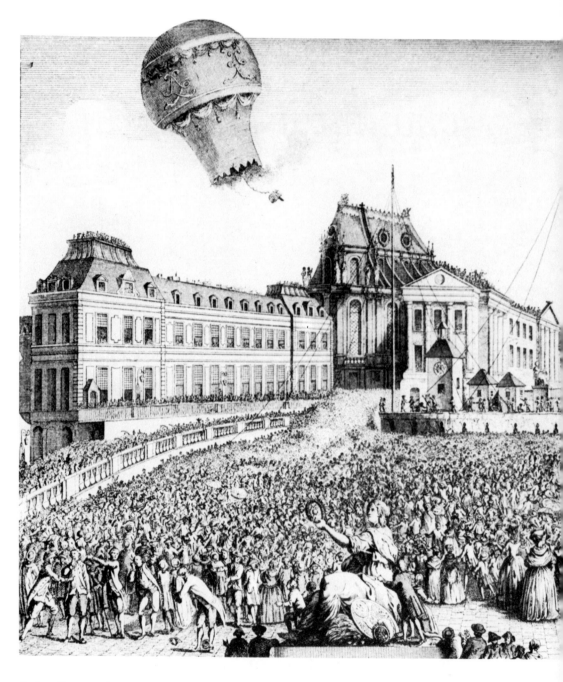

Before thousands of spectators, including Louis XVI and Marie Antoinette, a Mont-golfier balloon rises from the courtyard of Versailles on September 19, 1783, with a sheep, a cock, and a duck aboard.

who offered to use his considerable influence with the ladies at court to persuade Louis to allow scientific human ascension provided that he, d'Arlandes, was taken along.

Thus Pilâtre de Rozier (pē'lätr' də rō'zyā') became the first aeronaut. At twenty-six he was already a member of the Academy because of brainy scientific innovations. His favorite parlor trick was blowing hydrogen — over a lighted match.

His balloon was another of the Montgolfier hot-air line. In order to allow extended flight, it was necessary to replenish the hot air continually by fire from a grating set below the mouth of the big paper-lined, cloth balloon — a midair open furnace. He thought it might be prudent to take along a sponge and a bucket of water.

To make sure that the fire could be kept burning, the balloon was first tested at the end of a tethered line. Pilâtre de Rozier ascended to an altitude of about eighty feet and remained in the air for four and a half minutes. Then, assured that all was in readiness, at 2 P.M. on November 21, 1783, Man soared into the atmosphere from a site in the Bois de Boulogne (bwä' də bōō-lōn'). All went well at first, and the aeronauts Pilâtre de Rozier and d'Arlandes were greatly taken with the splendid view of Paris below — glimpsed between forking tidbits of straw into the flaming brazier. But then, "I perceived that the bottom of the cloth was coming away from the circle that surrounded it. . . . We were rapidly getting down to the roofs. We made more fire and rose again with the greatest ease. I looked down [and] it seemed to me we were going towards the towers of St. Sulpice [săn' sōol-pēs'] . . . but, on rising, a current of air made us quit this direction and bear more to the south. I saw on my left a sort of wood. . . . I cried 'Get to ground!' ''

The aeronauts had ascended over three thousand feet and had been aloft for twenty-five minutes. Ten days later Jacques Charles and an assistant went up in a hydrogen balloon. They descended twenty-seven miles from Paris; Charles then took off for a short solo.

Paris and Europe went balloon-crazy. Within a year more than fifty ascents were accomplished. French public attention and enthusiasm equaled, proportionally, that accorded our moon landing.

English science turned a blind public eye, but entrepreneurs were busy. A doughty Italian adventurer, Count Zambeccari (zăm-bā-kä'rē), came to London to try his hand at the balloon game. He failed on this occasion to obtain a backer, but an associate, Vincenzo Lunardi (vēn-chěn'zō lōo-när'dē), later managed to patch together commercial support. Thus the first man to ascend from London was an Italian.

Lunardi was an improbable aeronaut. A secretary to the Nea-politan Minister in London, he was young, softly handsome, and by nature more poet than prime mover. He liked balloons, but it was the ladies who really turned him on. "I love them all. . . . Ah! What glory to ascend my aerial chariot in their view! To be the object of *their* admiration! . . . My very brain turns giddy-with the thought. . . ."

Lunardi was ready on September 15, 1784. Hydrogen inflation of the balloon was torturously slow, and the delay angered the restless crowd, who almost believed they were being bilked anyhow. To the nervous Lunardi they seemed on the verge of breaking across the barrier. So Lunardi leaped aboard the incompletely inflated balloon and departed forthwith in some confusion. The balloon lifted to sixty feet, staggered, then recovered and rose evenly. Lunardi stumbled about waving a large flag so that all would realize he was aboard. A pigeon escaped, and he broke one of his oars (early aeronauts thought they could steer by waggling oars or fans in midair). He had forgotten his instruments. But it was a minor matter, for now the crowd "passed from incredulity and menace, into the most extravagant expressions of approbation and joy." His vain breast would have swelled even further had he known that at that moment George III had taken leave of his council and gone to the window saying, "We may resume our deliberations at pleasure, but we may never see poor Lunardi again."

But Lunardi himself was ignoring danger. "... Everything wore a new appearance and had a new effect ... the rivers meandering, the sea glistening with the rays of the sun; the immense district below me spotted with cities, towns, villages, and houses, pouring out their inhabitants to hail my appearance. . . ."

Lunardi coasted on into the English countryside, descending once to permit the cat to escape and after two and a quarter hours being drawn to earth with a rope held by — a lady, of course! He became a professional aeronaut and made ascents in Scotland, France, Italy, Spain, and Portugal. He went up in bad weather, was dunked in the sea on occasion, and died in bed.

The best-known early aeronaut was a Frenchman, Jean-Pierre Blanchard (zhän-pyâr' blän'shär'), first to fly across the English Channel. Blanchard was no Lunardi. He has been described as "a ruthless egotist, a mean-spirited and jealous man, a prima donna of the air. . . ." However, his professional abilities attracted a willing sponsor in Dr. John Jeffries, a middle-aged Boston physician then resident in London.

While Blanchard accepted Jeffries' funding of the project, he schemed to increase his fame by making the crossing solo, without the good doctor. He attempted among other stratagems to deceive his partner by wearing concealed leaded belts at balloon-lift trials, but he was found out. Dr. Jeffries accepted the faults of his associate with genial scorn — foibles of "my little hero."

After some days in wait for favorable winds, the pair got off from Dover at 1:15 P.M., January 7, 1785. Following a majestic ascent, the balloon began a series of dips; they almost didn't make it. Finally "40 minutes after two (having passed over a number of vessels, and being about three-quarters of the way over from Dover to the French coast . . .) found ourselves descending, and very rapidly. . . . We cast out all the little things we could find — apples, biscuits, etc., then one wing; still descending, we cast away the other wings; but not rising, cut away the damask curtains around the car, with gold cord tassels, etc., then stripped off all the silk lining. . . .

"Found ourselves still descending, and now approaching the sea within 120 yards, we proposed and began to strip, Mr. B. first casting away his surtout. . . . I then cast away my coat; then Mr. B. his new coat and long trousers; and we got on and adjusted our cork jackets and were preparing to get into the slings, when I found that we arose and that the pleasant view of France was opening to us every moment, as we arose to overlook the high grounds."

The transchannel balloon settled gently into a forest near Calais at 3:45 P.M., and into history.

Blanchard and Jeffries leave Dover to cross the English Channel January 7, 1785.

Blanchard, the commercial vaga-bond, later turned up in America and performed at Philadelphia, on January 9, 1793, the first manned ascension in the hemisphere before an audience including George Washington. Blanchard may have looked a bit bored — it was his forty-fifth ascent. No native Ameri-can got off the ground before

Charles Ferson Durant at New York City in 1830.

Count Zambeccari, the Italian nobleman who had been Lunardi's inspiration, endured, with two companions, perhaps the most grueling of the early balloon experiences. They made a night ascent from Milan, reaching a great and painful height, then descended in the darkness until they plainly heard the roaring of waves on a stormy ocean directly below. Frantically, they cast ballast and instruments overboard, afterward ascending to a tremendous altitude. But they had dragged their gallery in the sea and were soaked. Bleeding and vomiting, they endured in frost-stiffened clothes the miseries of high altitude.

Zambeccari's account details the final hours of the expedition. "After having traversed these regions for half an hour, at an immeasurable elevation, the balloon began to descend, and at last we fell again into the sea. . . . Although we descended gently, the gallery was sunk, and we were often entirely covered with water. The balloon . . . gave a purchase to the wind, which pressed against it as against a sail, so that by means of it we were dragged and beaten about at the mercy of the storm and the waves. . . . Certainly some boats happened to come within sight; but no sooner did they see the balloon floating and shining upon the water than they made all sail to get away from it. . . .

"Without the slightest doubt we should have drowned if heaven had not mercifully directed toward us a navigator who, better informed than those we had seen before, recognized our machine to be a balloon and quickly sent a longboat to our rescue. . . ."

Although Zambeccari had his fingers amputated after this experience, he persevered until a day when his balloon caught fire as it alighted in a treetop. Zambeccari was killed in the fall.

Considering the frail, unmanageable craft men set their lives upon, fatalities were few. A historian tells us that some five hundred aeronauts joined the profession (prior to 1865) and there were only ten deaths in the air.

Jean-Pierre Blanchard expired in bed a year after suffering a heart attack on his sixtieth ascent. Madame Blanchard then took up her late husband's profession to help make ends meet.

Women had been aloft early, as a lark. But Madame Blanchard went up for business and specialized in night ascensions over Paris. Her balloon glowed with colored lights and discharging fireworks, and the proximity of spurting flame to captive hydrogen sealed her fate. The balloon caught fire, descended, struck a rooftop, and threw Madame out to her death.

But ballooning soon was no longer looked upon as an agent of the millennium. The vagabond, county-fair aeronaut became a fixture in America and Europe.

Balloons are commonplace today as messengers of meteorologists and astronomical observers. Balloon clubs look after the weekend aeronaut, surveying his planet in sweet silence.

As the world turns its wondering eye from aeronautics to astronautics, the contrast is most apparent in scale and methods. The moon landing cost billions of dollars. Dr. Jeffries financed that first balloon channel crossing with seven hundred pounds sterling — approximately $3,300.

DISCUSSION

1. What were the early hot-air balloons made of? Why could they not hold hydrogen? What were hydrogen balloons made of?
2. Why were animals sent aloft with one of the earliest balloons?
3. What famous people are mentioned in the article as having witnessed early balloon flights?
4. Why was it necessary to heat the air used in hot-air balloons? Why were hydrogen balloons able to rise without heating?
5. The opening paragraph mentions early balloon flights "at altitudes ranging toward twenty thousand feet." Which of the flights described in the article probably reached that height? What makes you think that?
6. Why do you think the ships fled from Zambeccari's balloon after it had come down in the sea?
7. What do you think happened when Pilâtre de Rozier blew hydrogen over a lighted match?
8. Why were balloons impractical for transportation purposes?
9. Would you have wanted to go up in one of the early hot-air balloons? Why or why not? What do you think accounts for the fact that so few of the early professional balloonists were killed in the air?
10. In the final paragraph of the article, what contrast is made between early aeronautics and modern astronautics? What other contrasts can you make?

Roberto Clemente: *Superstar*

**by Arnold Hano and
The Editors of TIME**

Shortly before Christmas in 1972, the city of Managua, Nicaragua, was shaken by a series of tremors that, after hours of panic and confusion, reduced the capital to a heap of rubble. Thousands of people were killed; even more were left homeless, hungry, and destitute. In the wake of the earthquake, one of the worst ever recorded, efforts to aid the survivors were begun all over the world.

One such operation was instigated by Roberto Clemente, famous outfielder for the Pittsburgh Pirates. From his home in Puerto Rico, he organized an airlift of relief supplies. Fearing that the supplies might fall into the hands of profiteers, Clemente insisted on accompanying the plane to Managua to insure that its cargo would be properly distributed.

Minutes after takeoff on New Year's Eve, 1972, the plane developed engine trouble and crashed into stormy seas off the Puerto Rican coast. Everyone aboard was killed. Roberto Clemente, thirty-eight years old, died as he had lived — helping others. . . .

With Clemente's death, baseball lost one of its few genuine superstars. In eighteen storied seasons, he was named the National League's Most Valuable Player once (1966), led the league in hitting four times, won a dozen Golden Glove awards for fielding, and was elected to the league's All-Star team twelve times. His lifetime batting average of .317 was the highest among all active players. His finest hour came in the 1971 World Series when, with a blistering .414 average at bat and assorted marvels afield, all but single-handed he defeated the favored Baltimore Orioles. Such seasoned managers as Dick Williams of the Oakland A's and Harry Walker of the Houston Astros say the same thing: Roberto Walker Clemente was "the greatest ballplayer I ever saw."

He was also one of the quirkiest. Widely regarded as an unreconstructed hypochondriac, he had headaches, cramps, insomnia, and a nervous stomach from worrying — largely about his headaches, cramps, insomnia, and stomach. Though some of his ailments, like slipped discs, bone chips, blood clots, pulled muscles, and malaria, were undoubtedly for real, Pirate fans came to expect and even revel in the complaints of "Mr. Aches and Pains." It was almost axiomatic that the worse Roberto said he felt, the better he played. "If Clemente can walk," the New York Mets' Tommy Agee said before the 1972 season, "he can hit." Hit he did, registering a .300-plus average for the thirteenth time in his career. His last hit in his last regular season game — a ringing double to deep left center field — was the three thousandth of his career, a feat equaled by only ten other players in the history of the major leagues. . . .

Roberto Walker Clemente was born on August 18, 1934, in the town of Carolina, a suburb of San Juan, Puerto Rico. Life was more pleasant for young Roberto than it was for many Puerto Rican children. His father was not a laborer in a sugar plantation but the foreman of the plantation. Roberto's parents ran a grocery and a meat market for the plantation workers. His father also owned some trucks, which he used for small shipping jobs.

There were seven children, six boys and a girl. Roberto was the youngest. Latin-American families are very close, very protecting, very loving. The youngest is loved not only by his parents but by his older brothers and sisters. Thus Roberto was a well-cared-for child.

Though Roberto was born in the depression year of 1934, there was no depression in his family. "My father always worked," Clemente recalled. "We lived in a big wooden house, with a large front porch. Five bedrooms, living room, dining room, kitchen. Indoor bathroom."

Indoor bathroom. So many Latin-American families had no indoor plumbing, no water on their land at all. When he was a child in the Dominican Republic, the New York Yankees' Felipe Alou used to walk a mile to the river and carry water on his head and shoulders for the family.

Roberto had less difficult chores. In the summer, when his father would hire out his trucks for jobs, Roberto often helped out, loading or unloading sand. Not difficult, he insisted later.

But more important than the amount of physical labor were the attitude and atmosphere within the Clemente house.

"When I was a boy, I realized what lovely persons my mother and father were," Clemente said. "I was treated real good. I learned the right way to live. I never heard any hate in my house. Not for anybody. I never heard my mother say a bad word to my father, or my father to my mother. During the war, when food all over Puerto Rico was limited, we never went hungry. They always found a way to feed us. We kids were first, and they were second."

As a boy, Roberto played ball every day. Mainly it was softball, in playgrounds at first and, later, in a municipal league. He played shortstop or he pitched. When he was not playing ball, he squeezed a hard rubber handball hour after hour, to strengthen the muscles in his throwing arm. That arm was one of the strongest in baseball history.

When he did not play softball, he played sand-lot baseball. And when he played neither, he often crouched over the family radio, listening to reports of ball games in the Puerto Rican winter league. His idol, when he was a youngster, was Monte Irvin, the slugging Giants' outfielder who played ball in Puerto Rico in the winter. Irvin did two things Clemente admired: Monte could hit, and Monte could throw. For a while, Roberto's nickname was Monte Irvin.

If you think this obsession with baseball occasionally jangled his folks' nerves, you're right. Even in a permissive home where the children came first, Roberto's mother sometimes became edgy over her son's total occupation with ball.

"I would forget to eat because of baseball," Clemente said, "and one time my mother wanted to punish me. She started to burn my bat, but I got it out of the fire and saved it." Many times afterward she told him how wrong she was and how right he was to want to play baseball.

Roberto Clemente gets his 3,000th hit — his last one — September 30, 1972.

But Clemente's mother did not always oppose her son's involvement. She couldn't. We read today of ballplayers who inherit their skills from their fathers. With Clemente, it was his mother who passed on the natural talent. Clemente said that he got his arm from his mother and that, even in later years, she could throw a ball from second base to home plate. He told how his mother was invited to throw out the first ball of the amateur winter league in Puerto Rico, back in 1963. "She was seventy-three at the time," Clemente said. "She threw the ball from a box seat to home plate. She had something on it too."

Roberto intended to go to college and become an engineer. And though baseball was his life, at high school he managed to spread himself over other sports as well. He played baseball for his high-school team, but he also made the track team, where he became an all-round sensation. Roberto threw the javelin; he was a high jumper; he performed in what was then called the hop, skip, and jump, which today is the triple jump. His best marks were outstanding. He tossed the javelin 195 feet; he did a high jump of six feet and a triple jump of over forty-five feet. Roberto Clemente was considered a sure member of Puerto Rico's Olympics squad

for the 1956 event in Melbourne, Australia, but professional baseball interfered with such a schedule. . . .

In 1955, Clemente joined the Pittsburgh Pirates and quickly became one of the most feared scatter hitters in baseball. Standing a full yard away from the plate, cocking his extra-long bat, and twitching his neck like a nervous sparrow, he was a notorious bad-ball hitter who would rather swing at a wild pitch than settle for a walk. Opposing pitchers went crazy trying to figure out his weakness. In one game Cincinnati Reds' hurlers pitched him inside, down the middle, and outside, and he hit successive home runs to left, right center, and right field. "The big thing about Clemente," Giants' Pitcher Juan Marichal once said, "is that he can hit any pitch. I don't mean only strikes. He can hit a ball off his ankles or off his ear." Asked if he had found any effective way to pitch to Clemente, former Dodger Speedballer Sandy Koufax said, "Sure, roll the ball."

Afield, Clemente had to be seen to be believed. His circus catches and rifle arm were things of wonder. He saved one game against the Astros by making a diving, sliding catch of a humpback liner into short right.

In the same inning he took off after a home-run ball, leaped, twisted backward, and snared the ball as he slammed into the wall, injuring his ankle, knee, and elbow. "He took it full flight and hit the wall wide open," marveled Astro Manager Walker. "It was the best catch I've ever seen." Clemente also possessed the strongest throwing arm of any outfielder. From 420 feet away, he once fired a perfect strike to the plate to nip the runner trying to score from third. The accuracy he ascribed to his training as a high-school javelin thrower; the strength, to his mother.

In recent years, without fanfare or acclaim, Clemente was involved in many projects to benefit the youth and needy of his island. The father of three boys, he was working on his favorite project of a "sports city" for Puerto Rican children shortly before his death. "What we want to do," he said, "is exchange kids with every city in the United States and show all the kids how to live and play with other kids." As for himself, he said after the 1971 World Series, "I would like to be remembered as the type of player I was." That in itself would be enough.

DISCUSSION

1. How long did Roberto Clemente play major-league baseball? According to this selection, what was his "finest hour" as a ballplayer?
2. To whom did Clemente attribute the strength of his throwing arm? To what did he attribute his accuracy?
3. What were the circumstances of Roberto Clemente's death?
4. Did Clemente have a happy childhood? Why do you think that?
5. Clemente's baseball career is referred to in this selection as "eighteen storied seasons." What is the meaning of *storied* in this phrase?
6. Why do you think Clemente was looked on as an "unreconstructed hypochondriac"? How did his ailments, whether real or imagined, seem to affect his playing?
7. Why was Clemente regarded as a superstar?
8. What do you think Clemente meant when he said of himself, "I would like to be remembered as the type of player I was"? Do you think he will be long remembered? Why do you think that?

A Proposal of Marriage

by Anton Chekhov
Adapted by Paul T. Nolan

CHARACTERS

MR. STEPANOVITCH, *a farmer*
NATALIA, *his daughter*
LOMOV, *their bachelor neighbor*

TIME: *The late nineteenth century.*
SETTING: *The formal, nineteenth-century parlor of* STEPANOVITCH'S *home in rural Russia. There is one entrance up center and another at left center. A draped window is up right of the upstage entrance. In front of the window is a stiff-looking love seat. Everything about the room suggests that it is used only for formal occasions.*
AT RISE: STEPANOVITCH *is standing up center, peeking through the drapes.* NATALIA *is sitting in chair down right, knitting.*

STEPANOVITCH: I think I see him coming.

NATALIA (*starting to gather up her knitting*): I'll go to the kitchen.

STEPANOVITCH: Don't you like our good neighbor, Lomov?

NATALIA: I like Lomov well enough, but he's such a big baby. There is always something wrong with him — his heart, his liver, his lungs, his right arm, his left arm, his right eye, his left ear. Fifteen minutes with Lomov is like reading a medical book for an hour.

STEPANOVITCH: Men get like that when they live alone too long.

NATALIA: He doesn't have to be a bachelor. Of course, I would feel sorry for any woman married to a big baby like that. And then, he has too many opinions also.

STEPANOVITCH (*still looking out window*): Aha, he almost slipped and fell into the ditch.

NATALIA: He is also clumsy.

STEPANOVITCH: I like Lomov. He is an easy man to beat in an argument.

NATALIA: Good, then you talk to him.

STEPANOVITCH: I just had a thought. Suppose he has come to borrow money!

NATALIA: He's your friend, Papa.

STEPANOVITCH: I won't give him any. (*There is a knock on door up center.*) He's here.

NATALIA: I'm gone. (*She exits left center.*)

STEPANOVITCH (*as he opens door*): Who is this I see at my door? Why, Lomov! I am so glad to see you. (*as* LOMOV *enters*) How are you?

LOMOV (*coming down center, carrying his hat*): Thank you, Mr. Stepanovitch. I am all right, I guess. Hot and tired from the walk, but all right, I guess. How are you?

STEPANOVITCH: All right, I guess. Please sit down. (LOMOV *sits stiffly in love seat.*) It isn't right for people to forget their neighbors. (*He sits in chair down right, rises quickly, holding knitting needle.*) Natalia's needle. Women are forever leaving things around where they shouldn't be.

LOMOV: Yes, yes. And how is your daughter?

STEPANOVITCH: All right, I guess. But tell me, my good friend, what is the reason for such a formal visit? Coat and tie and your hat in your hand? Are you on your way to give a lecture or preach a sermon?

LOMOV: No, I have no engagement with anyone but you, Mr. Stepanovitch.

STEPANOVITCH: Then why are you all dressed up? This isn't New Year's Eve, you know.

LOMOV: Well, it's ... it's just ... (*rises, looks straight ahead*) I have come to you, Stepan Stepanovitch, to trouble you with a request. It is not the first time I have had the honor of turning to you for assistance, and you have always ... (*His voice breaks.*) Excuse me. I beg your pardon. I am a little excited. Could I have a glass of water? (STEPANOVITCH *goes down left to table with water pitcher and pours a glass of water.*)

STEPANOVITCH (*aside*): He's surely come to borrow money. I should have fled with Natalia. But he won't get a cent from me. (*giving water to* LOMOV) What is it you are asking of me, my good friend?

LOMOV: Well, you see, my dear Mr. Stepanovitch, my good friend, my old neighbor, my ... my ... (*drains glass and hands it back to* STEPANOVITCH) I am terribly nervous, as you can probably see.

STEPANOVITCH: To be sure. To be sure. Sit down, old fellow.

LOMOV (sitting): What I mean to say is ... you are the only man in the world who can help me. To be sure, I don't deserve it, and I have no right — no right at all — to make this request of you.

STEPANOVITCH: My dear Lomov, I have no idea what you are talking about. What is it you want from me?

LOMOV: I shall get to that. Immediately. In a minute or so.

STEPANOVITCH (going back to chair and sitting): How about now?

LOMOV: Here it is, then. I have come to ask for the hand of your daughter, Natalia Stepanovitch, in marriage.

STEPANOVITCH (rising; pleased): My dear friend, my good neighbor, dear Lomov, would you mind repeating that? I didn't quite hear you.

LOMOV: I have the honor to request the hand ...

STEPANOVITCH: Yes, of course, of course. My dear, dear man. (He goes to LOMOV, who rises.) I am so happy that everything is ... so ... so everything. (hugs him) I have wanted this to happen for so long. It has always been my dearest wish. It was Natalia's mother's dearest wish.

LOMOV: I didn't think Mrs. Stepanovitch liked me.

STEPANOVITCH: She loved you. If she were alive today, she would tell you so. And I have always loved you, too, my dear friend. I have loved you like a son. I've always wanted this marriage to take place. (moves away) But why am I standing here like a fool? I am overcome with pleasure, completely overwhelmed. This is the moment of the greatest happiness of my life. I'll call Natalia. (starts for door, left)

LOMOV: But, Mr. Stepanovitch, just a minute. What do you think? Will Natalia accept me?

STEPANOVITCH (turning): A good-looking, handsome fellow like you? What do you think? Natalia was telling me, just this very morning, how much she admires you. I think she has always loved you. But I shall fetch the lady herself. (exits center)

LOMOV (sitting, standing, then sitting): I'm cold. My whole body is trembling as though I were here for a medical examination. But I'll wait it out. The important thing is to be settled. Natalia is an excellent housekeeper, not bad-looking, and well educated. What more can I ask? I'm so excited that my ears are ringing. (He goes to table, pours a glass of water, and starts to drink *it.)* It doesn't do for a man to stay single. I must have a well-regulated life. I have a weak heart, continual palpitations, and I am very sensitive and always getting excited. *(He takes sip of water, sets glass down, returns to love seat.)* My lips are trembling. The pulse in my right temple throbs terribly. Ah, poor me. *(sits)*

NATALIA *(entering right)*: Oh, it's you, Lomov. Papa said there was a dealer out here who had come to buy something. He must have been joking. How have you been, Lomov?

LOMOV *(starting to rise)*: Very well, Natalia, and you?

NATALIA: No, no, keep your seat. *(sits in chair down right)* I can only stay a few minutes. I have a cake in the oven.

LOMOV: A few minutes will be fine.

NATALIA: I see that you are all dressed up. You will have to excuse my wearing my apron and this old dress. We are working today.

LOMOV: No, that is fine. Very fine.

NATALIA: Why don't you come around and see us more often? Would you like something to eat?

LOMOV: No, thank you, I just had my lunch.

NATALIA: Then rest. It's a fine day today. Only yesterday, it was rain-

ing so hard that the workmen couldn't do a stroke of work in the meadows. How are you coming with the wheat harvest? I was so anxious to have the hayfields mowed that I had the men work overtime, and they got everything out. Now I'm sorry they did. With the rain we've been having, the hay may rot. It would have been better if I had waited. *(looks at him)* Why are you all dressed up? You look like a city salesman or something. Are you on your way to a dance? *(observes him closely)* You know, Lomov, you're better-looking when you're dressed up. You really are. But what's the occasion?

LOMOV *(rising, pacing nervously)*: Well, you see, my dear Natalia Stepanovitch, it's ... it's simply this. *(looks at ceiling)* I have decided to ask you to ... to listen to me. Of course, it will be a surprise. Indeed, you might be angry. It's getting very cold, is it not? *(blows on his hands)*

NATALIA: I hadn't noticed, but then, of course, I have been working. *(pauses)* What is it exactly that you want, Lomov?

LOMOV *(sitting)*: Well, er ...

NATALIA *(folding her arms; impatiently)*: Well?

LOMOV: I'll try to be brief. My dear Natalia, as you know, for many years, since we were children, I have been a family friend. Longer than that. My poor aunt and her husband, from whom, as you know, I inherited the farm, were friends of your family. Our families have been friends for many years. *(wipes his brow)*

NATALIA *(impatiently)*: Where is all this leading?

LOMOV: What? Oh, yes. Well, as you know, our families have been not only friends but neighbors. *(smiles)* Our land runs right next to your land. My meadows, for example, stand right next to your birch woods.

NATALIA *(with irritation)*: What did you say? *Your* meadows?

LOMOV: Yes. You know, my meadows down east of your birch woods.

NATALIA: That's nonsense. Those meadows belong to us.

LOMOV *(rising)*: I mean the meadows by the birch woods.

NATALIA *(turning away)*: I know what meadows you mean. *(raises her voice)* They are ours, not yours.

LOMOV *(sitting; calmly)*: I am afraid you are mistaken, Natalia. Those are my meadows.

NATALIA *(going toward him)*: You must be confused. People who inherit property on which they were not born are often confused about such matters.

LOMOV: I am *not* confused. I looked at the will, and it is quite clear. Those meadows belong to my farm. *(He folds his arms and stares straight ahead.)*

NATALIA *(speaking with clenched teeth)*: You'll pardon my saying so, but it just isn't true.

LOMOV *(still staring off)*: It's all a matter of legal record. There really is no room for discussion. My aunt's grandmother, it is true, let your grandfather use them for a time. *(with emphasis)* But it was just for a time.

NATALIA: There's not a word of truth in what you are saying. *(She raises her voice and points her finger at him.)* My grandfather — and my great-grandfather — knew well that this farm ran all the way to the swamp. *(folds her arms)* You are not going to say that the meadows are on the other side of the swamp, are you?

LOMOV: Certainly not. *My* meadows are on this side of the swamp, but . . .

NATALIA: Bah! You are either joking or trying to make me angry. *(turns away)* I don't consider this at all neighborly. It isn't as if they were worth anything, but it's the injustice of your taking them that bothers me.

LOMOV *(going toward her)*: Would you listen to me for a minute? My aunt's grandmother allowed your grandfather . . .

NATALIA: Grandfather, Grandmother! *(turns and faces him)* The meadows belong to me, and that's the end of the matter. *(sits in chair and folds arms)*

LOMOV *(returning to his chair)*: They belong to me.

NATALIA: You can shout until you are blue in the face and put on ten new suits, and it won't change matters. The meadows are mine.

LOMOV *(turning toward her)*: Natalia, I am only concerned with what is right. If you want the meadows, I beg you to take them as a gift.

NATALIA *(calmly)*: How can you give me what's already mine? Until now, Lomov, I considered you a good friend. Just last season, we helped you harvest your crops. Now you offer to give me *my own* meadows. Good neighbors don't treat each other this way.

LOMOV *(gripping his chair and leaning toward her)*: Do you think I'm a thief? I never took anything that wasn't mine. And I don't let people call me names.

NATALIA *(shouting)*: The meadows are mine!

LOMOV *(shouting)*: Mine!

NATALIA *(shouting)*: Mine!

LOMOV *(rising)*: Mine!

NATALIA *(settling back in her chair)*: Really, you needn't scream. If you want to yell and scream and carry on in this fashion, you may do it in your home.

LOMOV *(sitting)*: Excuse me.

NATALIA *(speaking in very proper tone)*: While you are in my house, I'll thank you to behave yourself decently.

LOMOV *(trying to control his temper)*: I said I'm sorry. *(wipes his brow)* If it weren't that I am suffering from palpitation of the heart, I would deal with this whole matter differently. *(shouts)* The meadows are mine!

NATALIA *(shouting)*: Ours!

LOMOV *(shouting)*: Mine!

STEPANOVITCH *(entering left)*: What is all the yelling about? This is no way to . . .

NATALIA *(rushing to her father)*: Papa, would you tell this person whether the east meadows belong to us or to him?

STEPANOVITCH *(puzzled)*: They are of no value, but they are ours.

LOMOV *(turning away)*: You too? I thought at least you would be reasonable. *(rises, trying to be calm)* My aunt's grandmother gave the use of the meadows — free of charge, I might add — to your grandfather. It is true that your family was allowed to use the meadows for forty years, but later when . . .

STEPANOVITCH (*moving quickly to* LOMOV): My dear friend, you are forgetting the lawsuit. Besides, everyone knows the meadows are ours. Haven't you ever looked at a map of your property?

LOMOV: I can prove the meadows belong to me. I can take this matter to court.

STEPANOVITCH (*glaring at* LOMOV): I wouldn't try anything like that if I were you.

LOMOV (*nervously*): Well, I certainly will.

STEPANOVITCH: My dear friend, what are you so upset about? I don't ask for anything that doesn't belong to me. But I don't intend to be robbed. I'd rather give the meadows away than let you steal them.

LOMOV (*very angrily*): What's that! What right have you to give my meadows away? You can't do that.

STEPANOVITCH (*calmly; looking off*): I can do whatever I like with my own property. (*with rising anger*) And I want to tell you something. I am not used to having people address me in that tone of voice. (*draws himself up*) I, young man, am twice your age, and I'll thank you to treat me with proper respect.

LOMOV (*sitting*): So that's it. You think I'm a fool because I'm young. (*pouts*) You're making fun of me. You call my property yours, and you think I'll stand for it. (*attempts to be calm*) Mr. Stepanovitch, this is not the way good neighbors behave. (*shouts*) You're a land rustler, that's what you are.

STEPANOVITCH (*slowly; with great anger*): What did you say?

NATALIA (*going to her father*): Papa, send the workers to protect our meadows right now.

STEPANOVITCH (*ignoring* NATALIA): Young man, what was that you called me?

NATALIA (*to her father*): The meadows are ours, and I won't give them up. I won't. I won't. I won't.

LOMOV (*a little frightened*): I'll take this to court.

STEPANOVITCH (*with quiet contempt*): You can sue me if you like. I knew it would come to this. Your family always looked for an excuse to drag things into court, where they could plot and quarrel with their betters. (*shouts*) Your whole family were always plotters.

LOMOV: Don't insult my family. We don't have any embezzlers like your uncle.

STEPANOVITCH: The whole Lomov family was insane.

NATALIA: Every one of them.

STEPANOVITCH: Your grandmother dipped snuff, and your great aunt Natasia ran off with a salesman.

LOMOV: And your mother was a terrible cook. *(puts hand over his heart)* My heart. My palpitations. *(holds his head)* My poor head is bursting. I need water. Water.

STEPANOVITCH: And your grandfather was a gambler and a terrible glutton.

NATALIA: And your aunt was a gossip.

LOMOV: And you are schemers! Oh, my heart. And it's commonly known that you cheat in elections. Where is the door? I'm getting faint. My legs won't hold me. I'm going to have an attack. *(staggers to door up center and starts out)*

STEPANOVITCH *(following him and shouting)*: And don't ever come back!

NATALIA *(shouting)*: I hope you do bring this suit to court. It will show the whole world what a grasping schemer you are!

LOMOV: My heart, my head! I'm dying. *(exits)*

STEPANOVITCH: A loafer, scarecrow, monster.

NATALIA: A swindler too. And a weakling.

STEPANOVITCH: The nerve of such a man. He came here to propose marriage to you.

NATALIA *(aghast)*: What did you say, Papa? Lomov came to propose marriage . . . to me?

STEPANOVITCH: Yes, yes, the puppy.

NATALIA: Why didn't you tell me this before?

STEPANOVITCH: That's why he was all dressed up. The puppy.

NATALIA *(dropping into chair)*: Propose to me? Oh! Oh! Papa, Papa, bring him back.

STEPANOVITCH: What?

NATALIA: Run, Papa, run and bring him back. *(groans)* Or I shall die.

STEPANOVITCH: Bring him back? Are you crazy too?

NATALIA: I'm dying. Bring him back. *(wails loudly)*

STEPANOVITCH: All right, all right, I'll get him. Don't cry. *(starting out)* A man with a marriageable daughter should hide in the hills. *(exits up center)*

NATALIA: Bring him back. Bring him back! *(She looks up, sees her father has gone, straightens her hair and collar, takes off her apron and folds it, and sits demurely.)*

STEPANOVITCH *(entering)*: All right, he's coming back. We insult the man, throw him out, tell him not to come back — and five seconds later, I'm asking him to please come and call. It's all your fault, Natalia.

NATALIA: It's not my fault. It's yours, Papa. You're hard on people. If it hadn't been for you, he wouldn't have left.

STEPANOVITCH: Of course I'm to blame. The father is always to blame. Ask any young girl who is to blame. She'll tell you, "My father." (LOMOV *appears in doorway.*) There he is. There's the great lover. You talk to him. (*exits through door left*)

LOMOV (*staggering into room*): Palpitations. My leg is paralyzed. My side hurts. I feel faint.

NATALIA (*helping him to love seat, then sitting next to him*): You must excuse my father, Lomov. He is so unreasonable. I remember now that the meadows are yours.

LOMOV: My heart is beating terribly. My meadows ache. I mean my head aches. It wasn't the meadows I cared about. It was only the principle of the thing.

NATALIA: Of course, the principle. Let's forget the whole thing.

LOMOV: I have proof . . . in writing.

NATALIA: I know, but let's talk about something else. Are you going hunting soon?

LOMOV: I hope to, after the harvest. But I don't know. My dog, Blue, is limping.

NATALIA: That is too bad. How did it happen?

LOMOV: I'm not sure. (*sighs*) And he was the best dog I ever had. I paid one hundred and twenty-five for him.

NATALIA: A hundred and twenty-five! You're joking.

LOMOV: Indeed, I am not. And he was a bargain.

NATALIA: We only paid a hundred for our Rover, and Rover is a much better dog than your Blue.

LOMOV: Rover better than Blue! You're joking, of course. (*laughs*) That's really very funny.

NATALIA: Of course Rover is better. It's true Rover is young, but for pointing game or following, he's the best dog in the whole area.

LOMOV: Rover has a short lower jaw, and any dog that has a short lower jaw can't snap.

NATALIA: A short lower jaw? Our Rover? Nonsense.

LOMOV: I've seen your Rover. His lower jaw is shorter.

NATALIA: Have you measured it?

LOMOV: As a matter of fact, I have. I will admit he runs well.

NATALIA: Rover is purebred. Your Blue is a mongrel. Nobody could even figure out his pedigree. He's old and ugly and as skinny as a starving weasel.

LOMOV: He's not old. He's mature. I wouldn't take five of your Rovers for one Blue. Anyone can pick up a hound like your Rover on the streets. And it would be a public service to get rid of him.

NATALIA: Lomov, I must say that you are in a bad humor today. First, you say that you own our meadows. And now you're trying to pretend that your Blue is better than our Rover. I didn't think you were the kind of person who went around saying things he didn't believe. Our Rover is worth a hundred of your Blue, and you know it.

LOMOV: I can see, Natalia, that you think I'm either a blind man or an awful fool. Look, won't you please admit that your Rover has a short lower jaw?

NATALIA: No, I will not.

LOMOV: Rover has a pug jaw.

NATALIA: He has not!

LOMOV: He has!

NATALIA: He has not!

LOMOV: What are you shouting about? I thought you didn't like shouting.

NATALIA: When people talk nonsense, it's enough to make sane people shout. Rover is a better dog than Blue.

LOMOV: I don't wish to discuss this any further. I have palpitation of the heart.

NATALIA: A great hunter you are. Palpitation of the heart!

LOMOV: I ask you to be quiet, Natalia. I may have a heart attack.

NATALIA: No, you won't. Not until you admit that our Rover is worth a thousand of your old Blue.

STEPANOVITCH (entering): Well, I see that it has started again. Forget the meadows.

NATALIA: This has nothing to do with the meadows, Papa. We'll leave it to you. Which is the better dog — our Rover or Lomov's Blue?

LOMOV: First, answer this question, Mr. Stepanovitch. Does Rover have a pug jaw or does he not?

STEPANOVITCH: What if he has? A pug jaw is a good thing in a dog. It shows courage. Our Rover is the best dog in the whole country.

LOMOV: But not better than my Blue. Now, tell the truth.

STEPANOVITCH: Don't get excited. We can discuss these things like sensible people. Your Blue certainly has his good points — he's from a good breed and has a good stride. But he has two faults. First, he is old. Secondly, he has a long lower jaw. He's buck-toothed.

LOMOV: Buck-toothed! *(rises)* I feel faint. *(puts his hand on his heart)* Palpitations, I can feel them. *(takes a deep breath)* All right, let's keep to the facts. Do you remember at the last hunt that Blue ran away from your Rover?

STEPANOVITCH: But he ran in the wrong direction.

LOMOV: He did not. The game circled. If your Rover hadn't become confused and made so much noise, Blue would have found the game.

STEPANOVITCH: Your Blue should be retired.

NATALIA: Or else you should get crutches for him. The poor dog should be put out of his misery.

LOMOV: Oh, palpitation. My leg is lame. I'm blacking out.

NATALIA: Palpitation! What kind of hunter are you? You and your old Blue should sit on the porch and keep out of the way of real hunters with real dogs. Palpitation.

STEPANOVITCH: Yes, what kind of hunter are you? A man with your diseases ought to stay at home where it is safe. If you were a hunter, you'd know that Rover is a better dog than Blue. I really am

very much upset. Let's drop the whole subject. It's foolish to talk to you. You are no hunter.

LOMOV *(feeling his chest)*: It's happened. I'm having an attack. I can feel it. My heart's breaking into little pieces.

STEPANOVITCH: You're not only not a hunter but your housekeeper tells you what to do. You're not even the head of your own house.

LOMOV: I'm dying. That's what's happening. *(staggers downstage and falls into chair)*

STEPANOVITCH: You baby! Weakling. Milk-toast.

LOMOV: I can't breathe. Air! Air! *(He flops back in chair.)*

NATALIA *(going to him)*: He is dead! *(shakes him)* Lomov. Lomov! *(turns toward STEPANOVITCH)* What have we done? He is dead. *(sinks into chair)* The doctor. The doctor. *(stands up, shouting)* Somebody call a doctor!

STEPANOVITCH: And now what's the matter with you? You're as bad as he is.

NATALIA: He's dead. Dead.

STEPANOVITCH *(going down and pouring glass of water)*: That's nonsense. He's not dead. Why would he be dead? Just because we were having a quiet discussion. *(goes to LOMOV and tries to pour water into*

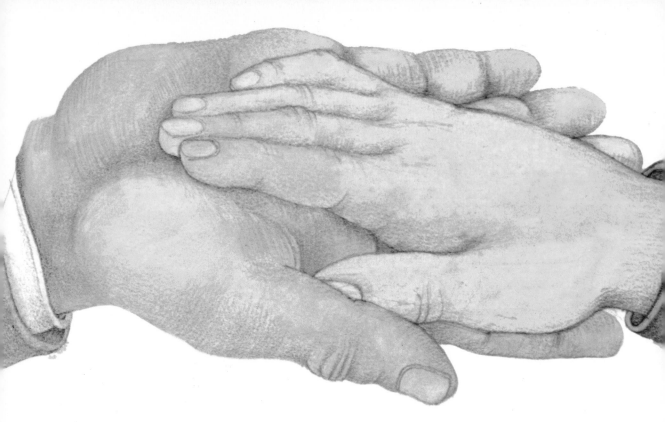

his mouth) Drink. Come on, be a good fellow and drink the water. *(He lets* LOMOV's *head fall back.)* He won't drink. He *is* dead! This is a terrible situation. Why didn't I shoot myself when I thought of it this morning? It would have saved the whole day. Why don't I do it now? What am I waiting for? *(again puts glass to* LOMOV's *lips)* Come on, don't be difficult. Drink the water. All right, be hard to get along with. Go ahead and stay dead. A fine neighbor you are. *(He throws water in* LOMOV's *face.)*

LOMOV *(leaping up)*: I am being drowned! Help, I'm going down for the third time! *(looks around)* Where am I?

STEPANOVITCH: Oh, you just passed out — with joy, I guess. You proposed to my Natalia, and she accepted. I give you my blessing. Now, please, let's have a little peace and quiet around here.

LOMOV: What? What are you saying? Did I propose?

STEPANOVITCH: Yes, and Natalia is willing. Go ahead, kiss the bride.

NATALIA: He lives. He lives. My Lomov lives! Yes, Lomov, I will marry you.

STEPANOVITCH: Well, go ahead, then. Kiss her.

LOMOV: Who? Oh. *(takes* NATALIA's *hand and kisses it)* Oh, yes.

Now I think I remember. I am very happy. I am very happy, Natalia.

NATALIA: And I am very happy, too, Lomov.

LOMOV: But my leg. I think it may be paralyzed.

NATALIA: Sit down, my darling. Rest.

LOMOV (sitting): That's the important thing, to rest.

STEPANOVITCH: Well, now it is all settled. Finally. We have no more problems. This certainly takes a load off my back.

NATALIA: And now, my darling, that it is all settled about our marrying, you will do one thing for me.

LOMOV: Anything, my love.

NATALIA: Admit Rover is a better dog than Blue.

LOMOV: He's not.

NATALIA: He is.

LOMOV: Not!

NATALIA: Is!

STEPANOVITCH (starting off up center): Don't go away. I'll go and bring the preacher. (fast curtain)

DISCUSSION

1. Before Lomov arrived, what faults of his did Natalia mention to her father?
2. What was the purpose of Lomov's visit? Why did he never actually state his purpose to Natalia?
3. What did Natalia and Lomov argue about first? How did that argument end?
4. After Lomov left, what made Natalia insist that her father call him back? What happened after Lomov returned?
5. What seemed to be the one thing about Lomov that appealed to both Natalia and her father? Why do you think that?
6. Why had Lomov decided to marry? Why do you think he had chosen Natalia as his future wife? How do you think he really felt about Natalia?
7. What evidence is there in the play that Stepanovitch was eager to have Natalia marry?
8. Why do you think Natalia accepted Lomov's proposal?

9. What sort of married life do you predict for Natalia and Lomov? Why?
10. In portraying his characters, how did Chekhov use exaggeration to add to the humor of the play?
11. Do you think that, in writing this play, the author's sole purpose was to amuse? If not, what serious message do you think lies beneath the humor?
12. Could you like people in real life who behave as the characters did in the play? Why or why not? Do you think Chekhov liked such people? Why do you think that?

AUTHOR

Anton Pavlovich Chekhov, author of "A Proposal of Marriage," was one of Russia's foremost writers of short stories and plays. He studied medicine at Moscow University and, while he was a student, began writing skits for newspapers in order to earn extra money. By the time he was twenty-six, his short stories had become so popular that he decided to turn to writing as a profession. He continued to think of himself as a doctor rather than a writer, but he did not practice medicine much except during a cholera epidemic in 1892–1893.

Although Chekhov's short stories were unusually successful, his early full-length plays were failures. Consequently, he abandoned his efforts at drama and for many years wrote only short stories and magazine articles. Later, however, he concentrated on the playwright's craft and eventually wrote several plays that were acclaimed as masterpieces. Among them are *Uncle Vanya*, *The Three Sisters*, *The Seagull*, and *The Cherry Orchard*, which are still performed frequently today before enthusiastic audiences in many parts of the world.

Chekhov's work influenced the writing of countless later authors and playwrights. In 1904, at the height of his career, he died of tuberculosis at the age of forty-four.

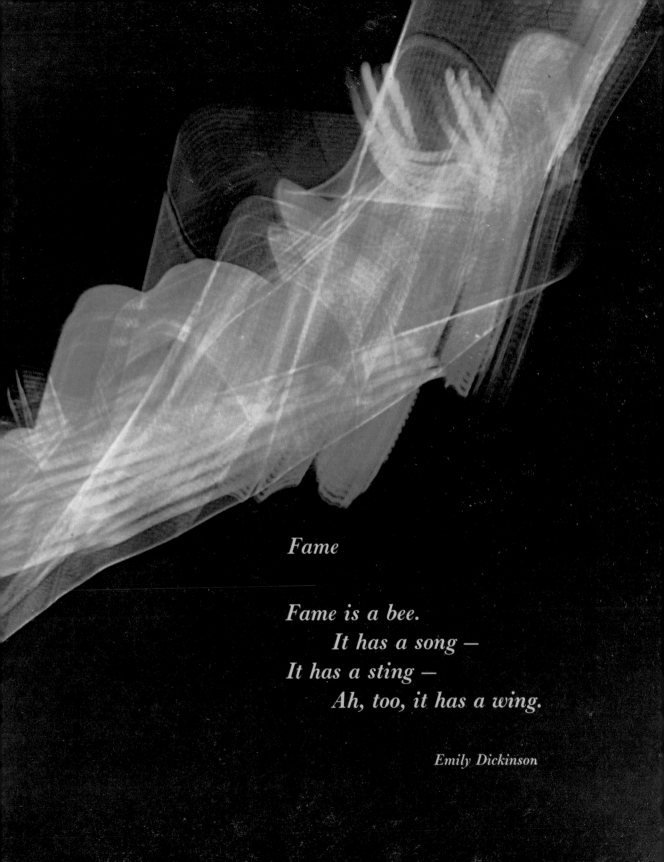

Fame

Fame is a bee.
  It has a song —
It has a sting —
  Ah, too, it has a wing.

Emily Dickinson

BUCK

by Jack London

A cross between a Saint Bernard and a Scotch shepherd dog, Buck was stolen from a comfortable existence at Judge Miller's estate in California and transported to the Yukon Territory to be used as a sled dog for men eager to get rich in the gold fields of the Klondike. He passed from master to master, learning with each experience how to endure hunger and man's brutality and how to survive with half-wild sled dogs in the rugged surroundings. But the beatings of one cruel master would have been too much for Buck if John Thornton had not intervened and nursed him back to health.

Love — genuine, passionate love — was Buck's for the first time. This he had never experienced at Judge Miller's down in the sun-kissed Santa Clara Valley. With the judge's sons, hunting and tramping, it had been a working partnership; with the judge's grandsons, a sort of pompous guardianship; and with the judge himself, a stately and dignified friendship. But love that was feverish and burning, that was adoration, that was madness, it had taken John Thornton to arouse.

This man had saved his life, which was something; but, further, he was the ideal master. Other men saw to the welfare of their dogs from a sense of duty and business expediency; he saw to the welfare of his as if they were his own children, because he could not help it. And he saw further. He never forgot a kindly greeting or a cheering word, and to sit down for a long talk with them ("gas" he called it) was as much his delight as theirs. He had a way of taking Buck's head

roughly between his hands and resting his head upon Buck's, of shaking him back and forth, all the while calling him ill names that to Buck were love names. Buck knew no greater joy than that rough embrace and the sound of murmured oaths, and at each jerk back and forth it seemed that his heart would be shaken out of his body, so great was its ecstasy. And when, released, he sprang to his feet, his mouth laughing, his eyes eloquent, his throat vibrant with unuttered sound, and in that fashion remained without movement, John Thornton would reverently exclaim, "You can all but speak!"

Buck had a trick of love expression that was akin to hurt. He would often seize Thornton's hand in his mouth and close so fiercely that the flesh bore the impress of his teeth for some time afterward. And as Buck understood the oaths to be love words, so the man understood this feigned bite for a caress.

For the most part, however, Buck's love was expressed in adoration. While he went wild with happiness when Thornton touched him or spoke to him, he did not seek these tokens. Unlike Skeet, who was wont to shove her nose under Thornton's hand and nudge and nudge till petted, Buck was content to adore at a distance. He would lie by the hour, eager, alert, at Thornton's feet, looking up into his face, dwelling upon it, studying it, following with keenest interest each fleeting expression, every movement or change of feature. Or, as chance might have it, he would lie farther away, to the side or rear, watching the outlines of the man and the occasional movements of his body. And often, such was the communion in which they lived, the strength of Buck's gaze would draw John Thornton's head around, and he would return the gaze, without speech, his heart shining out of his eyes as Buck's heart shone out.

For a long time after his rescue, Buck did not like Thornton to get out of his sight. From the moment Thornton left the tent to when he entered it again, Buck would follow at his heels. His transient masters since he had come into the Northland had bred in him a fear that no master could be permanent. He was afraid that Thornton would pass out of his life, as others had passed out. Even in the night, in his dreams, he was haunted by this fear. At such times he would shake off sleep and creep through the chill to the flap of the tent, where he would stand and listen to the sound of his master's breathing.

But in spite of this great love he bore John Thornton, which seemed to bespeak the soft civilizing influence, the strain of the primitive, which the Northland had aroused in him, remained alive and active. Faithfulness and devotion, things born of fire and roof, were his; yet he retained his wildness and wiliness. He was a thing of the wild, come in from the wild to sit by John Thornton's fire, rather than a dog of the soft Southland, stamped with the marks of generations of civilization. Because of his very great love, he could not steal from this man, but from any other man, in any other camp, he did not hesitate an instant; while the cunning with which he stole enabled him to escape detection.

His face and body were scored by the teeth of many dogs, and he fought as fiercely as ever and more shrewdly. Skeet was too good-natured for quarreling — besides, she belonged to John Thornton; but a strange dog, no matter what the breed or valor, swiftly acknowledged Buck's supremacy or found himself struggling for life with a terrible antagonist. And Buck was merciless. He had learned well the law of club and fang, and he never forewent an advantage or drew back from a foe he had started on the way to death. He had been lessoned by fighting dogs and knew there was no middle course. He must master or be mastered; to show mercy was a weakness. Mercy was misunderstood for fear, and such misunderstandings made for death. Kill or be killed, eat or be eaten, was the law; and this mandate, down out of the depths of time, he obeyed.

He was older than the days he had seen and the breaths he had drawn. He linked the past with the present, and the eternity behind him throbbed through him in a mighty rhythm to which he swayed as the tides and seasons swayed. He sat by John Thornton's fire, a broad-breasted dog, white-fanged and long-furred; but behind him were the shades of all manner of dogs, half-wolves and wild wolves, urgent and prompting, tasting the savor of the meat he ate, thirsting for the water he drank, scenting the wind with him, listening with him and telling him the sounds made by the wild life in the forest, dictating his moods, directing his actions, lying down to sleep with him when he lay down, and dreaming with him and beyond him and becoming themselves the stuff of his dreams.

So insistently did these shades beckon him that each day mankind and the claims of mankind slipped farther from him. Deep in the forest a call was sounding, and as often as he heard this call, mysteriously thrilling and luring, he felt compelled to turn his back upon the fire and the beaten earth around it and to plunge into the forest, and on and on, he knew not where or why; nor did he wonder where or why, the call sounding imperiously, deep in the forest. But as often as he gained the soft unbroken earth and the green shade, the love for John Thornton drew him back to the fire again.

Thornton alone held him. The rest of mankind was as nothing. Chance travelers might praise or pet him, but he was cold under it all, and from a too demonstrative man he would get up and walk away. When Thornton's partners, Hans and Pete, arrived on a raft, Buck refused to notice them till he saw they were close to Thornton.

After that he did tolerate them in a passive sort of way, accepting favors from them as though he favored them by accepting. They were of the same large type as Thornton, living close to the earth, thinking simply, and seeing clearly; and ere they swung the raft into the big eddy by the sawmill at Dawson, they understood Buck and his ways and did not insist upon an intimacy such as obtained with Skeet.

For Thornton, however, his love seemed to grow and grow. He, alone among men, could put a pack upon Buck's back in the summer traveling. Nothing was too great for Buck to do when Thornton commanded. One day (they had grubstaked themselves from the proceeds of the raft and left Dawson for the headwaters of the Tanana) the men and dogs were sitting on the crest of a cliff which fell away, straight down, to naked bedrock three hundred feet below. John Thornton was sitting near the edge, Buck at his shoulder. A thoughtless whim seized Thornton, and he drew the attention of Hans and Pete to the experiment he had in mind. "Jump, Buck!" he commanded, sweeping his arm out and over the chasm. The next instant he was grappling with Buck on the extreme edge, while Hans and Pete were dragging them back into safety.

"It's uncanny," Pete said, after it was over and they had caught their speech.

Thornton shook his head. "No, it is splendid, and it is terrible too. Do you know, it sometimes makes me afraid."

"I'm not hankering to be the man that lays hands on you while he's around," Pete announced conclusively, nodding his head toward Buck.

"Py Jingo!" was Hans's contribution. "Not mineself either."

It was at Circle City, ere the year was out, that Pete's apprehensions were realized. Joe Burton, a man evil-tempered and malicious, had been picking a quarrel with a tenderfoot at the bar when Thornton stepped good-naturedly between. Buck, as was his custom, was lying in a corner, head on paws, watching his master's every action. Burton struck out, without warning, straight from the shoulder. Thornton was sent spinning and saved himself from falling only by clutching the rail of the bar.

Those who were looking on heard what was neither bark nor yelp but a something which is best described as a roar, and they saw Buck's body rise up in the air as he left the floor for Burton's throat. The man saved his life by instinctively throwing out his arm, but he was hurled backward to the floor with Buck on top of him. Buck loosed his teeth from the flesh of the arm and drove in again for the throat. This time the man succeeded only in partly blocking, and his throat was torn open. Then the crowd was upon Buck, and he was driven off; but while a surgeon checked the bleeding, he prowled up and down, growling furiously, attempting to rush in, and being forced back by an array of hostile clubs. A "miners' meeting," called on the spot, decided that the dog had had sufficient provocation, and Buck was discharged. But his reputation was made, and from that day his name spread through every camp in Alaska.

Later on, in the fall of the year, he saved John Thornton's life in quite another fashion. The three partners were lining a long and narrow poling-boat down a bad stretch of rapids on the Forty-Mile Creek. Hans and Pete moved along the bank, snubbing with a thin Manila rope from tree to tree, while Thornton remained in the boat, helping its descent by means of a pole and shouting directions to the shore. Buck, on the bank, worried and anxious, kept abreast of the boat, his eyes never off his master.

At a particularly bad spot, where a ledge of barely submerged rocks jutted out into the river, Hans cast off the rope and, as Thornton poled the boat out into the stream, ran down the bank with the end in his hand to snub the boat when it had cleared the ledge. This it did and was flying downstream in a current as swift as a millrace when Hans checked it with the rope and checked too suddenly. The boat flipped over, and Thornton, flung sheer out of it, was carried downstream toward the worst part of the rapids, a stretch of wild water in which no swimmer could live.

Buck had sprung in on the instant, and at the end of three hundred yards, amid a mad swirl of water, he overhauled Thornton. When he felt Thornton grasp his tail, Buck headed for the bank, swimming with all his splendid strength. But the progress shoreward was slow, the progress downstream amazingly rapid. From below came the fatal roaring where the wild current went wilder and was rent in shreds and spray by the rocks which thrust through like the teeth of an enormous comb. The suck of the water as it took the beginning of the last steep pitch was frightful, and Thornton knew that the shore was impossible. He scraped furiously over a rock, bruised across a second, and struck a third with crushing force. He clutched its slippery top with both hands, releasing Buck, and above the roar of the churning water shouted, "Go, Buck! Go!"

Buck could not hold his own and swept on downstream, struggling desperately but unable to win back. When he heard Thornton's command repeated, he partly reared out of the water, throwing his head high, as though for a last look, then turned obediently toward the bank. He swam powerfully and was dragged ashore by Pete and Hans at the very point where swimming ceased to be possible and destruction began.

They knew that the time a man could cling to a slippery rock in the face of that driving current was a matter of minutes, and they ran as fast as they could up the bank to a point far above where Thornton was hanging

on. They attached to Buck's neck and shoulders the line with which they had been snubbing the boat, being careful that it should neither strangle him nor impede his swimming, and launched him into the stream. He struck out boldly but not straight enough into the stream. He discovered the mistake too late, when Thornton was abreast of him and a bare half-dozen strokes away, while he was being carried helplessly past.

Hans promptly snubbed with the rope, as though Buck were a boat. The rope thus tightening on him in the sweep of the current, he was jerked under the surface, and under the surface he remained till his body struck against the bank and he was hauled out. He was half-drowned, and Hans and Pete threw themselves upon him, pounding the breath into him and the water out of him. He staggered to his feet and fell down. The faint sound of Thornton's voice came to them, and though they could not make out the words of it, they knew that he was in his extremity. His master's voice acted on Buck like an electric shock. He sprang to his feet and ran up the bank ahead of the men to the point of his previous departure.

Again the rope was attached and he was launched, and again he struck out, but this time straight into the stream. He had miscalculated once, but he would not be guilty a second time. Hans paid out the rope, permitting no slack, while Pete kept it clear of coils. Buck held on till he was on a line straight above Thornton; then he turned and, with the speed of an express train, headed down upon him. Thornton saw him coming, and as Buck struck him like a battering-ram, with the whole force of the current behind him, Thornton reached up and closed with both arms around the shaggy neck. Hans snubbed the rope around a tree, and Buck and Thornton were jerked under the water. Strangling, suffocating, sometimes one uppermost and sometimes the other, dragging over the jagged bottom, smashing against rocks and snags, they veered in to the bank.

Thornton came to, his belly downward, being violently propelled back and forth across a drift log by Hans and Pete. His first glance was for Buck, whose wet face and closed eyes Skeet was licking. Thornton was himself bruised and battered, and he went carefully over Buck's body, when he had been brought around, finding three broken ribs.

"That settles it," he announced. "We camp right here." And camp they did, till Buck's ribs knitted and he was able to travel.

DISCUSSION

1. How did Buck's feelings for Thornton differ from his feelings for any previous master?
2. For a long time after Thornton rescued him, why did Buck try not to let Thornton out of his sight?
3. Briefly describe two incidents that reveal the extent of Buck's love for Thornton.
4. What does the phrase "fire and roof" mean in the following sentence: "Faithfulness and devotion, things born of fire and roof, were his; yet he retained his wildness and wiliness"?
5. What was "the law of club and fang" that Buck had learned?
6. Explain this sentence: "He was older than the days he had seen and the breaths he had drawn." If necessary, turn to page 553 and reread the paragraph that begins with this sentence.

7. What was the "call" that Buck continually heard, and what prevented him from answering it?
8. Buck is portrayed as being influenced by two strong opposing forces. What were they, and which appeared to be the stronger?
9. Do you think the call that Buck kept hearing represents something beautiful or something ugly and fearful? Why do you think that? Cite specific passages in the story, if possible, to prove your point.
10. Buck had lived in both "the Northland" and "the Southland." In which place had he heard the call? What two opposing forces do "the Northland" and "the Southland" represent?

AUTHOR

Jack London was an American author whose forty years of life were filled with action and adventure. His love of life is evident in all his writing. He joined the gold rush to the Yukon in 1897; he went to sea on a sealing schooner; he managed to travel all over the world.

Born in San Francisco, London had little formal education. Even as a boy, he had to work at various jobs in order to help support his family. But he always enjoyed reading, and he found escape from the poverty and hardship of his youth in exciting books about exploration and travel.

The year London spent in the Klondike was probably the most important year of his life. It was there that he found material for the stories that later made him famous, and it was there that he decided to turn his adventures into money by writing about them. An outstanding storyteller, London made over a million dollars, and he spent it all before he died in 1916.

"Buck" is an excerpt from London's best-known book, *Call of the Wild,* which was based on his experiences in the Yukon. In this novel and in others like *White Fang, The Son of the Wolf,* and *The Sea-Wolf,* London reveals his great interest in the emotions of men struggling for survival.

Several publishers were so enthusiastic about London's work that they gave him monthly allowances so that he could write without financial worries. He was the author of about fifty volumes of short stories, novels, plays, and essays, many of which were translated into other languages.

FROM THE BOOKSHELF

S IS FOR SPACE, *by Ray Bradbury*
This includes some of Ray Bradbury's best science-fiction stories.

THE COLOR OF MAN, *by Robert C. Cohen*
The author discusses the biological basis of skin color, the development of variations in color, and man's attempts to deal with color prejudice.

GANDHI, *by Olivia E. Coolidge*
This biography of the unique leader of the people of India reveals his weaknesses as well as his genius.

UP FROM THE MINOR LEAGUES OF HOCKEY, *by Stan and Shirley Fischler*
The authors have based these biographical sketches on tape-recorded interviews with hockey players who have made it in the big leagues.

LADIES OF HORROR: TWO CENTURIES OF SUPERNATURAL STORIES BY THE GENTLE SEX, *edited by Seon Manley and Gogo Lewis*
Fourteen stories of the occult, science fiction, and other dimensions of time and human consciousness show how women writers have contributed to the literature of the supernatural.

STRANGER IN THE PINES, *by May McNeer*
In the early 1800's Adam Quinn, escaping from an enforced apprenticeship to a blacksmith, flees from the past and a terrible secret.

VILLAGE OF OUTCASTS, *by S. R. van Iterson*
A South American leper colony is the background for a story about young Claudio, his love for Pilar, and the secret that brings them together.

DEATHWATCH, *by Robb White*
Ben, a young geology student, guides a businessman on a hunting trip in the desert. When Ben discovers that a shot fired by his client has killed a man, the trip turns into a nightmare.

GLOSSARY

To learn the correct pronunciation of any word in this glossary, use the special spelling after the word and the pronunciation key at the bottom of each left-hand page.

The pronunciation key at the bottom of each left-hand page is a shortened form of the full key below, which shows how to pronounce each consonant and vowel in any special spelling.

FULL PRONUNCIATION KEY

CONSONANT SOUNDS

b	bib	k	cat, kick, pique	t	tight
ch	church	l	lid, needle	th	path, thin
d	deed	m	am, man, mum	*th*	bathe, this
f	fast, fife, off, phase, rough	n	no, sudden	v	cave, valve, vine
		ng	thing	w	with
g	gag	p	pop	y	yes
h	hat	r	roar	z	rose, size, xylophone, zebra
hw	which	s	miss, sauce, see		
j	judge	sh	dish, ship	zh	garage, pleasure, vision

VOWEL SOUNDS

ă	pat	ī	by, guy, pie	o͝o	took
ā	aid, they, pay	î	dear, deer, fierce, mere	o͞o	boot, fruit
â	air, care, wear			ŭ	cut, rough
ä	father	ŏ	horrible, pot	û	firm, heard, term, turn, word
ĕ	pet, pleasure	ō	go, row, toe		
ē	be, bee, easy, leisure	ô	alter, caught, for, paw	yo͞o	abuse, use
ĭ	pit	oi	boy, noise, oil	ə	about, silent, pencil, lemon, circus
		ou	cow, out	ər	butter

STRESS MARKS

Primary Stress ′
bi•ol′o•gy (bī ŏl′ə jē)

Secondary Stress ′
bi′o•log′i•cal (bī′ə lŏj′ĭ kəl)

Pronunciation key and word meanings adapted from *The American Heritage School Dictionary*, published by American Heritage Publishing Co., Inc., and Houghton Mifflin Company.

ab·a·lo·ne (ăb′ə lō′nē) *n.* A soft-bodied, edible sea animal having a large, shallow shell with a brightly colored, iridescent lining.

ab·do·men (ăb′də mən) *or* (ăb dō′-) *n.* **1.** In human beings and other mammals, the front part of the body from below the chest to about where the legs join, containing the stomach, intestines, and other organs of digestion. **2.** The hindmost division of the body of an insect.

ab·hor (ăb hôr′) *v.* **ab·horred, ab·hor·ring.** To regard with horror or loathing: *abhor violence in all forms.*

ab·ject·ly (ăb′jĕkt′lē) *or* (ăb′jĕkt′lē) *adv.* **1.** In a manner that lacks all self-respect or resolve. **2.** Hopelessly; miserably.

ab·o·li·tion·ist (ăb′ə lĭsh′ə nĭst) *n.* A person who favored the prohibition of slavery in the United States.

a·bom·i·na·tion (ə bŏm′ə nā′shən) *n.* **1.** A feeling of outrage and disgust. **2.** Something that produces outrage and disgust.

ab·o·rig·i·ne (ăb′ə rĭj′ə nē) *n.* Any member of a group of people who are the first known to have lived in a given region.

ab·stain (ăb stān′) *v.* To keep from doing something voluntarily; refrain: *He abstains from eating candy.* —**ab·stain′er** *n.*

a·byss (ə bĭs′) *n.* **1.** A very deep and large hole: *into the abyss of the volcano.* **2.** A huge emptiness: *voyaging through the abyss of outer space.*

ac·ces·si·ble (ăk sĕs′ə bəl) *adj.* Easy to reach, approach, or obtain: *The lake is easily accessible from the highway.* —**ac·ces′si·bil′i·ty** *n.* —**ac·ces′si·bly** *adv.*

ac·cli·ma·tize (ə klī′mə tīz′) *v.* **ac·cli·ma·tized, ac·cli·ma·tiz·ing.** To adapt or become adapted to new conditions.

ac·cou·ter·ments (ə kōō′tər mənts) *pl.n.* **1.** Articles of clothing or equipment; trappings. **2.** A soldier's equipment apart from his clothing and weapons.

ad·here (ăd hîr′) *v.* **ad·hered, ad·her·ing. 1.** To stick or hold fast: *The wallpaper adheres to the wall.* **2.** To remain loyal; give continuing support: *adhere to one's religious beliefs.* **3.** To follow closely, without changes: *They adhered to the original plan.*

a·dren·a·lin *or* **a·dren·a·line** (ə drĕn′ə lĭn) *n.* A hormone produced by the adrenal glands. It acts to quicken the pulse, raise blood pressure, and, in general, to prepare the body for vigorous action, as in response to danger.

ad·ver·sar·y (ăd′vər sĕr′ē) *n., pl.* **ad·ver·sar·ies.** An opponent or enemy.

ad·ver·si·ty (ăd vûr′sĭ tē) *n., pl.* **ad·ver·si·ties.** Great misfortune; hardship.

aes·thet·ic (ĕs thĕt′ĭk) *adj.* Of or sensitive to what is beautiful; artistic.

af·fi·da·vit (ăf′ĭ dā′vĭt) *n.* A written declaration made under oath before a notary public or other authorized officer.

a·gape (ə gāp′) *or* (ə găp′) *adv.* In a state of wonder or amazement, often with the mouth wide open. —**a·gape′** *adj.*

a·ghast (ə găst′) *or* (ə gäst′) *adj.* Shocked or horrified, as by something terrible.

agony column. A classified section of a newspaper containing advertisements chiefly about missing persons.

a·kin (ə kĭn′) *adj.* **1.** Related by blood. **2.** Derived from the same origin: *The word "maternal" is akin to the word "mother."*

al·a·bas·ter (ăl′ə băs′tər) *or* (-bä′stər) *n.* Any of various hard, translucent, often tinted or banded minerals that consist mainly of salts of calcium.

al·der (ôl′dər) *n.* Any of several trees or shrubs that grow in cool, damp places.

al·fil·a·ri·a (ăl fĭl′ə rē′ə) *n.* A plant found in North America, having finely divided leaves and small pink or purplish flowers.

al·gae (ăl′jē) *pl.n.* The less frequently used singular is **al·ga** (ăl′gə). Members of a large group of plants that lack true roots, stems,

---

ă pat/ā pay/â care/ä father/ĕ pet/ē be/ĭ pit/ī pie/î fierce/ŏ pot/ō go/ô paw, for/oi oil/ōō book/ ōō boot/ou out/ŭ cut/û fur/*th* the/th thin/hw which/zh vision/ə ago, item, pencil, atom, circus and leaves but often have green coloring and grow mostly in water.

al·ka·loid (ăl′kə loid′) *n.* Any one of a class of organic compounds that contain nitrogen and have powerful effects on living organisms. Many of them are derived from plants. Nicotine, quinine, and morphine are examples of alkaloids.

al·lot·ment (ə lŏt′mənt) *n.* **1.** The act of distributing. **2.** Something assigned or distributed for a particular purpose.

alms (ämz) *pl.n.* Money or goods given to the poor as charity.

al·um (ăl′əm) *n.* **1.** Any of various sulfates in which a trivalent metal, such as aluminum, chromium, or iron, is combined with a univalent metal, such as potassium or sodium. **2.** Aluminum potassium sulfate, $AlK(SO_4)_2$, a compound of this type.

a·men·i·ty (ə mĕn′ĭ tē) *n., pl.* **a·men·i·ties. 1.** A courteous act of polite social behavior. **2.** Anything that provides or increases comfort.

am·phi·the·a·ter, also **am·phi·the·a·tre** (ăm′fə thē′ə tər) *n.* **1.** An oval or round structure having tiers of seats rising gradually outward from an open space, or arena, at the center. **2.** A level area surrounded by ground that slopes upward.

am·poule or **am·pule** (ăm′pool) *or* (-pyool) *n.* A small, narrow glass container, sealed after filling and used chiefly to hold a hypodermic injection solution.

am·u·let (ăm′yə lĭt) *n.* A charm worn to ward off evil or injury, especially one worn around the neck.

an·a·tom·i·cal (ăn′ə tŏm′ĭ kəl) or **an·a·tom·ic** (ăn′ə tŏm′ĭk) *adj.* **1.** Of or concerned with the structure of a plant or an animal or of any of its parts. **2.** Of the structure of an organism as opposed to its functioning: *an interesting anatomical abnormality.* —**an′·a·tom′i·cal·ly** *adv.*

an·es·thet·ic (ăn′ĭs thĕt′ĭk) *adj.* Insensitive; without sensation or feeling. —*n.* Any drug or agent that causes a condition in which some or all of the senses, especially the sense

of touch, stop operating, either completely or in part.

an·gu·lar (ăng′gyə lər) *adj.* **1.** Of, having, forming, or consisting of an angle or angles. **2.** Bony and lean. **3.** Sharp-cornered: *bulky or angular packages.* **4.** Lacking grace or smoothness: *an angular gait.*

an·i·mos·i·ty (ăn′ə mŏs′ĭ tē) *n., pl.* **an·i·mos·i·ties.** Hatred, enmity, or hostility that is shown openly.

an·tag·o·nist (ăn tăg′ə nĭst) *n.* A person who opposes and actively competes with another; an adversary; opponent.

an·tag·o·nize (ăn tăg′ə nīz′) *v.* **an·tag·o·nized, an·tag·o·niz·ing.** To earn the dislike of: *He antagonized his father by acting bored.*

an·thro·poid (ăn′thrə poid′) *adj.* Resembling a human being; manlike: *Gorillas and chimpanzees are anthropoid apes.* —*n.* An anthropoid ape.

an·ti·bi·ot·ic (ăn′tē bī ŏt′ĭk) *n.* Any of a group of substances such as penicillin and streptomycin, produced by certain fungi, bacteria, and other organisms, that are capable of destroying microorganisms or stopping their growth. They are widely used in the treatment and prevention of diseases. —*adj.* Of, using, or acting as an antibiotic or antibiotics: *antibiotic therapy; an important antibiotic drug.*

an·ti·dote (ăn′tĭ dōt′) *n.* **1.** A substance that counteracts the effects of a poison. **2.** Anything that counteracts something injurious.

ap·pend·age (ə pĕn′dĭj) *n.* **1.** Something added or attached. **2.** Any part or organ of the body that hangs or projects from another part: *A finger is an appendage of the hand.*

ap·pren·tice·ship (ə prĕn′tĭs shĭp′) *n.* A period during which a person works for another without pay in return for instruction in a craft or trade.

ap·pro·ba·tion (ăp′rə bā′shən) *n.* **1.** The act of approving, especially officially; approval. **2.** Praise; commendation: *not a murmur of approbation or blame.*

ap·pro·pri·a·tion (ə prō′prē ā′shən) *n.* **1.** The act of setting something aside for oneself or for a specific use. **2.** Public funds set aside for a specific purpose.

ar·a·ble (ăr′ə bəl) *adj.* Fit for cultivation.

ar·chae·ol·o·gist (är′kē ŏl′ə jĭst) *n.* A person who scientifically studies the remains of past human activities, such as burials, buildings, tools, and pottery.

ar·du·ous (är′jōō əs) *adj.* Demanding great effort; difficult: *arduous training; an arduous task.* —**ar′du·ous·ly** *adv.* —**ar′du·ous·ness** *n.*

a·ris·to·crat·ic (ə rĭs′tə krăt′ĭk) *or* (ăr′ĭs tə-) *adj.* **1.** Of or like the upper classes; noble: *aristocratic manners.* **2.** Having an aristocracy as a form of government: *aristocratic city-states.* —**a·ris′to·crat′i·cal·ly** *adv.*

ar·ro·gant (ăr′ə gənt) *adj.* Excessively and unpleasantly self-important, as in disregarding all other opinions but one's own. —**ar′ro·gant·ly** *adv.*

ar·se·nic (är′sə nĭk) *n.* Symbol **As** One of the elements, the most common form of which is a brittle, gray, highly poisonous metal.

artificial respiration. Any of several methods by which a living person who has stopped breathing may be revived. These methods usually involve forcing air rhythmically in and out of the lungs.

as·cer·tain (ăs′ər tān′) *v.* To find out: *ascertain the truth.* —**as′cer·tain′a·ble** *adj.*

as·tute (ə stōōt′) *or* (ə styōōt′) *adj.* Keen in judgment; shrewd: *an astute appraisal.* —**as·tute′ly** *adv.* —**as·tute′ness** *n.*

au·di·to·ry (ô′dĭ tôr′ē) *or* (-tōr′ē) *adj.* Of hearing or the organs of hearing.

aus·tere (ô stîr′) *adj.* **1.** Having a stern personality or appearance; somber. **2.** Severely simple, as in living habits. **3.** Harsh or barren: *They found it an austere land in which to live.* —**aus·tere′ly** *adv.*

av·a·lanche (ăv′ə lănch′) *or* (-länch′) *n.* A large mass of material such as snow, ice, or earth that falls or slides down the side of a mountain.

a·vi·ar·y (ā′vē ĕr′ē) *n., pl.* **a·vi·ar·ies.** A large cage or enclosure for birds, as in a zoo.

av·id (ăv′ĭd) *adj.* **1.** Eager: *avid for power.* **2.** Ardent; enthusiastic: *an avid reader.* —**a·vid′i·ty** (ə vĭd′ĭ tē) *n.* —**av′id·ly** *adv.*

ax·i·o·mat·ic (ăk′sē ə măt′ĭk) or **ax·i·o·mat·i·cal** (ăk′sē ə măt′ĭ kəl) *adj.* Self-evident. —**ax′i·o·mat′i·cal·ly** *adv.*

bac·te·ri·ol·o·gy (băk tîr′ē ŏl′ə jē) *n.* The scientific study of very small one-celled organisms often considered to be plants, although they usually lack green coloring.

baf·fle (băf′əl) *v.* **baf·fled, baf·fling.** To cause uncertainty in; puzzle: *Use the dictionary for any word that baffles you.* —**baf′fled** *adj.: a baffled look.* —**baf′fling** *adj.: a baffling problem.* —**baf′fle·ment** *n.*

balk (bôk) *v.* **1.** To stop short and refuse to go on. **2.** To refuse; recoil; shrink: *They balked at the terms of the settlement.* **3.** To check or thwart: *The policemen balked the robbers' escape plans.*

bal·last (băl′əst) *n.* **1.** Any heavy material carried in a vehicle mainly to provide weight. **2.** Gravel or small stones used to form a foundation for a roadway or for railroad tracks. —*v.* To provide with or fill in with ballast.

bar·ba·rism (bär′bə rĭz′əm) *n.* **1.** Existence in a crude, uncivilized state: *mankind's progress from barbarism toward civilization.* **2.** A brutal or cruel condition, act, or custom.

bar·rage (bə räzh′) *n.* **1.** A concentrated firing of guns or missiles, often as a screen or protection for military troops. **2.** An overwhelming attack or outpouring, as of blows or words: *a barrage of fists; a barrage of questions.*

bat·ting (băt′ĭng) *n.* Cotton or wool fibers wadded into rolls or sheets, used to stuff mattresses, line quilts, etc.

ă pat/ā pay/â care/ä father/ĕ pet/ē be/ĭ pit/ī pie/î fierce/ŏ pot/ō go/ô paw, for/oi oil/ŏŏ book/
ōō boot/ou out/ŭ cut/û fur/*th* the/th thin/hw which/zh vision/ə ago, item, pencil, atom, circus

be·hold·en (bĭ hōl′dən) *adj.* Indebted: *Electricity has now made man beholden to the machine.*

bell·weth·er (bĕl′wĕth′ər) *n.* A male sheep that wears a bell and leads a flock.

ber·serk (bər sûrk′) *or* (-zûrk′) *adj.* In or into a crazed or violent frenzy: *He went berserk and started firing at everyone in sight.*

be·sieged (bĭ sējd′) *adj.* **1.** Surrounded and blockaded: *Everyone in the besieged city suffered from hunger.* **2.** Hemmed in.

be·trothed (bĭ trōth d′) *or* (-trôtht′) *n.* A person engaged to be married.

bide (bīd) *v.* **bid·ed** *or* **bode** (bōd), **bid·ed, bid· ing.** To stay; to be left; remain.

bilk (bĭlk) *v.* To cheat, defraud, or swindle.

bi·ped (bī′pĕd′) *n.* An animal with two feet. Birds and human beings are bipeds.

bit (bĭt) *n.* **1.** A tool for drilling that fits into a brace or electric drill. **2.** The metal mouthpiece of a bridle, used to control the horse. **3.** The part of a key that enters the lock and works the mechanism.

bla·sé (blä zā′) *or* (blä′zā) *adj.* Uninterested, unexcited, or bored because of constant exposure or indulgence: *New Yorkers tend to be blasé about tall buildings.*

blear·i·ly (blîr′ə lē) *adv.* **1.** In a way that is blurred, by or as if by tears. **2.** Vaguely or indistinctly.

blitz (blĭts) *n.* **1.** A blitzkrieg. **2.** An intense air raid or series of air raids. **3.** Any intense, swift attack. *—v.* To subject to a blitz.

block and tackle. An arrangement of pulleys and ropes used for lifting heavy objects.

blue law. **1.** A law passed in colonial New England to govern personal behavior and particularly to state which activities are prohibited on Sunday. **2.** Any law restricting Sunday activities.

Bo·he·mi·an (bō hē′mē ən) *n.* Often **bohemian.** A person, especially an artist, who does not follow conventional standards of behavior.

boo·ty (bōō′tē) *n., pl.* **boo·ties. 1.** Loot taken from an enemy in war. **2.** Any seized or stolen goods. **3.** Treasure.

bore (bôr) *or* (bōr) *v.* **bored, bor·ing. 1.** To make (a hole, tunnel, well, etc.) by drilling or digging. **2.** To seem to penetrate like a drill: *deep-set eyes boring into his. —n.* **1.** The inside diameter of a hole, tube, cylinder, etc. **2.** A bored hole, as in a pipe or the barrel of a firearm.

bor·ough (bûr′ō) *or* (bŭr′ō) *n.* An incorporated self-governing town.

bou·le·var·dier (bōō′lə vär dyā′) *or* (bōō′ə- vär dîr′) *n.* A man about town.

bou·tique (bōō tēk′) *n.* A small retail shop that sells gifts, fashionable clothes, etc.

bou·ton·niere *or* **bou·ton·nière** (bōōt′n îr′) *or* (bōōt′n yâr′) *n.* A flower worn in a buttonhole, usually on a lapel.

bra·zier (brā′zhər) *n.* A metal pan for holding burning coals or charcoal.

breech·clout (brēch′klout′) *n.* A cloth worn to cover the loins.

brood (brōōd) *n.* A group, as of young birds, hatched from eggs laid at the same time by the same mother. *—v.* **1.** To sit on and hatch (eggs). **2.** To think at length and unhappily; worry anxiously.

brusque (brŭsk) *adj.* Rudely abrupt in manner or speech; curt; blunt. **—brusque′ly** *adv.* **—brusque′ness** *n.*

buc·ca·neer (bŭk′ə nîr′) *n.* A pirate.

bul·wark (bōōl′wərk) *or* (bŭl′-) *n.* **1.** A wall or barrier serving as a fortification. **2.** Any protection or defense.

bump·er (bŭm′pər) *n.* A drinking vessel filled to the top. *—adj.* Abundant: *a bumper crop.*

buoy·ant (boi′ənt) *or* (bōō′yənt) *adj.* **1.** Capable of floating or of keeping things afloat. **2.** Animated; sprightly. **3.** Resilient; elastic: *a buoyant step.* **—buoy′ant·ly** *adv.*

bush·el (bōōsh′əl) *n.* **1.** A unit of volume or capacity used in dry measure in the United States and equal to 4 pecks or 2,150.42 cubic inches. **2.** A container with approximately this capacity.

cache (kăsh) *n.* **1.** A hiding place for a supply of provisions, weapons, etc. **2.** A supply of

something hidden in such a place. —*v.*
cached, cach·ing. To hide or store away in
a cache.

ca·dav·er·ous (kə dăv′ər əs) *adj.* Resembling
a corpse; pale and gaunt.

cal·a·bash (kăl′ə băsh′) *n.* **1.** A large gourd
with a tough, shell-like rind. **2.** A bowl,
ladle, pipe, etc., made from the hollowed-
out shell of such a gourd or fruit.

cal·i·ber (kăl′ə bər) *n.* **1.** Degree of worth or
distinction: *a man of high caliber.* **2.** The
diameter of the inside of a tube, especially
the bore of a firearm. **3.** The diameter of a
bullet or other projectile intended for a firearm: *a .45-caliber bullet.*

cal·i·co (kăl′ĭ kō) *n., pl.* **cal·i·coes** or **cal·i·cos.**
A cotton cloth with a figured pattern printed
on it in color.

cal·lous (kăl′əs) *adj.* **1.** Having calluses. **2.**
Unfeeling; unsympathetic. —*v.* To make or
become callous.

cam·ou·flaged (kăm′ə fläzhd′) *adj.* Concealed or disguised through the use of
colors or patterns in order to appear to be
part of the natural surroundings.

can·ker (kăng′kər) *n.* An ulcerlike sore on
the lips or in the mouth.

can·ny (kăn′ē) *adj.* **can·ni·er, can·ni·est.** Careful and shrewd in one's actions and dealings.
—**can′ni·ly** *adv.* —**can′ni·ness** *n.*

can·o·py (kăn′ə pē) *n., pl.* **can·o·pies. 1.** A
kind of tentlike roof, usually held up on
posts, covering a bed, entrance, sacred object, or important person. **2.** Any similar
covering: *a canopy of leafy branches.*

can·tank·er·ous (kăn tăng′kər əs) *adj.* Ill-
tempered and quarrelsome; disagreeable;
contrary. —**can·tank′er·ous·ly** *adv.*

ca·pit·u·late (kə pĭch′ə lāt′) *v.* **ca·pit·u·lat·ed,
ca·pit·u·lat·ing.** To surrender under stated
conditions; give in; yield.

ca·pri·cious (kə prĭsh′əs) *or* (-prē′shəs) *adj.* **1.**
Subject to sudden, unpredictable changes;

impulsive; fickle: *a capricious child.* **2.** Often
changing; unreliable; irregular: *capricious
weather conditions.* —**ca·pri′cious·ly** *adv.*
—**ca·pri′cious·ness** *n.*

ca·rafe (kə răf′) *or* (-räf′) *n.* A glass bottle for
serving water or wine at the table.

car·cass (kär′kəs) *n.* **1.** The dead body of an
animal. **2.** Anything likened to a carcass.

ca·reen (kə rēn′) *v.* **1.** To tilt (a ship) onto its
side, on the shore, in order to clean or repair
its bottom. **2.** To lurch or swerve while in
motion: *The car careened on the icy road.*

car·i·ca·tured (kăr′ĭ kə chŏŏrd′) *or* (-chərd)
adj. Pictured or described in a greatly exaggerated or distorted way in order to produce
a comic effect.

car·nel·ian (kär nēl′yən) *n.* A pale to deep
red type of clear quartz used as a gem.

cast (kăst) *or* (käst) *n.* **1.** A hue or shade. **2.**
Outward form or appearance: *This puts a
different cast on the matter.* **3.** The act of
throwing: *a cast of the dice.* **4.** The actors
in a play, movie, etc.: *There were only four
people in the cast.* **5. a.** An object cast in or
as if in a mold. **b.** An impression formed in
a mold: *a cast in plaster of a face.*

cat·a·clysm (kăt′ə klĭz′əm) *n.* **1.** A sudden
and violent change in the earth's crust. **2.** A
great upheaval or disaster, such as a flood,
earthquake, revolution, or war. —**cat′a·clys′-
mic** (kăt′ə klĭz′mĭk) *adj.*

ca·tas·tro·phe (kə tăs′trə fē) *n.* A great and
sudden calamity, such as an earthquake or
flood.

cav·a·lier (kăv′ə lîr′) *n.* **1.** An armed horse-
man; a knight. **2.** A gallant or chivalrous
gentleman.

ca·vort (kə vôrt′) *v.* To leap about playfully;
romp; frolic.

cel·an·dine (sĕl′ən dīn′) *or* (-dēn′) *n.* A plant
having deeply divided leaves, yellow flowers,
and yellow-orange juice, native to Europe
and Asia.

ă pat/ā pay/â care/ä father/ĕ pet/ē be/ĭ pit/ī pie/î fierce/ŏ pot/ō go/ô paw, for/oi oil/ŏŏ book/
ŏŏ boot/ou out/ŭ cut/û fur/*th* the/th thin/hw which/zh vision/ə ago, item, pencil, atom, circus

cen·trif·u·gal (sĕn **trĭf′**yə gəl) *or* (**-trĭf′**ə gəl) *adj.* Moving or directed away from a center or axis.

ce·ram·ic (sə **răm′**ĭk) *n.* A hard, brittle, heat-resistant and corrosion-resistant material made by treating clay or some other mineral with extreme heat and used in making pottery and other products.

chaff (chăf) *n.* **1.** Grain husks that have been separated from the seeds by threshing. **2.** Trivial or worthless matter.

cham·ois (shăm′ē) *n.* **1.** A goatlike animal of mountainous regions of Europe. **2.** Soft, yellowish leather originally made from the skin of this animal, used for washing and polishing.

chem·ist (kĕm′ĭst) *n.* **1.** A scientist who specializes in chemistry. **2.** *Chiefly British.* A pharmacist.

chev·ro·tain (shĕv′rə tān′) *n.* A small, hornless, deerlike animal native to Africa and Asia.

chlo·ro·phyll, also **chlo·ro·phyl** (klôr′ə fĭl) *or* (klōr′-) *n.* Any one of several green pigments composed of carbon, hydrogen, magnesium, nitrogen, and oxygen, found in green plants and other living things that carry on photosynthesis.

chol·er·a (kŏl′ər ə) *n.* A serious, often fatal disease that is infectious and often epidemic. It is caused by microorganisms, and its symptoms include diarrhea, vomiting, and cramps.

Cho·pin (shō′păn′), **Frédéric.** 1810–1849. Polish composer and pianist.

Chris·ten·dom (krĭs′ən dəm) *n.* **1.** Christians in general. **2.** The Christian world.

cler·gy (klûr′jē) *n., pl.* **cler·gies.** Ministers, priests, and rabbis in general.

co·ag·u·late (kō ăg′yə lāt′) *v.* **co·ag·u·lat·ed, co·ag·u·lat·ing. 1.** To change (a liquid) into a solid or nearly solid mass; clot. **2.** To undergo such a change: *Egg whites coagulate when heated.*

cof·fer·dam (kô′fər dăm′) *or* (kŏf′ər-) *n.* A temporary enclosure built in the water and pumped dry to allow construction work on the bottom of a river, harbor, etc.

coif·fure (kwä **fyōōr′**) *n.* A woman's hair style; hairdo.

col·ic (kŏl′ĭk) *n.* A sharp, severe pain or cramp in the abdomen.

col·league (kŏl′ēg′) *n.* A fellow member of a profession or organization; an associate.

co·los·sus (kə **lŏs′**əs) *n., pl.* **co·los·si** (kə **lŏs′**ī′) or **co·los·sus·es 1.** A huge statue. **2.** Anything of enormous size or importance.

comb·er (kō′mər) *n.* **1.** A person or instrument that combs. **2.** A long wave of the sea that has reached its peak or broken into foam.

com·mis·er·ate (kə **mĭz′**ə rāt′) *v.* **com·mis·er·at·ed, com·mis·er·at·ing.** To feel or express sorrow or pity for; sympathize.

com·plex (kŏm′plĕks′) *n.* A system or unit consisting of a large number of parts that are related in a complicated way: *a new radar complex; a complex of cities and suburbs.* *—adj.* (kəm **plĕks′**) *or* (kŏm′plĕks′). **1.** Consisting of many connected or interrelating parts, factors, etc.; intricately formed or organized. **2.** Difficult to understand or figure out; complicated.

con·cede (kən **sēd′**) *v.* **con·ced·ed, con·ced·ing. 1.** To admit as true or real, often unwillingly or hesitantly; acknowledge. **2.** To give; yield; grant: *After many years, the government conceded the right to vote to all citizens.*

con·ces·sion·aire (kən sĕsh′ə **nâr′**) *n.* A person who has a right to operate a business in a certain place.

con·duc·tion (kən **dŭk′**shən) *n.* The transmission or passage of something through a medium or along a path, especially when what passes is a flow of energy, such as electricity or heat, and the medium does not appear to move.

con·fec·tion·er (kən **fĕk′**shə nər) *n.* A person who makes or sells candy, preserves, and other confections.

con·fed·er·ate (kən **fĕd′**ər ĭt) *n.* An associate in a plot or crime; an accomplice.

con·fer (kən **fûr′**) *v.* **con·ferred, con·fer·ring. 1.** To hold a conference; consult together. **2.** To bestow or award: *The general conferred a medal on the marine officer.*

con·fi·dant (kŏn′fĭ dănt′) *or* (-dänt′) *or* (kŏn′-fĭ dănt′) *or* (-dänt′) *n.* A person to whom one confides personal matters or secrets.

con·niv·ance (kə nī′vəns) *n.* Secret or underhanded cooperation with something that should be reported or condemned.

con·serv·a·tive (kən sûr′və tĭv) *adj.* **1.** Tending to oppose change; favoring traditional values. **2.** Not showy: *a conservative dark suit.* **3.** Moderate; cautious; restrained.

con·spire (kən spīr′) *v.* **con·spired, con·spir·ing. 1.** To plan together secretly, especially to commit an illegal act. **2.** To work together; combine: *Many factors conspired to defeat him.*

consul general. The highest-ranking official appointed by a government to live in a foreign city, look after his country's commercial interests, and give assistance to its citizens who live or travel there.

con·sump·tion (kən sŭmp′shən) *n.* **1.** The act of using up. **2.** A quantity used up. **3.** A wasting away of body tissues. **4.** An old word for tuberculosis of the lungs.

con·ta·gious (kən tā′jəs) *adj.* **1.** Capable of being transmitted by direct or indirect contact: *a contagious disease.* **2.** Carrying or capable of carrying disease. **3.** Tending to spread: *contagious laughter.*

con·tem·plate (kŏn′təm plāt′) *v.* **con·tem·plat·ed, con·tem·plat·ing. 1.** To look at, often quietly and solemnly: *The men contemplated the treasure in blissful silence.* **2.** To think about, especially in a detached way: *I contemplated my strange situation.* **3.** To think about doing (something): *The student contemplated a career in science.* **4.** To expect: *They contemplated various kinds of trouble.*

con·tem·po·rar·y (kən tĕm′pə rĕr′ē) *adj.* **1.** Living or occurring during the same period of time. **2.** Current; modern: *contemporary history.* —*n., pl.* **con·tem·po·rar·ies. 1.** A person of the same age as another: *John and I are contemporaries.* **2.** A person living at the same time as another: *a composer much admired by his contemporaries.* **3.** A person of the present age.

con·trite (kən trīt′) *or* (kŏn′trīt′) *adj.* Feeling or caused by guilt: *a contrite sinner; contrite tears.* —**con·trite′ly** *adv.* —**con·trite′ness** *n.*

con·vey·ance (kən vā′əns) *n.* **1.** The act of carrying. **2.** Something used to transport goods or people, especially a vehicle, such as an automobile, bus, or train.

con·vul·sive (kən vŭl′sĭv) *adj.* **1.** Having or causing violent involuntary muscular contractions. **2.** Of or like a fit or seizure.

cope (kōp) *v.* **coped, cop·ing.** To contend or strive, especially successfully: *coped with heavy traffic.*

copse (kŏps) *n.* A thicket of small trees or bushes.

cor·o·ner (kôr′ə nər) *or* (kŏr′-) *n.* A public official who investigates any death not clearly due to natural causes.

cote (kōt) *n.* A shed or coop for small animals or birds.

coun·sel (koun′səl) *n.* **1.** Advice; guidance. **2.** *pl.* **counsel.** A lawyer or group of lawyers giving legal advice. —*v.* **coun·seled** *or* **coun·selled, coun·sel·ing** *or* **coun·sel·ling.** To give advice.

cov·ert (kŭv′ərt) *or* (kō′vərt) *adj.* **1.** Covered; sheltered. **2.** Concealed; secret: *a covert look.* —*n.* A covered or sheltered place; a hiding place. —**cov′ert·ly** *adv.*

cov·ey (kŭv′ē) *n., pl.* **cov·eys.** A group or small flock of partridges, grouse, or other birds.

craft (krăft) *or* (kräft) *n.* **1.** Skill or ability in something, especially in work done with the hands or in the arts. **2.** Skill in deception or evasion; cunning: *She kept her eyes down and with craft hid her tears from sight.* **3.** An occupation or trade: *masterpieces of the jeweler's craft.* **4.** *pl.* **craft.** A boat, ship, aircraft, or spacecraft.

ă pat/ā pay/â care/ä father/ĕ pet/ē be/ĭ pit/ī pie/i fierce/ŏ pot/ō go/ô paw, for/oi **oil**/o͝o **book**/
o͞o **boot**/ou **out**/ŭ **cut**/û **fur**/*th* **the**/th **thin**/hw **which**/zh **vision**/ə **ago, item, pencil, atom, circus**

cram·pon (krăm′pən) *n.* **1.** A hinged pair of curved iron bars used for raising weights. **2.** A spiked iron plate attached to the shoe to prevent slipping when climbing or walking on ice.

cre·vasse (krə văs′) *n.* **1.** A deep crack, as in a glacier. **2.** A crack in a dike or levee.

cri·te·ri·on (krī tîr′ē ən) *n., pl.* **cri·te·ri·a** (krī tîr′ē ə) or **cri·te·ri·ons.** A rule or standard on which a judgment can be based: *What are your criteria for judging his work?*

crook (krŏok) *n.* An implement or tool with a bent or curved part: *a shepherd's crook.*

crypt (krĭpt) *n.* An underground vault or chamber, especially one that is used as a tomb beneath a church.

cub·age (kyōō′bĭj) *n.* The content or volume of a cube.

cull (kŭl) *v.* **1.** To pick out from others; gather selectively: *cull passages from a poet's work.* **2.** To search through; comb: *cull the forests for firewood.*

cul·mi·nate (kŭl′mə nāt′) *v.* **cul·mi·nat·ed, cul·mi·nat·ing.** To reach the highest point or degree; climax: *A series of minor demonstrations yesterday culminated in open rebellion.* —**cul′mi·na′tion** *n.*

dam·ask (dăm′əsk) *n.* A rich, glossy fabric woven with patterns that show on both sides, as a silk used for draperies or a linen used for tablecloths.

de·bris, also **dé·bris** (də brē′) *or* (dā′brē′) *n.* The scattered remains of something broken, destroyed, or discarded; fragments; rubble.

de·camp (dĭ kămp′) *v.* **1.** To pack up and leave a camping ground; break camp. **2.** To leave secretly or suddenly; run away.

de·cid·u·ous (dĭ sĭj′ōō əs) *adj.* **1.** Falling off at the end of a season or growing period: *deer with deciduous antlers.* **2.** Shedding leaves at the end of the growing season.

de·ci·pher (dĭ sī′fər) *v.* **1.** To change (a message) from a code or cipher to ordinary language; decode. **2.** To read or interpret (something hard to understand or illegible).

de·coy (dē′koi′) *or* (dĭ koi′) *n.* **1.** A model of a duck or other bird, used by hunters to attract wild birds or animals. **2.** A person who leads another into danger or a trap. —*v.* (dĭ koi′). To lure into danger or a trap.

deft (dĕft) *adj.* Quick and skillful: *a deft motion; deft hands.* —**deft′ly** *adv.* —**deft′ness** *n.*

de·gen·er·ate (dĭ jĕn′ə rāt′) *v.* **de·gen·er·at·ed, de·gen·er·at·ing.** To sink into a much worse or lower condition; deteriorate.

de·lir·i·ous·ly (dĭ lîr′ē əs lē) *adv.* In a mentally confused or excited way.

del·ta (dĕl′tə) *n.* A usually triangular mass of sand, mud, and earth, as that accumulated at the mouth of a river.

delve (dĕlv) *v.* **delved, delv·ing.** To search deeply and laboriously in order to obtain information: *delve into the secrets of the universe.*

de·mure·ly (dĭ myōor′lē) *adv.* In a shy or modest way, sometimes falsely so.

dep·re·cat·ing·ly (dĕp′rĭ kāt′ĭng lē) *adv.* **1.** Disapprovingly. **2.** In a belittling way.

de·sal·i·ni·za·tion (dē săl′ə nĭ zā′shən) *n.* The removal of salts and other chemicals from sea water.

des·ig·na·tion (dĕz′ĭg nā′shən) *n.* **1.** The act of specifying or pointing out. **2.** An identifying name or title.

des·ti·tute (dĕs′tĭ tōōt′) *or* (-tyōot′) *adj.* Completely impoverished; penniless.

de·ter·rence (dĭ tûr′əns) *or* (-tûr′-) *n.* The act or a means of preventing or discouraging, as by fear.

det·o·nate (dĕt′n āt′) *v.* **det·o·nat·ed, det·o·nat·ing.** To explode or cause to explode: *detonate a bomb.* —**det′o·na′tion** *n.*

dex·ter·i·ty (dĕk stĕr′ĭ tē) *n.* **1.** Skill in the use of the hands or body. **2.** Mental skill or adroitness; cleverness.

di·gres·sion (dĭ grĕsh′ən) *or* (dī-) *n.* A straying from the main subject in writing or in speaking.

di·lat·ed (dĭ lā′tĭd) *or* (dī-) *or* (dī′lā′tĭd) *adj.* Made wider or larger.

dis·con·so·late (dĭs kŏn′sə lĭt) *adj.* Very sad; gloomy; dismal. —**dis·con′so·late·ly** *adv.*

dis·creet·ly (dĭ skrēt′lē) *adv.* **1.** In a cautious or prudent way. **2.** Modestly.

di·shev·eled (dĭ shĕv′əld) *adj.* Untidy; not orderly; disarranged: *disheveled hair.*

dis·patch·er (dĭ spăch′ər) *n.* A person employed to control the departure and movements of trains, taxicabs, or delivery trucks or to route telegraph communications.

dis·si·pat·ed (dĭs′ə pā′tĭd) *adj.* **1.** Indulging in pleasure to a degree harmful to health or morals. **2.** Wasted; squandered: *a dissipated fortune.*

dis·suade (dĭ swād′) *v.* **dis·suad·ed, dis·suad·ing.** To discourage or keep (someone) from a purpose or course of action. —**dis·sua′sion** (dĭ swā′zhən) *n.*

dis·tinc·tive (dĭ stĭngk′tĭv) *adj.* Serving to identify, characterize, or set apart from others: *Large red berries are a distinctive feature of this plant.* —**dis·tinc′tive·ly** *adv.* —**dis·tinc′tive·ness** *n.*

dis·tract·ed·ly (dĭ străk′tĭd lē) *adv.* **1.** In a confused or bewildered way. **2.** In a violently upset manner.

di·ver·gent (dĭ vûr′jənt) *or* (dī-) *adj.* **1.** Drawing apart from a common point; diverging. **2.** Differing: *widely divergent views on the subject.* —**di·ver′gent·ly** *adv.*

di·vulge (dĭ vŭlj′) *v.* **di·vulged, di·vulg·ing.** To make known; reveal; tell: *divulge a secret.*

dock (dŏk) *v.* **1.** To clip or cut off, as an animal's tail. **2. a.** To withhold a part of (a salary). **b.** To penalize (a worker) by such deduction.

dog·ged·ly (dô′gĭd lē) *or* (dŏg′ĭd lē) *adv.* In a persistent or stubborn way: *police detectives doggedly pursuing an escaped convict.*

do·gie (dō′gē) *n.* In the western United States, a motherless or stray calf.

dol·er·ite (dŏl′ə rīt′) *n.* A coarse, dark, igneous rock.

dor·sal (dôr′səl) *adj.* Of, toward, on, in, or near the back of an animal. —**dor′sal·ly** *adv.*

dos·si·er (dŏs′ē ā) *or* (-ē ər) *or* (dô′sē ā) *or* (-sē ər) *n.* A collection of papers or documents pertaining to a particular person or subject.

dough·ty (dou′tē) *adj.* **dough·ti·er, dough·ti·est.** Brave; courageous. —**dough′ti·ness** *n.*

dour (do͝or) *or* (dour) *adj.* **1.** Stern and forbidding. **2.** Gloomy; sullen. —**dour′ly** *adv.* —**dour′ness** *n.*

drag·net (drăg′nĕt′) *n.* A system of search, employed by the police, in which all available resources are used.

draw (drô) *n.* **1.** An act of drawing. **2.** An advantage; edge. **3.** A contest ending in a tie. **4.** A natural drainage basin; gully.

draw and quarter. To execute (someone) by tying each limb to a horse and driving the horses in different directions.

drove (drōv) *n.* **1.** A number of cattle, sheep, horses, etc., being driven in a group. **2.** A crowd; throng: *droves of visitors.*

drudge (drŭj) *n.* A person who does hard, tiresome, or menial work. —*v.* **drudged, drudg·ing.** To do hard, tiresome, or menial work.

du·bi·ous·ly (do͞o′bē əs lē) *or* (dyo͞o′-) *adv.* **1.** Doubtfully; uncertainly. **2.** Questionably; suspiciously.

dys·en·ter·y (dĭs′ən tĕr′ē) *n.* An infection of the lower intestines that produces pain, fever, and severe diarrhea.

eb·on (ĕb′ən) *adj.* Black. Used chiefly in poetry.

e·bul·lient (ĭ bŭl′yənt) *adj.* Full of bubbling excitement, enthusiasm, or high spirits. —**e·bul′lience** *n.*

ec·cen·tric·i·ty (ĕk′sĕn trĭs′ĭ tē) *n., pl.* **ec·cen·tric·i·ties.** The condition or quality of being odd or unusual in appearance or behavior.

ed·i·fice (ĕd′ə fĭs) *n.* A building, especially one of imposing size or appearance.

ă pat/ā pay/â care/ä father/ĕ pet/ē be/ĭ pit/ī pie/î fierce/ŏ pot/ō go/ô paw, for/oi oil/o͝o book/ o͞o boot/ou out/ŭ cut/û fur/*th* the/th thin/hw which/zh vision/ə ago, item, pencil, atom, circus

e·go·tist (ē′gə tĭst′) *n.* **1.** A person who talks about himself or herself excessively or boastfully. **2.** Someone with an inordinately large sense of self-importance.

e·lab·o·rate (ĭ lăb′ər ĭt) *adj.* Planned or made with great attention to numerous parts or details; complicated but carefully wrought; intricate: *a play with no elaborate scenery or costumes.* —*v.* (ĭ lăb′ə rāt′) **e·lab·o·rat·ed, e·lab·o·rat·ing.** To express oneself at greater length or in greater detail; provide further information: *After receiving only a brief answer to our question, we asked him to elaborate on the subject.*

e·lu·sive (ĭ lōō′sĭv) *adj.* **1.** Tending to avoid or escape, as by artfulness, cunning, or daring; evasive. **2.** Not able to be understood or detected.

em·a·nate (ĕm′ə nāt′) *v.* **em·a·nat·ed, em·a·nat·ing.** To come or send forth, as from a source or origin; issue or emit: *Sweet sounds emanated from a hidden cove.*

em·balm (ĕm bäm′) *v.* To treat (a corpse) with substances that prevent or retard decay. —**em·balm′er** *n.*

em·bel·lish·ment (ĕm bĕl′ĭsh mənt) *n.* **1.** An ornament. **2.** A fanciful or fictitious detail.

em·bez·zler (ĕm bĕz′lər) *n.* Someone who takes money or property for his own use in violation of a trust.

em·i·grant (ĕm′ĭ grənt) *n.* Someone who leaves a native country or region to settle in another: *wagon trains of emigrants from the East.*

em·i·nent (ĕm′ə nənt) *adj.* **1.** Outstanding in performance, character, or rank; distinguished. **2.** Remarkable; noteworthy: *eminent achievements.* —**em′i·nent·ly** *adv.*

em·u·late (ĕm′yə lāt′) *v.* **em·u·lat·ed, em·u·lat·ing.** To strive to equal or excel, especially through imitation. —**em′u·la′tion** *n.*

en·gross (ĕn grōs′) *v.* **1.** To occupy the complete attention of; absorb wholly. **2. a.** To write or transcribe in a large, clear hand. **b.** To prepare the text of an official document by an officially prescribed process, such as handwriting or printing.

e·nig·ma (ĭ nĭg′mə) *n.* Someone or something that is hard to figure out; a puzzle.

en·mi·ty (ĕn′mĭ tē) *n., pl.* **en·mi·ties.** Deep hatred or hostility, as between enemies or opponents; antagonism.

en·ti·ty (ĕn′tĭ tē) *n., pl.* **en·ti·ties.** Something that exists and may be distinguished from other things: *American English and British English are often considered separate entities.*

en·tre·pre·neur (än′trə prə **nûr′**) *or* (**-nōōr′**) *n.* A person who organizes and operates a business enterprise.

e·on (ē′ŏn′) *or* (ē′ən) *n.* **1.** An extremely long period of time. **2.** A division of geologic time that contains two or more eras.

e·qua·to·ri·al (ē′kwə tôr′ē əl) *or* (-tōr′-) *or* (ĕk′wə-) *adj.* **1.** Of or near the equator. **2.** Characteristic of the equator or the regions near it: *equatorial heat.*

er·rat·ic (ĭ răt′ĭk) *adj.* **1.** Irregular or uneven in quality, progress, etc. **2.** Odd; eccentric: *erratic behavior.* —**er·rat′i·cal·ly** *adv.*

es·carp·ment (ĭ skärp′mənt) *n.* **1.** A steep slope or long cliff formed by erosion or by vertical movement of the earth's crust along a fault. **2.** A steep slope or embankment in front of a fortification.

es·pres·so (ĕ sprĕs′ō) *n., pl.* **es·pres·sos.** A strong coffee brewed by forcing steam through long-roasted, powdered beans.

es·tu·ar·i·al (ĕs′chōō ĕr′ē əl) *adj.* Of or like the wide lower part of a river where its current is met and influenced by the tides of the ocean.

ex·alt·ed (ĭg zôl′tĭd) *adj.* **1.** Having high rank; dignified: *an exalted personage.* **2.** Lofty; noble: *an exalted literary style.*

ex·ot·ic (ĭg zŏt′ĭk) *adj.* **1.** From another part of the world; not native; foreign: *exotic customs.* **2.** Having the charm of the unfamiliar; strikingly or intriguingly unusual: *She is an exotic beauty.*

ex·pa·ti·ate (ĭk spā′shē āt′) *v.* **ex·pa·ti·at·ed, ex·pa·ti·at·ing.** To speak or write at length; elaborate: *He expatiated freely on the subjects about which he was most knowledgeable.* —**ex·pa′ti·a′tion** *n.*

ex·pe·di·en·cy (ĭk spē′dē ən sē) *n., pl.* **ex·pe·di·en·cies. 1.** Appropriateness to the purpose at hand. **2.** Selfish practicality.

ex·qui·site (ĕk′skwĭz ĭt) *or* (ĭk skwĭz′ĭt) *adj.* **1.** Of special beauty, charm, elegance, etc. **2.** Intense; keen: *He takes exquisite pleasure in his meals.* **3.** Keenly sensitive; discriminating. —**ex′qui·site·ly** *adv.*

ex·tro·vert (ĕk′strə vûrt′) *n.* A person whose interest tends to center on the people and things around him rather than on his own inner thoughts and feelings.

fair·ing (fâr′ĭng) *n.* An auxiliary structure or the external surface of an aircraft serving to reduce drag.

fal·ter (fôl′tər) *v.* **1.** To perform haltingly; lose strength or momentum: *The engine faltered.* **2.** To speak hesitatingly; stammer. **3.** To waver in purpose or action; hesitate.

fam·ine (făm′ĭn) *n.* A shortage of food resulting in widespread hunger and starvation.

fare (fâr) *v.* **fared, far·ing.** *British dialect.* To appear or seem.

fas·tid·i·ous (fă stĭd′ē əs) *adj.* **1.** Careful in all details. **2.** Overcritical: *a fastidious critic.* —**fas·tid′i·ous·ly** *adv.* —**fas·tid′i·ous·ness** *n.*

fe·cund·i·ty (fĭ kŭn′dĭ tē) *n.* Productiveness; fertility.

feigned (fānd) *adj.* False; pretended.

fem·i·nist (fĕm′ĭ nĭst) *n.* Someone who supports the doctrine that women should have the same rights and status as men.

fe·ro·cious (fə rō′shəs) *adj.* **1.** Extremely cruel and fierce; savage. **2.** Extreme; intense: *a ferocious speed.* —**fe·ro′cious·ly** *adv.*

fer·vent·ly (fûr′vənt lē) *adv.* In a way which shows deep feeling or great emotion.

fes·toon (fĕ stōōn′) *n.* A length or chain of leaves, flowers, ribbon, paper, etc., hung in a curve between two points for decoration. —*v.* To decorate with festoons.

fi·ber (fī′bər) *n.* **1.** A slender, threadlike strand, as of plant or animal tissue or of man-made material. **2.** A number of fibers forming a single substance: *muscle fiber.* **3.** Inner strength; character.

fil·a·ment (fĭl′ə mənt) *n.* Any fine or slender thread, strand, fiber, etc.

fin·ick·y (fĭn′ĭ kē) *adj.* Very fussy; difficult to please.

flail (flāl) *n.* A tool for threshing grain, consisting of a long wooden handle and a shorter, free-swinging stick attached to its end. —*v.* To thresh or beat with or as if with a flail.

flam·boy·ant (flăm boi′ənt) *adj.* **1.** Highly elaborate; ornate: *a flamboyant literary style.* **2.** Exaggerated or high-flown in style, manner, etc.; showy. **3.** Brilliant; vivid; sparkling. —**flam·boy′ance, flam·boy′an·cy** *n.* —**flam·boy′ant·ly** *adv.*

fla·men·co (flə mĕng′kō) *n.* **1.** A dance style of Spanish Gypsies characterized by forceful rhythms. **2.** The guitar music for this dance style.

flank (flăngk) *v.* To be placed or situated at the side of: *Two chairs flanked the couch.*

flo·ra (flôr′ə) *or* (flōr′ə) *n.* The plants of a particular region or time period: *desert flora.*

flo·til·la (flō tĭl′ə) *n.* A fleet of boats or other small vessels.

fluked (flōōkt) *adj.* Divided into two flattened, finlike divisions, as the tail of a whale.

focal length. 1. The distance from the surface of a lens to the focus located on that side of the lens. **2.** The distance from the surface of a reflector to its focus.

foi·ble (foi′bəl) *n.* A minor personal fault, failing, or peculiarity that is easy to forgive.

fo·li·age (fō′lē ĭj) *n.* The leaves of plants or trees; leaves in general.

fol·li·cle (fŏl′ĭ kəl) *n.* **1.** A rounded clump of cells, sometimes containing a cavity. **2.** A

ă pat/ā pay/â care/ä father/ĕ pet/ē be/ĭ pit/ī pie/ì fierce/ŏ pot/ō go/ô paw, for/oi oil/ŏŏ book/
ōō boot/ou out/ŭ cut/û fur/*th* the/th thin/hw which/zh vision/ə ago, item, pencil, atom, circus

tiny sac in the body, such as the depression in the skin from which a hair grows.

fools·cap (fōolz′kăp′) *n.* Writing paper in large sheets about 13 inches wide and 16 inches long.

for·age (fôr′ĭj) *or* (fŏr′-) *v.* **for·aged, for·ag·ing.** **1.** To search for food: *Raccoons forage in garbage dumps.* **2.** To search or hunt about, as for anything needed or desired. —*n.* **1.** Food for horses, cattle, or other animals, as plants or grass eaten while grazing. **2.** A search to find available food or supplies.

for·ay (fôr′ā′) *or* (fŏr′ā′) *n.* **1.** A sudden raid, expedition, or invasion, as to fight someone. **2.** A first attempt or venture in some field: *her opening foray into politics.* —*v.* To make a raid, as for plunder.

ford (fôrd) *or* (fōrd) *n.* A shallow place in a stream or river where one can wade, ride, or drive across. —*v.* To cross (a stream or river) by wading, riding, or driving through a ford.

for·mal·de·hyde (fôr măl′də hīd′) *n.* A colorless, gaseous compound of carbon, hydrogen, and oxygen that has a sharp, suffocating odor and the formula CH_2O.

for·tu·i·tous·ly (fôr tōo′ĭ təs lē) *or* (-tyōo′-) *adv.* **1.** In a chance or accidental way. **2.** Luckily; fortunately.

foun·dry (foun′drē) *n., pl.* **foun·dries.** A place in which metals are cast and molded.

fren·zied (frĕn′zēd) *adj.* Affected with or filled with frenzy; frantic. —**fren′zied·ly** *adv.*

fresh·et (frĕsh′ĭt) *n.* **1.** A sudden overflow of a stream as a result of heavy rain or a thaw. **2.** A stream of fresh water that runs into a body of salt water.

frig·ate (frĭg′ĭt) *n.* **1.** Any of various square-rigged fast-sailing warships built between the 17th and the mid-19th centuries. **2.** An antisubmarine ship, used as an escort.

friv·o·lous (frĭv′ə ləs) *adj.* **1.** Not worthy of serious attention; insignificant; trivial. **2.** Not serious or sensible in manner or behavior; silly; flippant: *He seemed to be frivolous and unaware of the crisis.* —**friv′o·lous·ly** *adv.* —**friv′o·lous·ness** *n.*

frond (frŏnd) *n.* The leaf of a fern, palm tree, etc., usually divided into smaller leaflets.

fume (fyōom) *v.* **fumed, fum·ing. 1.** To produce or give off fumes. **2.** To feel or show anger or agitation; seethe. —*n.* Any smoke, vapor, or gas, especially one that is irritating or that has an unpleasant odor.

fu·ror (fyōor′ôr′) *or* (-ōr′) *n.* A noisy outburst of anger, disapproval, enthusiasm, etc., as in a crowd; an uproar.

fu·tile (fyōot′l) *or* (fyōo′tīl′) *adj.* Having no useful result; useless. —**fu′tile·ly** *adv.*

gab·er·dine (găb′ər dēn′) *or* (găb′ər **dēn′**) *n.* **1.** A long, loose coat or smock. **2.** A firm, woven cloth with a smooth surface and slanting ribs; gabardine.

ga·ble (gā′bəl) *n.* The triangular wall section between the two slopes of a roof.

gal·ler·y (găl′ə rē) *or* (găl′rē) *n., pl.* **gal·ler·ies.** **1.** Any enclosed passageway, especially one used for a specified purpose. **2.** The balcony in a theater or church. **3.** A building or hall for displaying works of art. **4.** An underground tunnel or other passageway, as one dug for mining purposes. **5.** A basket or gondola suspended from a balloon.

gan·gren·ous (găng′grə nəs) *adj.* Dead and decayed, as the tissue in a living body, due to injury, disease, or failure of the blood supply.

gar (gär) *n.* A freshwater fish with a long, narrow body, sharp teeth, and long, narrow jaws.

gar·land (gär′lənd) *n.* A wreath or chain of flowers, leaves, etc., worn as a crown or used for ornament.

gaunt (gônt) *adj.* **gaunt·er, gaunt·est. 1.** Thin and bony; haggard; emaciated: *a gaunt face.* **2.** Bleak and desolate; stark. —**gaunt′ly** *adv.* —**gaunt′ness** *n.*

gauze (gôz) *n.* A loosely woven cloth that is thin enough to see through, used especially for bandages.

gen·ial (jēn′yəl) *or* (jē′nē əl) *adj.* **1.** Cheerful, friendly, and good-humored. **2.** Favorable to health or growth; warm and pleasant. —**ge·ni·al·i·ty** *n.* —**gen·ial·ly** *adv.*

ger·mi·nate (jûr′mə nāt′) *v.* **ger·mi·nat·ed, ger·mi·nat·ing.** To begin or cause to begin to grow; sprout: *Seeds need water and warmth to germinate.* —**ger′mi·na′tion** *n.*

ges·tic·u·late (jĕ stĭk′yə lāt′) *v.* **ges·tic·u·lat·ed, ges·tic·u·lat·ing.** To make motions, as by waving the arms while speaking, in order to emphasize one's meaning or express one's feelings. —**ges·tic·u·la′tion** *n.*

gilt (gĭlt) *n.* A thin layer of gold, such as gold leaf or gold-colored paint, applied to a surface: *ornate gilt on a picture frame.*

gird (gûrd) *v.* **gird·ed** or **girt** (gûrt), **gird·ing. 1.** To encircle or attach with a belt, band, etc.: *gird on their trusty swords.* **2.** To prepare (oneself) for action: *I shall bring you arms to gird yourselves for battle.* **3.** To encircle or surround.

girth (gûrth) *n.* **1.** The distance or measurement around something; circumference. **2.** A strap encircling the body of a horse or pack animal to secure a load or saddle on its back.

gist (jĭst) *n.* The central idea of something, such as a speech; essence.

glock·en·spiel (glŏk′ən spēl′) or (-shpēl′) *n.* A musical instrument consisting of a series of metal bars tuned to the tones of the chromatic scale. It is played by being struck with two light hammers.

gnarled (närld) *adj.* Having gnarls; knotty and misshapen.

gram·o·phone (grăm′ə fōn′) *n.* A record player; phonograph.

grate (grāt) *n.* A framework or network of parallel or interwoven bars or wires, used to block an opening or to separate things by straining them.

grat·ing (grā′tĭng) *n.* A set of parallel bars set across an opening, such as a window or doorway, in order to block it; a grate.

gray·back (grā′băk′) *n.* A body louse.

gre·gar·i·ous (grĭ gâr′ē əs) *adj.* **1.** Living in flocks, herds, colonies, or similar groups with others of the same kind. **2.** Seeking out and enjoying the company of others; sociable. —**gre·gar′i·ous·ly** *adv.* —**gre·gar′i·ous·ness** *n.*

grilled (grĭld) *adj.* Covered with metal grating, often of decorative design.

grim·ace (grĭm′əs) or (grĭ mās′) *n.* A facial contortion expressive of pain, disgust, etc. —*v.* **grim·aced, grim·ac·ing.** To make a grimace.

grub·stake (grŭb′stāk′) *n.* Supplies or funds advanced to a mining prospector or a person starting a business, in return for a promised share of the profits. —*v.* **grub·staked, grub·stak·ing.** To supply with a grubstake.

gru·el·ing (grōō′ə lĭng) *adj.* Exhausting; extremely tiring.

guil·lo·tine (gĭl′ə tēn′) or (gē′ə-) *n.* A machine for beheading a condemned prisoner, consisting of a heavy blade that falls freely between two upright posts. —*v.* (gĭl′ə tēn′) **guil·lo·tined, guil·lo·tin·ing.** To behead with a guillotine.

hack·a·more (hăk′ə môr′) or (-mōr′) *n.* A halter with a wide band that can be lowered over a horse's eyes, used in breaking horses to a bridle.

har·assed (hăr′əst) or (hə răst′) *adj.* Bothered by repeated interruptions, attacks, etc.

har·ry (hăr′ē) *v.* **har·ried, har·ry·ing, har·ries. 1.** To raid, as in a war; pillage. **2.** To disturb by constant attacks; harass.

hatch (hăch) *n.* **1.** A small door: *an escape hatch.* **2. a.** A trap door, especially one covering a hatchway on a ship. **b.** Any door or doorway on shipboard.

hearse (hûrs) *n.* A vehicle for carrying a dead person to a church or cemetery.

ă pat/ā pay/â care/ä father/ĕ pet/ē be/ĭ pit/ī pie/î fierce/ŏ pot/ō go/ô paw, for/oi oil/o͝o book/ o͞o boot/ou out/ŭ cut/û fur/*th* the/th thin/hw which/zh vision/ə ago, item, pencil, atom, circus

heist (hīst) *v.* **1.** *Slang.* To rob; steal. **2.** *Dialect.* To hoist; lift. —*n. Slang.* A robbery; burglary.

hemp (hĕmp) *n.* **1.** A tall plant with stems that yield a tough fiber used for making rope, cord, etc. **2.** The fiber of this plant.

hoar·y (hôr'ē) *or* (hōr'ē) *adj.* **hoar·i·er, hoar·i·est.** **1.** White or grayish. **2.** Very old.

hom·age (hŏm'ĭj) *or* (ŏm'-) *n.* **1.** Special honor or respect shown or expressed publicly. **2.** An action or ceremony, originating in feudal times, in which a person shows allegiance or loyalty to a ruler.

hov·er·craft (hŭv'ər krăft') *or* (-kräft') *n.* A motorized vehicle designed to skim over land or water at a height of a few inches. This vehicle is held aloft by air forced downward by an engine-driven fan and propelled and steered by another such fan.

hue (hyōō) *n.* **1.** Color: *all the hues of the rainbow.* **2.** A particular color seen as distinct from other colors; a shade; tint.

hum·mock (hŭm'ək) *n.* A low mound or ridge, as of earth or snow.

hu·mus (hyōō'məs) *n.* A dark-colored substance that consists of decayed plant and animal material and forms a part of the soil necessary for plant nourishment.

hun·ker (hŭng'kər) *v.* To squat close to the ground with the body leaning slightly forward, the weight resting on the calves.

hy·dro·dy·nam·ics (hī'drō dī năm'ĭks) *n.* *(used with a singular verb).* The part of physics that deals with the behavior of fluids in motion, especially fluids that cannot be compressed.

hy·po·chon·dri·ac (hī'pə kŏn'drē ăk') *n.* A person who is convinced that he is ill or about to become ill, and who often feels real pain when there is, in fact, no illness present.

hy·poth·e·sis (hī pŏth'ĭ sĭs) *n., pl.* **hy·poth·e·ses** (hī pŏth'ĭ sēz'). **1.** An explanation or statement that accounts for all of a set of known facts but for which there is no direct supporting evidence. **2.** Something that is assumed as a basis for action, discussion, etc.

hys·te·ri·a (hī stĕr'ē ə) *or* (-stîr'-) *n.* An extreme, uncontrollable fear or other strong emotion.

ig·no·ra·mus (ĭg'nə rā'məs) *or* (-răm'əs) *n., pl.* **ig·no·ra·mus·es.** An ignorant person.

im·pel (ĭm pĕl') *v.* **im·pelled, im·pel·ling.** **1.** To urge to action; spur: *the curiosity that impels rock collectors to learn more about minerals.* **2.** To drive forward; propel.

im·pen·e·tra·ble (ĭm pĕn'ĭ trə bəl) *adj.* **1.** Not capable of being entered or penetrated. **2.** Not capable of being understood or discerned; unfathomable: *her impenetrable secret.* —**im·pen'e·tra·bil'i·ty** *n.*

im·pe·ri·ous·ly (ĭm pîr'ē əs lē) *adv.* **1.** In an arrogant or domineering way. **2.** Urgently.

im·promp·tu (ĭm prŏmp'tōō) *or* (-tyōō) *adj.* Not prepared beforehand; not rehearsed. —*adv.* Without rehearsal or preparation. —*n.* Something made or done without rehearsal, as a musical composition or speech.

in·ad·ver·tent·ly (ĭn'əd vûr'tənt lē) *adv.* Accidentally; unintentionally.

in·bred (ĭn'brĕd') *adj.* **1.** Produced by or resulting from inbreeding. **2.** Existing from birth; inborn.

in·can·des·cent (ĭn'kən dĕs'ənt) *adj.* **1.** Giving off visible light as a result of being raised to a high temperature. **2.** Shining brilliantly; very bright. —**in'can·des'cence** *n.* —**in'can·des'cent·ly** *adv.*

in·cen·di·ar·y (ĭn sĕn'dē ĕr'ē) *adj.* **1.** Starting or designed to start fires. **2.** Tending to arouse strong feelings.

in·ces·sant (ĭn sĕs'ənt) *adj.* Continuing without interruption; constant: *her incessant talk.* —**in·ces'sant·ly** *adv.*

in·com·pre·hen·si·ble (ĭn'kŏm prĭ hĕn'sə bəl) *or* (ĭn kŏm'-) *adj.* Incapable of being understood or comprehended. —**in'com·pre·hen'si·bil'i·ty** *n.* —**in'com·pre·hen'si·bly** *adv.*

in·cor·po·ra·tion (ĭn kôr'pə rā'shən) *n.* **1.** The forming of a legal corporation. **2.** A combining or blending into a unified whole; the process of uniting.

in·cor·ri·gi·ble (ĭn kôr′ĭ jə bəl) *or* (-kŏr′-) *adj.* Not capable of being corrected or reformed. —*n.* A person who cannot be reformed. —**in·cor′ri·gi·bil′i·ty** *n.* —**in·cor′ri·gi·bly** *adv.*

in·cred·u·lous (ĭn krĕj′ə ləs) *adj.* **1.** Disbelieving; skeptical. **2.** Expressive of disbelief or astonishment. —**in′cre·du′li·ty** (ĭn′krĭ dōo′lĭ-tē) *or* (-dyōo′-) *n.* —**in·cred′u·lous·ly** *adv.*

in·den·ta·tion (ĭn′dĕn tā′shən) *n.* **1.** A deep recess along an edge or boundary. **2.** A notch or jagged cut in an edge, often one of a row forming toothlike projections. **3.** The blank space between a margin and the beginning of an indented line.

in·dic·a·tive (ĭn dĭk′ə tĭv) *adj.* Serving to point out or indicate.

in·dis·cre·tion (ĭn′dĭ skrĕsh′ən) *n.* **1.** Lack of caution or good judgment in speech or behavior. **2.** An unwise or tactless remark.

in·dis·put·a·ble (ĭn′dĭ spyōo′tə bəl) *adj.* Not capable of being disputed; beyond doubt; undeniable. —**in′dis·put′a·bly** *adv.*

in·dom·i·ta·ble (ĭn dŏm′ĭ tə bəl) *adj.* Not capable of being overcome or subdued; unconquerable. —**in·dom′i·ta·bly** *adv.*

in·er·tia (ĭ nûr′shə) *n.* **1.** The tendency of a physical body to remain at rest if at rest or, if moving, to continue moving in a straight line unless a force is applied to it. **2.** Resistance to move, act, or change.

in·ev·i·ta·ble (ĭn ĕv′ĭ tə bəl) *adj.* Not capable of being avoided or prevented: *an inevitable outcome.* —**in·ev′i·ta·bly** *adv.*

in·fa·mous (ĭn′fə məs) *adj.* **1.** Having an exceedingly bad reputation; notorious. **2.** Deserving universal condemnation; outrageous: *infamous deeds.* —**in′fa·mous·ly** *adv.*

in·gen·ious (ĭn jēn′yəs) *adj.* **1.** Clever at devising things; creative. **2.** Showing originality and resourcefulness. —**in·gen′ious·ly** *adv.*

in·her·ent (ĭn hîr′ənt) *or* (-hĕr′-) *adj.* Existing as a basic quality or characteristic; intrinsic: *inherent laziness.* —**in·her′ent·ly** *adv.*

in·junc·tion (ĭn jŭngk′shən) *n.* **1.** An order or command. **2.** A court order prohibiting or requiring a specific course of action.

in·no·va·tion (ĭn′ə vā′shən) *n.* **1.** The act or process of beginning (something new). **2.** Something newly introduced; a change.

in·scru·ta·ble (ĭn skrōo′tə bəl) *adj.* Difficult or impossible to understand or fathom; mysterious; enigmatic. —**in·scru′ta·bil′i·ty, in·scru′ta·ble·ness** *n.* —**in·scru′ta·bly** *adv.*

in·sight (ĭn′sīt′) *n.* **1.** The capacity to perceive the true nature of something. **2.** A perception of the true nature of something: *He had a brilliant insight about the meaning of the movie.*

in·som·ni·a (ĭn sŏm′nē ə) *n.* The inability to sleep, especially when persistent.

in·sti·gate (ĭn′stĭ gāt′) *v.* **in·sti·gat·ed, in·sti·gat·ing. 1.** To stir up; foment. **2.** To urge on; provoke: *instigate a rebellion.* —**in′sti·ga′tion** *n.* —**in′sti·ga′tor** *n.*

in·stinc·tive·ly (ĭn stĭngk′tĭv lē) *adv.* **1.** In a way that is not learned. **2.** In a manner prompted by instinct or natural impulse.

in·te·ger (ĭn′tĭ jər) *n.* Any member of the set (. . . −2, −1, 0, +1, +2, . . .), including all of the positive whole numbers, all of the negative whole numbers, and zero.

in·teg·ri·ty (ĭn tĕg′rĭ tē) *n.* **1.** Strict personal honesty and independence: *a man of integrity.* **2.** Completeness; unity: *The movie was shown without interruptions in order to maintain its integrity.*

in·ter·mi·na·ble (ĭn tûr′mə nə bəl) *adj.* Having or seeming to have no end; endless: *a seemingly interminable ball game.* —**in·ter′mi·na·bly** *adv.*

in·tern (ĭn′tûrn′) *n.* A recent graduate of a medical school who is undergoing supervised practical training. —*v.* **1.** (ĭn′tûrn′). To train or serve as an intern. **2.** (ĭn tûrn′). To detain or confine, especially in wartime: *intern a ship.* —**in·tern′ment** *n.*

ă pat/ā pay/â care/ä father/ĕ pet/ē be/ĭ pit/ī pie/î fierce/ŏ pot/ō go/ô paw, for/oi oil/ōo book/ ōo boot/ou out/ŭ cut/û fur/*th* the/th thin/hw which/zh vision/ə ago, item, pencil, atom, circus

in·ter·sect·ing (ĭn′tər sĕk′tĭng) *adj.* Crossing: *intersecting roads north of town.*

in·tim·i·date (ĭn tĭm′ĭ dāt′) *v.* **in·tim·i·dat·ed, in·tim·i·dat·ing.** To frighten or inhibit by or as if by threats: *The advancing forces did not intimidate the Romans.* —**in·tim′i·da′tion** *n.*

in·tri·cate (ĭn′trĭ kĭt) *adj.* **1.** Having a complicated structure, pattern, etc.; complex. **2.** Hard to understand. —**in′tri·cate·ly** *adv.*

in·ven·to·ry (ĭn′vən tôr′ē) *or* (-tōr′ē) *n., pl.* **in·ven·to·ries. 1.** A detailed list, as of goods or possessions. **2.** The process of making such a survey or list. **3.** The supply of goods on hand; stock: *The store's inventory is getting low.* —*v.* **in·ven·to·ried, in·ven·to·ry·ing, in·ven·to·ries.** To make an inventory of.

in·ver·te·brate (ĭn vûr′tə brĭt) *or* (-brāt′) *n.* An animal having no backbone, as a worm, clam, jellyfish, starfish, insect, or lobster. —*adj.* Having no backbone: *invertebrate animals.*

i·rate (ī rāt′) *or* (ī′rāt′) *adj.* Angry; enraged.

i·ris (ī′rĭs) *n.* The color membrane of the eye, located between the cornea and lens, that regulates the size of the pupil by expanding and contracting.

i·ro·ny (ī′rə nē) *n., pl.* **i·ro·nies. 1.** A wry, mocking way of using words or expressions so that they suggest the opposite of what they literally mean. **2.** A situation, outcome, or event that is opposite from or contrary to what might have been expected.

is·let (ī′lĭt) *n.* A very small island.

i·so·tope (ī′sə tōp′) *n.* Any of a set of atoms, or of a set of types of atoms, that contain in their nuclei the same number of protons but different numbers of neutrons.

i·tin·er·ant (ī tĭn′ər ənt) *or* (ī tĭn′-) *adj.* Traveling from place to place: *itinerant workers.* —*n.* A person who so travels.

jaun·diced (jôn′dĭst) *or* (jän′-) *adj.* **1.** Affected with jaundice. **2.** Showing or feeling jealousy, envy, etc.; prejudiced.

jaun·ty (jôn′tē) *or* (jän′-) *adj.* **jaun·ti·er, jaun·ti·est. 1.** Having a carefree, self-confident air. **2.** Stylish or smart in appearance: *A jaunty green hat completed his stylish outfit.* —**jaun′ti·ly** *adv.*

jave·lin (jăv′lĭn) *or* (jăv′ə lĭn) *n.* A light spear that is thrown for distance in an athletic contest.

jem·my (jĕm′ē) *n.* British form of the word **jimmy.**

jerk·y (jûr′kē) *n.* Meat, such as beef, that has been cut into strips and dried in the sun or cured with smoke.

jim·my (jĭm′ē) *n., pl.* **jim·mies.** A short crowbar with curved ends, often used by burglars to force open windows and doors. —*v.* **jim·mied, jim·my·ing, jim·mies.** To force open with a jimmy: *jimmy a door.*

Joshua tree. A large treelike plant of desert regions of the southwestern United States, having clusters of stiff, pointed leaves at the ends of its branches.

ju·bi·lant (jōō′bə lənt) *adj.* Full of joy; rejoicing: *a jubilant crowd.* —**ju′bi·lant·ly** *adv.*

ju·ni·per (jōō′nə pər) *n.* An evergreen tree or shrub related to the pines, having small scalelike or prickly leaves and bluish, aromatic berries.

ju·ve·nile (jōō′və nəl) *or* (-nīl′) *adj.* **1.** Young; immature; childish. **2.** Of or for young people. —*n.* **1.** A young person or animal. **2.** An actor who plays the roles of children. **3.** A book for children.

ka·lei·do·scope (kə līʹdə skōp′) *n.* **1.** A tube-shaped toy in which bits of loose, colored glass contained at one end reflect light into changing patterns visible from a hole at the other end. **2.** A constantly changing variety.

keen (kēn) *n.* A crying or wailing in sorrow for the dead. —*v.* To wail, as if in sorrow.

kelp (kĕlp) *n.* Any of several brown, often very large seaweeds.

kiln (kĭl) *or* (kĭln) *n.* Any of a variety of ovens used for hardening, burning, or drying things such as grain or lumber, especially a high-temperature oven used for firing pottery, porcelain, brick, etc.

kin·ka·jou (kĭng′kə jōō′) *n.* A tropical American mammal which lives in trees and has brownish fur and a long tail.

knoll (nōl) *n.* A small, rounded hill; a hillock.

ko·peck (kō′pĕk′) *n.* A coin of small value.

lam·i·nate (lăm′ə nāt′) *v.* **lam·i·nat·ed, lam·i·nat·ing. 1.** To beat or press into a thin plate or sheet. **2.** To split into thin layers. **3.** To make by joining several layers: *laminate plywood.*

lance (lăns) *or* (läns) *n.* **1.** A weapon, such as one used by knights or warriors on horseback, consisting of a long shaft and a sharp metal head. **2.** An implement resembling such a weapon, as a surgeon's lancet or a spear used by whalers.

lap·is laz·u·li (lăp′ĭs lăz′yōō lē) *or* (-lăzh′ōō-) *n.* An opaque, deep-blue mineral that is used as a gemstone.

lar·ce·ny (lär′sə nē) *n., pl.* **lar·ce·nies.** The crime of stealing; theft.

lark (lärk) *n.* A merry adventure, prank, or romp. —*v.* To engage in fun or merry pranks; frolic; romp.

la·ser (lā′zər) *n.* Any of a number of devices that use the radiating properties of systems of atoms or molecules to generate light that is of a single, precise wavelength, with all of the waves polarized, exactly aligned, and matching each other in their phases.

lat·i·tude (lăt′ĭ tōōd′) *or* (-tyōōd′) *n.* **1.** Distance north or south of the equator measured as the angle between the radius from the center of the earth to a point on its surface and the radius that intersects the equator and the meridian on which the point lies, usually expressed in degrees. **2.** Freedom from limitations or restrictions.

lay·man (lā′mən) *n., pl.* **-men** (-mən). **1.** A person who does not have the specialized knowledge or training of a member of a profession or highly skilled occupation. **2.** A person who is not a member of the religious clergy.

ledg·er (lĕj′ər) *n.* An account book in which sums of money received and paid out by a business are recorded.

le·thal (lē′thəl) *adj.* Causing or capable of causing death: *a lethal dose of a drug; a lethal weapon.* —**le′thal·ly** *adv.*

li·an·a (lē ăn′ə) *or* (-ä′nə) *n.* A high-climbing tropical vine with woody stems.

li·do (lē′dō) *n.* A fashionable resort.

loam (lōm) *n.* A soil that contains mainly sand, clay, silt, and decayed plant matter.

loin (loin) *n.* **1.** Often **loins.** The part of the sides and back of the body between the ribs and hipbones. **2. loins.** The region of the thighs and groin.

loss leader. A product offered by a retail store at cost or less to attract customers.

low·er·ing (lou′ər ĭng) *adj.* Dark or threatening, as the sky or weather.

lu·nar (lōō′nər) *adj.* Of, caused by, or affecting the moon: *a lunar orbit.*

mael·strom (māl′strəm) *n.* **1.** A large and violent whirlpool. **2.** A situation that resembles such a whirlpool in violence, turbulence, etc.: *caught in the maelstrom of war.*

mag·ni·tude (măg′nĭ tōōd′) *or* (-tyōōd′) *n.* Greatness, as of position, size, influence, etc.: *the magnitude of his achievements.*

main (mān) *adj.* Most important; major; principal. —*n.* A large pipe, duct, conduit, or conductor that is used to carry water, oil, gas, or electricity.

ma·jor·do·mo (mā′jər dō′mō) *n., pl.* **ma·jor·do·mos.** A head steward or butler, as one in the household of a great nobleman.

ma·lar·i·a (mə lâr′ē ə) *n.* A severe infectious disease whose symptoms are typically cycles of chills, fever, and sweating. It is caused by

---

ă pat/ā pay/â care/ä father/ĕ pet/ē be/ĭ pit/ī pie/î fierce/ŏ pot/ō go/ô paw, for/oi oil/ōō book/ ōō boot/ou out/ŭ cut/û fur/*th* the/th thin/hw which/zh vision/ə ago, item, pencil, atom, circus protozoan parasites that attack red blood cells and that are transmitted by the bite of a female mosquito. —**ma·lar′i·al** *adj.*

mal·func·tion (măl fŭngk′shən) *v.* **1.** To fail to operate. **2.** To function in an abnormal or improper way; perform imperfectly. —*n.* The process of malfunctioning or an example of malfunctioning.

mam·mal (măm′əl) *n.* Any of a group of animals that have hair or fur on their bodies and, in the females, special glands that produce milk for feeding their young. —**mam·ma′li·an** (mə mā′lē ən) *or* (-māl′yən) *adj.*

man·date (măn′dāt′) *n.* An authoritative command or instruction.

man·do·lin (măn′dl ĭn′) *or* (măn′dl ĭn′) *n.* A musical instrument having a pear-shaped body and a neck that has frets over which four pairs of strings are stretched.

mar·shal (mär′shəl) *v.* **mar·shaled** *or* **mar·shalled, mar·shal·ing** *or* **mar·shal·ling. 1.** To place in methodical order; organize: *The research team marshaled facts for the great debate.* **2.** To enlist and organize for a specified purpose.

mass (măs) *n.* **1.** A unified body of matter with no specific shape: *a mass of clay.* **2.** Any large amount or number that is not specified. **3.** The physical bulk of a solid body: *The huge mass of the central towers slowly appeared on the horizon.* **4.** A measure of the amount of matter contained in a physical body, equivalent to the quotient of a force acting on the body divided by the acceleration that the body undergoes as a result of that force.

mas·sif (mă sēf′) *n.* A large mountain mass or compact group of connected mountains forming an independent portion of a range.

mat·tock (măt′ək) *n.* A gardening tool with the blade set at right angles to the handle, used for cutting roots or breaking up soil.

me·an·der (mē ăn′dər) *v.* **1.** To follow a winding and turning course: *The river meanders through the town.* **2.** To wander aimlessly and idly. —**me·an′der·ing** *adj.*

me·di·e·val (mē′dē ē′vəl) *or* (měd′ē-) *or* (mĭd′ē-) *or* (mĭ dē′vəl) *adj.* Of or characteristic of the period in European history from the fall of the Roman Empire (about A.D. 500) to the rise of the Renaissance (about 1400).

men·ac·ing·ly (měn′ə sĭng lē) *adv.* **1.** In a threatening way. **2.** Dangerously.

Mer·cu·ry (mûr′kyə rē). The Roman god who served as messenger to the other gods and presided over the realms of commerce, travel, and thievery.

mesh (měsh) *n.* **1. a.** Any of the open spaces in a net, or sieve, or a wire screen. **b.** The size of these open spaces: *a fishnet of medium mesh.* **2.** Often **meshes.** The cords, threads, or wires forming a net or network. **3.** A knit or woven fabric with many small open spaces in it.

Mes·si·ah (mə sī′ə) *n.* **1.** The expected deliverer and king of the Jews, foretold by the prophets of the Old Testament. **2.** Christ, regarded by Christians as the fulfillment of this prophecy. **3. messiah.** Any person who is regarded as a savior or liberator of a people.

me·te·or·i·tic (mē′tē ə rĭt′ĭk) *adj.* Of or like the stony or metallic material of a meteoroid that survives passage through the atmosphere and reaches the earth's surface.

me·te·or·ol·o·gist (mē′tē ə rŏl′ə jĭst) *n.* Any person who specializes in the scientific study of the atmosphere and its effects, especially those effects that influence weather and weather conditions.

me·ter (mē′tər) *n.* The basic unit of length in the metric system, equal to 39.37 inches.

me·tic·u·lous·ly (mə tĭk′yə ləs lē) *adv.* In a very careful, precise way: *She meticulously recorded all her expenses.*

me·trop·o·lis (mə trŏp′ə lĭs) *n., pl.* **me·trop·o·lis·es. 1.** A large, busy city. **2.** The largest or most important city of a country, state, or region: *The town of Bend ranks as the metropolis of central Oregon.*

mi·cro·film (mī′krə fĭlm′) *n.* **1.** A film on which written or printed material can be photographed in greatly reduced size. **2.** A reproduction made on microfilm —*v.* To reproduce on microfilm.

mi·cro·or·gan·ism (mī′krō ôr′gə nĭz′əm) *n.* An organism, such as a bacterium or protozoan, so small that it can be seen only with the aid of a microscope.

mil·len·ni·um (mĭ lĕn′ē əm) *n., pl.* **mil·len·ni·ums** or **mil·len·ni·a** (mĭ lĕn′ē ə). **1.** A span of one thousand years. **2.** A thousand-year reign of Christ on earth, expected by the early Christians. **3.** Any hoped-for epoch of prosperity and peace. —**mil·len′ni·al** *adj.*

mil·li·ner (mĭl′ə nər) *n.* A person who makes, trims, designs, or sells women's hats.

mil·li·ner·y (mĭl′ə nĕr′ē) *n.* **1.** Women's hats, including trimmings for hats. **2.** The business of making, designing, or selling women's hats.

mill·race (mĭl′rās′) *n.* The fast-moving stream of water that drives a mill wheel.

mi·nute (mī nōōt′) *or* (-nyōōt′) *or* (mĭ-) *adj.* **1.** Exceptionally small; tiny. **2.** Marked by close examination or careful study of small details: *a minute inspection of bacteria.* —**mi·nute′ly** *adv.* —**mi·nute′ness** *n.*

Mon·gol (mŏng′gəl) *or* (-gōl′) *or* (mŏn′-) *n.* **1.** A native of Mongolia. **2.** A member of one of the nomadic tribes of Mongolia. **3.** The language of these people; Mongolian. —**Mon′gol** *adj.*

mo·not·o·nous (mə nŏt′n əs) *adj.* **1.** Uttered or sounded in one repeated tone; unvarying in pitch: *a monotonous drone that tires the listener and causes his attention to wander.* **2.** Never varied or enlivened; repetitiously dull: *a particularly strict and monotonous diet.* —**mo·not′o·nous·ly** *adv.*

mon·soon (mŏn sōōn′) *n.* A system of winds that influences the climate of a large area and that changes direction with the seasons, especially the wind system that produces the wet and dry seasons in southern Asia.

mon·u·men·tal (mŏn′yə mĕn′tl) *adj.* **1.** Of, like, or serving as a monument: *a monumental arch.* **2.** Impressively large and sturdy: *monumental dams, tunnels, and viaducts.* **3.** Of enduring importance; outstanding. **4.** Astounding; outrageous: *Suddenly he came to see his whole life as a monumental fraud.* —**mon′u·men′tal·ly** *adv.*

mope (mōp) *v.* **moped, mop·ing. 1.** To be gloomy or quietly resentful; sulk. **2.** To move or pass time aimlessly; dawdle. —*n.* **1.** A person who often has gloomy moods. **2. mopes.** Low spirits.

moray eel. Any of several tropical ocean eels that have sharp teeth and can be dangerous to swimmers.

mor·bid (môr′bĭd) *adj.* **1.** Of, caused by, or having to do with disease: *morbid changes in body tissues.* **2.** Abnormally intense or acute: *morbid curiosity.* **3.** Preoccupied with death, decay, or other unwholesome matters; gruesome: *a morbid chamber of horrors.* —**mor′bid·ly** *adv.* —**mor′bid·ness** *n.*

morgue (môrg) *n.* **1.** A place where the bodies of persons found dead are kept until identified or claimed. **2.** A file at a newspaper or magazine office for storing old issues and reference material.

mo·rose·ness (mə rōs′nĭs) *n.* The quality or state of being ill-humored, sullen, or gloomy: *His moroseness was depressing for those who worked with him.*

mor·ti·fied (môr′tə fīd′) *adj.* **1.** Restrained; disciplined. **2.** Ashamed or embarrassed; humiliated. **3.** Annoyed; frustrated.

mo·tor (mō′tər) *adj.* **1.** Propelled by an engine or motor: *a motor ski tow.* **2.** Of or involving vehicles propelled by engines: *motor accidents; a motor race.* **3.** Of, involving, or controlling muscle movements.

mu·nic·i·pal (myōō nĭs′ə pəl) *adj.* Of or relating to a city or its government: *municipal politics; the municipal airport.*

ă pat/ā pay/â care/ä father/ĕ pet/ē be/ĭ pit/ī pie/î fierce/ŏ pot/ō go/ô paw, for/oi oil/ŏŏ book/
ōō boot/ou out/ŭ cut/û fur/*th* **the**/th thin/hw **which**/zh vision/ə ago, item, pencil, atom, circus

mut·ton (mŭt′n) *n.* The meat of a full-grown sheep.

myr·i·ad (mîr′ē əd) *adj.* Amounting to a very large, indefinite number: *the moon, sun, planets, and myriad stars.* —*n.* A vast number.

na·ive *or* **na·ïve** (nä ēv′) *adj.* **1.** Simple and unaffected, as a child; artless: *a naive girl.* **2.** Showing a lack of experience, judgment, etc.; unsophisticated: *She frequently made naive remarks.* —**na·ive′ly** *adv.*

niche (nĭch) *n.* **1.** A recess or alcove in a wall, as for holding a statue. **2.** A cranny, hollow, or crevice, as in rock.

nit (nĭt) *n.* The egg or young of a louse, especially of the kind that infests human hair.

noc·tur·nal (nŏk tûr′nəl) *adj.* **1.** Of the night or occurring at night: *nocturnal stillness; a nocturnal breeze.* **2.** Active at night rather than by day: *Owls and bats are nocturnal creatures.* —**noc·tur′nal·ly** *adv.*

non·cha·lant·ly (nŏn′shə länt′lē) *adv.* In a way that is, or seems to be, cool, carefree, and casually unconcerned.

notch (nŏch) *n.* **1.** A V-shaped cut. **2.** A steep-sided gap in a ridge or mountain chain. **3.** *Informal.* A level; degree: *The defeat took him down a notch.* —*v.* **1.** To cut a notch in. **2.** To record by making notches: *notched the days and weeks on a pole outside his hut.*

no·to·ri·ous (nō tôr′ē əs) *or* (-tōr′-) *adj.* **1.** Known widely and regarded unfavorably; infamous: *a notorious swindler.* **2.** Well-known or famous for something, as a trait, a negative quality, etc.: *He was not notorious for his consistency.* —**no·to′ri·ous·ly** *adv.* —**no·to′ri·ous·ness** *n.*

no·va (nō′və) *n., pl.* **no·vae** (nō′vē) *or* **no·vas.** A star that suddenly becomes brighter than normal, returning to its original brightness after a period of time.

nu·ance (nōō′äns′) *or* (nyōō′-) *or* (nōō äns′) *or* (nyōō-) *n.* A subtle variation, as in meaning, color, or tone; a delicate shading.

nu·cle·us (nōō′klē əs) *or* (nyōō′-) *n., pl.* **nu·cle·i** (nōō′klē ī′) *or* (nyōō′-). **1.** A central or essential part around which other parts are grouped; a core: *the nucleus of a city; the hitters who formed the nucleus of the team.* **2.** A basis for future growth; a starting point: *a small colony designed to be the nucleus for a future empire.*

nymph (nĭmf) *n.* In Greek and Roman mythology, one of the female spirits dwelling in woodlands and waters.

ob·nox·ious (əb nŏk′shəs) *adj.* Extremely unpleasant or offensive. —**ob·nox′ious·ly** *adv.*

ob·so·lete (ŏb′sə lēt′) *or* (ŏb′sə lēt′) *adj.* No longer useful, in use, or in fashion: *an obsolete word; discarded their obsolete weapons.* —**ob′so·lete′ness** *n.*

Oc·ci·den·tal (ŏk′sĭ děn′tl) *adj.* **1.** occidental. Western, as distinguished from eastern, or Oriental. **2.** Of the Occident, the countries of Europe and the Western Hemisphere, or any of the peoples of the Occident.

o·dor·if·er·ous (ō′də rĭf′ər əs) *adj.* Having or giving off an odor, especially a pleasant one.

o·pi·um (ō′pē əm) *n.* A bitter yellowish-brown drug prepared from the pods of a certain variety of poppy, and from which codeine, morphine, heroin, and other alkaloid drugs are derived.

or·gan·dy, also **or·gan·die** (ôr′gən dē) *n., pl.* **or·gan·dies.** A light, sheer, crisp cotton cloth used for dresses, curtains, trimmings, etc.

o·ver·whelm·ing (ō′vər hwĕlm′ĭng) *or* (-wĕlm′-) *adj.* **1.** Engulfing. **2.** Completely overpowering: *an overwhelming desire to fall asleep.*

pag·eant (păj′ənt) *n.* **1.** A play or dramatic spectacle usually based on an event in history. **2.** A procession or celebration.

paint (pānt) *n.* **1.** A liquid mixture, usually of a finely ground solid pigment and a liquid, applied to surfaces as a protective or decorative coating. **2.** A cosmetic, such as rouge, that colors. **3.** A spotted horse or calf; a pinto.

pa·lav·er (pə lăv′ər) *or* (-lä′vər) *n.* Idle chatter, especially that meant to flatter or deceive. —*v.* To chatter idly.

pal·pi·ta·tion (păl′pĭ tā′shən) *n.* **1.** A shaking or quivering, as of a muscle. **2.** Rapid throbbing.

pa·py·rus (pə pī′rəs) *n.* **1.** A tall, reedlike water plant of northern Africa and nearby regions. **2.** A kind of paper made from the stems and pith of this plant by the ancient Egyptians. **3.** *pl.* **pa·py·ri** (pə pī′rī′). A document written on this material.

par·a·psy·chol·o·gy (păr′ə sī kŏl′ə jē) *n.* The study of things (such as telepathy or clairvoyance) that are not explainable by known natural laws.

parch·ment (pärch′mənt) *n.* **1.** The skin of a sheep or goat, prepared as a material to write on. **2.** A piece of writing on a sheet or roll of parchment. **3.** A diploma. **4.** Heavy paper that looks like parchment.

par·lia·men·ta·ry (pär′lə mĕn′tə rē) *or* (-trē) *adj.* **1.** Of or like an assembly of persons that makes the laws for a nation. **2.** Observing, following, or directing the rules of procedure of a parliament or similar body: *parliamentary debate.* **3.** Having a parliament: *parliamentary government.*

par·ry (păr′ē) *v.* **par·ried, par·ry·ing, par·ries. 1.** To turn aside; deflect: *parry a thrust in fencing.* **2.** To avoid skillfully; evade: *parried questions of the reporters.* —*n., pl.* **par·ries. 1.** The act or maneuver of deflecting a blow, especially in fencing. **2.** An evasive action or answer: *met the accusation with a deft parry.*

ped·i·gree (pĕd′ĭ grē′) *n.* **1.** A line of ancestors; ancestry. **2.** A list of ancestors. **3.** A list or record of the ancestors of a purebred animal.

pel·let (pĕl′ĭt) *n.* **1.** A small, densely packed ball, as of bread, wax, medicine, etc. **2.** A small bullet or shot.

pelt¹ (pĕlt) *n.* An animal skin, especially with the hair or fur still on it.

pelt² (pĕlt) *v.* To strike repeatedly with or as if with blows or missiles; bombard: *schoolboys pelting their friends with snowballs.*

pem·mi·can (pĕm′ĭ kən) *n.* A food made by North American Indians from a paste of lean meat mixed with fat and berries.

pen·ance (pĕn′əns) *n.* **1.** An act of devotion or self-mortification performed voluntarily to show sorrow for a sin or other wrongdoing. **2.** In some Christian churches, a sacrament that includes contrition, confession to a priest, acceptance of punishment, and absolution.

per·fo·ra·tion (pûr′fə rā′shən) *n.* **1.** The act of punching or boring a hole. **2.** A hole or series of holes, as those between postage stamps.

pe·rim·e·ter (pə rĭm′ĭ tər) *n.* **1. a.** The sum of the lengths of the segments that form the sides of a polygon. **b.** The total length of any closed curve, such as a circle or ellipse. **2.** A fortified strip or boundary protecting a military position.

per·i·scope (pĕr′ĭ skōp′) *n.* Any of several instruments in which mirrors or prisms allow observation of objects that are not in a direct line of sight.

per·pet·u·al (pər pĕch′oo əl) *adj.* **1.** Lasting forever or for an indefinitely long time: *the perpetual ice and snow of the polar regions.* **2.** Ceaselessly repeated or continuing without interruption: *perpetual nagging.* —**per·pet′u·al·ly** *adv.* —**per·pet′u·al·ness** *n.*

per·plex·i·ty (pər plĕk′sĭ tē) *n., pl.* **per·plex·i·ties. 1.** The condition of being confused or puzzled; bewilderment. **2.** Something that confuses or puzzles.

per·sim·mon (pər sĭm′ən) *n.* **1.** An orange-red fruit with pulp that is sweet and edible only when fully ripe. **2.** A tree that bears such fruit.

ă pat/ā pay/â care/ä father/ĕ pet/ē be/ĭ pit/ī pie/î fierce/ŏ pot/ō go/ô paw, for/oi oil/oo book/ oo boot/ou out/ŭ cut/û fur/*th* the/th thin/hw which/zh vision/ə ago, item, pencil, atom, circus

pes·ti·lence (pĕs′tə ləns) *n.* **1.** A deadly epidemic disease, especially bubonic plague. **2.** An epidemic of such a disease.

pet·rol (pĕt′rəl) *n. British.* Gasoline.

phan·tom (făn′təm) *n.* **1.** A ghost; apparition. **2.** An unreal mental image.

phos·pho·res·cent (fŏs′fə rĕs′ənt) *adj.* **1.** Emitting light as a result of and for some time after being exposed to radiation. **2.** Generating light.

pho·to·gen·ic (fō′tə jĕn′ĭk) *adj.* Attractive as a subject for photography: *She has a very photogenic smile.* —**pho′to·gen′i·cal·ly** *adv.*

phra·se·ol·o·gy (frā′zē ŏl′ə jē) *n., pl.* **phra·se·ol·o·gies.** **1.** A manner or style of speaking or writing: *flowery phraseology.* **2.** A set of expressions used by a particular person or group: *nautical phraseology.*

pick·et (pĭk′ĭt) *n.* **1.** A pointed stake or spike, as one driven into the ground to support a fence, secure a tent, or tether an animal. **2.** A detachment of one or more soldiers placed in a position to give warning of enemy approach. **3.** Someone stationed outside a building to express grievance or protest, as during a strike. **4.** A vehicle used for patrol or rescue operations. —*v.* **1.** To enclose, secure, tether, etc., with a picket. **2.** To demonstrate against, as during a strike.

pil·fer (pĭl′fər) *v.* To steal (small sums of money or things of little value): *He pilfered from his aunt's pantry.* —**pil′fer·er** *n.*

pin·na·cle (pĭn′ə kəl) *n.* **1.** A tall, pointed formation, as a mountain peak. **2.** The peak or summit of anything: *at the pinnacle of his fame.* **3.** A small turret or spire on a roof.

plague (plāg) *n.* **1.** A calamity or affliction, especially when regarded as a punishment from God. **2.** A very contagious, usually fatal, epidemic disease, especially bubonic plague or a closely related disease. **3.** A sudden influx or increase, as of anything evil. —*v.* **plagued, pla·guing.** To cause misery or trouble in or for: *Sleeping sickness has plagued Africa for many centuries.*

plain·tive·ly (plān′tĭv lē) *adv.* Sadly; mournfully: *The child cried plaintively.*

pla·teau (plă tō′) *n.* **1.** A relatively level area that is at a higher elevation than the land around it. **2.** A level or stage of growth or development: *The Japanese economy has reached a new plateau.*

plew (plōō) *n.* A beaver skin.

Plex·i·glas (plĕk′sĭ glăs′) *or* (-glăs′) *n.* A trademark for a light, strong, transparent plastic.

plum·age (plōō′mĭj) *n.* The feathers of a bird.

pomp (pŏmp) *n.* Showy or stately display: *The king was crowned with great pomp.*

pooh·bah (pōō′bä′) *n.* A pompous official, especially one who, holding many offices, fulfills none of them.

por·ce·lain (pôr′sə lĭn) *or* (pōr′-) *n.* **1.** A hard, white, translucent material made by baking a fine clay at a high temperature and glazing it with one of several variously colored materials. **2.** An object or objects made of this material.

pore (pôr) *or* (pōr) *n.* A tiny opening, as one of those in an animal's skin, through which perspiration passes or, on the surface of a leaf, through which water vapor, carbon dioxide, and oxygen pass.

po·rous (pôr′əs) *or* (pōr′-) *adj.* **1.** Full of or having pores. **2.** Full of small openings into or through which a liquid or gas can pass.

pos·ter·i·ty (pŏ stĕr′ĭ tē) *n.* **1.** Future generations: *He left a rich body of literature to posterity.* **2.** A person's descendants.

po·ten·tial (pə tĕn′shəl) *adj.* **1.** Possible or future, though not yet actual, definite, or real: *potential problems.* **2.** Capable of being developed, realized, or used: *the sea as a potential source of minerals.* —*n.* Capacity for further growth, development, or progress; promise: *a program to encourage students high in potential but low in hope.* —**po·ten′tial·ly** *adv.*

praying mantis. A large, grasshopperlike insect that preys on other insects and that holds its front legs folded up as if praying.

pre·car·i·ous (prĭ kâr′ē əs) *adj.* Dangerously insecure, unsafe, or uncertain: *dangling in a precarious position.* —**pre·car′i·ous·ly** *adv.*

pre·cept (prē′sĕpt′) *n.* A rule of conduct or procedure.

pre·cip·i·tous (prĭ sĭp′ə təs) *adj.* Like a very steep or overhanging mass of rock, such as the face of a cliff; sloping sharply.

pre·con·ceived (prē′kən sēvd′) *adj.* Formed (as an opinion or idea) before full or adequate knowledge is available; prejudiced.

pred·a·tor (prĕd′ə tər) *or* (-tôr′) *n.* **1.** An animal that lives by capturing and feeding on other animals; a preying animal. **2.** Someone who plunders or abuses other people for his own profit.

pred·e·ces·sor (prĕd′ĭ sĕs′ər) *or* (prē′dĭ-) *n.* **1.** Someone or something that comes before another in time, especially in an office or function: *The catapult was the predecessor of the present-day rocket launcher.* **2.** An ancestor.

pre·em·i·nent or **pre·em·i·nent** (prē ĕm′ə-nənt) *adj.* Superior to all others in importance, excellence, etc.; outstanding: *the pre-eminent artist of the movement.* —**pre-em′i·nence** *n.* —**pre-em′i·nent·ly** *adv.*

preen (prēn) *v.* **1.** To smooth or clean (the feathers) with the beak: *The parrot preened its feathers.* **2.** To dress or groom (oneself) with elaborate care; primp. **3.** To take self-satisfied pride in (oneself): *Mr. Holmes preened himself on his success as a writer.*

pre·hen·sile (prĭ hĕn′sĭl) *or* (-sīl′) *adj.* Used or suited for grasping or holding, especially by wrapping around something: *a monkey's prehensile tail.*

prem·ise (prĕm′ĭs) *n.* **1.** An idea or theory that forms a basis for action; a working assumption: *He started his business on the premise that people wanted durable, well-made clothes.* **2. premises.** Property under a single ownership; someone's land or building: *This is part of the school premises.* —*v.* **prem·ised, prem·is·ing.** To state in advance as a proposition or assumption.

pre·mo·ni·tion (prē′mə nĭsh′ən) *or* (prĕm′ə-) *n.* **1.** An advance warning: *gave no premonition of her plans.* **2.** A feeling that something is going to happen; a presentiment: *felt a sudden premonition of disaster.*

pre·pos·ter·ous (prĭ pŏs′tər əs) *adj.* **1.** Completely unreasonable or incredible; nonsensical; absurd. **2.** Ridiculous in appearance; grotesque: *a preposterous hat.* —**pre·pos′ter·ous·ly** *adv.*

pres·tige (prĕ stēzh′) *or* (-stēj′) *n.* Prominence or status in the eyes of others, achieved through success, fame, or wealth.

pre·sum·a·bly (prĭ zōō′mə blē) *adv.* Supposedly; probably.

prev·a·lent (prĕv′ə lənt) *adj.* Widely existing or commonly occurring: *Sickness is not as prevalent in the dry and cool areas as it is in the hot and humid areas.* —**prev′a·lence** *n.* —**prev′a·lent·ly** *adv.*

pri·ma don·na (prē′mə dŏn′ə) *or* (prĭm′ə) *n.* **1.** The principal female soloist of an opera company. **2.** A self-centered, temperamental person.

prime (prīm) *adj.* First in importance, degree, value, significance, etc.: *his prime concern; her prime accomplishments.* —*n.* The stage of ideal physical perfection or intellectual vigor in a person's life. —*v.* **primed, prim·ing.** **1.** To prepare a pump or similar device for operation by or as if by filling it with liquid. **2.** To prepare a surface for painting or finishing by covering with size, primer, or an undercoat. **3.** To make ready; prepare, as with information: *primed him for the contest.*

pri·me·val (prĭ mē′vəl) *adj.* Of the first or earliest age or ages of the world; primitive. —**pri·me′val·ly** *adv.*

pri·or·i·ty (prĭ ôr′ĭ tē) *or* (-ŏr′-) *n., pl.* **pri·or·i·ties. 1.** Precedence in importance or urgency: *Safety is given high priority in factories.* **2.** Something more important than

---

ă pat/ā pay/â care/ä father/ĕ pet/ē be/ĭ pit/ī pie/î fîerce/ŏ pot/ō go/ô paw, for/oi oil/ŏŏ book/
ōō boot/ou out/ŭ cut/û fur/*th* the/th thin/hw which/zh vision/ə ago, item, pencil, atom, circus

other considerations: *Her major priority is getting out of debt.*

pro·di·gious·ly (prə **dĭj′**əs lē) *adv.* In an impressive or extraordinary way.

prod·i·gy (**prŏd′**ə jē) *n., pl.* **prod·i·gies. 1.** A person with exceptional talents or powers: *a child prodigy.* **2.** Something extraordinary or rare; a marvel: *geysers and rock formations that are prodigies of nature.*

pro·fi·cient (prə **fĭsh′**ənt) *adj.* Performing correctly and skillfully; competent through training or practice; adept: *surprisingly proficient at playing the harmonica.* —**pro·fi′cien·cy** *n.* —**pro·fi′cient·ly** *adv.*

prof·i·teer (prŏf′ĭ **tîr′**) *n.* A person who makes excessive profits on the goods he sells, especially in a time of short supply. —*v.* To act as a profiteer.

pro·fu·sion (prə **fyōō′**zhən) *n.* Great quantity or amount: *A profusion of old chairs, books, crates, and picture frames filled the attic.*

pro·lif·er·ate (prə **lĭf′**ə rāt′) *v.* **pro·lif·er·at·ed, pro·lif·er·at·ing. 1.** To produce new growth or offspring rapidly and repeatedly; multiply at a fast rate: *Viruses proliferate in living tissue.* **2.** To increase or spread very rapidly. —**pro·lif′er·a′tion** *n.*

pro·lif·ic (prə **lĭf′**ĭk) *adj.* **1.** Producing offspring or fruit in great numbers: *prolific animals.* **2.** Causing or sustaining abundant growth: *the prolific tropical sun.* **3.** Producing numerous works: *an unusually prolific author.* —**pro·lif′i·cal·ly** *adv.*

prom·ul·gate (**prŏm′**əl gāt′) *or* (prō **mŭl′**-) *v.* **prom·ul·gat·ed, prom·ul·gat·ing.** To announce publicly and officially; proclaim: *joined in promulgating a new constitution.* —**prom′ul·ga′tion** *n.*

prone (prōn) *adj.* **1.** Lying with the front or face downward. **2.** Tending; inclined: *prone to make hasty judgments.* —**prone′ly** *adv.* —**prone′ness** *n.*

prop·a·gan·da (prŏp′ə **găn′**də) *n.* **1.** The communication of a given doctrine to large numbers of people, especially by constantly repeating the doctrine and by only giving information that supports it: *Government-*controlled radio can be an instrument of propaganda. **2.** Ideas, information, or other material distributed for the purpose of winning people over to a given doctrine, often without regard to truth or fairness.

prop·a·ga·tion (prŏp′ə **gā′**shən) *n.* **1.** The production of offspring or new individuals. **2.** The spreading about of information.

pro·té·gé (**prō′**tə zhā′) *n.* A person guided in his career by another, more influential or experienced person.

prov·o·ca·tion (prŏv′ə **kā′**shən) *n.* **1.** The act of provoking; incitement. **2.** An action that provokes anger or aggression: *Sharks will sometimes attack men without provocation.*

prox·im·i·ty (prŏk **sĭm′**ĭ tē) *n.* The quality or fact of being near; closeness: *the geographic proximity of Alaska and Siberia.*

pseu·do·nym (**sōōd′**n ĭm) *n.* A fictitious name, especially one assumed by an author.

psy·chi·cal (**sī′**kĭ kəl) *adj.* **1.** Of the human mind or psyche. **2. a.** Of extraordinary or apparently supernatural processes, such as extrasensory perception or mental telepathy. **b.** Of, produced by, or affected by such processes. —*n.* A person who is apparently responsive to supernatural phenomena; a psychic. —**psy′chi·cal·ly** *adv.*

psy·chol·o·gy (sī **kŏl′**ə jē) *n., pl.* **psy·chol·o·gies. 1.** The scientific study of mental processes and behavior. **2.** The emotional characteristics and behavior associated with an individual, group, or activity: *the psychology of war.* **3.** Action or behavior, often subtle, intended to persuade or manipulate: *He used poor psychology in showing his anger.*

pub (pŭb) *n.* A tavern; an inn.

pul·let (**pōōl′**ĭt) *n.* A young hen, especially one less than a year old.

pu·pil (**pyōō′**pəl) *n.* The opening in the center of the iris by which light enters the eye.

pur·chase (**pûr′**chĭs) *v.* **pur·chased, pur·chas·ing.** To obtain (something) by paying money or its equivalent; buy. —*n.* **1.** Something that is bought: *The car was a wise purchase.* **2.** The act of buying: *the purchase of land.* **3.** A secure position, grasp, or hold: *Using* *the ledge for a purchase, he paused in the climb.* —**pur′chas·a·ble** *adj.* —**pur′chas·er** *n.*

purge (pûrj) *v.* **purged, purg·ing. 1.** To rid of what is considered undesirable or harmful: *purge society of every possible evil.* **2.** To rid (a nation, political party, etc.) of persons considered undesirable, especially by harsh methods. —*n.* The act or process of purging.

purl (pûrl) *v. Dialect.* In surfing, to allow the nose of a surfboard to dip so deep that the board is greatly slowed down or actually submerged.

quail¹ (kwāl) *n., pl.* **quail** or **quails.** Any of several rather small, plump, short-tailed birds with brownish feathers.

quail² (kwāl) *v.* To lose courage; cower: *Harvey's dog looks ferocious, but he quails at the sight of a stranger.*

quar·ry¹ (kwôr′ē) or (kwŏr′ē) *n., pl.* **quar·ries.** An open excavation from which stone is obtained by digging, cutting, or blasting. —*v.* **quar·ried, quar·ry·ing, quar·ries. 1.** To obtain from a quarry. **2.** To make a quarry in: *quarry a mountain for its marble.*

quar·ry² (kwôr′ē) or (kwŏr′ē) *n., pl.* **quar·ries. 1.** An animal hunted or chased. **2.** Anything pursued in a similar manner.

qui·nine (kwī′nīn′) *n.* **1.** A bitter, colorless drug derived from certain cinchona barks and used to treat malaria. **2.** Any of various drugs or chemicals derived from quinine.

rab·bi (răb′ī′) *n.* **1.** The spiritual leader of a Jewish congregation. **2.** In former times, a scholar who interpreted Jewish law.

ra·di·o·ac·tive (rā′dē ō ăk′tĭv) *adj.* Of or showing the property by which atomic nuclei emit radiation.

rak·ish (rā′kĭsh) *adj.* Showy and jaunty in appearance. —**rak′ish·ly** *adv.*

rank¹ (răngk) *n.* **1.** A relative position on a scale of performance, production, value, quality, etc.: *in the middle rank of his class.* **2.** High position in society; eminence: *gentlemen of rank.* **3.** An official position or grade: *an adviser with cabinet rank.* **4.** A row or line, especially of people or things side by side: *The soldiers formed ranks for inspection.* —*v.* **1.** To hold a certain rank: *ranked eighth in a class of 160.* **2.** To assign a rank to; evaluate in a certain way: *Sports writers rank the team second in the nation.* **3.** To arrange in a row or on a scale: *ranked the children according to height.*

rank² (răngk) *adj.* **rank·er, rank·est. 1.** Growing thickly and without control: *rank weeds.* **2.** Strong and unpleasant in odor or taste: *a rank cigar.* **3.** Complete; out-and-out: *rank amateurs.*

rap·scal·lion (răp skăl′yən) *n.* A rascal; scamp; good-for-nothing.

rau·cous (rô′kəs) *adj.* **1.** Loud and harsh: *raucous cries.* **2.** Boisterous; disorderly: *their raucous party yesterday.* —**rau′cous·ly** *adv.* —**rau′cous·ness** *n.*

rav·ish·ing (răv′ĭ shĭng) *adj.* Filling one with delight or admiration; enchanting: *a ravishing symphony.* —**rav′ish·ing·ly** *adv.*

re·cip·ro·cate (rĭ sĭp′rə kāt′) *v.* **re·cip·ro·cat·ed, re·cip·ro·cat·ing. 1.** To give or take mutually: *reciprocating favors.* **2.** To make a return for something given or done. **3.** To show or feel in return: *reciprocated her love.* **4.** To move back and forth alternately, as a machine part. —**re·cip′ro·ca′tion** *n.*

re·gen·er·at·ing (rĭ jĕn′ə rā′tĭng) *adj.* **1.** Giving new life to; reviving. **2.** Replacing (a damaged or lost part) by growing new tissue.

reg·is·trar (rĕj′ĭ strär′) or (rĕj′ĭ strär′) *n.* An official of a college, corporation, etc., who is responsible for keeping records.

re·im·burse (rē′ĭm bûrs′) *v.* **re·im·bursed, re·im·burs·ing.** To pay back.

ă pat/ā pay/â care/ä father/ĕ pet/ē be/ĭ pit/ī pie/î fierce/ŏ pot/ō go/ô paw, for/oi oil/ŏŏ book/
ŏŏ boot/ou out/ŭ cut/û fur/*th* the/th thin/hw which/zh vision/ə ago, item, pencil, atom, circus

re·it·er·ate (rē ĭt′ə rāt′) v. **re·it·er·at·ed, re·it·er·at·ing.** To say over again; repeat: *The doctor reiterated his warning to the patient.* —**re′it·er·a′tion** n.

re·lent·less (rĭ lĕnt′lĭs) adj. **1.** Mercilessly harsh; unyielding; pitiless: *a relentless killer.* **2.** Steady and persistent; incessant; unremitting: *relentless heat.* —**re·lent′less·ly** adv.

re·lief (rĭ lēf′) n. **1. a.** The projection of a sculptured figure from a flat background. **b.** The apparent projection of a figure in a painting or drawing, as achieved by shading, coloring, etc. **2.** The variations in elevation of any area of the earth's surface: *a map that shows relief.* **3. in relief.** Carved, drawn, etc., so as to project or seem to project from a flat background.

rem·nant (rĕm′nənt) n. **1.** A portion or quantity left over; a remainder: *remnants of an old document.* **2.** A surviving trace or vestige: *the last remnants of an ancient empire.* **3.** A leftover piece of cloth remaining after the rest of the bolt has been sold.

re·mote (rĭ mōt′) adj. **re·mot·er, re·mot·est. 1.** Located far away: *a remote Arctic island.* **2.** Distant in time, relationship, etc.: *ideas remote from reality.* **3.** Barely perceptible; slight: *I haven't even a remote idea of what you are talking about.* **4.** Being distantly related by blood or marriage: *a remote cousin of mine.* **5.** Distant in manner; aloof. —**re·mote′ly** adv.

re·mu·da (rĭ mōo′də) n. *Southwestern U.S.* A herd of horses from which ranch hands select their mounts.

ren·dez·vous (rän′dā vōo′) or (-də-) n., pl. **ren·dez·vous** (rän′dā vōoz′) or (-də-). **1.** A prearranged meeting: *a rendezvous of the explorers in the wilderness.* **2.** A designated place for a meeting. —v. **ren·dez·voused** (rän′dā vōod′) or (-də-), **ren·dez·vous·ing** (rän′dā vōo′ĭng) or (-də-), **ren·dez·vous** (rän′dā vōoz′) or (-də-). To meet together or cause to meet together at a certain time and place.

rep·li·cate (rĕp′lĭ kāt′) v. **rep·li·cat·ed, rep·li·cat·ing.** To duplicate, copy, or repeat.

re·pos·i·to·ry (rĭ pŏz′ĭ tôr′ē) or (-tōr′ē) n., pl. **re·pos·i·to·ries.** A place where things may be put for safekeeping.

re·proach·ful·ly (rĭ prōch′fəl lē) adv. With blame or disapproval.

rep·u·ta·ble (rĕp′yə tə bəl) adj. Having a good reputation; honorable: *a reputable car dealer.*

req·ui·site (rĕk′wĭ zĭt) adj. Necessary to fulfill a certain requirement or quota: *the requisite number of teachers for a faculty.* —n. Something that is essential; a necessity.

re·sil·ient (rĭ zĭl′yənt) adj. **1.** Springing back to its original shape or position after being stretched, bent, or compressed; elastic. **2.** Snapping back quickly from illness, misfortune, etc. —**re·sil′ience** n.

res·ur·rec·tion (rĕz′ə rĕk′shən) n. **1.** The act of rising from the dead or returning to life. **2.** The act of bringing back into use; revival: *the resurrection of an ancient Oriental religious practice.*

ret·ro·spect (rĕt′rə spĕkt′) n. A review, survey, or contemplation of the past.

rev·el (rĕv′əl) v. **rev·eled** or **rev·elled, rev·el·ing** or **rev·el·ling. 1.** To take great pleasure or delight: *He revels in making fun of others.* **2.** To be festive in a riotous way: *The dancers reveled for an entire weekend.* —n. A noisy festivity. —**rev′el·er, rev′el·ler** n.

rev·e·la·tion (rĕv′ə lā′shən) n. **1.** Something revealed, especially something surprising. **2.** The act of revealing. **3.** In theology, a manifestation of divine will or truth.

re·vered (rĭ vîrd′) adj. Beloved; respected: *a revered professor.*

rho·do·den·dron (rō′də dĕn′drən) n. A shrub with evergreen leaves and clusters of white, pinkish, or purplish flowers.

rig·ma·role (rĭg′mə rōl′) n. **1.** Confused and rambling speech; nonsense. **2.** A complicated and petty set of procedures.

roil (roil) v. **1.** To make (a liquid) muddy or cloudy by stirring up sediment. **2.** To be in a state of agitation.

roof·tree (rōof′trē′) or (rŏof′-) n. **1.** A long horizontal beam extending along the ridge of a roof. **2.** A roof.

row (rou) *n.* **1.** A noisy quarrel or fight; a brawl. **2.** A loud noise; clamor; racket. —*v.* To quarrel noisily.

ru·di·men·ta·ry (rōō′də mĕn′tə rē) *adj.* **1.** Of basic principles or skills; elementary: *a rudimentary knowledge of economics.* **2.** Grown or developed in an imperfect or incomplete way: *the rudimentary tail of a Manx cat.*

rue (rōō) *v.* **rued, ru·ing.** To feel shame or sorrow for. —*n. Archaic.* Regret.

ru·in·a·tion (rōō′ə nā′shən) *n.* Destruction.

sac·ri·le·gious (săk′rə lĭj′əs) *or* (-lē′jəs) *adj.* Disrespectful or violent toward something sacred.

saf·fron (săf′rən) *n.* **1.** The dried orange-yellow stigmas from the flowers of a kind of crocus, used to flavor food and in making dye. **2.** An orange-yellow color. —*adj.* Orange yellow.

sage¹ (sāj) *n.* A very wise person, usually old and highly respected. —*adj.* **sag·er, sag·est.** Full of, showing, or noted for wisdom and sound judgment. —**sage′ly** *adv.*

sage² (sāj) *n.* **1.** A plant with grayish-green, spicy-smelling leaves used as flavoring in cooking. **2.** Sagebrush.

sa·lin·i·ty (sə lĭn′ĭ tē) *n.* **1.** The condition or property of being saline; saltiness. **2.** The degree to which something is saline or salty.

sal·vage (săl′vĭj) *v.* **sal·vaged, sal·vag·ing.** To save or rescue (anything of use or value) that would otherwise be lost, discarded, damaged, or destroyed. —*n.* The act of saving endangered property from total loss.

sal·va·tion (săl vā′shən) *n.* **1.** The act of saving or condition of being saved, as from loss, danger, or destruction; rescue. **2.** In the Christian religion, the saving of the soul from sin and death. **3.** Someone or something that saves, rescues, or preserves: *The emergency supplies were our salvation.*

salve (săv) *or* (säv) *n.* **1.** A soothing ointment applied to wounds, burns, sores, etc., to heal them or relieve pain. **2.** Anything that soothes or comforts; a balm: *The compliment was a salve to her wounded pride.* —*v.* **salved, salv·ing.** To soothe as if with salve: *Your praise salved their hurt feelings.*

sanc·tion (săngk′shən) *n.* **1.** Authoritative permission or approval. **2.** A measure or measures adopted by several nations taking action against a nation considered to have violated international law. —*v.* To give approval to; authorize.

sap·phire (săf′īr′) *n.* **1.** Any of several fairly pure forms of corundum, especially a blue form valued as a gem. **2.** A gem of this type.

sar·coph·a·gus (sär kŏf′ə gəs) *n., pl.* **sar·coph·a·gi** (sär kŏf′ə jī′). A stone coffin.

sar·don·ic (sär dŏn′ĭk) *adj.* Mocking; cynical; sarcastic. —**sar·don′i·cal·ly** *adv.*

sat·ur·nine (săt′ər nīn′) *adj.* Behaving like one born under the supposed astrological influence of Saturn; gloomy; glum: *a saturnine expression on his face.*

sa·vor·ing (sā′və rĭng) *n.* The act of tasting or enjoying with zest; relishing.

scav·en·ger (skăv′ĭn jər) *n.* **1.** An animal, such as a vulture, hyena, or catfish, that feeds on the remains of dead animals or on other dead or decaying plant or animal material. **2.** Someone who searches through rubbish for food, useful objects, etc.

scep·ter (sĕp′tər) *n.* A staff held by a sovereign as a sign of authority.

scrump·tious (skrŭmp′shəs) *adj. Informal.* **1.** Very tasty; delicious. **2.** Wonderful.

scru·pu·lous·ly (skrōō′pyə ləs lē) *adv.* **1.** Properly; honestly. **2.** In an exacting or conscientious way.

scru·ti·ny (skrōōt′n ē) *n., pl.* **scru·ti·nies. 1.** A close, careful look or study: *Sammy fidgeted under the cold, silent scrutiny of the headmaster.* **2.** Close observation; surveillance.

ă pat/ā pay/â care/ä father/ĕ pet/ē be/ĭ pit/ī pie/î fierce/ŏ pot/ō go/ô paw, for/oi oil/ŏŏ book/
ŏŏ boot/ou out/ŭ cut/û fur/*th* the/th thin/hw which/zh vision/ə ago, item, pencil, atom, circus

scul·ler·y (skŭl′ə rē) *n., pl.* **scul·ler·ies.** A room next to the kitchen in large houses, where dishwashing and other kitchen chores are done.

scythe (sīth) *n.* A tool used for mowing or reaping, having a long, curved blade with a long, bent handle. *—v.* **scythed, scyth·ing.** To cut with a scythe.

sea anemone. Any of several sea animals having a flexible, tube-shaped body that remains fastened to a surface at the lower end and has a mouth opening surrounded by many petal-like tentacles at the upper end.

sea urchin. Any of several sea animals having a soft body enclosed in a thin, round shell covered with spines.

sec·tor (sĕk′tər) *n.* **1.** The part of a circle bound by two radii and one of the arcs that they intercept. **2.** A particular military area or zone of action. **3.** A division of something: *the manufacturing sector of the economy.*

sec·u·lar (sĕk′yə lər) *adj.* **1.** Worldly or temporal rather than spiritual: *men's secular interests.* **2.** Not related to religion or a religious organization: *secular music.* **3.** Not living in a religious community: *the secular clergy.*

se·cu·ri·ty (sĭ kyoor′ĭ tē) *n., pl.* **se·cu·ri·ties.** Anything deposited or given to guarantee fulfillment of an obligation; a pledge: *The landlord insisted that an extra month's rent be given as security.*

sed·i·ment (sĕd′ə mənt) *n.* **1.** Finely divided solid matter that falls to the bottom of a liquid or sometimes a gas. **2.** Finely divided solid matter suspended in a liquid or gas.

seg·men·tal (sĕg mĕnt′l) *adj.* Divided or organized into parts or sections: *the segmental body of a worm.*

seis·mol·o·gist (sīz mŏl′ə jĭst) *n.* A scientist who studies earthquakes and the mechanical properties of the earth.

se·le·ni·um (sĭ lē′nē əm) *n.* Symbol **Se** One of the elements, a substance that can exist as a red powder, a black, glassy material, or a gray crystal, with chemical properties resembling those of sulfur.

selenium cell. A light-sensitive cell consisting of an insulated selenium strip between two electrodes.

sen·sor (sĕn′sər) *or* (-sôr′) *n.* A device, such as a photocell or thermocouple, that reacts in a characteristic way to a particular type of change in its condition or environment.

shard (shärd) *n.* **1.** A piece of broken pottery. **2.** A fragment of a brittle substance such as glass or metal.

sheathe (shēth) *v.* **sheathed, sheath·ing. 1.** To insert into a case or other protective covering: *sheathed his saber.* **2.** To provide with a protective covering or structure: *sheathe electric wires with rubber.*

Sher·pa (shûr′pə) *n.* A member of a Tibetan people living in northern Nepal.

shuck (shŭk) *n.* An outer covering, such as a corn husk, pea pod, or oyster shell. *—v.* To remove the husk or shell from: *shuck corn; shuck oysters.*

sig·ni·fy (sĭg′nə fī′) *v.* **sig·ni·fied, sig·ni·fy·ing, sig·ni·fies. 1.** To serve as a sign of: *What does this monument signify?* **2.** To make known: *Peter signified that he wanted to leave early.* **3.** *Dialect.* To make a direct or indirect implication of baiting or boasting in order to make fun of someone's appearance, relatives, or situation.

sil·hou·ette (sĭl′oo ĕt′) *n.* **1.** A drawing consisting of the outline of something, especially a human profile, filled in with a solid color. **2.** An outline of something that appears dark against a light background. *—v.* **sil·hou·et·ted, sil·hou·et·ting.** To cause to be seen as a silhouette.

sil·i·cate (sĭl′ĭ kĭt) *or* (-kāt′) *n.* Any of a large class of chemical compounds composed of silicon, oxygen, and at least one metal or a radical that can replace a metal, found widely in rocks and forming the principal substance of bricks and glass.

sil·i·co-mem·brane (sĭl′ĭ kō mĕm′brān′) *n.* A thin sheet of synthetic material through which dissolved substances can pass.

sim·u·lat·ed (sĭm′yə lāt′ĭd) *adj.* Imitative; pretended.

sin·is·ter (sĭn'ĭ stər) *adj.* **1.** Suggesting an evil force or motive: *a dark, sinister man.* **2.** Promising trouble; ominous: *words with a sinister sound.* **—sin'is·ter·ly** *adv.*

size¹ (sīz) *n.* **1.** The physical dimensions, proportions, or extent of something. **2.** Considerable extent, amount, or dimensions: *no difficulties of any size.* *—v.* **sized, siz·ing. 1.** To arrange, classify, or distribute according to size: *a chart that sizes skirts according to waist measurements.* **2.** To make, cut, or shape according to a required size: *sized and waterproofed material for tents.*

size² (sīz) *n.* Any of several jellylike or sticky substances made from glue, wax, or clay and used as a filler or glaze for porous materials such as paper, cloth, or wall surfaces. *—v.* **sized, siz·ing.** To treat or coat with size or a similar material.

skep·ti·cal (skĕp'tĭ kəl) *adj.* Of or characterized by doubt; doubting or disbelieving: *a skeptical attitude.* **—skep'ti·cal·ly** *adv.*

skir·mish (skûr'mĭsh) *n.* **1.** A minor encounter between small bodies of troops. **2.** Any minor conflict. *—v.* To engage in a skirmish.

slate (slāt) *n.* **1.** A fine-grained metamorphic rock that splits into thin layers with smooth surfaces. **2.** A writing tablet made of this or a similar material. **3.** A dark bluish gray. **4.** A record of past performance: *starting with a clean slate.* **5.** A list, especially of political candidates of the same party. *—v.* **slat·ed, slat·ing. 1.** To cover with slate: *slating a roof.* **2.** To assign a place to on a list or schedule.

sleuth·ing (slooth'ĭng) *n.* A search for information, as done by a detective.

slug·gish (slŭg'ĭsh) *adj.* **1.** Showing little activity or movement; slow: *a sluggish stream.* **2.** Lacking in alertness; dull; lazy: *a sluggish response.* **3.** Slow to perform or respond: *a sluggish child.* **—slug'gish·ly** *adv.*

snor·kel (snôr'kəl) *n.* **1.** A breathing apparatus used by skin divers, consisting of a plastic tube curved at one end and fitted with a mouthpiece. **2.** A retractable tube that can be extended from a submarine, allowing it to draw in fresh air and expel waste gases while submerged. *—v.* To swim using a snorkel.

snub (snŭb) *v.* **snubbed, snub·bing. 1.** To treat with scorn or contempt. **2.** To secure (a boat, horse, etc.) by means of a rope tied to a post. *—n.* **1.** A deliberate slight; scornful treatment. **2.** A sudden securing or checking of a rope.

snuff¹ (snŭf) *v.* **1.** To inhale (something) through the nose. **2.** To examine (something) by or as if by inhaling through the nose; sniff. *—n.* Finely pulverized tobacco that can be drawn up into the nostrils by inhaling.

snuff² (snŭf) *v.* **1.** To put out; extinguish: *snuff a candle.* **2.** To put an end to; kill: *The dictatorship eventually snuffed out all opposition.*

sod·den (sŏd'n) *adj.* **1.** Thoroughly soaked; saturated: *sodden land.* **2.** Bloated and dull from or as if from drink. **—sod'den·ly** *adv.*

so·nar (sō'när') *n.* **1.** A system, similar in principle to radar, that uses reflected sound waves to detect and locate underwater objects. **2.** An apparatus using such a system, as for detecting submarines.

son·ic (sŏn'ĭk) *adj.* **1.** Of sound, especially audible sound. **2.** Having a speed equal to that of sound in air, about 738 miles per hour at sea level at normal temperatures.

so·no·rous (sə nôr'əs) *or* (-nōr'-) *or* (sŏn'ər-) *adj.* **1.** Having or producing sound, especially full, deep, or rich sound. **2.** Impressive: *He read aloud in a deep and sonorous voice.* **—so·no'rous·ly** *adv.*

sor·rel¹ (sôr'əl) *n.* Any of several plants with sour-tasting leaves.

ă pat/ā pay/â care/ä father/ĕ pet/ē be/ĭ pit/ī pie/î fierce/ŏ pot/ō go/ô paw, for/oi oil/oo book/
oo boot/ou out/ŭ cut/û fur/*th* the/th thin/hw which/zh vision/ə ago, item, pencil, atom, circus

sor·rel² (sôr′əl) *n.* **1.** A yellowish brown. **2.** A yellowish-brown horse. —*adj.* Yellowish brown: *a sorrel horse.*

spon·ta·ne·ous (spŏn tā′nē əs) *adj.* **1.** Happening or arising without apparent outside cause; self-generated. **2.** Arising or occurring voluntarily and from impulse: *spontaneous cheers.* —**spon·ta′ne·ous·ly** *adv.*

spo·rad·ic (spô răd′ĭk) *or* (spō-) *adj.* Occurring at irregular intervals; having no pattern or order: *sporadic applause from the audience.* —**spo·rad′i·cal·ly** *adv.*

spore (spôr) *or* (spōr) *n.* **1.** One of the tiny, usually one-celled reproductive parts produced by nonflowering plants such as ferns, mosses, and fungi. **2.** An inactive form of certain bacteria and other microorganisms.

spume (spyōōm) *n.* Foam or froth on a liquid. —*v.* **spumed, spum·ing.** To froth or foam.

stac·ca·to (stə kä′tō) *adj.* **1.** Short and detached: *staccato musical tones.* **2.** Consisting of a series of distinct sounds: *staccato clapping.* —*adv.* In a short, detached manner: *playing a piano piece staccato.*

stam·i·na (stăm′ə nə) *n.* The power to resist fatigue or illness while working very hard; endurance.

stance (stăns) *n.* **1.** The position or manner in which a person or animal stands; posture: *an erect, almost military stance.* **2.** The position taken by an athlete or sportsman about to go into action: *the crouched stance of a football lineman.* **3.** An attitude regarding some issue: *a judge with a tough stance toward repeated offenders.*

stan·chion (stăn′chən) *or* (-shən) *n.* A vertical pole, post, or support. —*v.* To provide with stanchions for support: *stanchion a sagging roof.*

staunch·ly (stônch′lē) *or* (stänch′-) *adv.* Firmly supportive; loyally.

stip·u·late (stĭp′yə lāt′) *v.* **stip·u·lat·ed, stip·u·lat·ing.** To specify as a condition of an agreement; require by contract.

strat·a·gem (străt′ə jəm) *n.* Any plan or action intended to fool or deceive someone, especially an opponent.

stra·tum (strā′təm) *or* (străt′əm) *n., pl.* **stra·ta** (strā′tə) *or* (străt′ə). **1.** Any of a series of layers or levels, especially a series of approximately parallel layers. **2.** A bed or layer of rock whose composition is more or less the same throughout. **3.** A category regarded as occupying a level in a system or hierarchy: *the lowest strata of society.*

stu·pen·dous (stōō pĕn′dəs) *or* (styōō-) *adj.* **1.** Of astonishing force, volume, degree, etc.: *stupendous risks.* **2.** Amazingly large; huge: *stupendous ruins of an ancient temple.* —**stu·pen′dous·ly** *adv.*

sub·lim·i·ty (sə blĭm′ə tē) *n.* The state of being exalted, lofty, or awe-inspiring.

sub·soil (sŭb′soil′) *n.* The layer of earth below the surface soil.

sub·ter·ra·ne·an (sŭb′tə rā′nē ən) *adj.* **1.** Situated beneath the earth's surface. **2.** Hidden; secret.

sub·tly (sŭt′l ē) *adv.* **1.** In a way so slight as to be difficult to detect or analyze. **2.** In a way that is not immediately obvious. **3.** Slyly; deviously.

suc·cinct (sək sĭngkt′) *adj.* **1.** Clearly expressed in a few words; concise: *a succinct explanation.* **2.** Characterized by brevity and clarity: *a succinct style.* —**suc·cinct′ly** *adv.* —**suc·cinct′ness** *n.*

suc·cumb (sə kŭm′) *v.* **1.** To yield or submit to something overpowering or overwhelming: *succumb to the pressures of society.* **2.** To die.

suf·frage (sŭf′rĭj) *n.* **1.** The right or privilege of voting; franchise. **2.** The exercise of such a right.

suf·fra·gette (sŭf′rə jet′) *n.* A female who is in favor of a woman's right to vote.

sulfa drug. Any of a group of synthetic organic compounds capable of inhibiting bacterial growth and activity.

sul·len·ness (sŭl′ən ĕs) *n.* Brooding ill humor or resentment; sulkiness.

sul·tan (sŭl′tən) *n.* The ruler of a Moslem country.

summer stock. A theatrical activity, especially one outside a main theatrical center.

su·per·fi·cial (soo′pər fĭsh′əl) *adj.* **1.** Of, on, near, or affecting the surface: *a superficial wound.* **2.** Concerned only with what is apparent or obvious; shallow: *a superficial person.* **3.** Not deeply penetrating; trivial: *He has only a superficial knowledge of history.* —**su′per·fi′cial·ly** *adv.*

su·per·la·tive (sə pûr′lə tĭv) *or* (soo-) *adj.* Of the highest order, quality, or degree: *It was a superlative specimen.* —**su·per′la·tive·ly** *adv.* —**su·per′la·tive·ness** *n.*

su·per·sede (soo′pər sēd′) *v.* **su·per·sed·ed, su·per·sed·ing. 1.** To take the place of; replace or succeed: *Electric-light bulbs superseded candles and kerosene as the major source of indoor light.* **2.** To cause to be set aside or displaced: *Supreme Court decisions supersede those of lower courts.*

sur·mise (sər mīz′) *v.* **sur·mised, sur·mis·ing.** To conclude on slight evidence; suppose; guess: *Astronomers surmise that there is life elsewhere in the universe.* —*n.* An idea based on slight evidence; a guess.

sur·tout (sər too′) *or* (-toot′) *n.* A man's fitted coat or overcoat.

su·ture (soo′chər) *n.* **1. a.** The act or process of joining two thin pieces of material along a line by or as if by sewing. **b.** The material used in this process, as thread, gut, wire staples, or clips. **2.** The line along which two pieces, parts, bones, etc., are joined. —*v.* **su·tured, su·tur·ing.** To join by means of sutures; sew up, as in surgery.

swamp·er (swäm′pər) *or* (swôm-) *n.* **1.** A menial helper or lowly assistant. **2.** One who inhabits swamps or lowlands.

swathe (swŏth) *or* (swôth) *v.* **swathed, swath·ing. 1.** To wrap or bind with a strip or strips of cloth: *His right ankle was swathed in bandages.* **2.** To cover or wrap with something that envelops: *The actress was swathed in furs.* —*n.* A band, bandage, or other wrapping.

syn·co·pat·ed (sĭng′kə pā′tĭd) *or* (sĭn′-) *adj.* Rhythmically stressed, as words or musical notes.

syn·di·cate (sĭn′dĭ kĭt) *n.* An association of people formed to carry out any business or enterprise. —*v.* (sĭn′dĭ kāt′) **syn·di·cat·ed, syn·di·cat·ing.** To organize into a syndicate.

taint (tānt) *v.* **1.** To touch or affect, as with something undesirable. **2.** To make rotten; spoil. —*n.* A stain; a blemish.

tal·low (tăl′ō) *n.* A mixture of fats obtained from animals, such as cattle, sheep, or horses, and used to make candles, soaps, lubricants, etc.

Tal·mud (täl′mood′) *or* (täl′məd) *n.* A collection of ancient rabbinical writings, the basis of religious authority for orthodox Judaism.

tal·on (tăl′ən) *n.* The claw of a bird or animal that seizes other animals as prey.

tan·gi·ble (tăn′jə bəl) *adj.* **1.** Capable of being touched: *a tangible product like steel.* **2.** Capable of being understood or realized: *a tangible benefit.* **3.** Concrete; real: *tangible evidence.* —*n.* **tangibles.** Material assets. —**tan′gi·bly** *adv.*

Tar·tar (tär′tər) *n.* **1.** A member of any of the Mongolian peoples of central Asia who invaded western Asia and eastern Europe in the 13th century. **2.** A descendant of these peoples. —**Tar′tar** *adj.*

tat·too¹ (tă too′) *n.* **1.** A signal sounded on a drum or bugle to summon soldiers to their quarters. **2.** Any continuous, even drumming.

tat·too² (tă too′) *n.* A mark or design made on the skin by pricking and ingraining an indelible dye or by raising scars. —*v.* **tat·tooed, tat·too·ing, tat·toos.** To mark (the skin) with a tattoo.

taw·ny (tô′nē) *adj.* **taw·ni·er, taw·ni·est.** Light brown: *a tawny mountain lion.*

ă pat/ā pay/â care/ä father/ĕ pet/ē be/ĭ pit/ī pie/î fierce/ŏ pot/ō go/ô paw, for/oi oil/oo book/
oo boot/ou out/ŭ cut/û fur/*th* the/th thin/hw which/zh vision/ə ago, item, pencil, atom, circus

ten·ta·cle (tĕn′tə kəl) *n.* **1.** One of the narrow, flexible, unjointed parts extending from the body of certain animals, such as an octopus, jellyfish, or sea anemone, and used for grasping, moving, etc. **2.** Something resembling a tentacle, especially in the ability to grasp or hold.

te·pee (tē′pē) *n.* A cone-shaped tent of skins or bark used by North American Indians.

ter·rain (tə răn′) *or* (tĕ-) *n.* A tract of land, especially when considered with respect to its physical features: *rugged terrain.*

teth·er (tĕth′ər) *n.* **1.** A rope or chain for an animal, allowing it a short radius to move about in. **2.** The range or scope of one's resources or abilities. —*v.* To restrict with a tether.

tex·tile (tĕk′stəl) *or* (-stīl′) *n.* **1.** Cloth or fabric, especially when woven or knitted. **2.** Fiber or yarn that can be made into cloth.

throt·tle (thrŏt′l) *n.* **1.** A valve in internal-combustion engines by which the flow of fuel to the combustion chamber is controlled. **2.** A pedal or lever that controls a valve of this type. —*v.* **throt·tled, throt·tling.** **1.** To control (an engine, its fuel, or working fluid) with or as if with a throttle. **2.** To strangle; choke.

tier (tîr) *n.* Any of a series of rows placed one above another.

Tiffany lamp. A kind of lamp made from stained or iridescent glass, popular in the early 1900's.

tinge (tĭnj) *v.* **tinged, tinge·ing** *or* **ting·ing.** **1.** To color slightly; tint: *The sunset tinged the sky with red.* **2.** To give a slight trace or touch to; affect slightly: *admiration tinged with envy.* —*n.* A faint trace of color, flavor, etc.: *There was a tinge of sadness in her remarks.*

ti·pi (tē′pē) *n.* A form of the word **tepee.**

torch (tôrch) *n.* **1.** A portable light produced by the flame of an inflammable material wound about the end of a stick of wood. **2.** Anything that serves to enlighten, guide, inspire, etc. **3.** *British.* A flashlight.

tor·so (tôr′sō′) *n., pl.* **tor·sos** *or* **tor·si** (tôr′sē′). The human body except for the head and limbs; trunk.

tran·quil·li·ty, also **tran·quil·i·ty** (trăng-kwĭl′ĭ tē) *or* (trăn-) *n.* The quality or condition of being calm; peacefulness.

tran·sept (trăn′sĕpt′) *n.* Either of the two lateral arms of a church built in the shape of a cross.

trans·fu·sion (trăns fyōō′zhən) *n.* The direct injection of whole blood, plasma, or other fluid into the bloodstream.

tran·sient (trăn′shənt) *or* (-zhənt) *adj.* **1.** Passing away with time; transitory: *transient happiness.* **2.** Passing through from one place to another; stopping only briefly: *a transient guest at a hotel.* —*n.* Someone or something that is transient, especially a person making a very brief stay at a hotel. —**tran′sience, tran′sien·cy** *n.*

trek (trĕk) *v.* **trekked, trek·king.** To make a slow or arduous journey. —*n.* A journey, especially a long and difficult one.

tres·tle (trĕs′əl) *n.* **1.** A horizontal beam or bar extending between two pairs of legs that spread outward at an angle, used to support a vertical load. **2.** A framework made up of vertical, horizontal, and slanting supports, used to hold up a bridge.

trus·tee (trŭ stē′) *n.* **1.** A person or firm that administers another person's property or assets. **2.** A member of a group or board that manages the affairs of a college, foundation, institution, etc.

tulle (tōōl) *n.* A fine starched net used for veils, gowns, etc.

tur·moil (tûr′moil′) *n.* A condition of great confusion or disturbance: *The 17th and 18th centuries saw Europe in religious turmoil.*

two-di·men·sion·al (tōō′dĭ mĕn′shə nəl) *adj.* **1.** Having only two dimensions, especially length and width; flat. **2.** Limited in range or depth.

ty·phus (tī′fəs) *n.* Any of several forms of an infectious disease caused by microorganisms and characterized generally by high fever, depression, delirium, and red rashes.

u·biq·ui·tous (yo͞o bĭk′wĭ təs) *adj.* Being or seeming to be everywhere at the same time: *a pheasant ubiquitous throughout eastern and central South Dakota.* —**u·biq′ui·tous·ly** *adv.*

u·nan·i·mous (yo͞o năn′ə məs) *adj.* **1.** Sharing the same opinion: *Critics were unanimous about the play.* **2.** Based on complete agreement. —**u·nan′i·mous·ly** *adv.*

un·a·vail·ing (ŭn′ə vā′lĭng) *adj.* Useless; unsuccessful: *her unavailing efforts to apologize.*

un·can·ni·ly (ŭn kăn′ə lē) *adv.* **1.** In a way arousing wonder and fear; strangely. **2.** So perceptively as to seem supernatural.

un·du·lat·ing (ŭn′jə lā′tĭng) *or* (ŭn′dyə-) *or* (-də-) *adj.* Moving in a smooth, wavelike motion.

u·ni·corn (yo͞o′nĭ kôrn′) *n.* An imaginary animal of legend, resembling a horse with a single long horn projecting from its forehead.

u·nique (yo͞o nēk′) *adj.* **1.** Being the only one; sole: *Amassing a great fortune was his unique goal in life.* **2.** Having no equal or equivalent; being the only one in kind, excellence, etc. —**u·nique′ly** *adv.* —**u·nique′ness** *n.*

un·let (ŭn′lĕt′) *adj. British.* Not let or rented; unleased.

un·pal·at·a·ble (ŭn păl′ə tə bəl) *adj.* **1.** Not agreeable enough in flavor to be eaten. **2.** Not acceptable to the mind or sensibilities.

un·rec·on·ciled (ŭn rĕk′ən sīld′) *adj.* **1.** Unable to be friendly again. **2.** Unaccepting. **3.** Not in harmony or agreement.

un·sa·vor·y (ŭn sā′və rē) *adj.* **1.** Having a bad or dull taste; insipid. **2.** Morally offensive.

ve·he·ment·ly (vē′ə mənt lē) *adv.* **1.** Forcefully or intensely. **2.** Vigorously, violently, or energetically.

ver·i·ty (vĕr′ĭ tē) *n., pl.* **ver·i·ties. 1.** The condition of being real, accurate, or true: *the verity of his description of the castle.* **2.** Something that is true, as a principle, etc.

ver·te·brate (vûr′tə brāt′) *or* (-brĭt) *n.* Any of a large group of animals having a backbone, including the fishes, amphibians such as frogs and toads, reptiles, birds, and mammals. —*adj.* Having a backbone: *vertebrate animals.*

Vic·to·ri·an (vĭk tôr′ē ən) *or* (-tōr′-) *adj.* **1.** Of or typical of the time and taste of Queen Victoria's reign. **2.** Stuffy, conventional, or prudish in a manner considered typical of the time of Queen Victoria: *Victorian rules of conduct.* —**Vic·to′ri·an·ism′** *n.*

vis·cos·i·ty (vĭ skŏs′ĭ tē) *n.* **1.** The condition or property of resisting flow when pressure is applied. **2.** The degree to which a fluid resists flow when pressure is applied to it.

vi·sor (vī′zər) *or* (vĭz′ər) *n.* **1.** A projecting part, as on a cap or the windshield of a car, that protects the eyes from sun, wind, or rain. **2.** The movable front piece on a helmet that protects the face.

vol·u·ble (vŏl′yə bəl) *adj.* Talking very quickly and easily; fluent; glib: *a voluble speaker.* —**vol′u·bil′i·ty** *n.* —**vol′u·bly** *adv.*

waft (wäft) *or* (wăft) *v.* **1.** To carry gently through the air or over water: *feathers wafting downward from an eagle in flight.* **2.** To float or drift: *Strains of music wafted in through the window.* —*n.* Something, such as a scent or sound, carried lightly through the air: *a waft of perfume.*

wake¹ (wāk) *v.* **woke** (wōk) *or* **waked, waked, wak·ing. 1.** To come or bring from sleep to consciousness; awaken: *I woke before daybreak.* **2.** To be or remain awake: *whether he sleeps or wakes.* **3.** To rouse or stir: *He waked in her the need to weep.* —*n.* A watch or vigil kept over the body of a dead person before the burial.

wake² (wāk) *n.* **1.** The visible track of waves, ripples, or foam left behind something mov-

---

ă pat/ā pay/â care/ä father/ĕ pet/ē be/ĭ pit/ī pie/î fierce/ŏ pot/ō go/ô paw, for/oi oil/o͞o book/
o͞o boot/ou out/ŭ cut/û fur/*th* the/th thin/hw which/zh vision/ə ago, item, pencil, atom, circus

ing through water. **2.** The course or route over which anything has passed: *The hurricane left destruction in its wake.*

wan·ly (wŏn′lē) *adv.* Weakly or faintly.

war·bler¹ (wôr′blər) *n.* Any of a large number of small birds, the North American variety often having yellow feathers.

war·bler² (wôr′blər) *n.* A communications device that produces electronic tones which are varied in frequency over a fixed range.

wean (wēn) *v.* **1.** To cause (a young child or other young mammal) to become accustomed to food other than its mother's milk. **2.** To cause (someone) to give up a habit, interest, etc.

whale¹ (hwāl) *n.* Any of several very often large sea animals that resemble fish in form but are air-breathing mammals.

whale² (hwāl) *v.* To attack vehemently. Often used with *away: The poet whaled away at his critics.*

whet·stone (hwĕt′stōn′) *or* (wĕt′-) *n.* A stone used for sharpening knives and other cutting tools.

wick·er (wĭk′ər) *n.* Flexible twigs or shoots, as of a willow tree, woven into a material used for baskets, summer furniture, etc.

wil·i·ness (wī′lē nəs) *n.* The state of being guileful or calculating; slyness.

with·ers (wĭth′ərz) *pl.n.* The highest part of the back of a horse or similar animal, between the shoulder blades.

wiz·ened (wĭz′ənd) *adj.* Shriveled; withered.

wont (wônt) *or* (wōnt) *or* (wŭnt) *adj.* Accustomed, apt, or used to: *He was wont to lend money for charitable use.* —*n.* Habit; custom: *He shook playfully as was his wont.*

wretch·ed (rĕch′ĭd) *adj.* **1.** Full of or attended by misery or woe: *I'm lonely and wretched.* **2.** Shabby: *a wretched shack.* **3.** Hateful or contemptible: *a wretched person.* **4.** Inferior in quality: *a wretched performance.* —**wretch′ed·ly** *adv.*

writhe (rīth) *v.* **writhed, writh·ing. 1.** To twist or squirm or cause to twist or squirm, as in pain. **2.** To move with a twisting or contorted motion: *Snakes writhed in the pit.*

zo·di·ac (zō′dē ăk′) *n.* **1.** A band of the celestial sphere extending about eight degrees on both sides of the ecliptic that contains the paths of the sun, moon, and principal planets. **2.** The twelve divisions, or signs of the zodiac, into which this band is divided, each having the name of a constellation and often shown in a diagram or chart used in astrology.

INDEX

AUTHORS AND TITLES

LITERARY TYPES

ART CREDITS